Fundamental Principles
of Polymerization
RUBBERS, PLASTICS, AND FIBERS

Books by G. F. D'Alelio

FUNDAMENTAL PRINCIPLES
OF POLYMERIZATION

EXPERIMENTAL PLASTICS
AND SYNTHETIC RESINS

Fundamental Principles
of Polymerization

RUBBERS, PLASTICS, AND FIBERS

G. F. D'Alelio, A.B., Ph.D.

VICE PRESIDENT AND MANAGER OF RESEARCH
KOPPERS COMPANY, INC.
PITTSBURGH, PENNSYLVANIA

New York · JOHN WILEY & SONS, Inc.
London · CHAPMAN & HALL, Ltd.

PRINTED IN THE UNITED STATES OF AMERICA

Preface

The need for selected textbooks on polymers was impressed upon me a few years ago by a number of academic friends. It was pointed out that the first need was for a book to be used as a laboratory manual, which would demonstrate the chemical principles responsible for polymer formation and, at the same time, indicate certain techniques and processes of industry. This objective has been met, at least in part, by my *Experimental Plastics and Synthetic Resins*.

The field of polymerization has expanded at a considerable rate within the last few years, and, as a result, numerous publications have appeared on the subject, most of which, however, deal with the technology of applied polymerization, namely, the field of plastics. A rather limited number of books have appeared which deal with the fundamental principles of polymerizations.

This book, entitled *Fundamental Principles of Polymerization—Rubbers, Plastics, and Fibers*, is not encyclopedic in scope, but summarizes what I believe is the minimum fundamental knowledge that a scientist in the field of polymers should have. This minimum understanding is no longer limited to men in academic life, since today industry expects her scientists to be fundamental as well as practical. In this book I also attempt to reconcile the discrepancies of terminology in earlier literature, with the hope that it will establish a common meaning for the language in current use in this field.

Since this book includes sufficient historical data to indicate the effort and struggle expended in bringing this science to its present status, it is appropriate that my major acknowledgment should be to those men who preceded us and who by their persistent and diligent research efforts recorded so much for us to inherit. Much of their work was fundamental, even if later scientists proved some of their original theories to be wrong. They gave us the foundations on which to build, and we should be humble when we add stones to pyramids whose excavations and bases were the work of others.

I wish to express my gratitude to the Koppers Company, Inc., for the assistance which made this publication possible.

G. F. D'Alelio

May, 1952

Contents

Contents

Fractionation of Polymer Mixtures. Fractionation Efficiency and Polymer Distribution. Distribution Curves. Population Curve. Integral Weight Curve. Differential Weight Curve. Differential Number Curve. Mathematical Meaning of Distribution Curves. Weight Distribution Functions. Number Distribution Functions. Theoretical and Actual Distribution Curves in Addition Polymerization. Theoretical Distribution Curves for Condensation Polymers.

The Functionality Relationship. Use of the Functionality Equation. Functionality and Distribution Relationship. The Relationship of Weight Average, Viscosity Average, Number Average, and Sedimentation Average. Use of Functionality Equation in Crosslinking Equations. Limitations of the Functionality Equation. Difference between Addition and Condensation Polymerization. Kinetic Factors and Polymerization Mechanism. Gelation Activity. Interrupted Polymerization.

The Properties of Polymers. Generalized Relationship. Theoretical Strength of Polymers. Constitutional Factors in Polymers. Attractive Forces between Chains. Geometry of Linear Chains. Bond Angles. Bond Distances. Molecular Configuration. Branching and Rotational Isomerism. Evidence of Polymer Order. Identity Periods. Rubbers, Plastics, and Fibers. Segmer Ratios. Disorder and Fit Values. Molar Cohesion. Intensities of X-Ray Spacings.

Second-Order Phase Transition Temperatures. Interpretation of the Change in Slope. The Isoviscous State. Volume Relations. Heat Capacity. Compressibility. Thermal Conductivity. Refractive Index. Dielectric Properties. Modules of Elasticity. X-Ray Crystallinity. Effect of Molecular Weight on Transition Temperature. Crosslinking. Copolymerization. Stress. Orientation. Time Effects. Plasticizers.

Second-Order Transition and Molecular Structure. Elastomers. Rubbers. Plastics. Fibers. The Effect of Non-Polar and Polar Groups.

Plasticization. Melt Viscosities. Solvent Effects. Effect of Solvent Concentration. Polymer-Solvent Interaction. Characterization of μ. The Thermodynamics of Ideal Solutions. Deviations in Polymer Solutions. The Technical Importance of Plasticizers.

Crosslinked Polymers. Degree of Disorder. Molecular Flaws. Swelling and Solution as Function of Branching. Branching and Disproportionation. Linear and Crosslinked Polymers. Branched Polymers. Net and Space Polymers. Contrast of Linear and Crosslinked Polymers.

Intermolecular and Intramolecular Reactions. Ring Formations. Stability of Rings. Ease of Ring Formation. Condensation Polymerizations. The Reactions of Hydroxy Acids. Ring and Polymer Reversibility. Polymerizability and the Nature of the Ring. Addition Polyreactions. Reactions of Compounds with Olefinic Unsaturation. Re-

CHAPTER

actions of Carbon Heteroatom Compounds. Summary of Intermolecular and Intramolecular Reactions.

CHAPTER

CHAPTER 1

Polymers
Rubbers, Plastics, and Fibers

THE STATES OF MATTER

After the atomic concept of matter became firmly established in the nineteenth century, the developments in the fields of physics and chemistry led to the recognition of three basic states of matter, namely, the gaseous, the liquid, and the solid states. Most simple molecules fitted in this scheme. The kinetic theory of gases adequately explains the behavior of gases. This theory describes the gaseous molecules as small particles which are in constant motion, traveling in substantially straight lines, colliding with the walls of the container, and occasionally colliding with themselves. During these collisions the gaseous molecules behave as perfectly elastic spheres. The gaseous pressure is due to the dynamic effect of impact, and the motion of the molecules allows them to occupy whatever volume in which they are enclosed. The distance between neighboring molecules in a gas is relatively large, and the attractive forces are not sufficient to keep the molecules together. In normal gaseous molecules, the internal structure of the molecule may be disregarded in describing the kinetic motion of the gas. However, when the gaseous molecules are forced closer to each other, the details of structure, attractive forces, and composition become important. As the pressure on the gas is increased or as the temperature is lowered and thermal motion is reduced, the distance between neighboring molecules becomes shorter and the attractive forces become more effective. If the pressure is greatly increased or if the temperature is reduced sufficiently, the density of the gas increases. As a result liquefaction occurs, and the liquid is subject to flow. As a result of liquefaction, the compressibility of the liquid is less than that of the gas, the density of the liquid is higher than that of the gas, and the liquid now occupies a space equal to its own specific volume, not to the total volume of the container. Because of flow, however, the liquid shapes itself to that part of the container which it contacts. Furthermore, whereas all gases are completely miscible, many pairs of liquids are immiscible.

Herzfeld and Smallwood [1] state that the only fundamental difference between a gas and a liquid is the property of liquids forming an independent surface, that is, one not determined by the walls of the container, and that the other differences between gases and liquids are of degree and not fundamental. In a liquid there are three sources of pressure, the kinetic pressure, the cohesion pressure, and the external pressure.

As the temperature of a liquid is reduced, a change occurs resulting in a solid substance which has definite shape and volume and the qualities of rigidity and resistance. Solids are distinguished fundamentally from liquids and gases in that they are bounded by plane surfaces so oriented, one to the other, that they possess some degree of symmetry, a state called the crystalline state of aggregation. Every crystalline solid has a definite transition point at which it undergoes an abrupt change into a liquid, with the absorption of energy. In crystals, the constituent atoms are arranged in a definite pattern which is repeated regularly throughout the body of the crystal; in liquids, while the arrangement of the atoms in the molecules persists, the molecules themselves are distributed at random in respect to one another.

The solid, liquid, and gaseous states of matter are demonstrated readily by a number of simple compounds, such as acetamide or benzoic acid. Acetamide is crystalline at room temperature, and on heating at atmospheric pressure, it becomes a liquid at 82 C. On further heating, while the pressure is maintained constant, it remains liquid until it reaches a temperature of 222 C, and then it becomes gaseous. This process is reversible, and, on cooling, the liquid first and then the solid acetamide are obtained.

All other solid bodies which do not exhibit the crystalline state of aggregation were once classified as amorphous, and were to be regarded as nothing more than liquids of great viscosity.[2] There are a number of simple organic substances, such as glycerin, which on cooling crystallize with difficulty, and as the temperature is lowered, the viscosities of these liquids gradually increase. However, when these substances are induced to crystallize, they follow the pattern of the crystalline, liquid, and gaseous states of matter.

Many complex organic substances could not be adequately described by such an idealized scheme. Many of these complex substances have a direct bearing on life itself. Hair, the collogen in the tendons, the tissue in muscle, and many substances comprising vegetative and animal bodies are difficult to classify. Silk, cotton, wool, and rubber also fall in this category.

Our everyday living attests to the importance of these and many other natural products. Pound for pound, silk and cellulose are stronger than steel. Rubber possesses elastic extensibility in a remarkable combination with high strength. When we refer to these particular natural products, we point especially to those materials originating in living organisms. Nature was most thoughtful in giving man and animals hoofs and nails with the toughness of keratin. To survive, living organisms must have physical form and coherence. To accomplish these objectives, nature synthesizes those molecules that possess the requisite physical properties.

We immediately recognize that the properties attracting our attention are not only the specific properties, such as melting point, solubility, refractive index, or the like, by which a chemist characterizes organic substances, but also such outstanding mechanical properties as the tensile strength of silk and the impact strength of horn. These properties are outstanding because even though such strength properties are associated with molecular structure, organic structures are usually characterized by low values for their mechanical properties.

The particular mechanical and physical properties of these natural substances are reflected in other modes of behavior. Generally, but with many exceptions, they exist as complex mixtures of organic substances that show little or no tendency to "crystallize" nor do they exhibit definite melting points. They usually exist as a complexity of molecules of different molecular weights. When broken they show a concoidal fracture with a typical luster on the surface of the fracture. When they are dissolved in a volatile solvent and the solvent is allowed to evaporate, the solution at first becomes extremely viscous even though extremely dilute. These solutions, after complete elimination of the solvent, produce a vitreous or glassy mass or a continuous film.

Associated with high viscosities at low concentration, these materials exhibit many other remarkable properties. Their phenomena in diffusion, sedimentation, and osmotic processes, and their reaction toward thermal and mechanical treatment are not typical of the behavior of the ordinary organic compounds. Their ability to yield films and filaments has usually been associated with their non-crystalloidal character; and in a measure this conclusion is proper. Many of them normally show or may be mechanically or thermally processed to exhibit a marked degree of internal organization as indicated by birefringence, anistrophy, and diffraction of X-rays of 1 to 2 Å so that regular fiber patterns are obtained. Because they show these particular properties always found in crystals, they have been named *crystalloids*. This terminology is incorrect because in contrast to the norm for crystals they do not possess plane boundaries but exhibit a rod- or a ribbonlike form with dimensions ranging from 50 to 10,000 Å. The crystallized area of these substances contains intermicellar disorganized fractions indicating incomplete or partial crystallization, often called liquid areas.

These types of substances were left aside and classified as belonging to some vague borderland of the solid state. Some of them were classed as amorphous substances since they did not conform to the definitions of a crystal. Amorphous substances were to be regarded as nothing more than liquids of great viscosity, and among such substances were the glasses and the resins.

It was possible to describe rubber as glasslike at liquid-air temperatures, but at room temperature its elasticity, ductility, and softness distinguished it markedly from all other known glasses. When highly stretched and cooled, X-ray studies showed that it was crystalline. Cotton gave no external evidence of crystallinity, yet it was anisotropic when examined under X-ray, in contrast to glass, which has isotropic properties. When heated, cellulose did not melt; part of it became gaseous, but only because of decomposition.

Known also were a large number of synthetic organic substances, such as polystyrene,[3] that did not fit into the idealized scheme.

A significant characteristic of these synthetics is that they possess other properties that are comparable to many of the properties found in numerous products of an organic nature. Numerous investigations on the colloidal nature of these specific natural and synthetic substances led to the conclusion that the properties of these compounds were definitely due to their physical dimensions and great molecular weight.

Fischer's classical work [4] confirmed the high-molecular-weight nature of the proteins. Staudinger's investigations [5] established a number of synthetic high-molecular-weight molecules as models for a number of natural substances. He derived polystyrene as a model for rubber, polyoxymethylene as a model for cellulose, polyvinyl alcohol as a model for a polysaccharide, and polyvinyl acetate as a model for a polysaccharide ester.

Studies on the degradation of natural and synthetic substances into simpler units verified [6] their very high molecular weight. Those molecules showing these specific properties have been named polymers and macromolecules.

Within the last twenty-five years a considerable amount of study has been given to polymers. These studies have not led to the abandonment of the ideal scheme of the solid, the liquid, and the gaseous states.

Rather, they have shown that the scheme for the low-molecular-weight compounds must be expanded to include the polymers with molecular weights 100 to 100,000 times that of the simple molecules. These studies on polymers have been accelerated and stimulated for three major reasons:

1. The desire to understand those exceedingly important substances that play such an important part in the structures and functions of living entities.
2. The intent to utilize the naturally occurring materials to greatest advantage.
3. The wish purposefully to synthesize other molecules with properties designed for specific utilization.

As a result of these studies, another outstanding characteristic of polymers was recognized, namely, that regardless of the origin of the polymer, or wherever they are found or however they are used, their behavior and properties may be classified as belonging to one of the subclasses: (1) the rubber state, (2) the plastic state, or (3) the fiber state. The classification of the basic states of matter may be extended, therefore, from simple low-molecular-weight molecules to complex high-molecular-weight molecules.

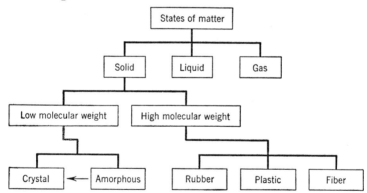

DEFINITION OF A POLYMER

A polymer substance possesses a very high molecular weight. The ranges of molecular weights found in a few ordinary organic compounds are contrasted with some synthetic and some natural polymers in Table 1. It is recognized in Table 1 that rubbers, plastics, and fibers are represented among the list of polymers. The molecular weights of the synthetic polymers in this table are representative of some of the industrial products and can be prepared with higher or lower values as desired.

TABLE 1

Ordinary Organic Substances		Polymers			
		Natural		Synthetic	
Substance	Molecular Weight	Substance	Molecular Weight	Substance	Typical Molecular Weight
Water	18.0	Amylose	10,000–80,000	Polystyrene	10,000–300,000
Ethyl alcohol	46.05	Pectin	ca. 270,000	Polyvinyl chloride	20,000–160,000
Benzene	78.05	Native cellulose	ca. 570,000	Polyisobutylene	10,000–100,000
Dextrose	198.11	Casein	15,000–375,000	Polymethyl methacrylate	50,000–140,000
Sucrose	342.18	Silk protein	ca. 150,000	Polyacrylonitrile	60,000–500,000
Glycerin	92.06	Gutta-percha	80,000–300,000	. . . .	. . . .

Comprehensive investigations have determined the structure and composition of many natural and synthetic polymers with certainty. These studies have shown that all polymers have in common one outstanding characteristic, a repeating structural unit in their molecules. This is true of both the natural and the synthetic products. This striking relationship may be observed in Table 2.

High-molecular-weight substances of this nature are called *high polymers*. The term *high* indicates a *high molecular weight*, the Greek term *poly* indicates *many*, and the Greek term *mer* indicates a *part* or *unit*. The combined terms mean that the unit is repeated many times in the molecular structure.

The classification of such diverse materials as rubbers, plastics, fibers, and a large number of natural products, such as high polymers, warrants fuller definitions of the terms *polymer* and *high polymers*. Historically, a number of definitions have been proposed.

In 1833, Berzelius [7] recognized polymers as compounds having different molecular weights in which the same atoms existed in the same proportions. This definition contains some of the elements that are common to polymers but does not exclude a larger number of compounds that are not polymeric. The compounds in Table 3 satisfy the terms of the Berzelius definition, yet, in the modern concept of polymers, none are recognized as such. Trioxane is a crystalline material which melts at 61 to 62 C and has a boiling point of 114 C. In solution it shows the viscosity normally associated with crystalloids and has no film-forming properties. Similarly, dioxane is a liquid boiling at 101 C, freezing in the neighborhood of 0 C, and containing the same atoms in the same proportions as ethylene oxide, yet dioxane does not possess any of the characteristics currently associated with polymers. A liquid distyrene [8-11] of the structure C_6H_5—CH—CH=CH—C_6H_5, with a

$$\overset{\displaystyle |}{CH_3}$$

boiling point of 310 to 312 C and a density of 1.016, has been prepared from styrene by room temperature reaction in the presence of one volume of sulfuric acid and nine volumes of glacial acetic acid. Stobbe reported [12] the isolation of a distyrene that is a saturated four-membered ring by treating styrene with a potassium iodide-iodine solution. Both these distyrenes have the same atoms in the same proportions as styrene, and still exhibit no polymeric properties.

The term polymer has likewise been defined in terms of monomer (*mono*, one; *mer*, part), and the conditions of this definition require that the polymer be of a larger molecular weight than the monomer, and that both have the same atoms in the same proportions. [13-15] These conditions are not satisfied by many polymers. Formaldehyde may be cyclicized under special conditions to produce trioxane, which contains the same atoms as formaldehyde in the same proportions. On the other hand, polyoxymethylene, a linear derivative of formaldehyde possessing polymer properties, contains terminal hydroxyl groups, and the polymer does not possess the same proportion of atoms as formaldehyde. It is obvious that as the value of n in polyoxymethylene diminishes, the deviation from this definition becomes larger, as is shown in the equations deriving trioxane and polyoxymethylene from formaldehyde.

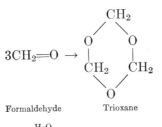

$$3CH_2{=}O \rightarrow$$

Formaldehyde   Trioxane

$$nCH_2{=}O \xrightarrow{\text{H}_2\text{O}} HO(CH_2O)_{n-1}CH_2OH$$

Formaldehyde   Polyoxymethylene

TABLE 2

POLYMER COMPOSITIONS

Name	Repeating Unit *	Structure
Polyethylene	$-CH_2-CH_2-$	$-CH_2CH_2CH_2CH_2CH_2CH_2CH_2CH_2CH_2CH_2CH_2CH_2CH_2CH_2CH_2CH_2-$
Polyisobutylene	$-CH_2-C(CH_3)(CH_3)-$	$-CH_2-C(CH_3)(CH_3)-CH_2-C(CH_3)(CH_3)-CH_2-C(CH_3)(CH_3)-CH_2-C(CH_3)(CH_3)-CH_2-C(CH_3)(CH_3)-$
Polystyrene	$-CH_2-CH(C_6H_5)-$	$-CH_2-CH(C_6H_5)-CH_2-CH(C_6H_5)-CH_2-CH(C_6H_5)-CH_2-CH(C_6H_5)-CH_2-CH(C_6H_5)-CH_2-CH(C_6H_5)-$
Polyvinyl alcohol	$-CH_2-CH(OH)-$	$-CH_2-CH(OH)-CH_2-CH(OH)-CH_2-CH(OH)-CH_2-CH(OH)-CH_2-CH(OH)-CH_2-CH(OH)-$
Polyvinyl formal	$-CH_2-CH-CH_2-CH-O-CH_2-O-$	$-CH_2-CH-CH_2-CH-CH_2-CH-CH_2-CH-CH_2-CH-CH_2-CH-$ (with $O-CH_2-O$ bridges)
Polyvinylidene chloride	$-CH_2-C(Cl)(Cl)-$	$-CH_2-C(Cl)(Cl)-CH_2-C(Cl)(Cl)-CH_2-C(Cl)(Cl)-CH_2-C(Cl)(Cl)-CH_2-C(Cl)(Cl)-CH_2-C(Cl)(Cl)-$
Polyacrylonitrile	$-CH_2-CH(CN)-$	$-CH_2-CH(CN)-CH_2-CH(CN)-CH_2-CH(CN)-CH_2-CH(CN)-CH_2-CH(CN)-CH_2-CH(CN)-$

Name	Segmer	Polymer structure
Polymethyl methacrylate		
Chloroprene		
Cresol formaldehyde resin		
Dibenzyl silicone resin		
Ethyl-cellulose		

* The repeating unit in a polymer is called a segmer, and the number of segmers represent the D.P. value or its Degree of Polymerization.

TABLE 2 (*Continued*)
POLYMER COMPOSITIONS

Structure	Name	Repeating Unit *
(glyceryl phthalate linoleate chemical structure)	Glyceryl phthalate linoleate	$-OC$ ... $COOCH_2-CH-CH_2O-$ $O=CC_{17}H_{31}$
(polydiallyl phthalate chemical structure)	Polydiallyl phthalate	$-CH_2-CH-$ ... $-CH_2-$ ... $C=O$ $C=O$ ... $-CH_2-$ ... $-CH_2-CH-$

NATURAL PRODUCTS

Structure	Name	Repeating Unit *
(protein molecule chemical structure)	Protein molecule	$-NH$ CO CH R

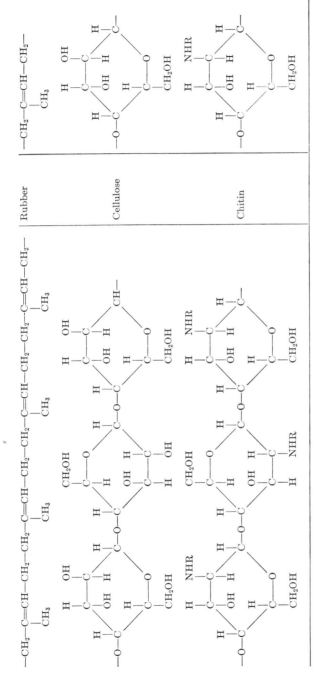

Rubber	
Cellulose	
Chitin	

* The repeating unit in a polymer is called a segmer, and the number of segmers represent the D.P. value or its Degree of Polymerization.

TABLE 3

Compound	Structural Formula	Empirical Formula	Melting Point	Boiling Point	Molecular Weight
Formaldehyde	$H_2C\!=\!O$	CH_2O	-92 C	-21 C	30
Methyl formate	$\overset{\overset{\text{O}}{\|\|}}{HC}\!-\!OCH_3$	$C_2H_4O_2$	-99.0 C	31.50 C	60
Trioxane	$CH_2 \overset{OCH_2}{\underset{OCH_2}{\diamond}} O$	$C_3H_6O_3$	64 C	Sublimes 46 C	90
Symmetrical Dihydroxyacetone	$HOCH_2\overset{\overset{\text{O}}{\|\|}}{C}\!-\!CH_2OH$	$C_3H_6O_3$	68–75 C	....	90
Glucose (anhydrous)	$\begin{array}{c} CH_2\!-\!CH\!-\!CH\!-\!CH\!-\!CH\!-\!CH \\ \;\mid\quad\;\mid\quad\;\mid\quad\;\mid\quad\;\mid\quad\;\|\; \\ OH\;\;OH\;\;OH\;\;OH\;\;OH\;\;O \end{array}$	$C_6H_{12}O_6$	(+1H$_2$O 118–120 C) Anhydrous 146 C	Decomposes	180

The same difficulty of definition is encountered when dioxane and polyethylene glycol are defined as polymers in terms of their monomer, ethylene oxide, as, for example:

$$2 \;\; \overset{\text{CH}_2-\text{CH}_2}{\underset{\text{O}}{\diagdown\diagup}} \;\; \rightarrow \;\; O \overset{\text{CH}_2-\text{CH}_2}{\underset{\text{CH}_2-\text{CH}_2}{\diamond}} O$$

Ethylene oxide   Dioxane

$$n \;\; \overset{\text{CH}_2-\text{CH}_2}{\underset{\text{O}}{\diagdown\diagup}} \;\; \overset{\text{H}_2\text{O}}{\longrightarrow} \;\; HO(CH_2CH_2O)_nH$$

Ethylene oxide   Polyoxyethylene

The difference between polymer and monomer composition in all these cases is in a water molecule that has added to the n number of basic starting molecules.

A similar discrepancy is evident in the polymers obtained through esterification or amidation reactions. In the intermolecular condensations of hydroxy or amino acids, a molecule of water is eliminated with the disappearance of each carboxyl group, as, for example:

$$n\text{HOCH}_2\text{CH}_2\text{CH}_2\text{CH}_2\text{CH}_2\text{COOH} \rightarrow$$
$$\text{H(OCH}_2\text{CH}_2\text{CH}_2\text{CH}_2\text{CH}_2\text{CO})_n\text{OH} + (n-1)\text{H}_2\text{O}$$

$$n\mathrm{H_2NCH_2CH_2CH_2CH_2CH_2COOH} \rightarrow$$
$$\mathrm{H(NHCH_2CH_2CH_2CH_2CH_2CO)}_n\mathrm{OH} + (n - 1)\mathrm{H_2O}$$

In a similar fashion, polymeric esters and amides are prepared by the condensation of polybasic acids with polyhydric alcohols and polyamines, respectively, by the elimination of water. The relation of polymer to monomer is further complicated by the mole ratios found in the reaction product as is indicated in Table 4.

TABLE 4

$n\mathrm{HOOCCH_2CH_2CH_2CH_2COOH} + n\mathrm{HOCH_2CH_2CH_2OH} \rightarrow$
$\qquad \mathrm{HO(OCCH_2CH_2CH_2CH_2COOCH_2CH_2CH_2O)}_n\mathrm{H} + (2n - 1)\mathrm{H_2O}$

$n\mathrm{HOOCCH_2CH_2CH_2CH_2COOH} + (n + 1)\mathrm{HOCH_2CH_2CH_2OH} \rightarrow$
$\qquad \mathrm{HOCH_2CH_2CH_2O(OCCH_2CH_2CH_2CH_2COOCH_2CH_2CH_2O)}_n\mathrm{H} + 2n\mathrm{H_2O}$

$(n + 1)\mathrm{HOOCCH_2CH_2CH_2CH_2COOH} + n\mathrm{HOCH_2CH_2CH_2OH} \rightarrow$
$\qquad \mathrm{HO(OCCH_2CH_2CH_2CH_2COOCH_2CH_2CH_2O)}_n\mathrm{OCCH_2CH_2CH_2CH_2COOH}$
$\qquad\qquad + 2n\mathrm{H_2O}$

$n\mathrm{HOOCCH_2CH_2CH_2CH_2COOH} + n\mathrm{H_2NCH_2CH_2CH_2NH_2} \rightarrow$
$\qquad \mathrm{HO(OCCH_2CH_2CH_2CH_2COHNCH_2CH_2CH_2NH)}_n\mathrm{H} + (2n - 1)\mathrm{H_2O}$

$n\mathrm{HOOCCH_2CH_2CH_2CH_2COOH} + (n + 1)\mathrm{H_2NCH_2CH_2CH_2NH_2} \rightarrow$
$\qquad \mathrm{H_2NCH_2CH_2CH_2NH(OCCH_2CH_2CH_2CH_2COHNCH_2CH_2CH_2NH)}_n\mathrm{H} + 2n\mathrm{H_2O}$

$(n + 1)\mathrm{HOOCCH_2CH_2CH_2CH_2COOH} + n\mathrm{H_2NCH_2CH_2CH_2NH_2} \rightarrow$
$\qquad \mathrm{HO(OCCH_2CH_2CH_2CH_2COHNCH_2CH_2CH_2NH)}_n\mathrm{OCCH_2CH_2CH_2CH_2COOH}$
$\qquad\qquad + 2n\mathrm{H_2O}$

The term *monomer* is likewise difficult to define especially when two entirely different classes of compounds, like the diamine and the dicarboxylic acid of Table 4, are reacted together to propagate the reaction. In such a case the term *monomer* designates the mixture of two starting molecules, when an intermediate reaction product, $\mathrm{HOOC(CH_2)_4CONH(CH_2)_3NH_2}$, would more truly represent the monomer.

The definition of polymer in terms of monomer composition cannot be satisfactorily applied to many polymers derived from olefinic molecules. A typical example is the polymerization of styrene, $\mathrm{C_6H_5CH{=}CH_2}$. The reaction is usually written

The equation is substantially correct if the process has occurred thermally or photochemically in the absolute absence of oxygen or peroxides or without other active catalysts such as aluminum chloride or sulfuric acid, so that the terminal valences are not utilized by a molecule other than the initial olefin. However, when they are present, many of these catalytic bodies are known to form part of the molecule. Parabromobenzoyl peroxide catalyzed reactions have been known [16] to contribute a bromophenyl radical to the polymer.

$$n CH_2\!\!=\!\!CH \xrightarrow{(p\text{-}BrC_6H_5CO)_2O_2} -\left[CH_2\!\!-\!\!CH\right]\!\!-\!\!CH_2\!\!-\!\!CH\!\!-\!\!C_6H_4Br$$

These findings were verified [17] by other investigators who also have shown that halobenzoate radicals are permanently attached to the polymer.

$$n CH_2\!\!=\!\!CH \xrightarrow{(p\text{-}ClC_6H_5CO)_2O_2} -\left[CH_2\!\!-\!\!CH\right]\!\!-\!\!CH_2\!\!-\!\!CH\!\!-\!\!O\!\!-\!\!C\!\!=\!\!O$$

Such polymers will not have the same atoms in the same proportion as the monomer, and the deviation from this proportion will be higher, the lower the molecular weight. Similarly, sulfuric acid may become the terminal part of the polymer molecule, as in the acid polymerization of styrene.

$$n CH_2\!\!=\!\!CH \xrightarrow{H_2SO_4} H\!\!-\!\!\left[CH_2\!\!-\!\!CH\right]\!\!-\!\!CH_2\!\!-\!\!CHOSO_3H$$

The same is true in the preparation [18] of polymers of isobutylene, for example,

$$2CH_2\!\!=\!\!C\!\!\begin{array}{c}CH_3\\CH_3\end{array} \xrightarrow{H_2SO_4} H\!\!-\!\!\left[\begin{array}{c}CH_3\\CH_2\!\!-\!\!C\!\!-\\CH_3\end{array}\right]\!\!-\!\!CH_2\!\!-\!\!C\!\!\begin{array}{c}CH_3\\CH_3\\OSO_3H\end{array}$$

In the early literature [19] it was believed that the property of undergoing polymerization was peculiar to unsaturated compounds and that polymerization occurred because of their natural tendency to saturate themselves. The compounds which showed this tendency to polymerize were those containing unsaturations, such as

$$\diagup \!\!\!\! C{=}C \diagup\!\!\!\!\diagdown \,, \; -C{\equiv}C-, \; \diagdown\!\!\!\! C{=}O, \; \diagdown\!\!\!\! C{=}S, \; -C{\equiv}N, \; -C{\equiv}N{=}O, \text{ etc.}$$

It was likewise thought [20] that a polymer is usually formed by the union of two or more molecules of the original compound united in such a manner that depolymerization into the parent substance is readily achieved. The reversible processes of converting anthracene to dianthracene under the influence of light [21-24]

$$\text{Anthracene} \; \underset{\text{dark}}{\overset{\text{light}}{\rightleftarrows}} \; \text{Dianthracene}$$

and of converting cinnamic acid to truxillic acid [25, 26] were considered polymerizations.

$$2C_6H_5CH{=}CHCOOH \; \rightleftharpoons \; \begin{array}{c} C_6H_5CH{-}CH{-}COOH \\ | \qquad | \\ C_6H_5CH{-}CH{-}COOH \end{array}$$

Cinnamic acid   Truxillic acid

Acetaldehyde may be converted to paraldehyde and aldol. The conversion to paraldehyde was considered a polymerization since acetaldehyde is regenerated readily by distillation in the presence of a small amount of sulfuric acid. Since acetaldehyde is not regenerated from aldol, its formation was classified as a condensation reaction and not as a polymerization.

$$CH_3CHO$$

condensation $\diagup$ $\diagdown$ polymerization

$$CH_3CHOHCH_2CHO \qquad\qquad CH_3\overset{}{C}H \qquad\qquad \begin{array}{c} CH_3 \\ | \\ O{-}CH \\ \diagup \qquad \diagdown \\ \qquad\qquad O \\ \diagdown \qquad \diagup \\ O{-}CH \\ | \\ CH_3 \end{array}$$

Aldol   Acetaldehyde   Paraldehyde

The properties of polymers are not found in either the aldol or the paraldehyde.

Carothers [27] defined polymerization as an intermolecular reaction functionally capable of proceeding indefinitely to molecules of infinite size.   In view of these investigations, *polymers are defined as the high-molecular-weight inter-reaction products of related polyfunctional molecules.* The component parts of this definition are derived as follows:

I. *High Molecular Weight.* The word *high* is necessary to distinguish these substances from the low-molecular-weight ones that exhibit *none* of the properties of high polymers.

II. *Polyfunctional Molecules.* These terms are needed to distinguish this reaction from the reaction of monofunctional molecules that are incapable of producing polymers.   This becomes evident when the reactions of monofunctional molecules are considered.   Functionality refers to the number of positions in a molecule normally available for reaction under the specific conditions of the experiment.   In the esterification reaction with ethyl alcohol, acetic acid has a functionality of one, for example,

$$CH_3COOH + C_2H_5OH \rightarrow CH_3COOC_2H_5 + H_2O \qquad (1)$$

If hexamethylene glycol is used as the alcohol, the functionality of the acetic acid remains one, even though the functionality of the glycol is two, for example,

$$
\begin{array}{ccc}
CH_3COOH & HOCH_2 & CH_3COOCH_2 \\
| & | & | \\
+ & (CH_2)_6 \rightarrow & (CH_2)_6 + 2H_2O \qquad (2) \\
| & | & | \\
CH_3COOH & HOCH_2 & CH_3COOCH_2
\end{array}
$$

In contrast to acetic acid, succinic acid has a functionality of two:

$$
\begin{array}{ccc}
CH_2COOH & HOC_2H_5 & CH_2COOC_2H_5 \\
| & + & \rightarrow | & + 2H_2O \qquad (3) \\
CH_2COOH & HOC_2H_5 & CH_2COOC_2H_5
\end{array}
$$

The products of the above reactions are low-molecular-weight esters and possess none of the properties of high polymers.   On the other hand, the esterification of succinic acid by hexamethylene glycol, a reaction in which both molecules have a functionality greater than one, produces an ester having the properties of a polymer.   When both molecules are polyfunctional, the molecules are capable of propagating the reaction indefinitely, even if thermodynamically this is never accomplished.   This concept is indicated graphically in Table 5 in the following series of reactions using n molecules of the acid and the glycol.

As a result of the propagation of the reaction the molecular weight may become very high.   The essential nature of a polyfunctional molecule is such that it is capable of extending the chemical reaction indefinitely in space. The causes for the termination of the reaction are beyond the scope of this discussion since free energy considerations, cyclization, condition of reaction, the nature of the reactants, the presence of modifying ingredients, and other causes may be direct factors that will be considered later.

TABLE 5

$HO(CH_2)_8OH + HOOC(CH_2)_2COOH \rightarrow HO(CH_2)_8OOC(CH_2)_2COOH$

$2HO(CH_2)_8OH + HOOC(CH_2)_2COOH \rightarrow HO(CH_2)_8OOC(CH_2)_2COO(CH_2)_8OH$

$2HO(CH_2)_8OH + 2HOOC(CH_2)_2COOH \rightarrow$
$\qquad HO(CH_2)_8OOC(CH_2)_2COO(CH_2)_8OOC(CH_2)_2COOH$

$3HO(CH_2)_8OH + 2HOOC(CH_2)_2COOH \rightarrow$
$\qquad HO(CH_2)_8OOC(CH_2)_2COO(CH_2)_8OOC(CH_2)_2COO(CH_2)_8OH$

$3HO(CH_2)_8OH + 3HOOC(CH_2)_2COOH \rightarrow$
$\qquad HO(CH_2)_8OOC(CH_2)_2COO(CH_2)_8OOC(CH_2)_2COO(CH_2)_8OOC(CH_2)_2COOH$

$10HO(CH_2)_8OH + 10HOOC(CH_2)_2COOH \rightarrow$
$\qquad HO(CH_2)_8OOC(CH_2)_2CO[O(CH_2)_8OOC(CH_2)_2CO]_8O(CH_2)_8OOC(CH_2)_2COOH$

$20HO(CH_2)_8OH + 20HOOC(CH_2)_2COOH \rightarrow$
$\qquad HO(CH_2)_8OOC(CH_2)_2CO[O(CH_2)_8OOC(CH_2)_2CO]_{18}O(CH_2)_8OOC(CH_2)_2COOH$

$nHO(CH_2)_8OH + nHOOC(CH_2)_2COOH \rightarrow$
$\qquad HO(CH_2)_8OOC(CH_2)_2CO[O(CH_2)_8OOC(CH_2)_2CO]_{n-2}O(CH_2)_8OOC(CH_2)_2COOH$

III. *Related Polyfunctional Molecules.* The word *related* is essential to the definition. It means that a substantial portion of the molecules must be polyfunctional; otherwise high-molecular-weight growth cannot occur. This was shown in the concept of polyfunctionality. It does not mean that monofunctional molecules cannot be used to modify the reaction provided a high-molecular-weight product is obtained. Monofunctional molecules are used in the preparation of polymers to control and lower the molecular weight.

IV. *Inter-reaction Product.* The term *inter-reaction* is in contrast to intrareaction. The reaction must occur between one molecule and another molecule. The distinction becomes clear when the self-esterification of a hydroxy acid is concerned. If the reaction is intramolecular, that is, within the same molecule, the product is a cyclic lactone:

$$nHO(CH_2)_3COOH \rightarrow n\begin{array}{c} CH_2 \\ \diagup \quad \diagdown \\ CH_2 \quad\quad CO \\ \diagdown \quad \diagup \\ CH_2O \end{array} + nH_2O$$

On the other hand, if the reaction is intermolecular and between different molecules, polymer formation will occur:

$$n\text{HO}(\text{CH}_2)_3\text{COOH} \rightarrow \text{H}[\text{O}(\text{CH}_2)_3\text{CO}]_n\text{OH} + (n-1)\text{H}_2\text{O}$$

The polymerization esterification reaction of hexamethylene glycol and succinic acid eliminates water and produces a polymer differing in composition from the starting materials. This fact is of no consequence to the present definition, since if by-products are required to achieve inter-reaction, they must occur simultaneously or subsequently to inter-reaction and thus be included or implied in the definition.

Similar reasoning applies to those reactions where a small amount of catalyst or water is required to bring about polymerization. If the added component is needed to cause the polymerization, it becomes an essential feature of the inter-reaction. The combined terms, *inter-reaction of related polyfunctional molecules*, likewise eliminate the difficulties found in describing the polymer in terms of the composition of the monomer.

Limiting Values of High Molecular Weight for a Polymer

In arriving at the definition of a polymer, two classes of molecules having repeating structures were recognized. One class of molecules possessed a large number of segmers, and they had polymer properties. The other class had only a few segmers in their molecules, and they were non-polymeric. The difference in the polymeric and non-polymeric compounds lies in the number of the segmers in the respective molecules.

Polymer means *many parts*, and ten as well as a hundred or a thousand can be considered "many" in contrast to one or two. Polymer, at the present time, implies that the number of *mers* united in the compound must be sufficiently large (*poly*) so that certain minimum chemical and physical properties are observed. There has been no absolute or satisfactory method of setting a limiting value to the number of segmers in a molecule before it is classified as a polymer primarily because the units or mers, numerous as they are, vary in molecular weight and molecular dimension, as may be observed in Table 2, where the unit weights of ethylene and of triethylcellulose are 28 and 245, respectively. Even in the simple case of polyethylene, as the number of segmer units is increased from a very small value to a high value, the transition in properties, from those of non-polymers to polymers, is gradual. In a certain transitional region the classification into polymeric and non-polymeric becomes arbitrary. However, certain generalizations as to the limiting values can be made.

Staudinger [28-30] studied this problem and subdivided polymers according to certain of their physical limitations. He defines a hemipolymer as a readily soluble polymer whose molecular weight lies above 1000 and below 10,000. Eupolymer is used to describe those high polymers with a molecular weight in excess of 10,000 since these substances are difficult to dissolve. In colloidal terms, he also classified them in values of chain length.

1. *Hemicolloids* are polymers with molecular weight up to 10,000. Their molecules have 20 to 100 segmers and chain lengths of 50 to 250 Å. Their colloid properties are not very pronounced, they dissolve without swelling, and their solutions have low viscosity. Films prepared from these polymers have low strength values. In this class typical polymer properties are evident to a low degree.

2. *Mesocolloids* are polymers having 100 to 1000 segmers whose chain length is 250 to 2500 Å. Their properties lie between those of the hemicolloids and eucolloids, and the polymer properties are very markedly evident.

3. *Eucolloids* are polymers that have over 1000 segmers whose chain length is over 2500 Å. Dissolution is accompanied by intense swelling; their solutions are very viscous even in low concentration and show high capacity for film formation. The solid eucolloids are very tough and hard.

TABLE 6

	Number of Segmers or D.P.	Appearance	Fiber and Film Properties	Solubility and Swelling in Schweitzer's Reagent	Viscosity of a 1% Solution in Schweitzer's Reagent
Oligosaccharide, α-cellulose, cellulose dextrine	1 to 10	Powdery	Brittle and no fiber- or film-forming properties	Rapid solubility without swelling	Very low viscosity
Hemicolloidal cellulose, β-cellulose	10 to 100	Powdery	Not very strong, little or no fiber- or film-forming properties	Solubility without swelling	Somewhat viscous
Mesocolloidal cellulose, α-cellulose, rayon, cellophane	100 to 500	Fibrous	Strong, possessing both film- and fiber-forming properties	Solubility after swelling	Viscous gel
Eucolloidal cellulose, α-cellulose, fibrous cellulose	500 to 3000	Very highly fibrous	Very strong and very marked fiber- and film-forming properties	Slight solubility after very strong swelling	Very high viscosity gel

TABLE 7

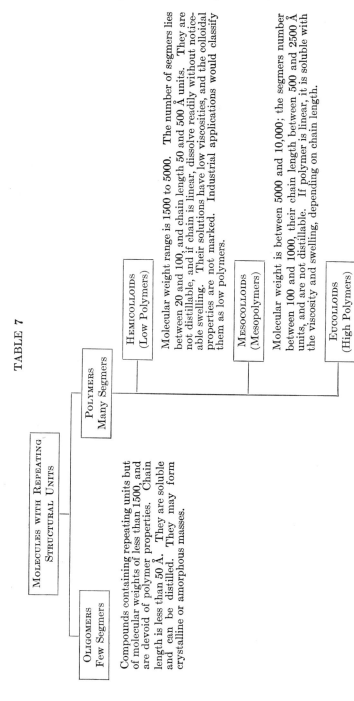

Molecules with Repeating Structural Units

Oligomers — Few Segmers

Compounds containing repeating units but of molecular weights of less than 1500, and are devoid of polymer properties. Chain length is less than 50 Å. They are soluble and can be distilled. They may form crystalline or amorphous masses.

Polymers — Many Segmers

Hemicolloids (Low Polymers)

Molecular weight range is 1500 to 5000. The number of segmers lies between 20 and 100, and chain length 50 and 500 Å units. They are not distillable, and if chain is linear, dissolve readily without noticeable swelling. Their solutions have low viscosities, and the colloidal properties are not marked. Industrial applications would classify them as low polymers.

Mesocolloids (Mesopolymers)

Molecular weight is between 5000 and 10,000; the segmers number between 100 and 1000, their chain length between 500 and 2500 Å units, and are not distillable. If polymer is linear, it is soluble with the viscosity and swelling, depending on chain length.

Eucolloids (High Polymers)

Molecular weight is usually over 10,000; segmers number over 1000 and chain length over 2500 Å. These polymers are not distillable. They dissolve with intense swelling if the chain is linear. Their dilute solutions are extremely viscous, and they usually form tough films and fibers.

Investigations [31] in 1930 showed that the molecular-weight limit of molecular distillation for organic substances lies between 1200 and 1500. As a generalization, it is in this molecular-weight range that polymer properties first become evident. Thereby a boundary may be established between polymers and non-polymers, whether the non-polymers contain repeating units or not. For those molecules that contain repeating units and have a molecular weight less than 1500, the term oligomer (*oligos*, Greek, few) is satisfactory. In no case should they be called polymers, since they do not contain "many" mers in the polymer sense and they do not have polymer properties. It must also be noted that oligomers are not hemicolloids. Staudinger [25] has applied the prefix *oligo* to those saccharides that have one to ten segmer units. These saccharides were devoid of polymer properties and were compared to those saccharides with sufficient segmers so that their polymer properties could be described (see Table 6).

In biology, a similar terminology is used:

Monomerous, having a single member in each whorl.

Oligomerous, having a few parts or members in a whorl.

Polymerous, having many parts or members in a whorl.

Accordingly, the primary distinction between oligomers and polymers becomes obvious, and those compounds belonging to the class of polymers may again be subclassified by Staudinger's colloidal relationship as hemicolloids, mesocolloids, and eucolloids. An equivalent classification is low polymers, mesopolymers, and high polymers. In general, the high polymers have a molecular weight of at least 10,000, the low polymers have a maximum molecular weight of about half this value, and the mesopolymers lie between the low and high polymers. The limits shown in the classification in Table 7 are not sharp. As an example, although the chain length expressed in terms of Ångström units may agree well with the molecular weight in one polymer, it may show a discrepancy for another polymer. In one case the segmer may be derived from ethylene with a molecular weight of 28, in another case it may be derived from a glucose unit with a molecular weight of 180 as in cellulose. However, in a molecular-weight series of one specific poly-

TABLE 8

	Melting Point	Solubility in Benzene
$C_{20}H_{42}$	38 C	Very soluble
$C_{30}H_{62}$	66 C	Soluble
$C_{60}H_{122}$	100 C	Difficultly soluble
$C_{100}H_{202}$	ca. 106 C	Very difficultly soluble
$C_{2000}H_{4002}$	ca. 110 C	Insoluble

mer, as in a series of polyethylenes, the molecular weight, the chain length, and the segmer number are equivalent. A marked division between low, meso, and high polymers is also readily made as is shown in the melting points and solubilities of the normal chain paraffins of Table 8.[26]

THE IMPORTANCE OF POLYMERS

Because of the infinite number of properties and sorts of behavior exhibited by polymers in their unlimited and diverse biological functions, their importance in living entities cannot be evaluated fully. They are an essential in the existence of life in the vegetative and animal kingdom from the lowest single-celled plant upward to man himself.

The polymeric saccharides are associated, in one form or another, with almost all plants, and the proteinic polymers are identified with animal tissue as well as with many plants. The cell wall of the alga, *Valonica ventricosa*, is known [32] to contain cellulose, and the polymeric carbohydrates, lichenin and isolichenin, are found in Icelandic moss.[33] As the plants become more complex, the polymer lignocellulose becomes evident, wherein the lignin appears to act as a connective substance. A number of various biological functions of the plant are carried on by various polymers such as the pectins, the gums, and the mucilages. Plants store the polysaccharides as starch, which is reconvertible to food as required. These polymers are found as reserve materials in seeds, fruits, tubers, and rhizomes. Inulin and konjakmannan are also found as reserve carbohydrates in a number of plants. Chlorophyll, which is an essential in plant life, appears to be associated with protein polymers.[34]

Whereas the polymeric saccharides are usually associated with plants, the proteins are identified with animals and their tissues. Four distinct proteins are found in muscle tissue: (1) myogen, which is water-soluble and albuminoid in character, with a molecular weight of about 81,000; (2) muscle globulin, with a molecular weight of about 160,000; (3) myosin, with a molecular weight of about 1,000,000; and (4) stroma protein. The principal constituent of the connective tissue in muscle as well as of the tendons is collogen fibers that are polymers of the amino acids. The protective elements of animals, hair, wool, horn, and nails, contain keratin as their principal polymer. The moth, *Bombyx mori*, protects itself with a cocoon of tough polymer, namely, silk. Hemoglobin, the coloring matter in the red blood corpuscles of vertebrates, has a molecular weight of 69,000 and appears to be polymeric. The coagulation of blood depends on the polymer, fibrinogen, which is dissolved in blood.

The fibrinogen is converted by the high-molecular-weight enzyme, thrombin, to fibrin, which precipitates and forms a clot.

In contrast to plants that store starches, many animals store glycogen for reserve energy. Once animal life exists, a large number of polymers play direct and important roles in the continued existence relative to health and disease. The polymers of one form of life may mean death to another form. Rattlesnake venom, crotoxin, is highly toxic to man and is a protein with a molecular weight of 33,000. A number of plant proteins, such as ricin, abrin, and crotin, are toxins inducing precipitation of red blood corpuscles. Such types of polymers are excellent arrow poisons. The bacterial toxins, such as have been isolated from the tubercle bacilli, are polymers with a molecular weight of 72,000.[35] Many micro-organisms such as *Acetobacter xylinum, B. mesentericus,* and *Penicillium Charlesii* produce polysaccharides from suitable sugar-containing media. This ability to form polysaccharides is associated with immunological specificity in certain pathogenic bacteria, such as in the Pneumococci I, II, and III.[36, 37] The serological importance of these polysaccharides resides in the fact that they form antigens when combined with proteins. The formation of antibodies, therefore, which is one of the most astounding and incomprehensible functions of living organisms, depends on the presence of polymers in the system.[38] There are a large number of infectious diseases which are due to pathogenic units known as viruses, many of which are polymers of high molecular weight and have a proteinic nature. The ferments or enzymes, which are considered as catalysts in processes involving living organisms, are polymeric. Some of the better known enzymes are urease, pepsin and trypsin. Some polymers exhibit the properties of hormones and are known [39] as proteohormones. Insulin is one of the proteohormones with a molecular weight of about 35,000. The lactation hormone, which has been isolated from the anterior lobe of the pituitary, is also a polymer. The active protein of the thyroid gland, thyreoglobuline, is a polymer with a molecular weight of 650,000.

These are some of the many bearings that polymers have on the existence and continuance of life. Once existence becomes a reality, the struggle for existence begins concurrently with existence. All living entities must have energy for continued existence. The ultimate material source of energy in life appears to be the sun; the sun transfers this energy to the lowest scale of life by means of a polymerization reaction; and carbon dioxide and water under the activation energy of the sun and in the presence of chlorophyll are transformed to sugars, starch, and cellulose. Often the fixing of atmospheric nitrogen through the roots of certain plants occurs simultaneously with this transformation.

The essentials of life in the lower and higher plants are transferred from one generation to another through the medium of, and in the custody and protection of, such polymers as are in seeds or in the protoplasms, the nucleoplasms, etc.

The ascending scale of life is plant, animal, and man. In this scale, the polymers of the lower scale supply the food and energy for the higher scale. Thus animals subsist primarily on plants, and man subsists on animals as well as on plants. With the recognition of this subsistence scale, man adapts himself to the favorable elements of his environment and attempts to improve those factors that contribute unfavorably to his environmental existence. The unfavorable factors are reflected in man's requirements in shelter, clothing, fuel, and luxuries. Wood, bamboo, and straw, all cellulosic polymers, have been used and still are necessary to man in the construction of shelter for himself and his domestic animals. All man's clothing is made of polymers: flax, ramie, cotton, wool, and silk. The polymers coal and wood are still man's basic fuel, in spite of oil; and even oil appears to have its origin in once living trees or fish or animals. Crude oil always contains some polymers.

Man's need for the polymer luxuries is evident in the size and scale of the rubber, plastics, and textile fiber industries.

RUBBERS

Rubbers are polymers characterized by a low initial elastic modulus of stretching in the range of 10^6 to 10^7 dynes per square centimeter and by a long range of almost instantaneously complete and reversible extensibility. As the temperature is lowered, the extensibility decreases markedly, and below some definite temperature rubbers become brittle.

TABLE 9

Year	Long Tons
1860	1,500
1875	9,000
1890	30,750
1900	48,000
1910	95,000
1915	155,000
1920	295,000
1925	525,000
1930	825,000
1935	873,000
1937	1,135,000

Plastics 25

Rubber and the products derived from rubber are considered to be indispensable to modern life. Natural rubber was the main source of this polymer almost exclusively up to the year 1940, as indicated by worldwide consumption (see Table 9). The volume of natural-rubber consumption was still increasing when the Second World War began, cutting off most of the sources of supply for natural rubber. A number of synthetic rubbers were produced on a large industrial scale. The outstanding synthetic rubbers were based on butadiene, which was copolymerized with either styrene or acrylonitrile. The butyl rubbers were copolymers of isobutylene with minor portions of butadiene or isoprene. The neoprene types of rubbers were based on 2-chlorobutadiene-1,3; and the thiokol rubbers are represented by the polyethylene polysulfides. The production of synthetic rubbers for the United States in the emergency periods of the war are tabulated in Table 10.

TABLE 10

U. S. PRODUCTION OF SYNTHETIC RUBBERS, LONG TONS

Year	Neoprene Type	Butadiene Type	Butyl Type	Thiokol Type	Total
1939	1,750	None	....	500	2,250
1940	2,500	60	....	700	3,260
1944	59,000	705,000	120,000	60,000	944,000

PLASTICS

Plastics are organic polymers with an initial elastic modulus ranging from 10^8 to 10^9 dynes per square centimeter. They also possess a marked range of deformability, of the order of 100 to 200 per cent, especially at elevated temperatures. Part of this deformation is reversible, and the remainder is permanent. The viscosity, extensibility, and modulus of elasticity are direct functions of temperature and are responsible for the plastic nature of the polymer.

Economically, the term plastics has now become associated with an industry in the United States that produced 5,000,000 pounds of products in 1920, approximately 500,000,000 pounds in 1941, and expanded further under the impact of "total" war to a figure of 800,000,000 pounds in 1944. Its dollar volume was indicated in 1945 as $330,000,000, and 42,000 people were employed in the industry. This industry was born in the United States in 1869. At that time ivory was extensively used in the manufacture of billiard balls. When an ivory shortage developed, the Phelan and Collender Company offered a $10,000 reward for a substitute material. John Wesley Hyatt, Jr., and his brother, Isaiah S. Hyatt, found a satisfactory substitute in a mixture of cellulose nitrate and camphor which became known as celluloid. The discovery was patented and issued as U. S. Patent 105,338 on July 12, 1870. A year later, the Celluloid Manufacturing Company was organized at Newark, N. J.

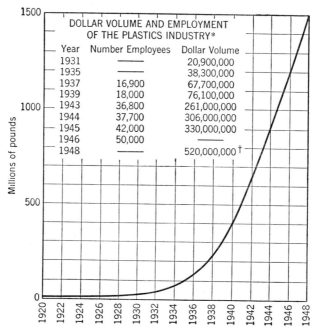

DOLLAR VOLUME AND EMPLOYMENT
OF THE PLASTICS INDUSTRY*

Year	Number Employees	Dollar Volume
1931	——	20,900,000
1935	——	38,300,000
1937	16,900	67,700,000
1939	18,000	76,100,000
1943	36,800	261,000,000
1944	37,700	306,000,000
1945	42,000	330,000,000
1946	50,000	——
1948	——	520,000,000 †

FIGURE 1.   The growth of the plastics industry.   * Data from the *Monthly Labor Review*, September 1947, Vol. 65, No. 3, p. 297.   † Estimated.

In 1880, the United States Census Bureau reported eight establishments with a total plastics sales volume of $1,261,540. This young industry showed signs of maturing when, on December 7, 1909, the basic United States Patent 942,699 was issued to L. P. Baekeland on resins obtained from formaldehyde and coal tar phenols and cresols. This new material found early and ready acceptance in the electrical industry because of its good mechanical strength and electrical properties. For many electrical applications it was far superior to shellac, which was widely used as an insulating material at that time.

Another reason for expansion of this industry is the diversity of the number of plastic compositions and their hosts of properties which fit them into a wide range. The real growth of the plastic industry began simultaneously with the expiration in 1926 of certain Bakelite patents, when a number of large volume users undertook the production of their own resins.

The pattern of growth may be seen in Figure 1. The data from the U. S. Tariff Commission Statistics have been adjusted to a smooth curve. The production for 1948 is estimated.

The scope of this *plastics industry* does not embrace any or all materials possessing plasticity. Rather it is limited to a very specific group of organic compounds capable of being processed while in a *plastic state* by the application of stress and thereafter able more or less permanently to retain the new and arbitrary form supplied by the stress. The industry thereby excludes such inorganic materials as the metals, glasses, ceramics, and clays.

Recently the D-20 Committee on plastics of the American Society for Testing Materials adopted the following definition of plastics:

"A plastic is any one of a large varied group of materials which consists of, or contains as an essential ingredient, an organic substance of large molecular weight; and which, while solid in the finished state, at some stage in its manufacture has been or can be formed (cast, calendered, extruded, molded, etc.) into various shapes by flow—usually through the application singly or together of heat and pressure."

Because of its fabrication step, the plastics industry may be defined as including the industrial fabrication of organic polymers.

FIBERS

Fibers are polymers characterized by a high initial modulus in the range of 10^{10} to 10^{11} dynes per square centimeter. They have a low range of extensibility of the order of 10 to 20 per cent. Part of this extensibility is permanent, part of it shows delayed recovery, and part of the elasticity is instantaneous. Most of the mechanical properties

TABLE 11

Fiber	Millions of Pounds
Cotton	4508
Rayon	768
Wool	648
Nylon	24
Casein	9
Saran	1
Vinyon	1
Total	5959

of fibers are relatively independent over a fairly long range from about −50 C to about 150 C, depending on the particular fiber.

The importance of fibers industrially may be realized by considering the volume of textile fibers utilized in the United States in the year 1945, such as are shown in Table 11, according to their decreasing volume of use.

REFERENCES

1. K. Herzfeld and H. M. Smallwood, *Treatise on Physical Chemistry*, Second Edition, Vol. I, p. 231, D. Van Nostrand Co., New York, 1931.
2. R. N. Pease, *Treatise on Physical Chemistry*, Second Edition, Vol. I, p. 251, D. Van Nostrand Co., New York, 1931.
3. E. Simon, *Ann.*, **31**, 267 (1839).
4. Emil Fischer, *Ber.*, **52**, 809–829 (1919).
5. H. Staudinger, *Die Hochmolekularen Organischen Verbindungen*, J. Springer, Berlin, 1932.
6. K. Freudenberg, *Ber.*, **76A**, 71–96 (1943).
7. J. Berzelius, *Jahres Bericht physischen Wissenschaften*, **12**, 63 (1833).
8. H. Stobbe and G. Posnjak, *Ann.*, **371**, 287 (1909).
9. H. Stobbe and G. Posnjak, *Ann.*, **371**, 292 (1909).
10. H. Stobbe and G. Posnjak, *Ann.*, **371**, 295 (1909).
11. R. Fittig and E. Erdmann, *Ann.*, **216**, 187 (1883).
12. J. Schiebar and K. Sandig, *Artificial Resins*, p. 91, translated by E. Flyeman, Pitman Publishing Corp., New York, 1931.
13. K. Hess, *Chemie der Zellulose und ihrer Begleiter*, Leipzig, 1928, Akademische Verlagsgesellschaft m.b.h., p. 577.
14. H. Meerwein, Houben-Weyl, *Die Methoden der organischen Chemie*, Leipzig, 1923, zweite Auflage, dritter Band, p. 1013.
15. H. Staudinger, *Ber.*, **58**, 1075 (1925).
16. C. C. Price, R. W. Kell, and E. Krebs, *J. Am. Chem. Soc.*, **64**, 1103 (1942).
17. P. D. Bartlett and S. G. Cohen, *J. Am. Chem. Soc.*, **65**, 543 (1944).
18. A. Butlerow, *Ann.*, **189**, 65 (1877).
19. J. B. Cohen, *Organic Chemistry*, Part I, pp. 192–193, Edward Arnold and Company, London, 1928.
20. H. Staudinger, *Ber.*, **53**, 1073 (1920).
21. J. Fritzsche, *J. prakt. Chem.*, **101**, 337 (1867).
22. J. Fritzsche, *J. prakt. Chem.*, **106**, 274 (1869).
23. R. Luther, *Z. physik. Chem.*, **30**, 628 (1899).
24. W. R. Orndorff and F. K. Cameron, *Am. Chem. J.*, **17**, 658 (1893).
25. H. Staudinger, *Organische Kolloid Chemie*, p. 130, Friedr. Vieweg und Sohn, Braunschireig, 1941.
26. H. Staudinger and E. O. Leupold, *Helv. Chim. Acta*, **15**, 222 (1932).
27. W. H. Carothers, *J. Am. Chem. Soc.*, **51**, 2548–2559 (1929).
28. H. Staudinger, *Ber.*, **59**, 3019 (1926).
29. H. Staudinger, *Ber.*, **62**, 2893 (1929).
30. H. Staudinger, *Ber.*, **68**, 1682 (1935).
31. W. H. Carothers, J. W. Hill, J. E. Kirby, and R. A. Jacobson, *J. Am. Chem. Soc.*, **52**, 5279 (1930).
32. O. L. Sponsler, *Protoplasma*, **12**, 241 (1931).

33. P. Karrer and B. Joos, *Biochem. Z.*, **136**, 537 (1923).
34. A. Stoll, *Naturwissenschaften*, **24**, 53 (1936).
35. A. M. Pappenheimer, Jr., *J. Biol. Chem.*, **125**, 200 (1938).
36. M. Heidelberger and O. T. Avery, *J. Exptl. Med.*, **38**, 73 (1923).
37. M. Heidelberger and O. T. Avery, *J. Exptl. Med.*, **40**, 301 (1924).
38. D. Obermayer and E. P. Pick, *Wien. klin. Wochschr.*, **19**, 327 (1936).
39. R. Ammon and W. Dirscherl, *Fermente, Vitamine und die Beziehungen dieser Wirkstoffe zireinander*, G. Thieme, Leipzig, 1938.

CHAPTER 2

Polymerization Reactions
and Functionality

POLYMERIZATION REACTIONS

Polymers are defined as the high-molecular-weight inter-reaction products of related polyfunctional molecules, and the process by which polymers are obtained is called polymerization. Polymerization reactions are the chemical reactions responsible for combining the polyfunctional molecules into polymers. An examination of the polymers in Table 2 of Chapter 1 shows that the structurally repeating unit or segmer in the polymers is a polyvalent radical. As an example, the bivalent radical, —CH$_2$—CH—, is the segmer of polystyrene.

It is a logical conclusion that such segmers must be polyvalent radicals since they were derived from polyfunctional molecules. As Carothers showed,[1] simple molecules can combine to form large molecules either by an addition or by a condensation reaction, and thus two corresponding types of polymerization processes are recognized.

CONDENSATION POLYMERIZATION

The term *condensation* is used to describe a reaction that results in a new bond between molecules not already joined, when such a reaction proceeds with the by-product elimination of simple compounds or of elements such as nitrogen, hydrogen, water, hydrogen chloride, sodium chloride, and the like. Examples of such condensation reactions are found in the esterification and amidation reactions of a carboxylic acid with an alcohol or an amine, respectively, whereby a molecule of water is eliminated for each carboxyl group that undergoes reaction.

30

The synthesis of ethyl acetate illustrates a typical condensation reaction:

$$CH_3COOH + C_2H_5OH \rightarrow CH_3COOC_2H_5 + H_2O$$

In an analogous manner the synthesis of polyethylene succinate from ethylene glycol and succinic acid illustrates a condensation polymerization:

$$nHOCH_2CH_2OH + nHOOC(CH_2)_4COOH \rightarrow$$
$$H[OCH_2CH_2OOC(CH_2)_4CO]_nOH + (2n - 1)H_2O$$

ADDITION POLYMERIZATION

Addition polymerization is used to describe a reaction that results in a new bond between molecules not already joined when such a reaction proceeds without the elimination of by-product molecules. The addition of water to ethylene to produce ethyl alcohol is a typical example of an addition reaction,

$$CH_2{=}CH_2 + H_2O \rightarrow CH_3CH_2OH$$

The alkylation of benzene with styrene represents another typical addition reaction,

In like manner, addition polymerization is illustrated by the synthesis of polyoxymethylene, polyethylene glycol, and polystyrene.

$$nCH_2O \xrightarrow{H_2O} HOCH_2O{-}(CH_2O)_{n-3}{-}CH_2OCH_2OH$$
Formaldehyde   Polyoxymethylene

$$n \begin{array}{c} CH_2 \\ \diagdown \\ \diagup \\ CH_2 \end{array} O \xrightarrow{H_2O} HOCH_2CH_2OCH_2CH_2O(CH_2CH_2O)_{n-3}{-}CH_2CH_2OH$$
Ethylene oxide   Polyethylene glycol

All polymer growth is obtained initially through either a condensation or an addition reaction. These two reactions may be subdivided as shown in the following classification.

CLASSIFICATION OF ADDITION AND CONDENSATION POLYMERIZATION REACTIONS

Addition Reactions

Addition polymers may be obtained by reactions of molecules involving a single molecular species, whereas in other cases at least two molecular species are required.

SINGLE-MOLECULAR SPECIES

Addition polymerization may be achieved with compounds, as singular-molecular species, when such compounds have the following basic types of structures:
Carbon to carbon unsaturation.
Carbon to heteroatom unsaturation.
Homocyclic carbon rings.
Heterocyclic rings.
Carbon to carbon unsaturation. Olefinic compounds of the structure $CR_2{=}CR_2$ are the simplest representatives of carbon to carbon unsaturation, and contain a single polymerizable unsaturated bond. R in this formula represents hydrogen or a substituted radical. The segmer is the bivalent radical corresponding to the opening of the double bond.

$$CR_2{=}CR_2 \rightarrow -CR_2{-}CR_2{-}$$
Monomer   Segmer

The parent olefin is ethylene. Substitution of the hydrogens results in a number of monomers such as vinyl chloride, styrene, isobutylene, methyl methacrylate, dimethyl itaconate, tetrafluoroethylene, vinylidene chloride, cyclohexene, and indene. Their structures are:

$$CH_2{=}CH \quad CH_2{=}CH \quad CH_2{=}C\overset{CH_3}{\underset{CH_3}{\diagup\diagdown}} \quad F_2C{=}CF_2 \quad CH_2{=}C\overset{Cl}{\underset{Cl}{\diagup\diagdown}}$$

| Vinyl chloride | Styrene | Isobutylene | Tetrafluoro-ethylene | Vinylidene chloride |

$$CH_2=C\begin{smallmatrix}CH_3\\[2pt]\\COOCH_3\end{smallmatrix}$$

Methyl methacrylate

$$CH_2=C-CH_2COOCH_3$$
$$|$$
$$COOCH_3$$

Dimethyl itaconate

$$CH=CH$$
$$CH_2 \qquad CH_2$$
$$CH_2-CH_2$$

Cyclohexene

$$HC=CH$$
$$CH_2$$

Indene

Acetylenic compounds of the structure, $CR\equiv CR$, of which acetylene is the parent substance, are illustrative of another subclass showing carbon to carbon unsaturation. A bivalent segmer is formed in these compounds during polymerization which corresponds to the opening of one of the triple bonds, and in this respect it corresponds to the ethylene derivative. However, a tetravalent radical can also form by the further opening of another bond, which is illustrated in the following.

$$CR\equiv CR \rightarrow -CR=CR- \rightarrow \ \ CR-CR$$

Bivalent
segmer

Tetravalent
segmer

Acetylene, methylacetylene, and diphenylacetylene are typical of this class of compounds, as represented by these structures:

$$HC\equiv CH \qquad HC\equiv C-CH_3 \qquad C_6H_5C\equiv C-C_6H_5$$

Acetylene   Methylacetylene   Diphenylacetylene

The non-conjugated compounds may be considered to be derived by the union of a multiplicity of olefinic radicals, $CR_2=CR-$, or of acetylenic radicals, $RC\equiv C-$, or of olefinic and acetylenic radicals so joined that conjugated unsaturation is absent. To avoid conjugation in these compounds, the unsaturated radicals must be separated by a polyvalent radical, Z', which does not introduce olefinic or acetylenic conjugation. It is obvious that the radical Z' must be at least difunctional and may have trifunctionality or a higher functionality. In these compounds the unsaturated residues function independently of each other and produce segmers corresponding to their substituted radical. The non-conjugated compounds may be represented generally by the structures

$$R_2C=\overset{\displaystyle R}{\overset{|}{C}}-Z'-\overset{\displaystyle R}{\overset{|}{C}}=CR_2; \quad R_2C=\overset{\displaystyle R}{\overset{|}{C}}-Z'-C\equiv CR; \quad RC\equiv C-Z'-C\equiv CR$$

In all cases the resulting segmer may be bivalent, tetravalent, hexavalent, etc., depending on the conditions of polymerization, on the compound itself, and on other factors, as illustrated.

$$R_2C{=}\overset{\overset{\displaystyle R}{|}}{C}{-}Z'{-}\overset{\overset{\displaystyle R}{|}}{C}{=}CR_2 \rightarrow$$

$$R_2C{-}\overset{\overset{\displaystyle R}{|}}{\underset{|}{C}}{-}Z'{-}\overset{\overset{\displaystyle R}{|}}{C}{=}CR_2 \rightarrow R_2C{-}\overset{\overset{\displaystyle R}{|}}{\underset{|}{C}}{-}Z'{-}\overset{\overset{\displaystyle R}{|}}{\underset{|}{C}}{-}CR_2$$

Bivalent segmer   Tetravalent segmer

Divinyl ether, diallyl ether, divinylbenzene, glycol dimethacrylate, allyl acrylate, pentadiene-1,4, and triallyl citrate are representative of the non-conjugated compounds.

$CH_2{=}CH$ $CH_2{=}CH{-}CH_2$ $CH_2{=}CH$ $CH_2{=}C{-}COO$

... (structural formulas)

Divinyl ether   Diallyl ether   Divinylbenzene   Glycol dimethacrylate

$CH_2{=}CHCOO$ $CH_2{=}CH$ $CH_2{-}COOCH_2CH{=}CH_2$

Allyl acrylate   Pentadiene-1,4   Triallyl citrate

The conjugated monomers have the structure

$$R_2C{=}\overset{\overset{\displaystyle R}{|}}{C}{-}\overset{\overset{\displaystyle R}{|}}{C}{=}CR_2$$

and are capable of forming a bivalent segmer with the valences on the 1,4-carbon atoms through a double-bond shift, which in turn can form a tetravalent segmer, as illustrated:

$$R_2C{=}\overset{\overset{\displaystyle R}{|}}{C}{-}\overset{\overset{\displaystyle R}{|}}{C}{=}CR_2 \rightarrow$$

$${-}CR_2{-}\overset{\overset{\displaystyle R}{|}}{C}{=}\overset{\overset{\displaystyle R}{|}}{C}{-}CR_2{-} \rightarrow {-}CR_2{-}\overset{\overset{\displaystyle R}{|}}{\underset{\underset{\displaystyle R}{|}}{C}}{-}\overset{\overset{\displaystyle R}{|}}{\underset{\underset{\displaystyle R}{|}}{C}}{-}CR_2{-}$$

Bivalent segmer   Tetravalent segmer

The formation of the initial bivalent segmer is in accord with the Diels-Alder reaction, which may be illustrated by the reaction of butadiene with maleic anhydride.

$$
\begin{array}{c}
CH_2 \\
\diagup\!\!\diagup \\
CH \\
| \\
CH \\
\diagdown\!\!\diagdown \\
CH_2
\end{array}
\quad + \quad
\begin{array}{c}
H \\
| \\
C\!-\!CO \\
\| \quad \diagdown \\
\quad\quad O \\
\| \quad \diagup \\
C\!-\!CO \\
| \\
H
\end{array}
\quad \rightarrow \quad
\begin{array}{c}
CH_2 \\
\diagup \quad \diagdown \\
CH \quad CH\!-\!CO \\
\| \quad\quad | \quad\quad \diagdown \\
\quad\quad\quad\quad\quad O \\
\| \quad\quad | \quad\quad \diagup \\
CH \quad CH\!-\!CO \\
\diagdown \quad \diagup \\
CH_2
\end{array}
$$

Isoprene, 2,3-dimethylbutadiene-1,3, hexatriene-1,3,5, and 2-chlorobutadiene-1,3 are typical compounds capable of forming a bivalent segmer through a double-bond shift. The structures of these compounds are:

$$
CH_2\!=\!CH\!-\!C\!=\!CH_2 \qquad CH_2\!=\!C\!-\!\!-\!C\!=\!CH_2 \qquad CH_2\!=\!C\!-\!CH\!=\!CH_2
$$
$$
\begin{array}{ccc}
\qquad | & | \quad\quad | & | \\
\quad CH_3 & CH_3 \; CH_3 & Cl
\end{array}
$$

Isoprene   2,3-dimethylbutadiene-1,3   2-chlorobutadiene-1,3

$$
CH_2\!=\!CH\!-\!CH\!=\!CH\!-\!CH\!=\!CH_2
$$
Hexatriene-1,3,5

Carbon to heteroatom unsaturation. The compounds of this class possess another atom, which is not carbon, attached to a carbon atom by at least a double bond.

The structure, $R_2C\!=\!Z$, represents those compounds wherein the heteroatom, Z, is attached directly to the carbon bond by a double bond. The aldehydes, $RCHO$, the ketones, R_2CO, the thioaldehydes, $RCHS$, the thioketones, R_2CS, the aldamines, $RCH\!=\!NR$, and the ketimines, $R_2C\!=\!NR$, are representative of this class of compounds. The segmer radical is equivalent to that derived by opening one of the bonds of the double bond attached to Z, for example,

$$
H_2C\!=\!O \quad \longrightarrow \quad
\begin{array}{c}
H \\
| \\
-\!C\!-\!O\!- \\
| \\
H
\end{array}
$$

Formaldehyde   Bivalent segmer of
                    polyoxymethylene

The structure, $RC\!\equiv\!Z$, represents those compounds wherein the heteroatom, Z, is attached directly to the carbon atom by a triple bond, and is represented only by the nitrogen atom in the nitriles, $RC\equiv N$. The segmer corresponds to the opening of either one or two of the bonds of the triple bond:

$$RC\equiv N \ \rightarrow \ \underset{\substack{\text{Bivalent} \\ \text{segmer}}}{RC=N} \ \rightarrow \ \underset{\substack{\text{Tetravalent} \\ \text{segmer}}}{RC-N}$$

However, the opening of a nitrile group to a tetravalent segmer is not common.

The trimerization of acetonitrile illustrates the formation of a bivalent segmer, such as,

$$3CH_3C\equiv N \ \rightarrow \ 3CH_3C=N \ \rightarrow$$

Homocyclic carbon ring compounds. These compounds, which are rings containing only carbon, may be represented by the structure, $(CR_2)_n$—CR_2, of which cyclopropane and cyclobutane are examples.
The polymers of these compounds contain segmers corresponding to a ring rupture, for example,

$$CR_2\text{---}CR_2 \ \rightarrow \ \text{---}CR_2\text{---}CR_2\text{---}CR_2\text{---}$$

Heterocyclic ring compounds. These compounds contain at least one heteroatom in a carbon ring compound.

The structure, $R-C\text{------}(C-R)_n$, represents those compounds which contain one heteroatom in the ring as illustrated by the ethylene imine, ethylene oxide, caprolactam, and propiolactone.

$$\begin{array}{c} CH_2\!\!-\!\!CH_2 \\ \diagdown \diagup \\ NH \end{array} \qquad \begin{array}{c} CH_2\!\!-\!\!CH_2 \\ \diagdown \diagup \\ O \end{array} \qquad \begin{array}{c} CH_2\!\!-\!\!CH_2 \\ | \quad\quad | \\ CH_2 \quad CH_2 \\ | \quad\quad | \\ CH_2 \quad CO \\ \diagdown \diagup \\ NH \end{array} \qquad \begin{array}{c} CH_2\!\!-\!\!CH_2 \\ | \quad\quad | \\ O\!\!-\!\!-\!\!CO \end{array}$$

| Ethylene imine | Ethylene oxide | Caprolactam | β-Propiolactone |

The segmer corresponds to a rupture of the ring,

$$\begin{array}{c} CH_2\!\!-\!\!CH_2 \\ \diagdown \diagup \\ O \end{array} \rightarrow -CH_2\!\!-\!\!CH_2\!\!-\!\!O-$$

The structure, $\begin{array}{c} R \\ | \\ (R\!\!-\!\!C)_m\!\!-\!\!Z \\ | \quad\quad | \\ Z\!\!-\!\!-\!\!(C\!\!-\!\!R)_m \\ | \\ R \end{array}$, represents those compounds that

contain two heteroatoms such as are illustrated by glycol succinate and diketopiperazine,

$$\begin{array}{c} CH_2\!\!-\!\!CH_2 \\ | \quad\quad | \\ O \quad\quad O \\ | \quad\quad | \\ C\!\!=\!\!O \quad C\!\!=\!\!O \\ | \quad\quad | \\ CH_2\!\!-\!\!CH_2 \end{array} \qquad\qquad \begin{array}{c} NH\!\!-\!\!CH_2 \\ | \quad\quad | \\ CO \quad CO \\ | \quad\quad | \\ CH_2\!\!-\!\!NH \end{array}$$

| Monomeric glycol succinate | Diketopiperazine |

The segmer radical corresponds to a rupture of the ring, as, for example,

$$\begin{array}{c} CH_2\!\!-\!\!CH_2 \\ | \quad\quad | \\ O \quad\quad O \\ | \quad\quad | \\ C\!\!=\!\!O \quad C\!\!=\!\!O \\ | \quad\quad | \\ CH_2\!\!-\!\!CH_2 \end{array} \rightarrow \begin{array}{c} O \\ \| \\ -C\!\!-\!\!CH_2CH_2COOCH_2CH_2\!\!-\!\!O- \end{array}$$

MULTIPLE-MOLECULAR SPECIES

Addition polymerization requiring multiple species involves molecules that react through groups containing carbon to heteroatom linkages, with at least a double bond between the carbon and the heteroatom. Since these reactions do not result in the elimination of a by-product molecule, they may be properly classified as addition polymerizations. However, in these reactions the initial addition product undergoes a molecular rearrangement to produce the final polymer. Such an addition polymerization is illustrated by the preparation of a polyurethane from a diisocyanate and a dihydric alcohol,

$$n\text{OCN(CH}_2)_6\text{NCO} + n\text{HOCH}_2\text{CH}_2\text{OH} \rightarrow$$

$$\overset{\displaystyle \text{H}}{\underset{\displaystyle |}{}} \quad \overset{\displaystyle \text{H}}{\underset{\displaystyle |}{}}$$
$$-[\text{OCN(CH}_2)_6\text{NCOOCH}_2\text{CH}_2\text{O}]_n-$$

The molecular rearrangement of the ester groups is demonstrated by the reaction of a monoisocyanate and a monohydric alcohol as follows:

$$\text{RNCO} + \text{C}_2\text{H}_5\text{OH} \rightarrow \text{RN}{=}\text{C}\overset{\displaystyle \text{OH}}{\underset{\displaystyle \text{OC}_2\text{H}_5}{}} \rightarrow \text{RN}-\overset{\displaystyle \text{H}}{\underset{}{\text{C}}}-\overset{\displaystyle \text{O}}{}\text{OC}_2\text{H}_5$$

The polyisocyanates react with other polyfunctional molecules containing active hydrogens, such as the carboxylic acids, the amines, the ureas, and the amides, as well as the alcohols.

The polyketene, having at least two $\diagdown\!\!\!\text{C}{=}\text{CO}\diagup$ groups, behaves similarly to the polyisocyanate, thus:

$$n\text{O}{=}\text{C}{=}\text{CH}-\text{CH}{=}\text{CO} + n\text{HOCH}_2\text{CH}_2\text{OH} \rightarrow$$

$$-(\text{OCCH}_2\text{CH}_2\text{COOCH}_2\text{CH}_2\text{O})_n-$$

Polymers prepared by addition polymerization involving multiple species usually can also be prepared by a direct condensation reaction, and the polyester derived from ethylene glycol and the *bis* ketene can be readily synthesized from ethylene glycol and succinic acid.

Condensation Reactions

Condensation polymers may be obtained by chemical reactions in which one molecular species is sufficient to produce the polymer, whereas, in other cases, at least two species of molecules are required.

SINGLE-MOLECULAR SPECIES

The first type of condensation polymerization can occur with a single-molecular species because at least two related functional groups are present in the same molecule, as, for example, in an amino acid,

$$\underset{A}{NH_2}(CH_2)_n\underset{B}{COOH} + \underset{A}{NH_2}(CH_2)_n\underset{B}{COOH} \rightarrow$$

$$NH_2(CH_2)_nCONH(CH_2)_nCOOH + H_2O$$

The amino group, A, of molecule 2, reacts with the carboxyl group, B, of molecule 1, accompanied by the elimination of water. This process is repeated by the addition of molecules 3, 4, 5, etc., until a polymer is produced.

MULTIPLE-MOLECULAR SPECIES

The second type of condensation polymerization requires more than one molecular species because the reactive functional groups are located in different species of the same molecule. This is exemplified by the reaction between hexamethylene diamine and adipic acid,

$$nH_2N(CH_2)_6NH_2 + nHOOC(CH_2)_4COOH \rightarrow$$

$$H[HN(CH_2)_6NHOC(CH_2)_4CO]nOH + (2n - 1)H_2O$$

Mixed Reactions

Many polymers are obtained in their final form through a combination of the addition and condensation types of polymerization. Such polymerizations are classified as addition-condensation polymers or condensation-addition polymers according to which type of polymerization reaction occurs first in the process.

CONDENSATION-ADDITION REACTIONS

In this category are those polymers which have been prepared first by a condensation reaction and then subjected to addition polymerization. A typical example of this class of polymers is the esterification of ethylene glycol with maleic anhydride to produce polymeric ethylene maleate. This polyester is then subjected to an addition polymerization of the double bonds of the maleic radical in the polymer. These phases are represented as follows.

Condensation phase

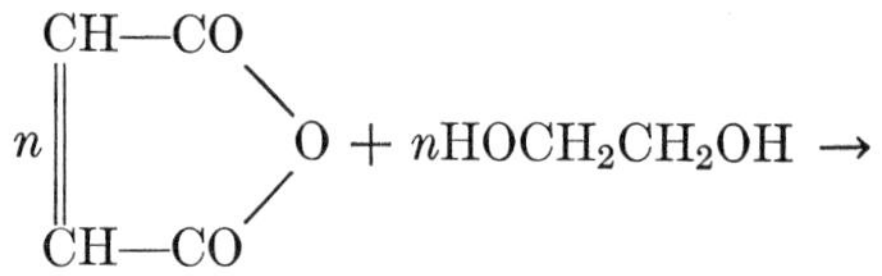

$$
n \underset{CH-CO}{\overset{CH-CO}{\|}} \Bigg\rangle O + n HOCH_2CH_2OH \rightarrow
$$

Maleic
anhydride

Ethylene
glycol

$$
H[OCH_2CH_2OOCCH=CHCO]_nOH + (n-1)H_2O
$$

Polyethylene maleate

Addition phase

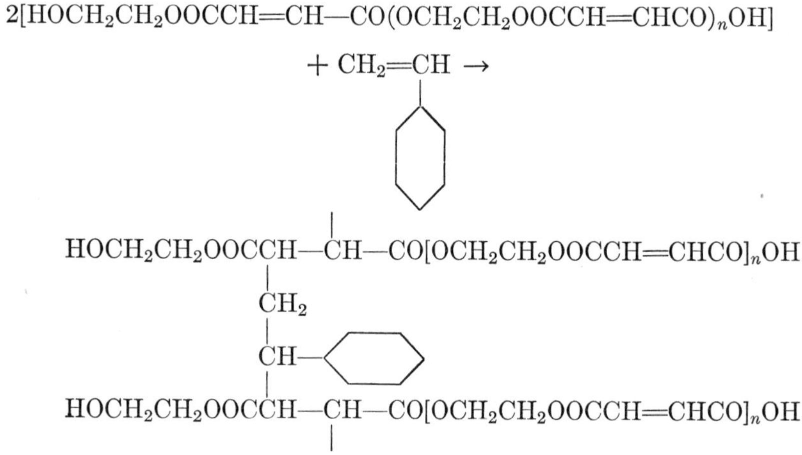

$$
2[HOCH_2CH_2OOCCH=CH-CO(OCH_2CH_2OOCCH=CHCO)_nOH]
$$

$$
+ CH_2=CH \rightarrow
$$

$$
HOCH_2CH_2OOCCH-CH-CO[OCH_2CH_2OOCCH=CHCO]_nOH
$$
$$
CH_2
$$
$$
CH-
$$
$$
HOCH_2CH_2OOCCH-CH-CO[OCH_2CH_2OOCCH=CHCO]_nOH
$$

ADDITION-CONDENSATION POLYMERIZATION

In this class the addition reaction occurs before the condensation polymerization. The phases are illustrated as follows.

Addition phase. Styrene and maleic acid are subjected to addition polymerization to give a polymer represented as follows:

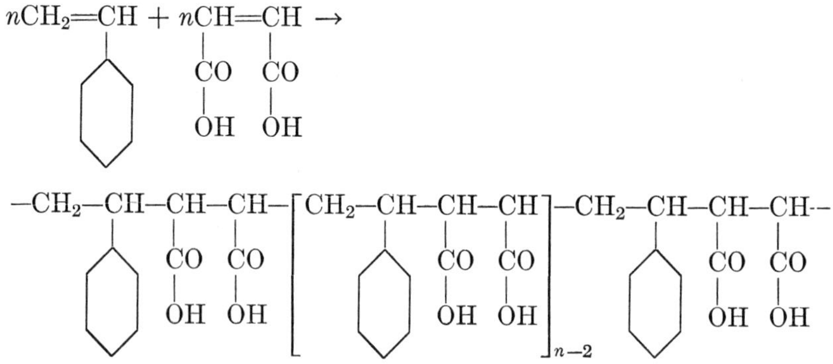

$$
nCH_2=CH + nCH=CH \rightarrow
$$
$$
\qquad\qquad CO \quad CO
$$
$$
\qquad\qquad OH \quad OH
$$

$$
-CH_2-CH-CH-CH-\left[CH_2-CH-CH-CH\right]-CH_2-CH-CH-CH--
$$
$$
\qquad CO\ CO \qquad\qquad CO\ CO \qquad\qquad CO\ CO
$$
$$
\qquad OH\ OH \qquad\qquad OH\ OH \Big]_{n-2} \qquad OH\ OH
$$

Usually this reaction is achieved by reacting styrene with maleic anhydride and then hydrolyzing the polymer.[2] However, the reaction using maleic acid is readily performed by using acetone as a solvent.

Condensation phase. The addition polymer is then condensed with a polyhydric alcohol or amine, for example, to produce even a larger polymer:

$$
2 \left[-CH_2\text{-}CH\text{-}CH\text{-}CH\text{-} \left[CH_2\text{-}CH\text{-}CH\text{-}CH \right]_{n-1} \right] + CH_2\text{-}CH_2 \rightarrow
$$

with the cyclohexane rings bearing CO CO / OH OH substituents, and CH_2-CH_2 bearing OH OH $\rightarrow$

$$
-CH_2\text{---}CH\text{---}CH\text{---}CH\text{---} \left[CH_2 \quad CH\text{---}CH\text{---}CH \right]_{n-1} -
$$

COOH / C=O / O / CH_2 / CH_2 / O / C=O

$$
-CH_2\text{---}CH\text{---}CH\text{---}CH\text{---} \left[CH_2\text{-}CH\text{---}CH\text{---}CH \right]_{n-1} -
$$

COOH

$$+ 2H_2O$$

Interrupted Polymerizations

Many addition polymerization products may be obtained in an intermediate stage through one type of addition and then carried to completion or a final form through another type of addition reaction. In some cases, two types of addition reactions may be proceeding simultaneously. Such polymers are called addition polymers since addition polymerization is used throughout the complete process. The same reasoning is applied to interrupted condensation polymers which have been carried to the final stage through condensation reactions.

CHOICE OF CLASSIFICATION

Many polymers can be prepared through either a condensation or an addition reaction as has already been shown in the case of ethylene succinate. Polyethylene imine can be derived at least to a low molecular weight value according to a condensation by reacting ethylene dibromide and ammonia or from the addition polymerization of ethylene imine:

$$n\text{CH}_2\text{---}\text{CH}_2 \underset{\text{NH}}{\diagdown\diagup} + \text{NH}_3 \rightarrow \text{H}_2\text{N}(\text{CH}_2\text{CH}_2\text{NH})_n\text{H}$$

or

$$n(\text{BrCH}_2\text{CH}_2\text{Br}) + (3n + 1)\text{NH}_3 \rightarrow \text{H}_2\text{N}(\text{CH}_2\text{CH}_2\text{NH})_n\text{H} + 2n\text{NH}_4\text{Br}$$

The question arises as to how polyethylene imine should be classified. If it is actually prepared by both processes, it is classified under both processes. However, if it has been experimentally proved that it can be prepared by only one process, it is classified under that process.

MONOMERS, COMERS, COMONOMERS, AND TELOMERS

All the preceding reactions are capable, under suitable conditions, of producing polymeric compositions characterized by a repeating unit or segmer. The segmer, which is the repeating polyvalent radical, has its origin in the starting polyfunctional molecules. It has been the custom to call such starting materials monomers. In the classification of polymeric reactions a number of condensation polymerization reactions were pointed out that required at least two molecular species to produce the polymer. In such reactions these species are not monomers or monomerous, and the term monomer is not only confusing but also misleading. However, the terminology of the starting materials can be related to and expressed in terms of the segmer. This is justified because the polymer consists of a sequence of these identical repeating units.

When this is done, the terms monomer, comer, and comonomer can be correlated to the classification of polymers as homopolymers or copolymers, as follows.

Monomer

When the segmer or repeating structural polyfunctional radical is directly derivable from a single molecular species, the starting material is called a monomer. Stating it differently, if the starting material, as a single molecular species, polymerizes alone under the specific conditions of the experiment to produce the segmer of the specific polymer, it is called a monomer. A few typical examples are:

Polymer	Segmer	Monomer

$-CH_2-CH-\left[\begin{array}{c}CH_2-CH\end{array}\right]-CH_2-CH-$ $-CH_2-CH-$ $CH_2=CH$

Polystyrene   Styrene

$NH_2(CH_2)_5CO[NH(CH_2)_5CO]_nNH(CH_2)_5COOH$ $-NH(CH_2)_5CO-$ $NH_2(CH_2)_5COOH$
Polycaprolactam ϵ-Amino caproic acid

$HO[OC(CH_2)_4COO]_nH$ $-OC(CH_2)_4COO-$ $HOOC(CH_2)_4COOH$
Polyadipic anhydride   Adipic acid

Comer

Since the segmer represents the repeating polyvalent radical in the polymer, the segmer indicates the starting materials that gave origin to the polyfunctional radical. If two or more reactants are required to produce the segmer in a specific polymer, neither of the reactants is a monomer. In such a case, an intermediate reaction product of the two reactants is the monomer; for example, the polymeric reaction of a diamine and a dicarboxylic produces a high molecular weight polymer:

$$nH_2N(CH_2)_6NH_2 + nHOOC(CH_2)_4COOH \rightarrow$$
$$H[NH(CH_2)_6NHOC(CH_2)_4CO]_nOH + (2n-1)H_2O$$

Since the segmer in this polymer is the radical $-NH(CH_2)_6-NHOC(CH_2)_4CO-$, the monomer could be represented only by the molecule $NH_2(CH_2)_6NHOC(CH_2)_4COOH$, which obviously is the intermediate reaction product between the diamine and the diacid,

$$NH_2(CH_2)_6NH_2 + HOOC(CH_2)_4COOH \rightarrow$$
$$NH_2(CH_2)_6NHOC(CH_2)_4COOH$$

It would seem advisable in such cases to call the reactants required to produce the segmer comers, and each reactant a comer. The prefix *co* indicates that it cannot produce the specific segmer by itself but it must do so with (*co*) another part (*mer*). The term comonomer would not be applicable since such a term would indicate that each reactant would be capable individually of producing segmer radical. Examples of comers are illustrated in the following:

$$n'HO(CH_2)_nOH + n'HOOC(CH_2)_mCOOH \rightarrow$$
   Comer   Comer

$$H[\underbrace{O(CH_2)_nOOC(CH_2)_mCO}_{\text{Segmer in polymer}}]_{n'}-OH$$

$$n'NH_2(CH_2)_nNH_2 + n'HOOC(CH_2)_mCOOH \rightarrow$$

Comer   Comer

$$H[\underbrace{NH(CH_2)_nNHOC(CH_2)_mCO}]_{n'}-OH$$

Segmer in polymer

This concept of comers embraces also those compounds that under a *specified* set of conditions do not polymerize, but when subjected to the same polymerizing condition in the presence of another compound or molecule, polymerize readily. Thus we may even have two comers producing polymers. Furthermore, in polymerization reactions, at least one molar equivalent of a complementary molecule must be used with a comer to produce a polymer.

Comonomer

The term comonomer describes a monomer polymerized in the presence of another monomer or comer, as indicated in the following:

(a) $nCH_2{=}CH \rightarrow -CH_2-CH-\left[CH_2-CH\right]-$

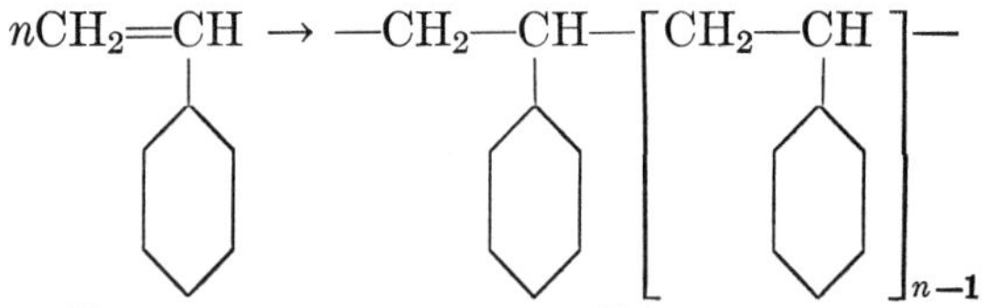

Monomer   Polymer $_{n-1}$

(b) $nCH_2{=}CH \rightarrow -CH_2-CH-\left[CH_2-CH\right]-$
$\phantom{nCH_2{=}}CN CN CN_{n-1}$

Monomer   Polymer

(c) $mCH_2{=}CH + nCH_2{=}CH \rightarrow$
$\phantom{mCH_2{=}CH + nCH_2{=}}CN$

Comonomer   Comonomer

$-CH_2-CH-CH_2-CH-\left[CH_2-CH\right]-\left[CH_2-CH\right]-$
$CN CN_{n-1}$
$_{m-1}$

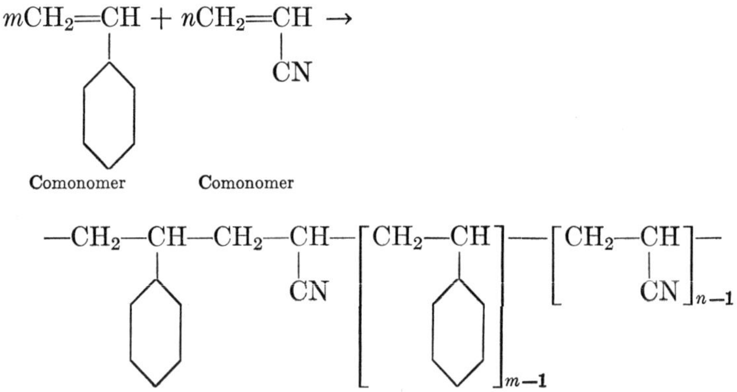

Polymer

(d) $CH{=}CH$
      $\underset{\diagdown O \diagup}{CO \qquad CO} \rightarrow$ no polymerization

(e) $nCH_2{=}CH + nCH{=}CH \rightarrow$
      $\underset{\text{Comonomer}}{\bigcirc} \qquad \underset{\text{Comer}}{\underset{\diagdown O \diagup}{CO \quad CO}}$

$-CH_2-CH-CH{-}CH-\left[CH_2-CH-CH{-}CH\right]-$
$\underset{\text{Polymer}}{\quad\;\bigcirc\quad\underset{\diagdown O \diagup}{CO\;\;CO}\qquad\quad\;\bigcirc\quad\underset{\diagdown O \diagup}{CO\;\;CO}\Big]_{n-1}}$

(f) $nCH_2{=}CH_2 + nCO \rightarrow -(CH_2-CH_2-CO)_n-$
      $\underset{\text{Comonomer}}{} \quad \underset{\text{Comer}}{} \qquad\quad \underset{\text{Polymer}}{}$

(g) $nCH_2{=}CCl_2 + nO_2 \rightarrow -(CH_2-CCl_2-O-O)_n-$
      $\underset{\text{Comonomer}}{} \quad \underset{\text{Comer}}{} \qquad\quad \underset{\text{Polymer}}{}$

When a comonomer is polymerized in the presence of another comonomer the molar ratio of one to the other may be widely varied between m and n, which may have the same or different numerical values over a range of zero to infinity. On the other hand, when a comonomer is polymerized with a comer, at least one equivalent mole of comonomer must be used for each mole of comer, and this is exemplified in reaction (e) when n equivalent moles of styrene and maleic anhydride are used to produce a polymer having a single segmer species:

$-CH_2-CH-CH{-}CH-$
$\quad\;\bigcirc\quad\underset{\diagdown O \diagup}{CO\;\;CO}$

However, m moles of comonomer may be used for each n moles of comer, provided that m is larger than n. Thus if m moles of styrene are polymerized with n moles of maleic anhydride, the polymer may be represented as

$$m\mathrm{CH_2}\!=\!\mathrm{CH} + n\mathrm{CH}\!=\!\mathrm{CH} \rightarrow$$

and the polymer contains two segmer species. This is explained [3] on the basis that styrene and maleic anhydride behave as if they form an unstable Diels-Alder type intermediate which produces a segmer independent of the styrene used in excess over the molar quantities required to produce the unstable intermediate, for example,

Similarly, the polymerization of olefins with sulfur dioxide appears to pass through an unstable intermediate:

$$n\mathrm{CR_2}\!=\!\mathrm{CR_2} + n\mathrm{SO_2} \rightarrow n\left[\begin{array}{c}\mathrm{CR_2}\!-\!\mathrm{CR_2}\\ \diagdown\diagup\\ \mathrm{SO_2}\end{array}\right] \rightarrow -[\mathrm{CR_2}\!-\!\mathrm{CR_2}\!-\!\mathrm{SO_2}]_n-$$

Telomer

A telomer is a chemical compound capable of forming the terminal part of the polymer. Telomers do not participate in the polymer growth but they do terminate it, and they may be compounds that have a functionality of one or produce monofunctional radicals.

Telomers exist for both condensation and addition reactions.

In a condensation reaction, as, for example, in a polyesterification of a dihydric alcohol with a dicarboxylic acid, either a monofunctional alcohol or an acid may act as the telomer:

$$n\mathrm{HO(CH_2)_yOH} + (n+1)\mathrm{HOOC(CH_2)_yCOOH} + 2\mathrm{ROH} \rightarrow$$

Comer   Comer   Telomer

$$\mathrm{ROOC(CH_2)_yCO[O(CH_2)_yOOC(CH_2)_yCO]_nOR}$$

Telomerized polymer

$$n\mathrm{HOOC(CH_2)_yCOOH} + (n+1)\mathrm{HO(CH_2)}y\mathrm{OH} + 2\mathrm{RCOOH} \rightarrow$$

Comer   Comer   Telomer

$$\mathrm{RCO[O(CH_2)_yOOC(CH_2)_yCO]_nO(CH_2)_yOOCR}$$

Telomerized polymer

In addition reactions the telomer likewise serves to terminate the chain by the production of monofunctional radicals, for example,

$$n\mathrm{CH_2{=}CH} + \mathrm{CCl_4} \rightarrow -\left[\mathrm{CH_2{-}CH}\right]-\mathrm{CCl_3} \qquad -\left[\mathrm{CH_2{-}CH}\right]-\mathrm{Cl}$$

Monomer   Telomer   or

Carbon tetrachloride telomerized polystyrene

$$n\mathrm{CH_2{=}CH} + \mathrm{HCCl_3} \rightarrow -\left[\mathrm{CH_2{-}CH}\right]-\mathrm{CCl_3} \qquad -\left[\mathrm{CH_2{-}CH}\right]-\mathrm{H}$$

Monomer   Telomer   or

Chloroform telomerized polystyrene

Carbon tetrachloride will also telomerize divinylbenzene so that soluble fusible polymers may be obtained.[4] In many cases the telomer may be a catalyst for the polymerization reactions, as when dimethyl amine is used as a catalyst in the polymerization of ethylene oxide or ethylene imine:

$$\mathrm{(CH_3)_2NH} + n\mathrm{CH_2CH_2} \rightarrow \mathrm{(CH_3)_2N(CH_2CH_2O)_nH}$$
$$\qquad\qquad\qquad\searrow\!\!\nearrow$$
$$\qquad\qquad\qquad\mathrm{O}$$

$$\mathrm{(CH_3)_2NH} + n\mathrm{CH_2CH_2} \rightarrow \mathrm{(CH_3)_2N(CH_2CH_2NH)_nH}$$
$$\qquad\qquad\qquad\searrow\!\!\nearrow$$
$$\qquad\qquad\qquad\mathrm{NH}$$

HOMOPOLYMERS, COPOLYMERS, AND HETEROPOLYMERS

The polymerization reactions of monomers, comonomers, and comers produce a number of polymers that can be classified according to the number of resulting segmer species in the polymer. These polymeric products may be classified as homopolymers and copolymers.

Homopolymers

The term *homopolymer* designates a polymer that has one and only one identical segmer characterizing the polymer:

(a) $n\text{HO(CH}_2)_5\text{COOH} \rightarrow \text{H[O(CH}_2)_5\text{CO]}_{n-1}\text{O(CH}_2)_5\text{COOH}$
     Monomer   Homopolymer

(b) $n\text{CH}_2{=}\text{CH} \rightarrow -\text{CH}_2-\text{CH}-\left[\text{CH}_2-\text{CH}\right]-\text{CH}_2-\text{CH}-$

                               $\Big]_{n-2}$

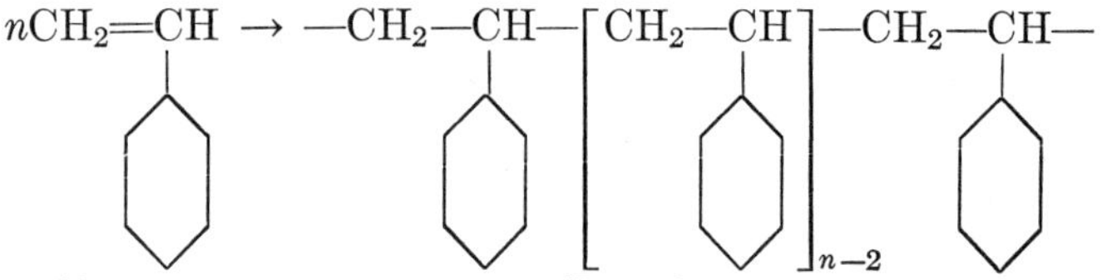

      Monomer   Homopolymer

(c) $n\text{NH}_2(\text{CH}_2)_6\text{NH}_2 + n\text{HOOC(CH}_2)_4\text{COOH} \rightarrow$
     Comer   Comer

                    $\text{H[NH(CH}_2)_6\text{NHOC(CH}_2)_4\text{CO]}_n\text{OH}$
                            Homopolymer

Copolymers

The term *copolymer* indicates a polymer with more than one segmer species. Typical examples of copolymers are:

(a) $n\text{CH}_2\text{---CH}_2 + m\text{CH}_2\text{---CH}_2 \rightarrow$
           $\diagdown\diagup$ $\diagdown\diagup$
           O   NH

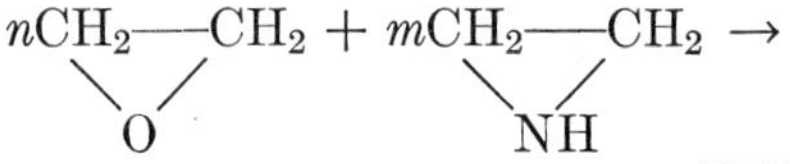

            $-(\text{CH}_2\text{CH}_2\text{O})_n-(\text{CH}_2\text{CH}_2\text{NH})_m-$

(b) $n\text{NH}_2(\text{CH}_2)_5\text{COOH} + m\text{NH}_2(\text{CH}_2)_6\text{COOH} \rightarrow$

            $\text{H[NH(CH}_2)_5\text{CO]}_n[\text{NH(CH}_2)_6\text{CO]}_m\text{OH}$

(c) $n\text{CH}_2{=}\text{CH} + m\text{CH}_2{=}\text{CH} \rightarrow$
                           COOR

               $-\left[\text{CH}_2-\text{CH}\right]-\left[\text{CH}_2-\text{CH}-\right]-$
                                        $\text{COOR}\Big]_m$

                          $\Big]_n$

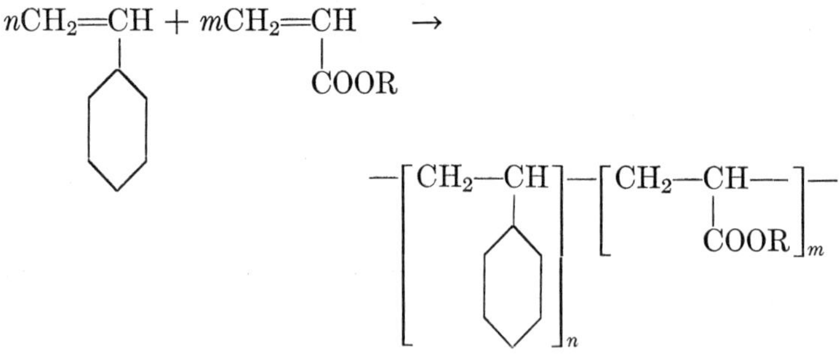

Copolymers may be subdivided into classes, according to the number of different types of segmers in the polymer. Thus a copolymer of vinyl acetate and vinyl chloride is a dipolymer, whereas a copolymer of styrene, acrylonitrile, and methyl acrylate is a tripolymer, because it contains three different segmer species. Similarly there are tetrapolymers, pentapolymers, etc.

Heteropolymers

The term *heteropolymer* was first used [5] by Wagner-Jauregg to describe those polymers obtained by reacting certain olefins with another material, such as maleic anhydride, which does not polymerize. A number of olefins were polymerized in the presence of maleic anhydride, and some were found to polymerize in boiling xylene and not in boiling benzene or toluene. In other cases the presence of a solvent prevented reaction which could be accomplished only in a molten state.

In boiling xylene, the reaction of stilbene and maleic anhydride produced a polymer with a constant composition independent of the variations of the initial concentration of the reactants. This suggests that the products were constructed according to a uniform principle of one mole of stilbene to one mole of maleic anhydride,

$$-\left[\begin{array}{cccc} CH & CH & CH & CH \\ | & | & | & | \\ C_6H_5 & C_6H_5 & CO & CO \\ & & \diagdown & \diagup \\ & & O & \end{array}\right]_n-$$

and contain only one segmer species.

Under the conditions of this experiment neither stilbene nor maleic anhydride polymerizes alone, and both reactants are comers. Benzal fluorene and anisal fluorene when reacted in a melt of maleic anhydride also formed a polymeric addition product of one mole of olefin with one mole of maleic anhydride with only one segmer species.

On the other hand, the reaction of 1,4-diphenylbutene-1 with maleic anhydride produced polymers wherein the ratio of maleic anhydride to styrene was greater than one. Some of these ratios were 1.5:1, 1.3:1, and 1.25:1. These ratios are explained by the presence of maleic anhydride in the terminal positions, for example:

$$-CH-CH-\left[\begin{array}{cccc} R & R & & \\ | & | & & \\ C-C-CH & CH \\ | & | & | & | \\ R & R & CO & CO \\ & & \diagdown & \diagup \\ & & O & \end{array}\right]_n-$$

In such polymers two segmer species are present. At very low molecular weights, as, for example when n is one, the ratio of maleic anhydride to the olefin, $CR_2{=}CR_2$, may be 2 to 1. This is especially true of asymmetric diphenylethylene, which gives a crystalline product, $C_{22}H_{16}O_{16}$, most probably a cyclic compound of the structure

If, on the other hand, the olefin is an active polymerizing material under the conditions of the experiments, the ratio of the olefin to the maleic derivative may be higher than one. This is illustrated in the polymerization of styrene and dimethyl maleate where ratios of styrene to maleate in the polymer are found [5] to be 4:1 to 5:1. In such a case the polymer has the possible structure

and two segmer species exist in the polymer.

Heteropolymers may be homopolymers or copolymers, depending on the number of segmer species in the polymer. In fact it is possible, as in the case of styrene and maleic, to prepare (1) homopolymers with a single segmer species, as when styrene and maleic anhydride are used in equivalent ratios, or (2) copolymers when styrene is used in excess of the molar quantities of maleic anhydride.

The preparation of homopolymers and copolymers from monomers, comers, and comonomers through addition and condensation polymerizations may be classified as in Table 1.

TABLE 1. HOMOPOLYMERS—SINGLE SEGMER SPECIES

Reactant to Produce Segmer	Typical Examples of Reactants	Repeating Structural Unit	Polymerization Reaction
1. Monomer	$n\text{CH}_2=\text{CH}-$ (C$_6$H$_5$)	$[-\text{CH}_2-\text{CH}-]_n$ (C$_6$H$_5$)	Addition
2. Monomer	$n\text{NH}_2(\text{CH}_2)_n\text{COOH}$	$[-\text{NH}(\text{CH}_2)_n\text{CO}-]_n$	Condensation
3. Comer and comer	$n\text{CH}=\text{CH}$ ($\overset{|}{\text{CN}}$ $\overset{|}{\text{COOCH}_3}$) $+ n\text{SO}_2$	$[-\text{CH}-\text{CH}-\text{SO}_2-]_n$ ($\overset{|}{\text{CN}}$ $\overset{|}{\text{COOCH}_3}$)	Addition
4. Comer and comer	$n\text{NH}_2(\text{CH}_2)_6\text{NH}_2 + n\text{HOOC}(\text{CH}_2)_4\text{COOH}$	$[-\text{NH}(\text{CH}_2)_6\text{NHOC}(\text{CH}_2)_4\text{CO}-]_n$	Condensation

COPOLYMERS—MULTIPLE SEGMER SPECIES

Reactant to Produce Segmer	Typical Examples of Reactants	Repeating Structural Unit	Polymerization Reaction
5. Comonomer and comonomer	$n\text{CH}_2=\text{CH}-$ (C$_6$H$_5$) $+ m\text{CH}_2=\text{CHCN}$	$\left[\left(-\text{CH}_2-\text{CH}- \right) \left(-\text{CH}_2-\text{CH}- \atop \text{CN} \right)_m \right]_n$	Addition
6. Comonomer and cononomer	$n\text{NH}_2(\text{CH}_2)_5\text{COOH} + m\text{NH}_2(\text{CH}_2)_6\text{COOH}$	$[-(\text{NH}(\text{CH}_2)_5\text{CO})_n-(\text{NH}(\text{CH}_2)_6\text{CO})_m-]$	Condensation
7. Comonomer and comer	$n\text{CH}_2=\text{CH}-$ (C$_6$H$_5$) $+ m\text{CH}=\text{CH}$ ($\overset{|}{\text{CN}}$ $\overset{|}{\text{CN}}$)	$\left[\left(-\text{CH}_2-\text{CH}- \right) \left(-\text{CH}-\text{CH}- \atop \text{CN} \;\; \text{CN} \right)_m \right]_n$	Addition
8. Comonomer and comers	$n\text{NH}_2(\text{CH}_2)_6\text{COOH} + m[\text{NH}_2(\text{CH}_2)_6\text{NH}_2 + \text{HOOC}(\text{CH}_2)_4\text{COOH}]$	$[-(\text{NH}(\text{CH}_2)_6\text{CO})_n-(\text{NH}(\text{CH}_2)_6\text{NHOC}(\text{CH}_2)_4\text{CO})_m-]$	Condensation
9. Comer and comer	$n\text{CH}=\text{CH}-$ (C$_6$H$_5$) $+ m\text{SO}_2$	$[-(\text{CH}-)_n-(\text{SO}_2)_m-]$	Addition
10. Comers and comers	$n[\text{NH}_2(\text{CH}_2)_6\text{NH}_2 + \text{HOOC}(\text{CH}_2)_4\text{COOH}] + m[\text{NH}_2(\text{CH}_2)_8\text{NH}_2 + \text{HOOC}(\text{CH}_2)_8\text{COOH}]$	$[-(\text{NH}(\text{CH}_2)_6\text{NHOC}(\text{CH}_2)_4\text{CO})_n-(\text{NH}(\text{CH}_2)_8\text{NHOC}(\text{CH}_2)_8\text{CO})_m-]$	Condensation

THE CONCEPT OF FUNCTIONALITY, FUSIBILITY, AND SOLUBILITY

In industry, reference is made to many plastic compositions as thermoplastic or thermosetting. This is a classification according to the behavior of the polymer under heat. It is implied in this classification that the polymer has not been subjected to decomposition temperatures.

A *thermoplastic polymer* is defined as a high polymer that is permanently fusible so that when subjected to heat below its decomposition temperature, it softens or melts, and rehardens when cooled.

A *thermosetting polymer* is defined as a high polymer that in its final stage of polymerization is permanently infusible. The thermosetting polymers pass through a stage during which they are thermoplastic before becoming thermosetting. This would indicate also that in some syntheses an intermediate polymerization stage can be obtained wherein the polymer is thermoplastic but is potentially thermosetting. Most thermoplastic resins are not even potentially thermosetting. It does not seem necessary to add a third classification to include thermoplastic polymers that are potentially thermosetting. If in an application, such a polymer is prevented from becoming converted to a thermoset condition, as by inhibitors or retarders, and it can be softened or melted indefinitely by reheating, it fulfills the definition required for a thermoplastic.

The difference between thermoplastic and thermosetting polymers is in their structural geometry, and the geometry responsible for the thermal behavior of the polymer is readily related to the functionality of the starting materials. It has already been shown that a monomer with a functionality of two is required to produce a high polymer, provided cyclization does not occur. Examples of such linear polymers obtained by addition and condensation polymerizations are indicated in Table 2, where reactions Type A and B represent polymers produced from monomers.

If the polymer is derived from comers such as hexamethylene diamine and adipic acid, the functionality of the system is the sum of the functionality of the comers divided by the number of comers as in types C and D. When such comers and comonomers are not used in molar equivalents, a suitable correction must be made.

If the functionality of the reactants is greater than two, the polymer will not be linear but will possess a network structure of chains attached to each other by direct chemical bonds. For purposes of demonstration, idealized structures of such molecules are presented as examples in reactions E and F in Table 3.

TABLE 2

Type of Reaction	Reactants	Indicated Functionality of Reactants	Total Functionality	Polymer
(A) Addition	$nCH_2=CH$—[benzene]	*—CH_2—CH—* [benzene]	2	—CH_2—CH—$[CH_2$—CH$]_{n-2}$ [benzene rings]
(B) Condensation	$nNH_2(CH_2)_5COOH$	*$NH_2(CH_2)_5COOH$*	2	$H[NH(CH_2)_5CO]_nOH$
(C) Condensation	$NH_2(CH_2)_6NH_2$ + $HOOC(CH_2)_4COOH$	*$NH_2(CH_2)_6NH_2$* + *$HOOC(CH_2)_4COOH$*	2	$H[NH(CH_2)_6NHOC(CH_2)_4CO]_nOH$
	$NH_2(CH_2)_6NHOC(CH_2)_4COOH$	*$NH_2(CH_2)_6NHOC(CH_2)_4COOH$*	$4/2 = 2$	
(D) Condensation	$HO(CH_2)_6OH$ + $HOOC(CH_2)_4COOH$	*$HO(CH_2)_6OH$* + *$HOOC(CH_2)_4COOH$*	2	$H[O(CH_2)_6OC(CH_2)_4CO]_nOH$
	$HO(CH_2)_6OC(CH_2)_4COOH$	*$HO(CH_2)_6OC(CH_2)_4COOH$*	$4/2 = 2$	

TABLE 3

Type of Reaction	Reactants	Indicated Functionality of Reactants	Total Functionality	Polymer
(E) Addition	CH$_2$=CH—⬡—CH=CH$_2$	*CH$_2$—CH$_2$*—⬡—*CH$_2$—CH$_2$*	4	
(F) Condensation			6 / 6 / 12/5 = 2.4	

The average functionality for reaction F is calculated as follows. Three moles of phthalic acid or anhydride are required as molar equivalents for 2 moles of glycerin. Thus a total of 5 moles of reactants are used. The 3 moles of phthalic acid have a functionality of six, or six reactive groups, and the 2 moles of glycerin have six reactive groups. The two reactants thus offer a functionality of twelve for 5 moles, that is, twelve divided by five or a 2.4 functionality ($f = 2.4$).

An examination of reactions E and F shows that a rigid three-dimensional structure is obtained when the average functionality is greater than two. Polymers of this class normally belong to the infusible or thermosetting class; polymers of reactions A, B, C, and D belong to the thermoplastic class.

It has been common practice to add to the definition of a thermoplastic polymer that it is soluble as well as fusible and that a thermosetting polymer is insoluble as well as infusible. Generally, it is true that most thermosetting polymers are insoluble. However, it is obvious that polymers are possible whereby a copolymer may be made with a large amount of monomer with a functionality of two and a trace of a comonomer of a functionality greater than two, and that such a copolymer would be fusible and not soluble. It would be swollen, however, in a liquid normally a very active solvent for the unmodified homopolymer. A typical example of such a copolymer is one made from styrene with very small quantities of divinylbenzene. If sufficient crosslinks are introduced by large amounts of divinylbenzene, both insolubility and infusibility result.

If a polymer is infusible or insoluble, the conclusion cannot be drawn that the polymer is crosslinked, since the substituents in a linear polymer, because of high secondary valence forces, may produce insolubility or infusibility without direct chemical bonds between the polymer chains. Polyacrylonitrile is a polymer of this kind, and it does not melt without decomposition and it is not crosslinked. For some time aqueous zinc chloride and calcium thiocyanate solutions have been used as solvents for polyacrylonitrile, but preliminary evidence indicates that some of the nitrile groups in the polymer are converted to amides or ammonium salts and that degradation of the polymer occurs. Concentrated sulfuric acid also dissolves polyacrylonitrile. Solution in these cases occurs only by reaction, and the polymers recovered from solution contain many nitrile groups which have been converted to other derivatives.

Exhaustive studies have been carried out on the solubility of polyacrylonitrile, and N, N-dimethylacetamide was found to be a true solvent.[3] Dimethylacetamide is not a common solvent, and obviously a linear polymer must not be considered insoluble without caution.

TABLE 4

EXAMPLES OF FUNCTIONALITY IN MOLECULES

Monomer or Comer	Name	Indicated Functionality	Type	Functionality Number
$CH_2{=}CH$ (benzene ring)	Styrene	$-CH_2-CH-$ (benzene ring)	Addition	2
$CH_2{=}CH$ $\diagdown$ O $CH_2{=}CH$ $\diagup$	Divinyl ether	$-CH_2-CH-$ $\|$ O $\|$ $-CH_2-CH-$	Addition	4
$H_2N(CH_2)_4COOH$	Amino caproic acid	$-NH(CH_2)_5CO-$	Condensation	2
$CH_2{-}CH_2$ $\diagdown O \diagup$	Ethylene oxide	$-CH_2-CH_2O-$	Addition	2
$CH_2-CH-CH_2$ $\|$ $\|$ $\|$ OH OH OH	Glycerin	$CH_2-CH-CH_2$ $\|$ $\|$ $\|$ O O O $\|$ $\|$ $\|$	Condensation	3
OH (benzene ring)	Phenol	HO (benzene ring with bonds)	Condensation	3
$CH_2-CH{-}{-}CH_2$ $\|$ $\diagdown \diagup$ OH O	Epihydrin	$CH_2-CH-CH_2-O-$ $\|$ $\|$ O $\|$	Addition and condensation	3
$CH{=}{=}CH$ $\|$ $\|$ $COOH$ $COOH$	Maleic acid	$-CH{-}{-}CH-$ $\|$ $\|$ $COOH$ $COOH$	Addition	2
$CH{=}{=}CH$ $\|$ $\|$ $COOH$ $COOH$	Maleic acid	$CH{=}CH$ $\|$ $\|$ CO CO $\|$ $\|$	Condensation	2
$CH{=}{=}CH$ $\|$ $\|$ $COOH$ $COOH$	Maleic acid	$-CH-CH-$ $\|$ $\|$ CO CO $\|$ $\|$	Addition and condensation	4

It is conceivable that a thermoplastic polymer can be fusible or infusible and still fall within one of four solubility categories:

Soluble in common or a large number of solvents.
Not soluble but swollen by solvents.
Insoluble in an extremely large number of solvents.
Insoluble in any solvent.

To the present time, no true solvent has been found for the high polymers of tetrafluorethylene; they are considered "insoluble" thermoplastics. In fact, polytetrafluorethylene does not melt but may be fabricated by a sintering process, although the polymer is linear and was derived from the monomer, $CF_2{=}CF_2$, whose functionality is two.

A number of examples of the types of functionality observed in molecules used in polymerization reactions are given in Table 4.

In Table 4 it may be noted that certain compounds like maleic acid can react by addition or condensation and exert polyfunctionality in both types of reaction. If such a reactant is used under conditions where all its functionality is utilized, the functionality of that reactant is the sum of all its functionalities. Maleic anhydride has a total functionality of 4, and thermosetting polymers will result; this is illustrated in the preparation of ethylene maleate. The first or condensation stage, followed by an addition polymerization, is as follows:

First Stage—Condensation

$$n\text{HOCH}_2\text{CH}_2\text{OH} + n\text{CH}{=\!=}\text{CH} \quad \rightarrow$$
$$\underset{\text{COOH}}{|} \quad \underset{\text{COOH}}{|}$$

$$-\text{OCH}_2\text{CH}_2\text{OOCCH}{=}\text{CHCO}(\text{OCH}_2\text{CH}_2\text{OOCCH}{=}\text{CHCO})_{n-1}-$$

Second Stage—Addition

$$-\text{OCH}_2\text{CH}_2\text{OOCCH}{=}\text{CHCO}(\text{OCH}_2\text{CH}_2\text{OOCCH}{=}\text{CHCO})_n-\ \Big|$$
$$+\ -\text{OCH}_2\text{CH}_2\text{OOCCH}{=}\text{CHCO}(\text{OCH}_2\text{CH}_2\text{OOCCH}{=}\text{CHCO})_n-\ \Big| \quad \rightarrow$$

$$-\text{OCH}_2\text{CH}_2\text{OOCCH}{=}\text{CHCO}(\text{OCH}_2\text{CH}_2\text{OOCCH}{-}\text{CHCO})_n-$$
$$-\text{OCH}_2\text{CH}_2\text{OOCCH}{=}\text{CHCO}(\text{OCH}_2\text{CH}_2\text{OOCCH}{-}\text{CHCO})_n-$$

The functionality of these monomers, comonomers, or comers is responsible for the formation of synthetic polymers. During the process of, or as a result of, polymer formation, a number of changes occur in a polymerization system. Some of the changes that occur are:

Monomers, comers, comonomers, or telomers disappear.
The density increases.
The refractive index increases.
Film-forming characteristics appear.
The viscosity increases.
The physical properties, such as flexural and impact strengths, increase.
Solubilities change.
Melting points and boiling points change.
Colloidal properties become evident.
Molecular weights increase.

The appearance of these new characteristics is related to a fundamental change that involves the reacting materials. Two theories have been offered to explain these properties; one is the micellar theory, the other is the macromolecular theory.

REFERENCES

1. W. H. Carothers, *Chem. Revs.*, **8**, 353–426 (1931).
2. G. F. D'Alelio, *Experimental Plastics and Synthetic Resins*, p. 113, John Wiley and Sons, New York, 1946.
3. G. F. D'Alelio, unpublished results.
4. G. F. D'Alelio, U. S. Patent 2,378,196 (June 12, 1945).
5. Th. Wagner-Jauregg, *Ber.*, **63**, 3213 (1930).

CHAPTER 3

The Existence of Macromolecules

THE MICELLAR VERSUS THE MACROMOLECULAR THEORY

The colloidal and physical properties of synthetic polymers initiated a controversy as to whether these substances were built up from micelles [1-3] or from macromolecules.[1,4-6] These two theories have also been called the *association theory* versus the *structural theory*.

This controversy was a continuation of the conflict which started when the micellar theory was offered to explain the colloidal properties of many high molecular natural substances.

The Association or Micellar Theory

The micellar theory stated that the high molecular weight and colloidal and physical properties of the synthetic polymers were the result of molecular aggregation of simple molecules into a micelle of colloidal dimension. The molecules associated in the micelle were held together by secondary valence forces alone, and no primary chemical bond existed between the molecules. In 1899 Thiele[7] considered polystyrene as molecules of monomeric styrene bound together by partial valences. In the dissertation on the *glassy modification* of acrylic esters, Pechmann and Rohm[8] in 1901 explained the transformation of monomeric acrylic esters into products having colloidal properties as the result not of a chemical reaction but of an allotropic change.

Schroeter[9,10] suggested that the change of ketene to diketene and of salicylic acid to the tetrasalicylide produced no change in the actual structure of the starting or monomeric materials. He said that the change was due to an excess of external peripheral force about the monomeric molecules. During the years 1924 to 1926 the association theory was widely accepted as an explanation of the properties of natural high polymers.[1,11-14]. Proteins were considered to have been

59

built up by the mutual association or attraction of small units, for example from the diketopiperazines:

$$2n \quad \begin{matrix} NH_2 \\ \diagdown \\ CH_2 \\ \diagup \\ HOOC \end{matrix} \rightarrow n \begin{matrix} NH \\ \diagup \diagdown \\ CO \quad CH_2 \\ | \quad \quad | \\ CH_2 \quad CO \\ \diagdown \diagup \\ NH \end{matrix} \xrightarrow{\text{Association}} \left[\begin{matrix} NH \\ \diagup \diagdown \\ CO \quad CH_2 \\ | \quad \quad | \\ CH_2 \quad CO \\ \diagdown \diagup \\ NH \end{matrix} \right]_n$$

Glycine   Diketopiperazine   Protein molecule

The diketopiperazine was claimed to exhibit such enormous secondary valence forces that it behaved physically as though it were of very high molecular weight.

During this same period, cellulose was considered to be the associated form of an anhydroglucose, and the molecular formula of cellulose was $C_6H_{10}O_5$.

In support of this association theory, evidence was offered that it was possible, by using freezing point and boiling point methods, to obtain small molecular weights for proteins and other natural substances, such as the polysaccharides and rubber. Later investigations showed that the low molecular weight values obtained were due to technique errors.

The Structural or Macromolecular Theory

The macromolecular theory held that the properties of polymer molecules were primarily the result of primary valence bonds. In other words, the molecules are large because of true chemical bonds, and the amino acids form a polymer by means of direct valence bonds:

$$nNH_2CH_2COOH \rightarrow NH_2CH_2CO(NHCH_2CO)_{n-2}—NHCH_2COOH$$

and the colloidal properties were inherent to its high molecular weight.

The resolution of the conflict over which theory is correct involved a large number of chemical and physical investigations, a number of which are given below.

CHEMICAL INVESTIGATIONS

End group analyses. The relative amount of reactive end groups is determined by chemical analysis. It is obvious that if the polymer is a macromolecule, the amount of end groups in the molecule is inversely proportional to its size. If the polymer is built up by micellar association, the end group ratio remains constant. Fischer's synthetic preparation of the polypeptides demonstrates this concept. If we use glycine and condense it with itself we obtain diketopiperazine, whose end group number is zero.

$$2NH_2CH_2COOH \rightarrow \begin{matrix} CH_2 \\ / \quad \backslash \\ NH_2 \quad COOH \\ HOOC \quad NH_2 \\ \backslash \quad / \\ CH_2 \end{matrix} \rightarrow \begin{matrix} NH---CH_2 \\ | \qquad | \\ OC \qquad CO \\ | \qquad | \\ CH_2---NH \end{matrix}$$

Glycine   Diketopiperazine
(zero end groups)

The association theory postulates the protein as being diketopiperazine associated so strongly n times that it behaves as a high molecular weight compound. The number of end groups in such a polymer should be zero. If, however, polypeptides higher than diketopiperazine are prepared, a series of compounds is found in which the molecular weight increases but the number of end groups remains constant as in Table 1.

TABLE 1

	Molecular Weight	Number End Groups
NH_2CH_2COOH Glycine	75	1
$NH_2CH_2CONHCH_2COOH$ Glycylglycine	132	1
$NH_2CH_2CO(NHCH_2CO)NHCH_2COOH$ Triglycine	189	1
$NH_2CH_2CO(NHCH_2CO)_2NHCH_2COOH$ Tetraglycine	246	1
$NH_2CH_2CO(NHCH_2CO)_8NHCH_2COOH$ Decaglycine	588	1

The fact that the end group remains one as the molecular weight is increased offers proof that association has not occurred and that polymerization took place as follows:

$$HNHCH_2CO\boxed{OH + H}NHCH_2CO\boxed{OH + H}NHCH_2CO\boxed{OH + H}NHCH_2COOH, \text{ etc.}$$

In many substances, it was possible to prove that the ratio between the end groups and the mass of the whole molecule decreases according to calculation as the molecular weight increases.

End group analysis [15] can be readily carried out on the polymers of the methyl ester of alanyl-glycyl-glycine, $\overset{\displaystyle CH_3}{\overset{|}{N}}HCH_2CONHCH_2$-$CONHCH_2COOCH_3$, and on the polymers of glycine esters.[16, 17]

Emil Fischer's systematic investigation [18,19] of the structure of poly-peptides likewise substantiated the structural theory.

Staudinger and co-workers [20-22] applied end group analysis to the polyoxymethylene dimethyl ethers, the polyoxymethylene diacetates, and the polyethylene oxide diacetates.

A series of ethylene oxide polymers were prepared according to the reaction, $H_2O + nCH_2$——$CH_2 \rightarrow$ polymer. According to the asso-
$$\diagdown \diagup$$
$$O$$
ciation theory, the polymer should form n diacetates since n molecules of ethylene oxide would react with acetic anhydride.

Staudinger gives the following data in Table 2 from one of these studies on ethylene oxide polymers:

TABLE 2

Degree of Polymerization *	Acetyl, %	Molecular Weight Calculated from Acetyl	Molecular Weight, Cryoscopic Method
5	26.7	236	220
9	17.6	405	415
18	9.5	820	790
20	8.4	940	900
27	6.5	1,240	1,170
37	4.6	1,890	1,230
39	4.4	1,750	1,610
59	2.8	3,000	2,200
70	2.6	3,200	3,040
140	1.3	6,500	5,900
145	1.25	6,800	5,900
210	0.92	9,300	9,200
290	0.62	13,800	12,000

* The number of segmers in the polymer is equal to the D.P. number.
From H. Staudinger, *Die Hochmolekularen organischen Verbindungen*, p. 298 (1932).

In the process of converting the polyethylene glycols to their acetates no change in molecular weight was observed. If the polyethylene oxide was in the associated form, equivalent quantities of ethylene diacetate should have been obtained. Ethylene diacetate is a low-boiling liquid which does not polymerize, and if it had been obtained it would have been isolated readily.

Carothers and co-workers [23] have shown that high polymeric materials were produced in condensation reactions by the direct elimination of simple molecules; that is, the ratio of the number of reactive groups to the number of starting molecules decreased during the reaction as the molecular weight increased. Typical examples included polymers of hydroxy acids, amino acids, dihydric alcohols, and dibasic acids; hence, with by-product elimination the question of association was removed. All Carothers' experimental work verified these conclusions.[24-28]

Voerman [29] prepared adipic anhydride in 1904 and recorded a melting point of 98 C. He apparently regarded its anomalous properties as due to the association of simple rings and not to the existence of a chain structure. Hill [30] prepared monomeric adipic anhydride and recorded a melting point of about 20 C and a boiling point of about 100 C at 0.1 millimeter. On being heated at 100 C for a few hours it became polymeric, with melting point of 81 to 85 C. The molecular weight of the oligomer was between 710 and 860.

Hill also showed [30] polyadipic anhydride as a linear chain structure and not a ring structure by the reaction with aniline, in which reaction both the monoanilide and dianilide were obtained. Monomeric adipic anhydride itself, $(CH_2)_4(CO)_2O$, produces only the monoanilide. In the linear polymeric anhydride, the product formed depends on which side of the oxygen atom the next anhydride group along the chain breaks. Hill represents the scheme leading to three reaction products of polyadipic anhydride and aniline in this way:

$$HOOC(CH_2)_4CO\text{---}:O\text{---}\overset{\overset{O}{\|}}{C}\text{---}(CH_2)_4\overset{\overset{O}{\|}}{C}\text{---}O\text{---}:OC(CH_2)_4CO\text{-----------}:O\text{---}[CO(CH_2)_4CO]_nOH$$

$\overset{+}{C_6H_5NH}$---:H	⟍⟋ ---H	---:$\overset{+}{NHC_6H_5}$ ⟍ C_6H_5NH---:H	
$\overset{\downarrow}{COOH}$	$\overset{\downarrow}{COOH}$	$CONHC_6H_5$	
$(CH_2)_4$	$(CH_2)_4$	$:(CH_2)_4$	
$CONHC_6H_5$:	$COOH$	$CONHC_6H_5$	
Monoanilide :	Adipic acid :	Dianilide :	

Other important evidence for the macromolecular theory is obtained by the transformation of a polymer into a polymer-analogue. If polystyrene is the associated form of the monomer, styrene, hydrogenation should produce ethylcyclohexane,

$$\left[\begin{array}{c} CH_2{=}CH \\ | \\ \bigcirc \end{array}\right]_n \xrightarrow[\text{}]{H_2} n\,\begin{array}{c} CH_3\text{---}CH_2 \\ | \\ CH \\ \diagup \diagdown \\ CH_2 \quad CH_2 \\ | \qquad | \\ CH_2 \quad CH_2 \\ \diagdown \diagup \\ CH_2 \end{array}$$

Associated styrene monomers   Ethylcyclohexane

which is completely saturated and hence should not associate to give a very high molecular weight. If the polymer derived from styrene is a macromolecule through direct chemical valences, hydrogenation should produce a polymer-analogue of the same degree of polymerization. Staudinger and co-workers [31-33] carried out the catalyzed reduction of a number of polystyrenes of different molecular weight and obtained polyhexahydrostyrenes of the same molecular weight order (see Table 3).

TABLE 3 [33]

Average Molecular Weight of Polystyrene Used	Average Molecular Weight of Polyhexahydrostyrene Obtained
1800	1800
3000	3300
5000	4500

Similarly, caoutchouc, with a molecular weight of 64,000, has been reduced to a hydrocaoutchouc of the same degree of polymerization. In an analogous way many natural and synthetic polymers can be converted into polymeric analogues and then reconverted, if desired, into the original polymer without breaking the polymer chain, or changing its degree of polymerization.[34-36] Such conversions cannot be carried out under drastic chemical conditions, because the skeletal structure of the macromolecule is sensitive to heat, oxygen, chemical reagents, etc. Of course the destructive nature of these agents depends somewhat on the chemical nature of the macromolecule. Other examples of the transformations into polymeric analogues are:

Cellulose → cellulose acetate → cellulose → ethylcellulose

Polyvinyl acetate → polyvinyl alcohol → polyvinyl acetate

Cellulose → cellulose acetate → cellulose → cellulose nitrate

Polystyrene is aliphatically saturated and does not react with bromine by addition under conditions in which such an addition should occur. If it were an "associated" polymer, this reaction with bromine should be expected:

$$\left[CH_2{=}CH \right]_n + nBr_2 \rightarrow nBr{-}CH_2{-}CHBr$$

The results of the degradation [37-41] of polymers into smaller units support the structural theory. If polystyrene was the associated form of styrene, monomeric styrene should be obtained through depolymerization. Table 4 gives Staudinger's results on depolymerizing 104 grams of polystyrene.

TABLE 4

| | | | Weight in Grams | | | | |
Pressure	Temper-ature	Time, Hours	Mon-omer	Di-mers	Tri-mers	Tetra-mers	Residue
1 atmosphere	310–350	6	65	20	4	..	10
Vacuum	290–320	12	40	20	24	4	12

The dimers and trimers were shown [42] to have these structures:

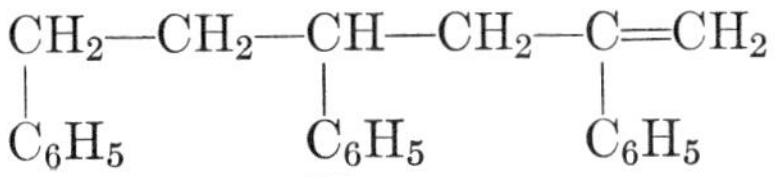

$$CH_2—CH_2—CH—CH_2—C=CH_2$$
| | |
C_6H_5 C_6H_5 C_6H_5
Tristyrene

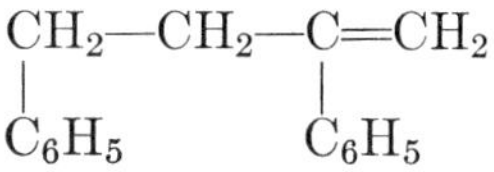

$$CH_2—CH_2—C=CH_2$$
| |
C_6H_5 C_6H_5
Distyrene

Identified also among the products of degradation of polystyrene were [41]

1,3-diphenylpropane,

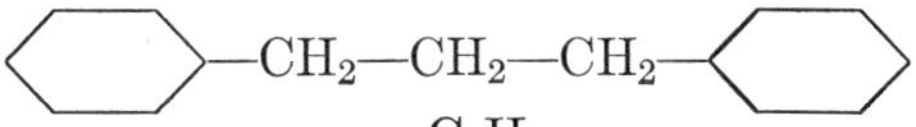

1,3,5-triphenylbenzene,

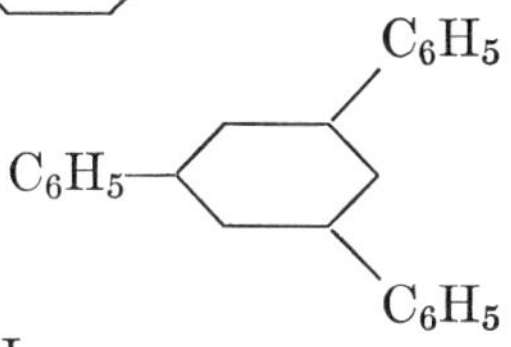

Toluene,

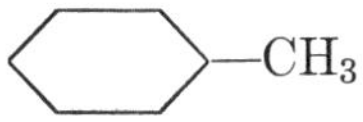

Isopropenylbenzene,

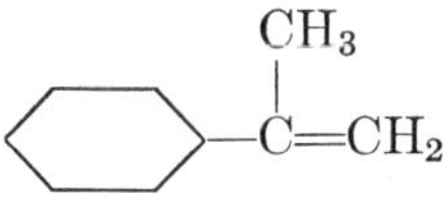

All these products can be explained only by the pyrolysis of an organic compound having a direct carbon to carbon chain:

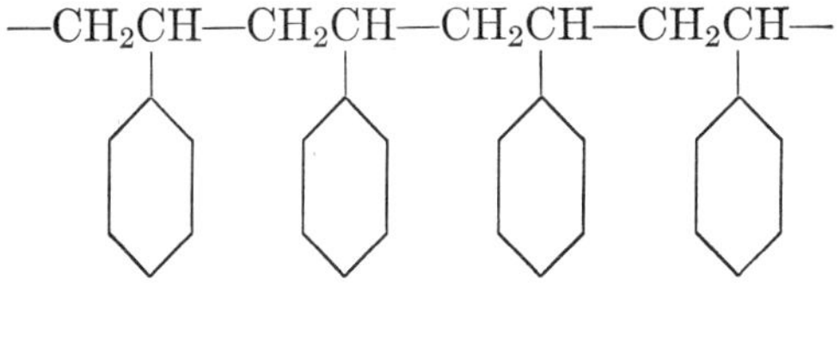

Physical properties. Staudinger [43] changed the condition of polymerization and obtained from one and the same monomer a polymeric series which exhibited the normal differences in properties found in the members of a low molecular weight homologous series. That is, the physical properties of the solids as well as their solutions change gradually with the growing length of the molecule. Specific details on a number of polymers can be considered individually, but generally as the degree of polymerization increases the tensile strength increases, film-forming characteristics appear, toughness increases, the viscosity increases, the solubility decreases, the impact strength increases, the melting points increase, etc. The increase in properties or decrease in solubility however is not directly proportional to the molecular weight. As the molecular weights increase, there is a rapid rise to a limiting value in the form of an asymptotic curve.

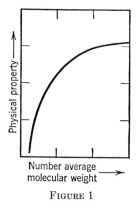

Physical property ⟶

Number average ⟶
molecular weight

FIGURE 1

Staudinger[43] gives the following relative data, which indicate the change of properties versus molecular weight, as in Table 5.

TABLE 5

Molecular Weight	Condition of Polymer	Sintering Temperature, °C	Solubility in Ether	Behavior in Benzene	Specific Viscosity
208	Liquid	Fluid at room temperature	Easily soluble	Immediately soluble, no swelling	0.17
312	Liquid	Fluid at room temperature	Easily soluble	Immediately soluble, no swelling	0.24
3,000	White brittle powder	105–110	Soluble	Immediately soluble, no swelling	0.78
23,000	White powder	120–130	Partly soluble	Immediately soluble, no swelling	4.2
120,000	White fiber-like	160–180	Insoluble	Noticeable swelling before solution	22.0
200,000	White fiber-like	>180	Insoluble	High swelling before solution	39.0
600,000	White fiber-like	>180	Insoluble	Very great swelling before solution	110.0

A general curve of properties versus molecular weight[44] is shown in Figure 1.

Dipole moments. W. B. Bridgman[45] through measurements of refraction and polarization in dilute benzene solution obtained the values of the dipole moments of the polymers of oxydecanoic acid of molecular weights between 900 and 14,000. The calculated values were in excellent agreement with the observed data for a macromolecular structure; they are summarized in Table 6.

TABLE 6

DIPOLE MOMENTS OF POLYOXYDECANOIC ACID

Degree of Polymerization	Molecular Weight	$\mu \times 10^{18}$, Observed	$\mu \times 10^{18}$, Calculated
5	905	5.0	4.2
12	2,120	6.7	6.6
24	4,140	10.2	9.1
46	7,780	12.4	12.4
53	9,070	15.7	13.3
82	13,900	19.0	16.4

The physical and chemical methods discussed represent only part of the evidence which in its cumulative quantity proves that the primary properties of high polymers are a result of their macromolecular nature, involving primary valence bonds and not association forces. These macromolecules can be subdivided, as with other atoms and molecules, into homopolar and heteropolar molecules, depending on the character of the segmers that constitute the chain. The homopolar or heteropolar nature of the polymer has a direct bearing on the secondary physical properties of the polymer.

HOMOPOLAR AND HETEROPOLAR MOLECULES AND POLYMERS

It is known that the ordinary inorganic and organic molecules of very low molecular weight, even after the saturation of primary valences, are always capable of exerting a force or influence on other molecules of the same or different species. These forces are usually called secondary valences, cohesive forces, or van der Waals forces, etc., and they are much weaker than the primary valences. These are the forces primarily responsible for condensing gases into liquids and liquids into crystals, or, in different terminology, these are the forces that cause molecules to associate or aggregate.

Homopolar bonds exist between neutral and non-ionic molecules. The alcohols, esters, and ethers are examples of simple homopolar compounds. Heteropolar bonds exist in compounds having ionic groups. The salts of organic acids and bases are examples of simple heteropolar compounds. These same types of secondary forces are also found in macromolecules; they are responsible, in a large measure, for some of the secondary properties observed in polymers.

Homopolar polymers are represented by such macromolecules as polystyrene, polyvinyl alcohol, polymethylmethacrylate. Sodium polyacrylate and the salts of proteins are typical heteropolar polymers. The homopolar and heteropolar polymers can associate to form micelles as a result of their secondary valence forces. Thus two type of micelles are recognized, molecular and macromolecular.

Molecular Micelles

Low molecular weight atoms or molecules associate to form a chain without direct valency bonds, and the associated molecules behave as if they were of a high molecular weight. The colloidal properties are the result of chain formation due to secondary valence forces only. These chains are temperature-sensitive, that is, the apparent molecular weight changes with temperature. These materials are colloidal in

FIGURE 2

some solvents but not in others. They also give low molecular weight derivatives. Colloidal ferric hydroxide in water and concentrated aqueous dispersions of soap represent

the typical molecular colloids. Graphically, the molecular chains may be represented as in Figure 2, with each (—) representing a single low-molecular-weight molecule.

As an example, Debye [46,47] has shown that 66 single molecules of dodecylamine hydrochloride, an acid soap with a molecular weight of 240.5, agglomerate in water to a micellar weight of 17,300, and in 0.046 M solution of sodium chloride, to a molecular weight of 37,200. The difference between micellar weight and molecular weight becomes obvious. Similarly, most organic dyes in water and tetraisoamyl ammonium iodide in carbon tetrachloride form micelles.[48-51]

Macromolecular Chains and Micelles

A macromolecular chain consists of a high molecular weight molecule; the molecular weight is the function of primary valences only. The

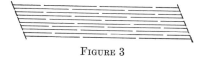

FIGURE 3

colloidal properties are due to the length of the polymer chain, and they give derivatives of the same molecular weight. These derivatives produce colloidal solutions. The polymers may be divided into homopolar and heteropolar types, which exert secondary valence forces to form polymer micelles. Graphically, the polymer micelles may be represented as in Figure 3, with each line representing a macromolecule or polymer.

The classification in Figure 4 distinguishes between molecular and macromolecular chains and micelles.

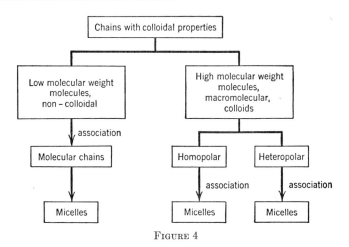

FIGURE 4

REFERENCES

1. M. Bergmann, *Ber.*, **59**, 2973 (1926).
2. K. H. Meyer, *Z. angew. Chemie*, **41**, 935 (1928).
3. P. Karrer, *Einführung in die Chemie der Polymeren Kohlenhydrate*, Akademische Verlagsgesellschaft m.b.H., Leipzig, 1925.
4. H. Staudinger and J. Fritschi, *Helv. Chim. Acta*, **5**, 785 (1922).
5. H. Staudinger, *Z. angew. Chem.*, **42**, 37 (1929).
6. H. Staudinger, *Z. angew. Chem.*, **42**, 67 (1929).
7. J. Thiele, *Ann.*, **306**, 92 (1899).
8. H. von Pechmann and O. Rohm, *Ber.*, **34**, 427, 573 (1901).
9. G. Schroeter, *Ber.*, **49**, 2697 (1916).
10. G. Schroeter, *Ber.*, **52**, 2224 (1919).
11. E. Abderhalden, *Naturwissenschaften*, **12**, 716 (1924).
12. M. Bergmann, *Naturwissenschaften*, **13**, 1045 (1925).
13. H. Pringsheim, *Naturwissenschaften*, **13**, 1084 (1925).
14. K. Hess, W. Weltzien, and E. Messmer, *Ann.*, **435**, 1 (1924).
15. E. Fischer, *Ber.*, **39**, 2924 (1906).
16. M. Frankel and E. Katchalski, *Nature*, **144**, 330 (1939).
17. M. Frankel and E. Katchalski, *J. Am. Chem. Soc.*, **64**, 2268 (1942).
18. E. Fischer, *Ber.*, **52**, 809 (1919).
19. E. Fischer, *Untersuchungen über Aminosäuren Polypeptide und Proteine*, J. Springer, Berlin, 1909.
20. H. Staudinger and H. Johner, *Ann.*, **474**, 205 (1929).

21. H. Staudinger and M. Lüthy, *Helv. Chim. Acta*, **8**, 41 (1925).
22. H. Staudinger and R. Signer, *Ann.*, **474**, 172 (1929).
23. W. H. Carothers and J. A. Arvin, *J. Am. Chem. Soc.*, **51**, 2560–2570 (1929).
24. W. H. Carothers and G. L. Dorough, *J. Am. Chem. Soc.*, **52**, 711–721 (1930).
25. W. H. Carothers and G. L. Berchet, *J. Am. Chem. Soc.*, **52**, 5289–5291 (1930).
26. W. H. Carothers and J. W. Hill, *J. Am. Chem. Soc.*, **54**, 1557–1559 (1932).
27. W. H. Carothers and J. W. Hill, *J. Am. Chem. Soc.*, **54**, 1559–1566 (1932).
28. W. H. Carothers and F. J. van Natta, *J. Am. Chem. Soc.*, **55**, 4714–4719 (1933).
29. G. L. Voerman, *Rec. trav. chim.*, **23**, 265 (1904).
30. J. W. Hill, *J. Am. Chem. Soc.*, **52**, 4110–4114 (1930).
31. H. Staudinger, *Ber.*, **59**, 3033 (1926).
32. H. Staudinger and E. O. Leupold, *Ber.*, **67**, 304 (1934).
33. H. Staudinger, *Ber.*, **62**, 2406 (1929).
34. H. Staudinger and H. Eilers, *Ber.*, **68**, 1611 (1935).
35. H. Staudinger and O. Schweitzer, *Ber.*, **63**, 3132 (1930).
36. H. Staudinger and G. V. Schulz, *Ber.*, **68**, 2320 (1935).
37. H. Staudinger, K. Frey, P. Garbsch, and S. Wehrli, *Ber.*, **62**, 2912 (1929).
38. H. Staudinger and W. Heuer, *Ber.*, **67**, 1159 (1934).
39. H. Staudinger and A. Steinhofer, *Ann.*, **517**, 35 (1935).
40. G. S. Whitby, *Trans. Faraday Soc.*, **32**, 315 (1936).
41. I. Allen, Gibson Island Conference, July 12, 1939.
42. H. Staudinger and A. Steinhofer, *Ann.*, **517**, 35 (1935).
43. H. Staudinger, *Die Hochmolekularen organischen Verbindungen*, p. 186, J. Springer, Berlin, 1932.
44. H. Staudinger, *Kunststoffe*, **29**, 1 (1939).
45. W. B. Bridgman, *J. Am. Chem. Soc.*, **60**, 530 (1938).
46. P. Debye, *J. Colloid Sci.*, p. 407 (August 1948).
47. P. Debye, *J. Phys. & Colloid Chem.*, **51**, 18 (1947).
48. P. Walden, *Kolloid-Z.*, **27**, 97 (1920).
49. P. Walden, *Z. physik. Chem.*, **94**, 295 (1920).
50. P. Walden, *Z. physik. Chem.*, **94**, 352 (1920).
51. Wo. Ostwald and K. Röderer, *Kolloid-Z.*, **82**, 174 (1908).

CHAPTER 4

The Non-Homogeneity of Polymers and Their Properties

A polymer mass is not homogeneous in the sense that it consists of macromolecules or individual polymer chains of identical size. It consists of a mixture of individual polymers which, in most cases, have the same empirical formula but are of different molecular weights. In many instances the chains differ not only in length but also in composition. Partially hydrolyzed polyvinyl acetate and partially acylated cellulose fall in this class. Because these polymers are a mixture of macromolecules, the molecular weight value assigned to the mixture does not have the same meaning as it has for such homogeneous molecules as acetone, or urea, or sucrose. The molecular weights assigned to such polymer mixtures obviously must refer to an average molecular weight, which is the sum of the weights of all the macromolecules of various molecular weights divided by the number of macromolecules. The very high molecular weight and the correspondingly large size of the polymers make molecular weight determinations more difficult than for ordinary small molecules. Polymer molecular weights are usually derived by one or more of the following methods, which will be considered in more detail later.

Chemical end group analysis.
Viscosity determination.
Sedimentation in an ultracentrifuge.
Osmotic pressure.
Light scattering.

The non-homogeneity of a polymer mass is determined by, first, separating the mixture into a number of fractions, second, measuring the molecular weight of each fraction, and, third, plotting a distribution curve of the fractions.

71

FRACTIONATION OF POLYMER MIXTURES

The separation of a polymer mixture into fractions is based on the primary property of the individual polymer molecules, namely, the size of the molecule. Such properties as diffusion, sedimentation, solubility, and volatility are related to molecular weight, and as a result the fractionation of macromolecules may be accomplished in a number of ways. The methods of separating materials into fractions have been tabulated by Cragg and Hammerschlag and are given in Table 1.[1]

TABLE 1

SEPARATION OF MIXTURES INTO FRACTIONS

Method	*Principle on Which Separation Is Based*
I. Solubility methods	Solubility decreases with molecular weight.
1. Fractional precipitation	
a. By addition of precipitant	
b. By cooling	
2. Fractional solution	
a. Solvent of varying composition	
b. Varying temperature	
3. Distribution between two immiscible solvents	Distribution coefficient depends on molecular weight.
II. Rate-of-solution method (diffusion into a single solvent)	Smaller molecules diffuse faster.
III. Ultracentrifuge	Sedimentation velocity increases with molecular weight.
IV. Chromatographic adsorption	Smaller molecules are preferentially adsorbed.
V. Ultrafiltration through graded membranes	Sieving action.
VI. Molecular distillation	Larger molecules are less volatile.

From L. H. Cragg and H. Hammerschlag, "The Fractionation of High Polymeric Substances," *Chem. Revs.*, **39**, 83 (1946). The Williams and Wilkins Company, Baltimore, publisher.

The fractionation of polymers is much more difficult and more complex than the fractionation of ordinary low molecular weight compounds. For example, in the fractionation of acetanilide or sucrose, a fraction is eventually obtained that consists of pure acetanilide or sucrose, in which each molecule is identical with each neighbor molecule. In high polymers, however, such a condition is never reached since further processing of these fractions shows that they are heterogeneous and contain polymers of different chain length.

The solubility method is probably the method in most common use for polymer fractionations. This separation is accomplished either by the addition of a precipitant to the solution of the polymer, or by cooling of a solution of the polymer, or by a combination of cooling and precipitant. Regardless of the method used, the objective of the separation is to obtain fractions as narrow and as sharp as possible. To obtain this sharp distribution, it may be necessary to refractionate the isolated fraction, and to combine all fractions within the same molecular weight range.

FRACTIONATION EFFICIENCY AND POLYMER DISTRIBUTION

The efficiency of the fractionation process determines the sharpness, or slopes, of the distribution curves, and inefficient fractionation distorts the distribution curve. The difference in the nature of the distribution curve between a good and poor fractionation is readily demonstrable by using a fractional-precipitation method. As a general rule, fractional precipitation by the addition of a precipitant to a concentrated solution of the polymer produces unsatisfactory results. Douglas and Stoops[2] have shown that the separation of a polymer into fractions is more accurate when a dilute rather than a concentrated solution of polymer is used. They compared the separation of fractions on solutions of resins of various concentrations of vinyl chloride and vinyl acetate copolymers dissolved in acetone, to which was added acetone-water (50-50) mixtures. Table 2 summarizes the results obtained.

TABLE 2

PERCENTAGE PRECIPITATED IN MOLECULAR WEIGHT RANGE

Figure	Resin Solution, %	Fraction 1, 16–20,000 mol. wt.	Fraction 2, 12–16,000 mol. wt.	Fraction 3, 8–12,000 mol. wt.	Fraction 4, 4–8000 mol. wt.	Fraction 5, below 4000 mol. wt.
1	10.00	0%	57%	25%	13%	5%
2	5.25	0	46	29	18	7
3	2.70	0	35	31	24	10
4	1.64	5	28	30	23	14
5	1.10	6	26	23	21	24

Reprinted by permission from *Industrial and Engineering Chemistry.*

The integral weight step distribution curves obtained from each of these five solutions are compared in Figures 1 to 5. It will be observed that the fractionation becomes poorer as more concentrated solutions

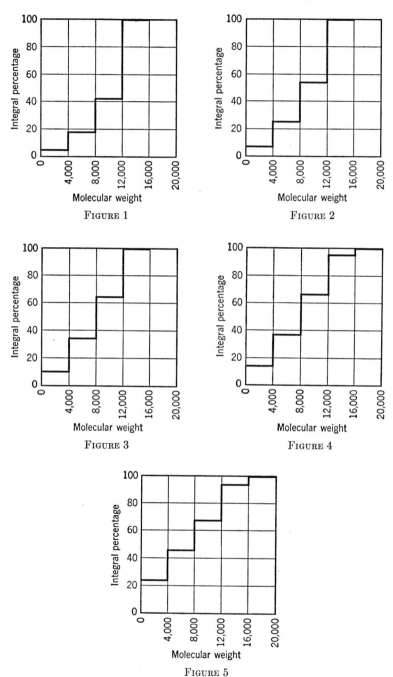

FIGURE 1

FIGURE 2

FIGURE 3

FIGURE 4

FIGURE 5

are used, and that a significant difference in distribution occurs even in the use of a 1.64 per cent solution as compared to a 1 per cent solution.

DISTRIBUTION CURVES

When sufficient sharp fractions have been isolated from a polymer, and the molecular weights of the fractions have been determined, the distribution of the fractions of the various molecular weights isolated from the original sample may be represented in a number of ways. A typical representation is illustrated using a sample of polyvinylnaphthalene.[3] The vinylnaphthalene was bulk polymerized at 70 C for 1560 minutes to an 83 per cent conversion. The fractionation was accomplished, using toluene as a solvent and methyl alcohol as a precipitant. The fractions of the highest molecular weights were refractionated, using cyclohexanone as the solvent and methyl alcohol as the precipitant. The data of the fraction are summarized in Table 3.

TABLE 3

Molecular Distribution Data
2-Vinylnaphthalene Polymerized in Bulk at 70 C

Fraction Number	Weight Polymer, Grams	Percentage Polymer, Based on Total	Cumulative Percentage Polymer	$\eta_{sp,}$ 0.5%	$[\eta]$	Molecular Weight	D.P.
B–1	3.57	8.44	8.44	0.035	0.0693	72,250	466
B–2	1.17	2.76	11.20	0.09	0.175	130,100	840
B–3	3.43	8.10	19.30	0.12	0.230	155,100	1000
B–4	3.74	8.84	28.14	0.14	0.280	176,000	1130
B–5	4.93	11.70	39.84	0.18	0.336	197,400	1270
B–6	3.88	15.83 { 9.15	48.99	0.23	0.423	229,000	1480
B–7	2.82	6.68	55.67	0.23	0.423	229,000	1480
B–8	4.72	11.20	66.87	0.25	0.455	239,500	1540
B–9	1.80	4.26	71.13	0.28	0.505	256,200	1650
B–10	2.78	6.56	77.69	0.33	0.583	280,800	1810
B–11	4.83	11.40	89.09	0.56	0.920	375,500	2420
B–12	4.64	10.91	100.00	0.80	1.21	446,600	2880

The data of Table 3 may be plotted as a population curve, as in Figure 6, by plotting the percentage weight of the fraction as determined against the molecular weight or its equivalent value such as the degree of polymerization or viscosity. While such a plot does give a distribution picture, it is of little value in the comparison of one distribution curve to another, and it is not as important as an integral weight or a differential weight distribution curve.

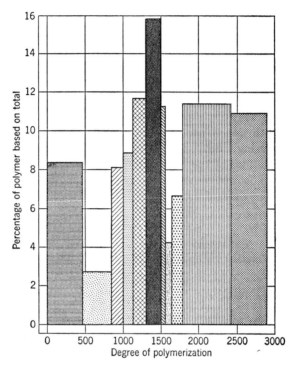

FIGURE 6.   Population curve of 2-vinylnaphthalene polymerized in bulk.

The integral weight distribution curve is obtained by plotting the cumulative weight percentage of the polymer fractions against the molecular weight, as in Figure 7. Such a plot results in a step curve, through which a continuous curve is drawn.

The differential weight distribution curve, shown in Figure 8, is obtained by the graphic differentiation of the continuous integral weight distribution curve by dividing ΔW, the change in the weight fraction, by ΔDP, the change in the degree of polymerization.

Fractional precipitation methods have been more widely used than any other method to isolate smaller fractions of macromolecules for determination of molecular weight distribution. The ultracentrifuge has also been used for this purpose, but not as extensively as the solution and precipitation method because of the specialized equipment required. However, the centrifugal method possesses an advantage in

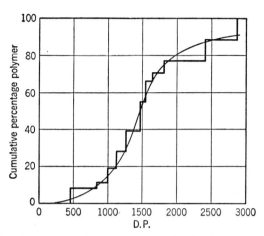

FIGURE 7. Cumulative percentage and integral distribution curve of 2-vinylnaphthalene polymerized in bulk.

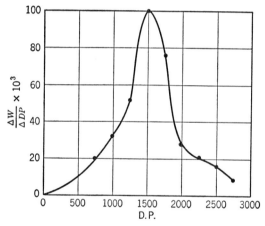

FIGURE 8. Differential distribution curve of 2-vinylnaphthalene polymerized in bulk.

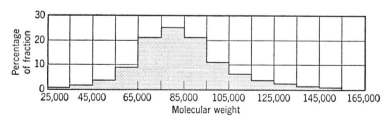

FIGURE 9. Population curve of a polystyrene sample.

that it may be used not only to separate the polymer into fractions but also to determine the molecular weight of the fractions.

Signer and Gross,[4-6] determining the distribution curve in an ultracentrifuge on a 100-gram sample of polystyrene whose average molecular weight was 80,000, obtained the data of Table 4.

TABLE 4

Weight of Fraction	Molecular Weight Range
0.2	25– 35,000
1.7	35– 45,000
3.6	45– 55,000
8.4	55– 65,000
20.0	65– 75,000
23.8	75– 85,000
20.2	85– 95,000
10.4	95–105,000
6.0	105–115,000
3.3	115–125,000
1.7	125–135,000
0.5	135–145,000
0.2	145–155,000

These data are represented in Figure 9 as a population curve, in Figure 10 as an integral weight distribution curve, in Figure 11 as a differential weight distribution curve, and in Figure 12 as a differential number distribution curve.

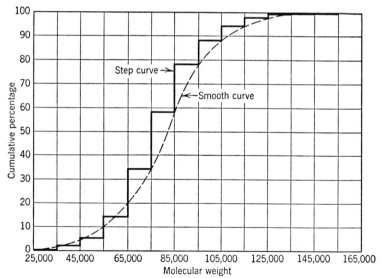

FIGURE 10.   Integral weight distribution curve of a polystyrene sample.

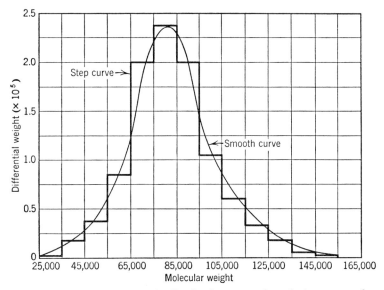

FIGURE 11.   Differential weight distribution curve of a polystyrene sample.

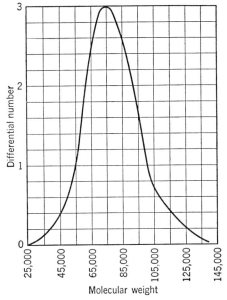

FIGURE 12.   Differential number distribution function of a polystyrene sample.

A comparison of the population curve of polystyrene in Figure 9 and of polyvinylnaphthalene in Figure 6 shows that the polystyrene sample is more homogeneous than the polyvinylnaphthalene sample; in fact, the population curve for polystyrene is quite similar to its own differential weight distribution curve in Figure 11.

MATHEMATICAL MEANING OF THE DISTRIBUTION CURVES

The meaning of the integral and differential curves is summarized briefly in the following equations.

If M_0 = molecular weight of the monomer and n = number of monomers of chain length n, the molecular weight of the polymer is

$$M_n = nM_0 \tag{1}$$

If more than one monomer is involved in the reaction, the molecular weight of the polymer is

$$M_n = n \left[\frac{M'_0 + M''_0}{2} \right] \tag{2}$$

if M'_0 and M''_0 are used in equivalent quantities and if the polymerization reaction does not result in by-product elimination.

In a condensation reaction which proceeds by the elimination of a molecule of condensation product, M''', the equation becomes

$$M_n = n \left[\frac{M'_0 + M''_0}{2} - M''' \right] \tag{3}$$

when M'_0 and M''_0 are used in equivalent quantities. If M'_0 and M''_0 are not equal, the value of n is odd, and the polymer chain may be terminated by M'_0 or M''_0. The molecular weights of these chains terminated respectively by M'_0 and M''_0 are

$$M'_n = \frac{n+1}{2} \cdot M'_0 + \frac{n-1}{2} \cdot M''_0 - (n-1)M''' \tag{4}$$

$$M''_n = \frac{n-1}{2} \cdot M'_0 + \frac{n+1}{2} \cdot M''_0 - (n-1)M''' \tag{5}$$

However, when n becomes sufficiently large, greater than 50, for example, equations 4 and 5 are reduced to equation 3. These equations are simple and valid only if we have a single polymer chain. If the weight of M_n in grams corresponds to the molecular weight in grams of the monomer M_0, then M_n corresponds to one base mole (Staudinger's basal mole), which contains 6.06×10^{23} fundamental units (Avogadro's number) united in chains of different lengths. The chains of different lengths are separated theoretically by fractionation. In actual practice, fractionation processes result in the isolation of chains within certain chain length limits. The simplest manner of representing the results of a fractionation is to plot either the total weight or the total number of chains of length N against the value of n to give an integral distribution function. The plot of these data results in a step curve. If there are sufficient fractions, the step curve can be replaced by a continuous curve to obtain the integral weight and integral number distribution functions, $R'(n)$ and $Z'(n)$, respectively.

The major interest in polymer distribution, however, is in knowing the *weight* or the *number* of the molecules in the range between n and dn. Correspondingly, two distribution functions are used, the weight distribution function and the number distribution function. However, the weight distribution functions are used most often.

WEIGHT DISTRIBUTION FUNCTIONS

The differential weight distribution curve gives the weights of the different fractions. Thus the weight of one chain of links is given by $M_n = nM_0$ (equation 1) and the weight of $f(n)$ chains is

$$M_n = f(n) \cdot n \cdot M_0 \tag{6}$$

whose differential is

$$dM_n = f(n) \cdot n \cdot M_0 \, dn = R'(n) \cdot dn \tag{7}$$

The total weight of chains whose polymerization degree lies between zero and n is given in integration equation 7. Then

$$M(0, n) = \int_0^n f(n) \cdot n \cdot M_0 \, dn \tag{8}$$

and by integrating over all possible degrees of polymerization, we obtain the expression

$$M = M_0 = \int_0^\infty f(n) \cdot n \cdot M_0 \cdot dn \tag{9}$$

wherein

$$\int_0^\infty f(n) \cdot n \cdot dn = 1$$

Equation 9 represents the continuous integral weight distribution curve of Figure 10; and Figure 11 represents its graphical differentiation. In fractionation experiments, the fractions are represented from a limit of monomer ($n = 1$) to a degree of polymerization n_1, and the next fraction to a degree of polymerization n_2, the next fraction to a degree of polymerization n_3, etc. The weights of the chains of these fractions are given as

$$M_1(1, n_1) = \int_1^{n_1} f(n)M_0 \cdot n \cdot dn \tag{10}$$

$$M_2(n_1, n_2) = \int_{n_1}^{n_2} f(n)M_0 \cdot n \cdot dn \tag{11}$$

$$M_3(n_2, n_3) = \int_{n_2}^{n_3} f(n)M_0 \cdot n \cdot dn \tag{12}$$

NUMBER DISTRIBUTION FUNCTIONS

In a manner similar to the manner of obtaining the weight functions, the number distribution functions may be obtained.

The differential number distribution equation is given by

$$dN = f(n) \, dn = Z'(n) \, dn \tag{13}$$

By integrating equation 13 over all possible degrees of polymerization, that is, from $n = 0$ to ∞, the total number of chain molecules in one basal mole is given as

$$N = \int_0^\infty f(n) \, dn \tag{14}$$

while the total number of chains with lengths between a degree of polymerization of 0 to n is given as

$$N(0, n) = \int_0^n f(n) \, dn \tag{15}$$

The differential number distribution curve is obtained by dividing each function of the weight differential curve by the corresponding molecular weight of that function. Figure 12, the differential number distribution curve of the polystyrene sample of Signer and Gross, was derived from the differential weight distribution curve of Figure 11.

In distribution function plots, any value equivalent to the length of the polymer chain or its molecular weight may be used as the abscissa; the intrinsic viscosity $[\eta]$ is often used.

THEORETICAL AND ACTUAL DISTRIBUTION CURVES IN ADDITION POLYMERS

It is interesting to note that Schulz [7-10] has derived a theoretical expression for the form of integral distribution curves of addition polymers by considering the relation of polymer propagation to polymer termination. This relationship is expressed as

$$f(n)\, dn = \ln^2 \alpha \cdot \alpha^n\, dn \qquad (16)$$

α has the meaning of $1 - K_x$, where K_x is the ratio of the rate of the termination and the propagation reactions or

$$\alpha = 1 - K_x = \frac{W_p - W_c}{W_p} \qquad (17)$$

where W_p is the probability of propagation, and W_c is the probability of cessation. The actual and theoretical differential weight distribution curve for a polystyrene sample is shown in Figure 13. Schulz,

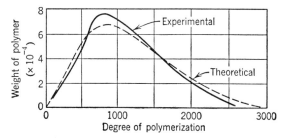

FIGURE 13.   Differential weight distribution curve of polystyrene.

Dinglinger, and Husemann [7, 8, 11] polymerized the styrene for this sample at 140 C until it was 60 per cent polymerized and obtained the following data on the fractions of the polymer. The unfractionated polymer had an intrinsic viscosity of 9.2 and an average polymerization degree of 1280, or a molecular weight of about 130,000. The polymer was dissolved in methyl ethyl ketone and fractionally precipitated with methanol. The data are given in Table 5.

TABLE 5

Fraction	Weight, %	Intrinsic Viscosity	Degree of Polymerization
1	2.3	0.51	102
2	4.4	2.46	495
3	5.2	3.70	740
4	6.1	4.6	900
5	12.4	6.0	1210
6	7.3	7.2	1450
7	23.7	8.7	1780
8	15.3	10.5	2110
9	8.3	12.3	2610
10	10.1	15.5	3110
11	4.9	19.4	3880

A similar comparison of the experimental and theoretical integral weight distribution curve for a polyisobutylene sample according to Schulz is shown in Figure 14.

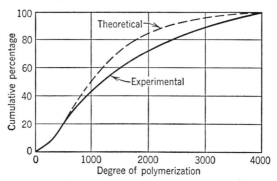

FIGURE 14.   Integral weight curves of polyisobutylene.

THEORETICAL DISTRIBUTION CURVES FOR CONDENSATION POLYMERS

Carothers [12] and Flory [13-19] derived a relation between functionality and the conditions under which linear polymers of a definite size are formed. These equations were further extended to predict the degree of reaction at which gelation due to crosslinking occurs. These relationships may be summarized as follows:

$$2(N_0 - N) = \text{number of functions lost (since two functions disappear with the formation of a new bond)} \qquad (18)$$

where f = degree of functionality of the starting molecules, N_0 = number of molecules at start of the reaction, N_0 = number of functional groups at the start of the reaction, and N = number of molecules at end of the reaction.

$$\frac{2(N_0 - N)}{Nf} = p = \text{extent of the reaction} \qquad (19)$$

$$\frac{N_0}{N} = \overline{DP} = \text{average degree of polymerization} = n \qquad (20)$$

$$p = \frac{2N_0}{N_0 f} - \frac{2N}{N_0 f} \qquad (21)$$

and

$$p = \frac{2}{f} - \frac{1}{f \cdot \overline{DP}} \qquad (22)$$

USE OF FUNCTIONALITY EQUATION WITH
BIFUNCTIONAL MOLECULES

If all the molecules are bifunctional, as in the condensation of a
hydroxy acid, $HO(CH_2)_nCOOH$, then f equals 2, and equation 22
becomes

$$p = 1 - \frac{1}{\overline{DP}} = 1 - \frac{N}{N_0} = \frac{N_0 - N}{N_0} \tag{23}$$

Table 6 shows the polymerization degree or $\overline{DP}$ obtained with the
extent of the reaction. The data are plotted in Figure 15.

TABLE 6

p	$\overline{DP}$
0.50	2
0.66	3
0.75	4
0.80	5
0.90	10
0.95	20
0.98	50
0.99	100
0.995	200

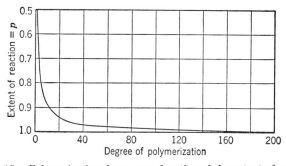

FIGURE 15.   Polymerization degree as a function of the extent of reaction.

However, it must be borne in mind that the application of this equation to condensation polymers shows only the polymer whose degree of
polymerization is formed in the greatest amount. As with addition
polymerization, condensation polymerization produces a mixture of
polymers of different molecular weights. Thus the above table and
curve show only that at 98 per cent condensation reaction, the polymer
formed from 50 units is present in the greatest amount. However, they
do not show the distribution of the polymer mixture.

Flory extended his work to include the relationship between polymer distribution and the extent of the reaction. His results were in excellent agreement with the composition of polymers determined experimentally and prepared by Carothers and his co-workers.[20] The polymers prepared and studied were polyesters derived from (1) hydroxy acids and (2) dicarboxylic acids and dihydric alcohols. In these condensation reactions it was assumed that one functional group was as active as any other, which assumption was verified [15] experimentally in the polyesters.

Under the conditions of equation 23, $p = 1 - (N/N_0)$, the probability that a particular reactive group has reacted is given as p, and the probability that no bond has formed is given as $(1 - p)$. In forming a polymer containing n segmers, $(n - 1)$ bonds must form since the two terminal groups have not reacted. The probability that the $(n - 1)$ bonds have formed is obviously given by p^{n-1}, and the probability that the two terminal groups have not formed bonds is given by $(1 - p)^2$. Hence the probability of a molecule entering a chain is given as p^{n-1}. $(1 - p)^2$, and the probability of its presence in a chain of n-mer units is given by

$$W_n = n(1 - p)^2 \cdot p^{n-1} \qquad (24)$$

wherein W_n is the total number of primary molecules in n-mer chains divided by the total number, N_0, of the monomeric components initially present. This equation gives the weight fraction of each polymer at any extent of reaction.

The number of chains of length n is proportional to the probability that a primary molecule will be found in such a chain and is given as:

$$N_n = \frac{N_0 W_n}{n} = N_0 p^{n-1} \cdot (1 - p)^2 \qquad (25)$$

If P_n represents the molecular fraction of n-mers, then

$$P_n = \frac{N_n}{N_0} = \frac{N_0 W_n}{N_0 n} = p^{n-1} \cdot (1 - p)^2 \qquad (26)$$

The weight fractions are represented in Figures 16 and 17 for different degrees of reaction p. Figure 16 represents the differential weight distribution for low degrees of polycondensation, $p = 0.5$ to 0.9, and Figure 15 for high degree of reaction, from $p = 0.9$ to 0.99. These curves indicate that a certain polymer occurs most frequently, that this maximum is progressively displaced toward greater chain length with a greater degree of reaction, and that this maximum tends to flatten out. These curves also show that the polymerization products are non-homogeneous.

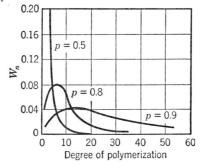

FIGURE 16. Differential weight distribution curves for low degrees of polycondensation.[14] (By permission from the authors and the *Journal of the American Chemical Society*.)

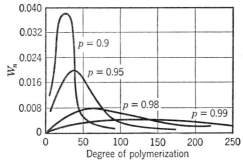

FIGURE 17. Differential weight distribution curves for higher degrees of polycondensation.[14] (By permission from the authors and the *Journal of the American Chemical Society*.)

The differential number distribution curves are shown in Figures 18 and 19.

By differentiating and equating the weight fraction distribution equation to zero, we obtain the maximum of the distribution curve as

$$W_n(\text{max}) = -\frac{(1-p)^2}{\ln p} \cdot e^{-(1+ln\,p)} = -\frac{(1-p)^2}{\ln p} \cdot e^{-(1+ln\,p)} \quad (27)$$

and as p approaches one the equation becomes

$$W_n(\text{max}) = \frac{1-p}{e} \quad (28)$$

The dependence of the weight distribution upon p is shown in Figure 20. The $\overline{DP}$ values chosen were $n = 5$, 10, and 20, and the weight distributions are plotted against p.

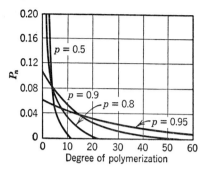

FIGURE 18.   Differential number distribution curves for low degrees of polycondensation.[14]   (By permission from the authors and the *Journal of the American Chemical Society.*)

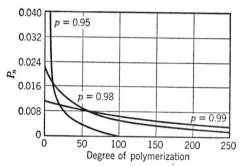

FIGURE 19.   Differential number distribution curves for higher degrees of polycondensation.[14]   (By permission from the authors and the *Journal of the American Chemical Society.*)

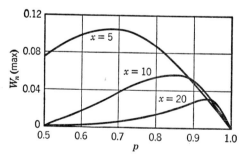

FIGURE 20.   Amounts of polycondensations as functions of p.[14]   (By permission from the authors and the *Journal of the American Chemical Society.*)

RELATIONSHIP OF WEIGHT, VISCOSITY, NUMBER, AND SEDIMENTATION AVERAGE MOLECULAR WEIGHTS

The molecular weights of the polymer mixture, before separation, and of the fractions, are average molecular weights. These average molecular weight values are obtained readily by viscosity, diffusion, and sedimentation measurements in dilute solutions. Three primary molecular weight values are recognized—the weight average, the number average, and the sedimentation average molecular weights.

Weight Average Molecular Weight

The weight average molecular weight, $\overline{M}_w$, is expressed mathematically as [21]

$$\overline{M}_w = \frac{\Sigma M_i^2 N_i}{\Sigma M_i N_i} \qquad (29)$$

where M_i is the molecular weight of particles of chain length i, and N_i is the number of particles of chain length i. The $\overline{M}_w$ value is obtained in light scattering measurements and also in certain viscosity measurements. Viscosity measurements give either a weight average molecular weight or a more complex average, which Flory [22] defines as the viscosity average molecular weight, $\overline{M}_\eta$, depending on the observed experimental viscosity law. The viscosity average is expressed as

$$\overline{M}_\eta = \left[\frac{\Sigma N_i M_i^{\beta+1}}{\Sigma N_i M_i} \right]^{1/\beta} \qquad (30)$$

where β is a constant, and when β becomes one, then $\overline{M}_\eta$ equals $\overline{M}_w$.

Number Average Molecular Weight

The number average molecular weight, $\overline{M}_n$, is expressed [21] as

$$\overline{M}_n = \frac{\Sigma M_i N_i}{\Sigma N_i} \qquad (31)$$

where $\overline{M}_n$ is the molecular weight averaged over the number of particles, M_i is the molecular weight of particles of chain length i, and N_i is the number of particles of chain length i.

The $\overline{M}_n$ value is obtained by methods which determine end groups analytically and through osmotic pressure measurements. Examples of end group determinations are the copper and iodine numbers of cellulose, the bromine number of polystyrene, the acylation of polyethylene glycol, etc. This value is called a number average, since the molecular weight determination depends on the number of molecules present and is also the basis for molecular weight determinations through melting point depression, boiling point elevation, etc.

Sedimentation Average Molecular Weight

For molecular weight values obtained by sedimentation equilibrium in a centrifuge, average molecular weight is expressed [21] as

$$\bar{M}_z = \frac{\Sigma M_i^3 N_i}{\Sigma M_i^2 N_i} \tag{32}$$

An examination of these equations for $\bar{M}_w$, $\bar{M}_n$, and $\bar{M}_z$ shows that only when there is *one* molecular species of M_i molecular weight will $M_n = M_w = M_z$, and that molecular weights of polymers should be referred to with caution.

This picture is readily clarified if we consider a polymer containing a number of different molecular species. Each species will contribute equally to the number average, whereas those species that have the greater molecular weight will contribute more to the weight average. Therefore, $\bar{M}_w$ will always be greater than $\bar{M}_n$, and a wide distribution curve will produce a larger difference between $\bar{M}_w$ and $\bar{M}_n$, and in a narrow distribution curve $\bar{M}_w$ and $\bar{M}_n$ approach each other.

However, Flory [13] shows that in addition polymerization of ethylene oxide, for example, the ratio of the weight average molecular weight to the number average molecular weight, $\bar{M}_w/\bar{M}_n$, does approach one, and that the distribution curve in this addition polymerization is narrower than that obtained in condensation polymerizations as, for example, that of the organic ω-hydroxy carboxylic acids. He also shows [23] that when the molecular weight in condensation polymers is high, the ratio becomes approximately $\bar{M}_n:\bar{M}_w:\bar{M}_z = 1:2:3$.

Flory obtained this ratio of molecular weight average by evaluating the expression, $M_i N_i$, in terms of the value, p, which designates the extent of the reaction according to the equations:

$$\bar{M}_n = M_0 \cdot \frac{1}{1-p} \tag{33}$$

$$\bar{M}_w = M_0 \cdot \frac{1+p}{1-p} \tag{34}$$

$$\bar{M}_z = M_0 \cdot \frac{1+4p+p^2}{1-p^2} \tag{35}$$

and

$$\bar{M}_n:\bar{M}_w:\bar{M}_z = \frac{1}{1-p} : \frac{1+p}{1-p} : \frac{1+4p+p^2}{1-p^2}$$

and it can be shown that as p becomes greater, that is, approaches 1, then $\bar{M}_n:\bar{M}_w:\bar{M}_z$ as 1:2:3, for example,

$$\text{at } p = 0.5 \text{ then } M_n:M_w:M_z = 1:1.5:2.16$$

$$\text{at } p = 0.9 \text{ then } M_n:M_w:M_z = 1:1.9:2.85$$

$$\text{at } p = 0.99 \text{ then } M_n:M_w:M_z = 1:1.99:2.97$$

Likewise, Kraemer and Lansing [21] have shown that in a mixture of equal weights of molecules of molecular weight 10,000 and 100,000, the ratio of

$$\frac{\bar{M}_w}{\bar{M}_n} = \frac{91,818}{55,000} = 1.67$$

It is evident, as Kraemer originally said, that extreme caution should be used in comparing molecular weights obtained by different experimental methods.

Another example of the difference in values between M_w and M_n may be seen in a system containing two molecules of molecular weight 200 and one of molecular weight 400, wherein the molecular weights of the two species are closer than in the previous example.

$$\Sigma \bar{M}_w = \frac{2(200)^2 + 1(400)^2}{2(200) + 1(400)} = 300 = \text{weight average}$$

$$\Sigma \bar{M}_n = \frac{2(200) + 1(400)}{2 + 1} = 266 = \text{number average}$$

In this case $\bar{M}_w/\bar{M}_n = 1.13$, that is, the distribution curve becomes narrower as $\bar{M}_w/\bar{M}_n$ approaches 1. The meaning of the ratio of $\bar{M}_w$ to $\bar{M}_n$ may be shown also in the following manner. The total number of molecules in a basal mole is given by

$$N = \int_0^\infty f(n)\, dn \qquad (36)$$

and, if no polymerization has taken place, $N = N_a = 6.06 \times 10^{23}$ = Avogadro's number. When polymerization does occur, the average degree of polymerization, $\bar{P}$, is expressed as

$$\bar{P} = \frac{N_a}{N} = \frac{N_a}{\displaystyle\int_0^\infty f(n)\, dn} \qquad (37)$$

and the number average molecular weight, $\bar{M}_n$, becomes

$$\bar{M}_n = \frac{N_a}{N} = \frac{M_0}{\displaystyle\int_0^{\infty} f(n)\, dn} \tag{38}$$

Where the number distribution function (Figure 12) [2,7] is symmetrical or nearly so, the function can be represented approximately by

$$f(n)\, dn = \frac{q}{n_{\max}} \exp\left[-\pi q^2 (n - n_{\max})^2\right] \tag{39}$$

wherein the average polymerization degree corresponds to the most frequent chain length with $n_{\max}$ links and

$$\bar{P} = P_{\max} \tag{40}$$

In contrast, the polymerization degree from a viscometric measurement is considered as follows.[11,24-26] The full meaning of the viscosity equation is considered in a later chapter. In the following equations, η_{sp} is the specific viscosity and is given as

$$\eta_{sp} = K_n \cdot c \cdot n \tag{41}$$

whose differential is

$$d\eta_{sp} = K_n \cdot n \cdot dc \tag{42}$$

In a number distribution function, $f(n)$, the concentration corresponding to a degree of polymerization n is given as

$$dc = n \cdot f(n) \cdot c \cdot dn \tag{43}$$

and the corresponding viscosity is

$$d\eta_{sp} = K_n \cdot c \cdot n^2 f(n)\, dn \tag{42a}$$

and the viscosity integral is

$$\eta_{sp} = K_n \cdot c \cdot n^2 \cdot f(n)\, dn = \bar{P}\eta \tag{44}$$

$\bar{P}\eta$ has been called by Schulz the viscometric polymerization degree. If it is compared with $\bar{P}$, the following relation is obtained:

$$\frac{\bar{P}\eta}{\bar{P}} = \int_0^{\infty} n^2 \cdot f(n)\, dn \int_0^{\infty} f(n)\, dn = 1 + \frac{1}{2\pi q^2 n^2_{\max}} = 1 + \frac{1}{B'} \tag{45}$$

This equation shows that the viscometric value is always higher than the number average value. In the term $1/B'$, the quantity of q, that is, the width of the distribution curve relation, is the critical value. When $n_{\max}$ becomes large, 300 or more, the value of $1/B'$ becomes small, provided q is not large. If the maximum in the distribution curve becomes flat, q becomes small. If n_{max} is not large, the value of $1/B'$ is no longer negligible, and the ratio, $\bar{P}_n$, must be greater than one.

USE OF FUNCTIONALITY EQUATION IN CROSSLINKING REACTIONS

Gelation may be defined as the critical value at which an infinite network becomes possible, the network being a result of crosslinking of the functional molecules. The functionality equation, $p = \dfrac{2}{f} - \dfrac{2}{f\overline{DP}}$, may be used to predict [27] the point at which gelation will occur with reactants or a mixture of reactants whose average functionality is greater than 2. If $\overline{DP}$ is very large, the equation becomes

$$p = \frac{2}{f} \tag{46}$$

With bifunctional molecules, $p = 2/f = 1$, and, since this value is never reached, gelation does not occur. With trifunctional molecules, such as a monohydroxy dicarboxylic acid, the reaction limit is reached at $p = 2/3$, that is, gelation will occur when 66 per cent of the functional groups in the trifunctional reactants have reacted. For tetrafunctional reactants, the limit of reaction is $p = 2/4 = 1/2$, or at some point below 50 per cent reaction the molecular weight will change from a low value to a very high molecular weight. Figure 21 shows the theoretical curve for gelation with respect to functionality. This curve shows that only a small quantity of a reactant whose functionality is greater than 2 is required to produce effective crosslinkages. A verification of this fact may be found in Staudinger's

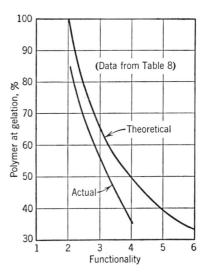

FIGURE 21. Relation of functionality to gelation.

work, wherein he found that only 300 parts per million of divinylbenzene ($f = 4$) were required to produce an insoluble copolymer of styrene. This corresponded to 0.03 per cent of divinylbenzene on the weight of the styrene, and the average functionality was approximately 2.00059.

The following example illustrates the method of calculating function-ality and of predicting the gelation point with mixed reactants, such as the reaction between glycerin and phthalic anhydride.

$$2\begin{array}{c} CH_2OH \\ | \\ CHOH \\ | \\ CH_2OH \end{array} + 3 \left[\begin{array}{c} CO \\ \diagdown \\ O \\ \diagup \\ CO \end{array} \right] \rightarrow \text{glyceryl phthalate}$$

The reaction involves 5 molecules that contain 12 reactive groups, and the average functionality $f = 12/5 = 2.4$.
Gelation will occur at

$$p = \frac{2}{2.4} = 83.3 \text{ per cent}$$

It will be noted that the equation $p = 2/f$ shows no dependence on temperature but only on the functionality of the reactants. Table 7 shows [28] that esters from glycerin and phthalic anhydride in equivalent quantities gel at approximately the same point irrespective of the temperature.

TABLE 7

Temperature, C	Time to Gel, Minutes	Percentage Esterified as Determined by H_2O Evolved	
160	860	79.5%	7.98 cc water
185	255	79.6	7.99 cc water
200	105	79.6	7.99 cc water
215	50	79.5	7.98 cc water

Reprinted by permission from the authors and the *Journal of the American Chemical Society.*

The reaction of one mole of glycerin with one mole of phthalic anhy-dride and one mole of a monocarboxylic acid may readily be shown to have a functionality of 2. It can be shown also that gelation will not occur unless the monocarboxylic acid has unsaturation which can polymerize further by addition polymerization. This is the basic principle embodied in the application of certain alkyd resins as paints.

LIMITATIONS OF THE FUNCTIONALITY EQUATION

The application of the equation, $p = 2/f$, to all polymerization systems must be treated with caution since many factors, mostly chemical, must be taken into account. The gelation equation was derived for condensation systems. Furthermore, the existence of a double bond does not necessarily imply that its functionality is 2. Butadiene, $CH_2=CH-CH=CH_2$, may be taken as a typical example. Under certain conditions it may be polymerized as divinyl:

$$\begin{array}{ccc} CH_2=CH & & -CH_2-CH- \\ | & \to & | \\ CH_2=CH & & -CH_2-CH- \end{array}$$

with a functionality of 4 to produce crosslinked polymeric systems. Under other conditions, it behaves as a 1,4 addition type, $-CH_2-CH=CH-CH_2-$, to give linear compounds. In most cases it behaves both as a bis (1,2) compound, with a functionality of 4, and as a 1,4 monomer, with a functionality of 2. The functionality, in any particular system, lies between 2 and 4.

Apparent discrepancies result [29] when the p equation is used to predict the gelation point in an addition copolymerization of a mixture of monomers, one of which has a functionality of 2 and the other has a functionality greater than 2. Table 8 also exemplifies [30] these discrepancies.

TABLE 8

Moles of Monomer, $f = 2$	Moles of Monomer, $f = 4$	Average Functionality	Predicted Gelation Point	Resin Found at Gelation, %	Deviation from Predicted
Styrene	Diallyl succinate				
0	1	4.00	50.00	36.14	13.86
1	1	3.00	66.00	54.3	11.7
2	1	2.66	75.00	64.0	11.0
3	1	2.50	80.00	68.9	12.1
4	1	2.40	83.33	71.4	11.9
5	1	2.33	85.71	75.1	10.64

These polymers were prepared, using 0.1 per cent of benzoyl peroxide on the weight of the monomers and heating the mixture at 90 C until gelation occurred. At this point the mixture was poured into methyl alcohol, and the insoluble fraction was isolated and vacuum-dried at 50 C to constant weight. These data are summarized in Figure 21.

In vinyl polymerizations, the conditions under which the polymerization occurs are also important. Divinylbenzene has a functionality of

4 and, when polymerized alone, gelation will occur between 15 to 35 per cent, depending on its purity and on the conditions under which it is polymerized. Theoretically it should gel at 50 per cent reaction. If a 20 per cent solution of divinylbenzene in diethylbenzene is polymerized under reflux in the presence of 0.01 per cent of benzoyl peroxide, about a 75 per cent yield of a soluble fusible polymer of divinylbenzene can be isolated before gelation occurs. If a 10 per cent solution in diethylbenzene is polymerized, the isolation of soluble fusible polymer will amount to almost 90 per cent. However, if a trace of a copper is included in the 10 to 20 per cent diethylbenzene solution of divinylbenzene, practically a quantitative yield of fusible soluble polymer may be obtained.[31] In all of these divinylbenzene polymerizations, the diethylbenzene reacted with the growing polymer and telomerized the polymer chain.[30]

Walling [29] compared the calculated and observed gel points for systems involving a monovinyl and divinyl monomer to explain discrepancies when the gelation equation is used for addition polymers. The gel condition was expressed as

$$2pr = \frac{q}{1 - q} \tag{47}$$

where p equals the probability that a vinyl group has reacted, q that a reacted vinyl group ends a chain, and r that a unit contains two reacted or unreacted vinyl groups.

If A and B are the concentrations of the unreacted monomers and A_0 and B_0 are the initial concentration, and if all groups have the same reactivity,

$$p = 1 - \frac{A}{A_0} = 1 - \left[\frac{B}{B_0}\right]^{\frac{1}{2}} \tag{48}$$

and

$$r = \frac{2B_0}{A_0 + B_0} \tag{49}$$

and

$$q = \frac{1}{\lambda} \tag{50}$$

the average kinetic chain length; then the gelation point is given as

$$1 - \frac{A}{A_0} = 1 - \left[\frac{B}{B_0}\right]^{\frac{1}{2}} = \frac{A_0 + 2B_0}{4B_0(\lambda - 1)} \tag{51}$$

The amount of divinyl compound was varied between 0.05 and 100 per cent, and in the presence and absence of solvents. The systems studied were methyl methacrylate–ethylene methacrylate and vinyl acetate–divinyl adipate. The results were in good agreement with prediction only if the concentration of divinyl compound was 0.2 mole per cent or less. The experimental results obtained when more than 0.2 per cent of crosslinking agent is used are explained qualitatively on the basis that the reaction mixture consists of swollen polymer molecules whose rate of diffusion is slow compared to the rate of growth.

Breitenbach [32] has presented by means of kinetic experiments experimental evidence that the two vinyl groups of crosslinking divinyl compounds are incorporated independently into growing chains. He also shows that the number of crosslinkages in the polymer molecule is not identical with the number of molecules of divinyl compound, but that the number of linkages is determined by the various rates of reactions involved, that is, the reactivity and specificity constants. If the number of crosslinkages formed is equal to the number of molecules of divinyl compounds, the polymer first formed is the same as those formed later in the polymerization. Otherwise, the polymer first formed is essentially the same as those formed from a monovinyl compound in the absence of crosslinking agents. Table 9 shows the effect of crosslinking of styrene by meta-divinylbenzene (DVB) at 110 C, and the data indicate that the two vinyl groups of a crosslinking monomer react independently.

TABLE 9

Polymeriza-tion Time, in Hours		Styrene	Styrene plus 8.88×10^{-5} moles DVB	Styrene plus 4.08×10^{-4} moles DVB
3	Conversion, %	13.4	13.4	11.0
3	η	0.143	0.145	0.161
7	Conversion, %	......	29.4	......
7	η	......	0.150	......
10	Conversion, %	42.5	42.1	38.6
10	η	0.139	0.158	0.278
21	Conversion, %	......	73.9	......
21	η	......	0.179	......
44	Conversion, %	......	85.7	......
44	η	......	0.193	......
100	Conversion, %	94	93	Insoluble
100	η	0.147	0.20	

Large discrepancies between the actual and theoretical values are found in the polymerizations of such related monomers as diallyl maleate and diallyl itaconate, both of which have a potential functionality of 6, whose structural formulas are represented by

$$\begin{array}{l} CH\text{—}COOCH_2\text{—}CH{=}CH_2 \\ \| \\ CH\text{—}COOCH_2\text{—}CH{=}CH_2 \end{array} \qquad \begin{array}{l} CH_2{=}C\text{—}COOCH_2\text{—}CH{=}CH_2 \\ \quad\;\; | \\ \quad\;\; COOCH_2\text{—}CH{=}CH_2 \end{array}$$

Their differences in gelation may be explained by the different reactivities and selectivities of the olefinic groupings,

$$>CH{=}CH< \quad \text{and} \quad CH_2{=}C<$$

In the preparation of crosslinked copolymers, discrepancies are found even when the monomers belong to the same family as, for example, in copolymers of the systems of methyl methacrylate with glycol dimethacrylate, and of vinyl acetate with vinyl succinate, whose structural formulas are represented by

$$\begin{array}{c} CH_3 \\ | \\ CH_2{=}C\text{—}COOCH_3 \\ \text{Methyl methacrylate} \end{array} + \begin{array}{l} \quad\;\; CH_3 \\ \quad\;\; | \\ CH_2{=}C\text{—}COOCH_2 \\ \quad\;\; CH_3 \qquad\quad | \\ \quad\;\; | \qquad\qquad\;\; | \\ CH_2{=}C\text{—}COOCH_2 \\ \text{Glycol dimethacrylate} \end{array}$$

$$\begin{array}{c} CH_2{=}CH\text{—}OCO\text{—}CH_3 \\ \\ \text{Vinyl acetate} \end{array} + \begin{array}{l} CH_2{=}CH\text{—}OCO\text{—}CH_2 \\ \qquad\qquad\qquad\qquad\;\; | \\ CH_2{=}CH\text{—}OCO\text{—}CH_2 \\ \text{Vinyl succinate} \end{array}$$

DIFFERENCES BETWEEN ADDITION AND CONDENSATION POLYMERIZATION

It becomes obvious that the theoretical distribution curves were derived for condensation polymers and should be applied with caution to addition polymers since the mechanisms of addition and condensation polymerizations are substantially different. Some of these differences are given in the following paragraphs.

Polymerization Mechanism

Addition polymerization is a kinetic chain reaction. Polymer growth is not accomplished by the addition of one polymer chain already formed to another polymer chain already formed, but by the addition in succession of a monomer, M, to an activated monomer or polymer molecule, M^*, thus

$$M \xrightarrow[\text{or initiation}]{\text{activation}} M^* \xrightarrow{M_1} MM_1^* \xrightarrow{M_2} MM_1M_2^* \rightarrow \text{etc.}$$

until deactivation occurs.

In condensation polymerization, such as is represented by the poly-amidification of aminocaproic acid, $NH_2(CH_2)_5COOH = M_0$, the first step is the intermolecular reaction.

Step 1: $2M_0 = MM$

The second step may be the reaction of the dimer with itself or another monomer.

Step 2: $MMMM \xleftarrow{MM} MM \xrightarrow{M_0} MMM_0$

At this step there may exist five species of molecules, with the result that the trimers and tetramers of Step 2 may react with monomers, M_0, or dimers, MM, or with themselves, that is, trimers or tetramers.

Kinetic Factors

The differences in the time intervals for the synthesis of a given polymer molecule by addition and condensation reactions are large.

In addition polymerization, an individual polymer molecule is synthesized at the beginning of the reaction in a matter of 10^{-2} to 10^{-6} second. The yield, or amount of polymer, is a function of time, but the molecular weight of the polymer is not determined by time since addition polymers of the normal type (that is, derived from monomers whose maximum, including potential functionality, is 2) do not interreact with one another. An addition polymerization system therefore contains monomers and polymers, not only at the initiation but at all stages of the process, until deactivation of the system occurs.

In condensation polymerization, the synthesis of a given polymer molecule is accomplished by a series of independent steps which occur over a definite time period, usually measured in terms of hours, or days, and even at the early stages of condensation the polymer will contain a very small amount of monomer or comers. Thus, in condensation polymerization, the monomers disappear during the initial part of the polymerization process.

Termination

In addition polymerization, the reaction of two growing polymer chains results in a termination, and no further growth of the polymer occurs:

$$MM_1M_2^* + MM_1M_2^* \rightarrow MM_1M_2M_2M_1M$$

The reactive growing ends of the chain are lost.

In condensation polymerization the reaction of two growing polymers is a propagation and not a termination reaction, since the new molecule still possesses reactive terminals:

$$H[NH(CH_2)_5CO]_3OH + H[NH(CH_2)_5CO]_3OH \rightarrow$$

$$H_2O + H[NH(CH_2)_5CO]_6OH$$

Gelation Activity

When two or more monomers are used in addition copolymerization, it must be borne in mind that these monomers usually have specific reactivity rates and selectivities and, therefore, the possibility of different rates of entry into the chain. In the examples of crosslinked copolymerization of the addition type previously described, polymer chains are formed and crosslinked at the same time, and the rate is not uniform in systems that crosslink at low conversions. It may be noted in Figure 21 that those compositions that gel at higher conversions approach the theoretical curve, and that the gelation equation is not broadly valid.

The gelation equation quite accurately describes the formation of crosslinked networks in condensation polymers.

Interrupted Polymerizations

In addition polymerization, certain chemical modifications of the polymer already formed cannot be accomplished by interrupting the polymerization before complete conversion. Thus, if the polymerization of styrene is interrupted at a 50 per cent conversion, and another monomer is added to the system and the polymerization continued, copolymerization of the newly added monomer will occur only with the unconverted monomer and not with the polymer already formed.

In condensation polymerization, all the species of polymer chains present may be modified by interruption of the polymerization, since all polymer species still possess reactive terminals.

THE PROPERTIES OF POLYMERS

The Theoretical Strength of Linear Polymers

The strength of a carbon to carbon bond is calculated to be about 5.6×10^{-4} dyne. In a bundle of perfectly oriented chains of repeating —CH_2— units, such as in polyethylene or a paraffin, the theoretical tensile strength is about 4,000,000 pounds per square inch. The actual value of commercial polyethylene is about 5300 to 7500 pounds per square inch at −70 F, 1800 to 2000 at 70 F, and 730 to 1000 at 170 F.

The actual tensile strengths of a number of polymers are indicated in Table 10.

TABLE 10

Polymer	Tensile Strengths at Room Temperature, Pounds per Square Inch
Methyl methacrylate	6,000–15,000
Polystyrene	5,000–14,000
Vinyl chloride–vinyl acetate	8,000–10,000
Nylon fiber, regular	60,000–70,000
Rubber–GRS	2,000– 5,000
Cellulose-cotton	35,000–70,000
Cellulose acetate–rayon	10,000–30,000
Native silk	50,000–80,000
Cast phenolic resin	2,000– 8,000

It is obvious that the analogy to a perfect bundle fails in many respects. Our assumptions have been that our chain is perfectly oriented, as in Figure 22. It follows then that if a tensile stress were applied to the end of the bundle and if the chains were not perfectly oriented, as in Figure 23, the stress could not be uniformly distributed among the cross sections of the chain. As shall be observed in many specific examples, a very high degree of orientation is not found except in some natural cellulosic products. The orientation in most synthetics at best is only partial.

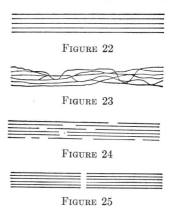

FIGURE 22

FIGURE 23

FIGURE 24

FIGURE 25

Types of Orientation in Polymer Bundles.

Our second assumption is that the stress is distributed among the number of chains present. This assumes that all the chains in the bundle begin and end at approximately the same position, as in Figure 25, whereas Figure 24 more properly describes the actual condition. When Figures 23 and 24 are combined, the discrepancies in the actual and the theoretical values are those to be expected.

THE RELATION BETWEEN PHYSICAL PROPERTIES AND MOLECULAR WEIGHT

The length of the chain in a polymer is probably its most important structural characteristic. The chain length explains the high viscosity and the intense swelling of such molecules as well as the production of films and fibers. The colloidal properties of macromolecules is proportional to chain length and is the same for different polymers of the same chain length, and as far as colloidal properties are concerned the actual chemical composition in non-polar molecules is of secondary importance. Certain physical properties, such as tensile strength, depend also on the composition as well as the chain length. A number of properties as a function of chain length is generalized [33] in Figures 26, 27, and 28.

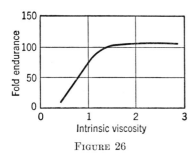

FIGURE 26

(Reprinted by permission from *Industrial and Engineering Chemistry*.)

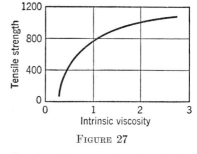

FIGURE 27

(Reprinted by permission from *Industrial and Engineering Chemistry*.)

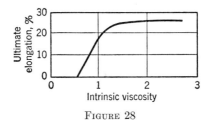

FIGURE 28

(Reprinted by permission from *Industrial and Engineering Chemistry*.)

With specific reference to cellulose acetate, Sookne and Harris [33] have shown that the tensile strength depends on the number-average molecular weight of the polymer. They also found that the tensile strength of a blend composed of a mixture of cellulose acetate fractions equals the weight average of the tensile strengths of the components, thus,

$$T_m = \Sigma_i w_i T_i \tag{52}$$

where w_i is the weight fraction of the components with tensile strength T_i, and T_m is the tensile strength of the mixture.

Flory [34] developed these relationships further to define the relationship between tensile strength and molecular weight as follows.

If T is expressed as a function of $1/M$ and then expanded as a power series, the expression becomes

$$T = f\left(\frac{1}{M}\right) = a_0 + \frac{a_1}{M} + \frac{a_2}{M^2} + \cdots \qquad (53)$$

According to the equation $T_m = \Sigma_i w_i T_i$, the equation becomes

$$T_m = f\left(\frac{1}{\overline{M}_n}\right) = f\left(\frac{\Sigma_i w_i}{M_i}\right) \qquad (54)$$

where $\overline{M}_n$ is the number-average molecular weight and M_i is the molecular weight of the ith species. If the series expansion is employed, the equation becomes

$$T_m = a_0 + a_i \Sigma_i \left(\frac{w_i}{M_i}\right) + a_2 \left(\frac{\Sigma_i w_i}{M_i}\right)^2 + \cdots \qquad (55)$$

Additivity of the tensile strength according to the weight fractions of the components, as expressed in equation 52, required that

$$T_m = \Sigma w_i f\left(\frac{1}{M_i}\right) = a_0 + a_1 \Sigma_i \left(\frac{w_i}{M_i}\right) + a_2 \Sigma \left(\frac{w_i}{M_i^2}\right) + \cdots \qquad (56)$$

The first two terms of equations 55 and 56 are identical, but the higher terms differ. The equations are consistent only if a_2 and the higher coefficients in the series expansion are equal to zero. It follows that

$$T = a_0 + \frac{a_1}{M} \qquad (57)$$

and when dealing with a heterogeneous mixture of polymers, M is replaced by $\overline{M}_n$,

$$T = a_0 + \frac{a_1}{\overline{M}_n} \qquad (58)$$

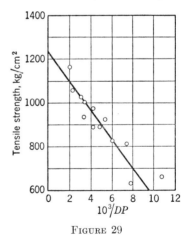

FIGURE 29

(By permission from the authors and the *Journal of the American Chemical Society*.)

Flory applies the same analysis to other properties which seem to depend on the number-average molecular weight and seem to exhibit additivity in their weight fractions.

The tensile strength data of Sookne and Harris [33] are plotted in Figure 29.[34]

Bunn [35] has recently summarized the relationship of molecular weight as a function of temperature to the solid, liquid, and viscous states of polymers, distinguishing between those polymers that crystallize and those that do not. These relationships are summarized broadly in the diagrams of Figures 30 and 31, respectively.

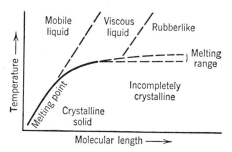

FIGURE 30. Relation between physical properties and molecular weight of crystalline polymers. (From C. W. Bunn, "Molecular Structure and Physical Properties of Polymers," *Research*, I, No. 14, 632 [1948].)

Figure 30 shows that substances composed of small molecules form completely crystalline solids which melt sharply to mobile liquids. In a homologous series, such as in the paraffin hydrocarbons, the melting point rises as does the viscosity of the liquid with an increase in molecular weight. As the molecular length is increased, the melting point does not rise continuously, but practically becomes constant at high molecular weight. The viscosity of the liquid continues to rise until it becomes so high that it has properties similar to a solid, and is said to be rubberlike. All polymers do not crystallize, and the corresponding diagram for such substances is given in Figure 31. At high temperatures these substances are rubberlike; at low temperatures they are glasslike.

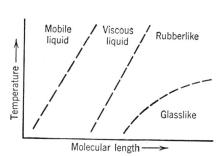

FIGURE 31. Relation between physical properties and molecular weight of non-crystalline polymers. (From C. W. Bunn, "Molecular Structure and Physical Properties of Polymers," *Research*, I, No. 14, 632 [1948].)

The difference in behavior between non-crystalline and crystalline polymers resides in the molecular constitution of the polymer.

CONSTITUTIONAL FACTORS IN POLYMERS

The factors that contribute to a specific molecular constitution are:

Attractive forces between the chains.

The actual shape or geometry of the chain.

The temperature at which the strength measurement is made.

The presence of plasticizers.

Attractive Forces between Chains

All atoms, including neutral atoms, exert secondary electronic forces on molecules of the same or different species. These forces arise from three sources.

DIPOLES IN EACH CHAIN

The dipole-dipole effect [36, 37] is relatively strong at considerable distances and fades very slowly.

DIPOLES IN ONE CHAIN INDUCING A DIPOLE IN A POLARIZABLE GROUP IN ANOTHER CHAIN

This second source of attractive force between a dipole and a polarizable group [38, 39] arises when the dipole in one chain approaches a polarizable group, attraction occurs, and because of its proximity a dipole is induced in the polarizable group. These forces fade rapidly with distance.

DISPERSION EFFECTS OR THE ELECTRONIC FLUCTUATION IN ATOMS OR MOLECULES

The dispersion effect or the electronic fluctuation in molecules results [40, 41] when the electrical fluctuations in molecules or atoms that are close to each other are out of phase and therefore attract each other. The sum of the three component forces comprise van der Waals' forces. This sum is small compared to the force of a carbon to carbon bond of about 5.6×10^{-4} dyne (20,000 to 200,000 calories per mole) and has been estimated to be about 1 per cent of this value or about 5×10^{-6} dyne (500 to 7000 calories per atom or atomic group). This is indeed a small value, but these forces become considerable when the chains are very long and their orientation is such that substantial sections of the chain are close to each other.

A number of molar cohesion forces for different groups has been derived by Dunkel, [42, 43] in which the values are given in calories per mole of such groups. The molar cohesion of different groups, given in calories per mole of such groups, is shown in Table 11.

TABLE 11

Group	Molar Cohesion, Kg Cal per Mole	Group	Molar Cohesion, Kg Cal per Mole
—CH$_3$	1,800	—COO—CH$_3$	5,600
=CH$_2$	1,800	—COO—C$_2$H$_5$	6,230
—CH$_2$—	990	—NH$_2$	3,530
=CH—	990	—Cl	3,400
—O—	1,630	—F	2,060
—OH	7,250	—Br	4,300
=CO	4,270	—NO$_2$	7,200
—COH	4,700	—SH	4,250
—COOH	8,970	—CONH—	16,200
—I	5,040	—CONH$_2$—	13,200

Most polymers have strength values even lower than those calculated for van der Waals' forces, which, as shown, are much smaller than even the primary valence forces. It is most improbable that, in cases of rupture of polymeric materials, primary bonds are broken; rather, the secondary valence forces have been overcome, and, in this manner, polymers with high secondary valence forces have higher tensile strengths. The melting point of a polymer also depends on the magnitude of the forces between molecules because the stronger the bonding forces, the less the amplitude of vibration at any given temperature. However, the nature of the bonding group between chains is not the sole factor that contributes to the properties of the polymer because polymer chains are not rigid and the geometry of the chain may keep the chains sufficiently distorted so that the bonding forces are inefficient.

The Geometry of the Linear Chain

The geometry of a polymer chain may be characterized by its linear form, its disorder, and its identity period.

LINEAR FORM

The secondary or molar cohesion forces theoretically should produce bonding strengths in proportion to their forces. This would be true if linear molecules existed in straight lines and if the chains could be parallel to each other. The geometry of the chain depends on the valency angle between the atoms as well as the distance between atoms. The bond distance of a carbon to carbon bond is given as 1.53 Å, and the bond angle of a system C—C—C is given as approximately 110 degrees.

Van't Hoff's theory of the tetrahedral carbon atom first pointed out the importance of the fact that the linkages in organic molecules form definite angles with each other that are responsible for specific geometric or spatial structures. Table 12 gives a list of bond angles found in a number of simple organic molecules.[44-46]

TABLE 12 [44]

Type of Bond	Compound Studied	Bond Angle
H—N—H	NH_3	108°
C—N—C	$N(CH_3)_3$	108°
H—C—H	CH_4	110°
C—C—C	$CH_3CH_2CH_3$	111°30′
C—C=C	$CH_2{=}C{\Big<}{\,}^{CH_3}_{CH_3}$	124°20′
H—C≡	$CH{\equiv}CH$	180°
H—O—H	H_2O	105°
H—S—H	H_2S	92°

Pauling and co-workers also measured the nuclear distance in a number of bonds and showed how the distance in Ångström units changed with substitutions on the bonds. Table 13 summarizes a few examples.

TABLE 13 [45]

Substance Studied	Type of Bond	Distance in Ångström Units
$CH_3{-}CH_3$	C—C	1.547
$CH_3{-}CH_2{-}CH_3$	C—C	1.541
$CH_3CH{\Big<}{\,}^{CH_3}_{CH_3}$	C—C	1.538
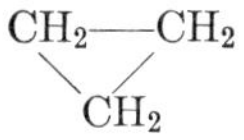 $CH_2{-}CH_2$ with CH_2	C—C	1.526
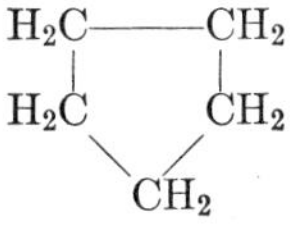 $H_2C{-}CH_2$ / H_2C CH_2 / CH_2	C—C	1.520
$CH_2{=}CH{-}CH{=}CH_2$	C—C	1.46
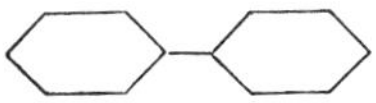 ⬡—⬡	C—C	1.48
$CH{\equiv}C{-}C{\equiv}CH$	C—C	1.36
$CH_2{=}CH{-}Cl$	C—Cl	1.69
$CH_2{=}C{\Big<}{\,}^{Cl}_{Cl}$	C—Cl	1.69
$^{Cl}_{Cl}{\Big>}C{=}C{\Big<}{\,}^{Cl}_{Cl}$	C—Cl	1.73

In a linear chain, the chain can be extended only as far as is consistent with these bond angles. Because of these bond angles, a normal carbon-carbon chain would be expected to be a planar zig-zag configuration.[47] The configurations sometimes may take the form of a spiral. The classification of the chain configuration is, therefore:

1. Planar, zig-zag.
2. Unidirectional spiral of uniform pitch.

Huggins [48] considers a planar zig-zag chain to be a special case of spiral.

DISORDER

The shape and the geometry of the chain determine the packing or the "fit" of one chain to another, and the resulting crystallization may be far from ideal, if the chains are disordered and do not possess a regularity of structure.

Baker and Fuller have classified [49] the different types of disorder that can occur in high polymer chains as lateral disorder, longitudinal disorder, and steric disorder.

Lateral disorder is found especially in copolymers of vinyl compounds, as, for example, in copolymers of acrylonitrile and methyl acrylate. As the quantity of the acrylate is increased, crystallization becomes poorer because of side chain bulk; the polymer molecule no longer consists of a regular repetition, in all directions and in space, of a basic pattern of atoms.

Similarly, longitudinal disorder may be found along the length of chain, as in condensation copolymers of two amino acids, as, for example, of aminocaproic and aminoheptoic acids. Lateral and linear disorder may be achieved simultaneously in copolymers of aminoheptoic acid, and N-methylaminocaproic acid.

Steric disorder in a polymer is the result of the stereochemical configuration of the polymer molecules. Steric disorder then represents a special case of isomerism.

Isomerism. Isomerism in polymers is concerned with the structural arrangement of monomeric units in regard to the sequence of such monomers. This sequence contributes to the geometry of the polymer, and therefore to its properties. Isomerism occurs essentially in polymers derived by the addition polymerization of olefinic and acetylenic compounds. If the polymer chains under observation are considered to possess the same molecular weight values, a number of isomeric polymer chains is possibly due to the arrangement of the monomers, as indicated in the following systems.

Substitution Isomerization. If ethylene is polymerized so that a simple hydrocarbon chain is obtained, to each end of which is attached the initiating catalyst radicals, R, then the polymer may be represented ideally by the structure

$$n\text{CH}_2\!\!=\!\!\text{CH}_2 \rightarrow \text{RCH}_2\text{CH}_2\text{CH}_2\text{CH}_2(\text{CH}_2\text{CH}_2)_{n-4}\text{CH}_2\text{CH}_2\text{CH}_2\text{CH}_2\text{R}$$

If a substituted ethylene, $\text{CH}_2\!\!=\!\!\text{CH}\!\!-\!\!\text{X}$, such as vinyl chloride or vinyl acetate is polymerized,[50] two essentially different polymer structures are obtainable from such vinyl compounds, namely, the head-to-head and the head-to-tail polymers. The head-to-tail polymer has the structure,

$$n\text{CH}_2\!\!=\!\!\text{CH}\!\!-\!\!\text{X} \rightarrow \underset{\substack{| \\ \text{X}}}{\text{RCH}_2\text{CH}}\underset{\substack{| \\ \text{X}}}{\text{CH}_2\text{CH}}\underset{\substack{| \\ \text{X}}}{(\text{CH}_2\text{CH})_{n-4}}\!\!-\!\!\underset{\substack{| \\ \text{X}}}{\text{CH}_2\text{CH}}\underset{\substack{| \\ \text{X}}}{\text{CH}_2\text{CHR}}$$
Head-to-tail structure

whereas a head-to-head form has the structure,

$$n\text{CH}_2\!\!=\!\!\text{CH}\!\!-\!\!\text{X} \rightarrow$$

$$\underset{\substack{| \quad | \\ \text{X} \;\; \text{X}}}{\text{RCH}_2\text{CHCHCH}_2}\underset{\substack{| \quad | \\ \text{X} \;\; \text{X}}}{(\text{CH}_2\text{CHCHCH}_2)_{n-4}}\!\!-\!\!\underset{\substack{| \quad | \\ \text{X} \;\; \text{X}}}{\text{CH}_2\text{CHCHCH}_2\text{R}}$$
Head-to-head structure

Normally, polyvinyl chloride and polyvinyl acetate exist essentially as a head-to-tail structure, whereas polyvinyl ketones and polyacrylic ester derivatives exist in a head-to-head structure. Both forms are possible for each class of polymers, and thereby give mixed head-to-head structures alternating with head-to-tail structures. The extent to which this alternation takes place determines the number of isomers obtained, thus:

$$\underset{\substack{| \qquad | \\ \text{X} \quad\; \text{X}}}{\text{RCH}_2\text{CHCH}_2\text{CH}}\!\!-\!\!\underset{\substack{| \quad | \\ \text{X} \;\; \text{X}}}{\text{CH}_2\text{CHCHCH}_2}\!\!-\!\!\underset{\substack{| \qquad | \\ \text{X} \quad\; \text{X}}}{\text{CH}_2\text{CHCH}_2\text{CH}}\!\!-\!\!\underset{\substack{| \quad | \\ \text{X} \;\; \text{X}}}{\text{CH}_2\text{CHCHCH}_2}\!\!-, \text{ etc.}$$

or

$$\underset{\substack{| \quad | \\ \text{X} \;\; \text{X}}}{\text{RCH}_2\text{CHCHCH}_2}\underset{\substack{| \\ \text{X}}}{\text{CH}_2\text{CHCH}_2}\underset{\substack{| \\ \text{X}}}{\text{CHCH}_2}\underset{\substack{| \\ \text{X}}}{\text{CHCH}_2}\underset{\substack{| \\ \text{X}}}{\text{CHCH}_2}\underset{\substack{| \\ \text{X}}}{\text{CHCH}_2\text{CH}}\!\!-, \text{ etc.}$$

Copolymer Isomerism. If two different monomers, $\text{CH}_2\!\!=\!\!\underset{\substack{| \\ \text{X}}}{\text{CH}}$ and $\text{CH}_2\!\!=\!\!\underset{\substack{| \\ \text{Y}}}{\text{CH}}$ are copolymerized, for example, in equal molar proportions, the copolymer product may be written as

$$n\text{CH}_2\!\!=\!\!\text{CH} + n\text{CH}_2\!\!=\!\!\text{CH} \rightarrow \text{R(CH}_2\text{CH)}_n\!-\!\text{(CH}_2\text{CH)}_n\text{R}$$
$$\begin{array}{cccc} | & | & | & | \\ \text{X} & \text{Y} & \text{X} & \text{Y} \end{array}$$

However, such a representation does not describe the structure of the polymer that can exist in a number of isomeric states, for example:

$$\text{RCH}_2\text{CHCH}_2\text{CHCH}_2\text{CHCH}_2\text{CHCH}_2\text{CHCH}_2\text{CHCH}_2\text{CHCH}_2\text{CH}\!-\!, \text{ etc.}$$
$$\begin{array}{cccccccc} | & | & | & | & | & | & | & | \\ \text{X} & \text{Y} & \text{X} & \text{Y} & \text{X} & \text{Y} & \text{X} & \text{Y} \end{array}$$

or

$$\text{RCH}_2\text{CHCH}_2\text{CHCH}_2\text{CHCH}_2\text{CHCH}_2\text{CHCH}_2\text{CHCH}_2\text{CHCH}_2\text{CH}\!-\!, \text{ etc.}$$
$$\begin{array}{cccccccc} | & | & | & | & | & | & | & | \\ \text{X} & \text{X} & \text{Y} & \text{Y} & \text{X} & \text{X} & \text{Y} & \text{Y} \end{array}$$

or

$$\text{RCH}_2\text{CHCH}_2\text{CHCH}_2\text{CHCH}_2\text{CHCH}_2\text{CHCH}_2\text{CHCH}_2\text{CHCH}_2\text{CH}\!-\!, \text{ etc.}$$
$$\begin{array}{cccccccc} | & | & | & | & | & | & | & | \\ \text{Y} & \text{Y} & \text{Y} & \text{X} & \text{X} & \text{Y} & \text{X} & \text{X} \end{array}$$

Furthermore, any of the sequences of monomers in the copolymer can also exist in a head-to-head structure rather than only in the head-to-tail structure indicated above, thus:

$$\text{RCH}_2\text{CHCHCH}_2\text{CH}_2\text{CHCHCH}_2\text{CH}_2\text{CHCHCH}_2\text{CH}_2\text{CHCHCH}_2\!-\!, \text{ etc.}$$
$$\begin{array}{cccccccc} | & | & & | & | & & | & | & & | & | \\ \text{Y} & \text{Y} & & \text{Y} & \text{X} & & \text{X} & \text{X} & & \text{Y} & \text{X} \end{array}$$

Branching Isomerism. The idealized polymerization of a vinyl monomer is illustrated as producing a strictly linear chain,

$$\text{RCH}_2\text{CHCH}_2\text{CHCH}_2\text{CHCH}_2\text{CH(CH}_2\text{CH)}_n\text{R}$$
$$\begin{array}{ccccc} | & | & | & | & | \\ \text{X} & \text{X} & \text{X} & \text{X} & \text{X} \end{array}$$

During the process of polymerization, however, branching of the linear chain can occur by a number of means, such as by a kinetic chain transfer, to produce a branched polymer, for example,

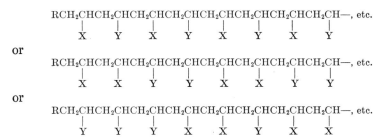

The presence of methyl groups in polyethylene has been attributed to branching,[51] the extent of which depends on the manner in which the polymer was prepared, the amount of catalyst, and other factors. The degree of branching has a profound effect on the properties of the polymer. Highly branched polyethylenes are softer, have lower melting points, and less tendency to crystallize than unbranched or slightly branched polymers.

Rotational Isomerism. Huggins [52] originally suggested that all vinyl polymers are capable of stereoisomerism and that this isomerism can explain the different behavior of polymers prepared under different conditions. It has been shown [53] that vinyl isobutyl ether could be polymerized to give products of essentially the same molecular weight but with entirely different properties. The rapid low-temperature polymerization of vinyl isobutyl ether with boron trifluoride results in a rubbery polymer of low softening point. In contrast, the use of boron trifluoride–dimethyl ether catalyst results in a fibrous polymer of high softening point with a distinct tendency to crystallize. The rubbery and fibrous polymers are readily isolated from their solutions by use of a precipitant at room temperature. If the rubbery polymer is dissolved in a high-boiling solvent and maintained at elevated temperatures for a certain period of time, the fibrous and not the original rubbery modification is isolated by precipitation. This change from the rubbery to the fibrous polymer is explained by assuming that the comparatively large isobutyl ether group sufficiently hinders the carbon to carbon bond rotation in the chain so as to stabilize certain strongly kinked configurations which are responsible for rubbery properties. By dissolving such a polymer, the kink in the chain due to restricted rotation is eliminated.

Another example of rotational isomerism is observed in certain copolymers where one of the components in the copolymer was derived from a monomer, or comer which could exist in *cis* or *trans* configuration.[30] The copolymers of styrene with dimethyl maleate and dimethyl fumarate, respectively, are illustrative of such copolymers. Dimethyl maleate is the *cis* form of the α,β-ethylene dicarboxylic acid; the fumarate is the *trans* form:

$$CH—COOCH_3 \qquad\qquad CH—COOCH_3$$
$$\|\qquad\qquad\qquad\qquad\qquad \|$$
$$CH—COOCH_3 \qquad\qquad H_3COOC—CH$$

Cis form   Trans form
Dimethyl maleate   Dimethyl fumarate

If free rotation occurs along the carbon-carbon atoms of a polymer chain, the same copolymer should be obtained with styrene whether the maleate or the fumarate is used. If rotation is restricted, the copolymers of the maleate and the fumarate should be different. They may be represented structurally as follows if equivalent molar ratios of styrene and ester are used:

$$-CH_2-CH-CH——CH-CH_2-CH—CH——CH-CH_2-CH—CH——CH-$$

$$\underset{C_6H_5}{|}\ \underset{COOCH_3}{|}\ \underset{COOCH_3}{|}\quad \underset{C_6H_5}{|}\ \underset{COOCH_3}{|}\ \underset{COOCH_3}{|}\quad \underset{C_6H_5}{|}\ \underset{COOCH_3}{|}\ \underset{COOCH_3}{|}$$

Maleate copolymer

$$\qquad\qquad COOCH_3\qquad\qquad COOCH_3\qquad\qquad COOCH_3$$
$$\qquad\qquad|\qquad\qquad\qquad|\qquad\qquad\qquad|$$
$$-CH_2-CH—CH-CH-CH_2-CH—CH-CH-CH_2-CH—CH-CH-$$
$$\underset{C_6H_5}{|}\ \underset{COOCH_3}{|}\quad \underset{C_6H_5}{|}\ \underset{COOCH_3}{|}\quad \underset{C_6H_5}{|}\ \underset{COOCH_2}{|}\qquad|$$

Fumarate copolymer

Actually, the copolymer of equivalent molar quantities of styrene and dimethyl maleate is quite soft and rubbery, whereas the fumarate copolymer is relatively hard and brittle.[30] This difference is attributable to the stereoisomerism of the polymers with the ester substituents of the chain restricted in different arrangements along the chain.

EVIDENCE OF POLYMER ORDER

X-ray diffraction studies have shown definitely that polymeric substances of long chain length tend to form crystalline arrangements along the chain axes that lie parallel to each other. If these crystalline areas are not normally present, the long axes of the molecules may be oriented by cold drawing or stretching, the classical example [54] of which is natural rubber.

These X-ray patterns produce characteristic identity periods (fiber periods) and can be used for qualitative determinations. Table 14 gives the identity periods of a number of high polymers in Ångström units.

TABLE 14

	Identity Period, Ångström Units Fiber Period
Polyethylene	2.53
Polyvinyl alcohol	2.52
Polyethylenetetrasulfide	4.32
Polyvinylidene chloride	4.67
Polychloroprene	4.8
Polyvinyl chloride	5.0
Polybutadiene	5.0
Polyisoprene (cis rubber)	8.2
Polyethylene succinate	8.32
Polyethylene adipate	11.7
Polyhexamethylene adipamide	17.0
Polyisobutylene	18.8
Polyethylene oxide	17.0
Polyethylene azeleate	31.2

The identity or fiber period as determined by X-rays is not to be confused with the segmer or repeating unit of the polymer. The identity period is the distance between consecutive-like points of crystals, that is, crystallographically equivalent positions. Its actual dimension may correspond to the atomic distances of a segmer but not necessarily so, because of spatial configurations of the chain itself, and, as well, of the side chain arrangement.

Fuller, Frosch, and Erickson [55, 56] have compared the observed and calculated fiber periods of a number of polyesters (shown in Table 15 [56]),

TABLE 15

Polyester	Segmer	Identity Period, Ångström Units	
		Calculated (from Segmer)	Observed
Polyethylene succinate	$-O(CH_2)_2OCO(CH_2)_2CO-$	9.70	8.32
Polyethylene adipate	$-O(CH_2)_2OCO(CH_2)_4CO-$	12.21	11.71
Polyethylene suberate	$-O(CH_2)_2OCO(CH_2)_6CO-$	14.73	14.1
Polyethylene sebacate	$-O(CH_2)_2OCO(CH_2)_8CO-$	17.24	16.83

Reprinted by permission from the authors and the *Journal of the American Chemical Society.*

in which the identity period and the segmer were of the same approximate value. These calculations were made on the assumption of the tetrahedral angle and that the carbon to carbon bond was 1.54 Å and the carbon to oxygen bond 1.43 Å.

Their values are summarized in Figure 32, which is a plot of the calculated length of the repeating segmer and the observed length of the fiber or identity period.

The polyesters of Table 15 show a high degree of orientation. Most linear polymers as prepared do not possess a high degree of orientation. However, in a large number of cases this may be achieved by cold drawing of the entangled mass of chains. When the chains are slightly pulled, some disentanglement occurs, and the bundles are

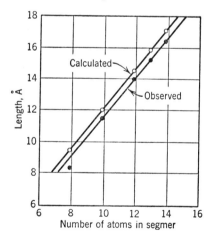

FIGURE 32. Calculated and observed identity period for a number of polyesters.

pulled closer together, with the result that the mutual attraction of polar groups belonging to different chains increases appreciably and produces the secondary effect of making it more easy for neighboring groups to fit into a crystalline structure. The final condition of the polymer should be highly crystallized and oriented. This condition, however, is never completely reached because crystallization does not start at one single point but at many points. The growing crystals interfere with each other so that a certain amount of disordered material always remains. These imperfections, or incomplete orientation, naturally lead to unequal distribution of strain when a sample is submitted to stress. It is most probable that the points of stress are concentrated on those molecules that extend from one crystalline area to another through a region where looping may exist to a considerable degree.

RUBBERS, PLASTICS, AND FIBERS

The distinction between rubbers, plastics, and fibers has been considered [57] on the basis of the magnitude of the attractive forces between long-chain molecules and the ease with which they fit into a crystal lattice. These data are summarized in Table 16.

TABLE 16

MOLAR COHESION VALUES IN CALORIES PER MOLE

Group 1

Polyethylene	1000	(CH_2); (CH_2)
Polyisobutylene	1200	(CH_2); (CH_3)
Polybutadiene	1100	(CH_2); $(CH=CH)$
Rubber	1300	(CH_2); $(CH=C—CH_3)$
Polychloroprene	1600	(CH_2); $(CH=CHCl)$

Group 2

Polyvinyl chloride	2600	(CH_2); $(CHCl)$
Polyvinyl acetate	3200	(CH_2); $(CHOCOCH_3)$
Polystyrene	4000	(CH_2); (C_6H_5)
Polyvinyl alcohol	4200	(CH_2); $(CHOH)$

Group 3

Cellulose acetate	4800	$(—O—)$; $(OOCCH_3)$
Polyamides	5800	(CH_2); $(CONH)$
Cellulose	6200	$(—O—)$; (OH)
Silk fibroin	9800	$(—CHR)$; $(CONH)$

Reprinted by permission from *Industrial and Engineering Chemistry.*

The molar cohesion value is given for 5 Å chain length with a coordination number of four. On the basis of molar cohesion, the substances in group 1, having values between 1000 and 2000 calories, behave as typical rubbers; those between 2000 and 5000 calories, as typical plastics; and those above 5000, as fibers.

It appears, however, that molar cohesion value alone cannot be used as a criterion for such a classification. Polyethylene exhibits an excellent fit of the straight zig-zag hydrocarbon chain into a crystal lattice and has very marked fiber characteristics. It is not rubbery except at high temperatures, that is, in excess of 100 C. This property of becoming rubbery at high temperatures is characteristic of many plastics.

Polyvinyl alcohol, according to this classification, should behave as a plastic, yet it exhibits excellent fiber properties with crystalline characteristics somewhat similar to polyethylene.

It does appear possible, however, to characterize the fit value of the chains quantitatively according to the ratio of their segmer to identity period, and a number of examples are considered below. As will be noted, a number of other values appear to be important in determining the properties of a polymer, that is, whether it can be classified as a fiber, a plastic, or a rubber.

Polyethylene, whose segmer is —CH_2—CH_2—, has an identity period of 2.5 Å which is in excellent agreement with a bond angle of about 112 degrees and a carbon to carbon distance of 1.53 Å, and corresponds to the segmer length.

The shape of such a molecule is planar zig-zag,[47, 58] and the fit value equals 1.

Identity period 2.5 Å

Polyethylene

Polyvinyl chloride has a segmer —CH_2—CH—, and its identity period
$$\quad\quad\quad\quad\quad\quad\quad\quad\quad\quad\quad\quad\quad\quad\quad\quad\quad | $$
$$\quad\quad\quad\quad\quad\quad\quad\quad\quad\quad\quad\quad\quad\quad\quad\quad\quad Cl$$
would be expected to be about 2.5 Å. Since the actual observed value [59] is 5, there are four carbon atoms per identity distance. This value is expected if the chlorine atoms are alternately placed first on one side and then on the other with respect to the plane of zig-zag, and thus only the alternate chlorine atoms are in the same plane. The fit value of polyvinyl chloride is 0.5.

Cl   Cl Cl   Cl Cl   Cl
Polyvinyl chloride

Polyvinyl alcohol, whose segmer is —CH_2CH—, has an identity period

$$OH$$

of 2.52, which likewise means that all the hydroxyl groups of one chain
are in the same plane,[59, 60] and is likewise a planar zig-zag with a fit
value of one.

OH   OH   OH   OH   OH   OH
Polyvinyl alcohol

Polyvinylidene chloride has as its segmer the grouping, —CH_2C<,

with an identity period of 4.67, and therefore a fit value of 0.54, which
indicates a deviation from a zig-zag chain, since a value similar to that
of polyvinyl chloride would be expected.

Cl   Cl Cl   Cl Cl   Cl

Cl   Cl Cl   Cl Cl   Cl
Polyvinylidene chloride

The substitution of hydrogen by one chlorine atom in polyethylene
chain did not interfere seriously with the configuration of the polymer
chain. Its fit value is 0.52. However, as observed in polyvinylidene
chloride, the substitution of two chlorine atoms on the same carbon
atom produces a large discrepancy between the calculated (2 × 2.5 Å)
and observed distance, 4.67 Å. As shown in Table 9, the atomic distances may change with substitution.

The most probable shapes of the chains in the crystallized areas of
polyethylene, polyvinyl chloride, polyvinyl alcohol, and polyvinylidene
chloride are given in Figure 33.

Bunn [61] has questioned the structure of polyvinyl alcohol and has
shown that the observed repeat distance of 2.52 Å is compatible with a
structure in which the hydroxyl groups are randomly placed on either
side of the plane zig-zag. He shows that a two-molecule monoclinic
unit cell for which $a = 7.81$ Å, $b = 2.52$ Å, and $c = 5.51$ Å, and $\beta =
91°42'$ is consistent with other data.[60] The structure consists of a
double layer of molecules held together by hydroxyl bonds. A particular arrangement with the hydroxyl groups randomly placed in left- and
right-hand positions accounts in a very satisfactory manner for the en-

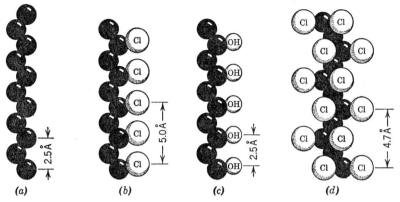

FIGURE 33. Most probable shapes of chains in the crystallized areas of polyethylene (a), polyvinyl chloride (b), polyvinyl alcohol (c), and polyvinylidene chloride (d).

tire X-ray diffraction pattern as well as the relative intensities. In this structure the adjacent double layers are held together by weaker van der Waals' forces. The proposed projections are shown in Figures 34 and 35,[61] wherein the dotted lines are hydrogen bonds.

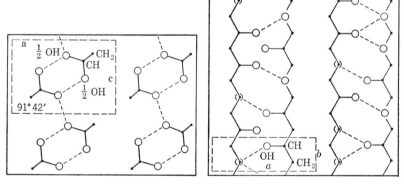

FIGURE 34. Projection of polyvinyl alcohol.   FIGURE 35. Projection of polyvinyl alcohol.

(Both from C. W. Bunn, "Crystal Structure of Polyvinyl Alcohol," *Nature*, **161**, 929 [1948]. By permission of the publishers, The Macmillan Company, New York.)

Polyisobutylene has as a segmer the unit, $-CH_2-\overset{\displaystyle CH_3}{\underset{\displaystyle CH_3}{C}}-$, with an identity period of 18.63 Å.[62] This value represents a 16-atom chain, side chains excluded, per identity period, which is in agreement [63] with the assumptions of a uniform spiral with tetrahedral bond angles and the usual carbon to carbon bond distances, and represents *seven revolutions* per identity period. Its fit value is 0.14. A number of other probable shapes for the shape of the polyisobutylene chains in the crystallized areas are given in Figure 36.[62] It seems that highly substituted chains need a large number of segmer units to produce an identity period.

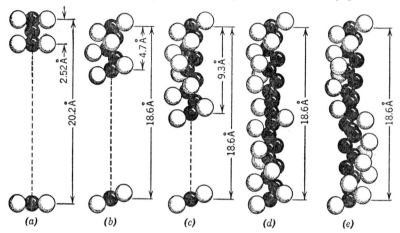

(a)   (b)   (c)   (d)   (e)

FIGURE 36.   Planar zigzag forms, (b) to (e), non-planar forms that produce the required shortening. The larger spheres represent methyl groups. (Reprinted by permission from the authors and the *Journal of the American Chemical Society.*)

From these few examples, we may be led to believe that a fit value of 1 represents the ideal situation, whereby, in the crystallite regions of a polymer, the secondary valence forces are utilized to a high degree of efficiency, approaching 100 per cent. In polyvinyl alcohol, for example, the bonding forces due to the —OH group are utilized for every vinyl alcohol radical, —CH_2—CH—, *found in the crystallite*. Such polymers
OH
should be crystalline and have definite fiber properties. The physical values of such fibers depend on the nature of the substituent group responsible for the secondary valence forces. This is obvious in the comparison of polyethylene and polyvinyl alcohol. It may be postulated that deviations from the fit value of 1 would produce changes from fiber to plastic to rubbery types progressively. These deviations may result from (1) disorder in the linear chain itself, as in copolymers, (2) disorder in the substitution along the linear chain, as exemplified in polyvinyl chloride, and (3) the bulkiness of the substitution along the chains,

thereby either spreading the chains apart or causing the chain to assume the shape of a spiral. As has been noted already, polyvinyl chloride,

$$\left[-CH_2-CH- \atop \qquad\quad | \atop \qquad\quad Cl \right]_n$$, has the same generic segmer unit, $-CH_2-CH-$, as $\quad\quad | \atop \quad\quad X$

polyvinyl alcohol and polyethylene, and would be expected to have the same fit value. Because the chlorine atoms in the polymer are alternately placed first on one side and then on the other side with respect to the zig-zag plane, the fit value becomes 0.5. From this value we should expect the fiber properties to decrease and the plastic properties to become evident. This is actually so in the industrial polyvinyl chloride product, which is used primarily as a plastic and only to a minor degree as a fiber. Polyvinyl acetate,

$$\left[-CH_2-CH- \atop \qquad\qquad\quad | \atop \qquad\qquad OCOCH_3 \right]_n$$, has

the same generic segmer, $-CH_2-CH-$, as polyethylene, polyvinyl alco-
$\qquad\qquad\qquad\qquad\qquad\qquad | \atop \qquad\qquad\qquad\qquad\qquad\quad X$

hol, and polyvinyl chloride. However, the acetyl side chain has considerable bulk. This polymer was subjected to X-ray studies by a number of investigators,[59, 64, 65] and only amorphous patterns were obtained. Polyvinyl acetate is a plastic that has rubber properties.

Polyvinylidene chloride has a fit value of 0.54. Correlated to polyvinyl chloride, it should have fiber and plastic properties. Because of the two chlorine atoms attached to the same carbon atom in each segmer, the value of the secondary valence forces should be higher than for polyvinyl chloride. This is verified in the physical and chemical properties of the polymer in fiber and plastic forms.

Polyisobutylene $\left[\begin{matrix} CH_3 \\ | \\ -CH_2-C- \\ | \\ CH_3 \end{matrix} \right]_n$ has the same generic segmer unit,

$\quad X \atop \quad | \atop -CH_2-C-$, as polyvinylidene chloride. However, a chain having
$\quad | \atop \quad X$

high bulk substitution needs a large number of segmer units to produce an identity period. The fit value of this polymer is 0.14, which removes it considerably from the fiber state and into the plastic and rubber classification. Polyisobutylene has certain plastic properties, dominated, however, by rubber properties.

In Table 14 the identity periods of a number of polymers almost universally acknowledged to have properties associated with the "rubber" state are given.

The identity periods for chloroprene and polybutadiene are given as 4.8 and 5.0, respectively. These values correspond roughly to their segmer lengths and therefore have a fit value of 1. However, this fit value is not the normal value for these materials since, in the unstretched state, their X-ray diagrams are amorphous and they have a fit value of zero.

A classification, distinguishing rubbers, plastics, and fibers solely on the basis of fit values is incomplete. The identity periods used in determining this value are based on X-ray patterns, and give the value only for the crystallite (oriented) regions. However, this orientation in a cluster of polymer chains, at best, is only partial, and there are large areas of amorphous regions. If we represented, as extremes, a polymer of a fit value of one with 100 per cent crystallite areas as the "perfect fiber pattern" and a completely amorphous pattern with a fit value of zero as the "perfect rubber pattern," the intermediate regions would represent the region known as plastics.

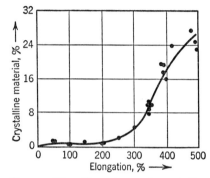

FIGURE 37.   Percentage of crystalline material in stretched vulcanized natural rubber at 20 C. (Reprinted by permission from the American Institute of Physics, New York.)

One border line would be fibers dominated by plastic properties, and the other would be plastics dominated by rubber properties. Likewise, we should hardly expect the "perfect fiber"—and as an actual result we find that even the best fibers have amorphous regions. In the natural fibers, particularly of a protein nature, we find that the ratio of the crystallite area to the amorphous area, that is, whether it has a long or short identity period, in relation to the amorphous area, determines many of its properties, such as elasticity, elongation, and resiliency. Similarly, we cannot expect the "perfect rubber," and as an actual result we find that most rubbers show an identity period when stretched. Wildschut [66] concludes that orientation occurs on the stretching of rubber by the systematic addition of secondary valence forces, and as elongation is increased the percentage of crystallization increases, as shown in Figure 37.

TABLE 17 [67]

PRINCIPAL EQUATORIAL SPACINGS, IN ÅNGSTRÖM UNITS, OF ORIENTED LINEAR POLYMERS

Polymer	A_1	A_2	A_3	A_4	A_5	A_6	A_7	A_8
1. Polyethylene	4.18 VS	3.71 VS	2.97 W	2.63 VW	2.47 S			
2. Polydecanoate	4.17 VS	3.73 VS	3.00 MW	2.49 MW				
3. Polyundecanoate	4.12 VS	3.69 S	3.26 M	3.02 S	2.55 S	2.41 W	2.26 S	2.11 S
4. Polyethylene sebacate	4.17 VS	3.67 S	3.42 W	2.96 M				Typical even polyester
5. Polytrimethylene azelate	4.51 VS	3.96 M	3.67 M	3.00 W				Typical odd polyester
6. Polyhexamethylene adipamide	4.40 VS	3.71 VS	3.28 S	2.37 VS				Typical even polyamide
Polyhexamethylene adipamide (quenched)	4.18 VSf							
7. Polynonamethylene azelamide	4.09 VS	2.34 M						Typical odd polyamide
8. Polyundecanamide	4.36 VS	3.81 VSf	3.09 W	2.39 M				
9. Poly-N-methylundec- anamide	4.39 VS	2.52 M						
10. Polyvinyl alcohol	4.54 VS	3.89 VS	3.20 S	2.79 S				
11. Polyvinyl chloride	5.32 M	4.74 M	3.71 M	3.24 M				
12. Polyvinyl cyanide	5.20 S	3.01 M						
13. Polyvinyl butyral	10.7 M	4.54 A						
14. Polyvinyl isobutyl ether	9.90 S	8.30 S	6.47 W	4.82 S	4.21 S			
15. Polyvinyl acetate	7.05 M							Diffuse X-ray pattern
16. Polystyrene	(10.05)							Diffuse pattern
17. Poly-p-chlorostyrene	(12.15)							
18. Poly-(2,5)dichloro- styrene	9.85							
19. Polyvinyl pyridine	(8.95)							
20. Polyvinyl carbazole	11.95							
21. Polyethylene succinate	5.37 VW	4.41 VS	3.85 S	3.12 W	2.70 W	2.29 VW	1.92 W	
22. Polyisobutylene	5.98 VS	3.47 W	2.98 S	2.73 W	2.24 M			Diffuse X-ray pattern when unoriented
23. Polyvinylidenechloride	5.65 VS	3.41 M	3.16 M	2.83 S	2.44 M	2.18 W	2.08 M	
24. Rubber hydrochloride	6.0 M	5.2 VS						
25. Polymethyl metha- crylate	6.65 Vf							Diffuse X-ray pattern
26. Poly-n-propyl metha- crylate	11.48 S	(7.95 f)						Diffuse X-ray pattern
27. Poly-i-butyl metha- crylate	10.93 S							
28. Poly-n-butyl metha- crylate	(12.25 VS)							
29. Polyisoprene-cis (nat- ural rubber)	6.20 VS	4.19 VS	3.10 W					
30. Polyisoprene-trans (gutta percha)	6.00 M	5.34 M	4.77 VS	3.87 VS	3.25 W	2.95 S	2.76 S	2.35 S
31. Polychloroprene	5.07 M	4.42 VS	4.01 VS	3.30 S	3.02 W	2.52 M		

Relative intensities are shown by letters beside the spacings: S, strong; M, moderate; W, weak; V, very; f, diffuse; A, arc. Position of spacings in parentheses is uncertain.

Reprinted by permission from the author and the Reinhold Publishing Corporation.

Baker [67] has published the principal equatorial spacings in Ångströms of a number of oriented polymers. The relative intensities are shown in Table 17 beside these spacings, and it will be noted that even in those polymers that are considered to be excellent fiber-forming materials intensities ranging from very strong to very weak are found.

SECOND-ORDER PHASE TRANSITION TEMPERATURE

It has been shown that the physical properties of polymers may be correlated to their intermolecular and intramolecular forces and order. The problem arises then as to the conditions under which one polymer should be compared to another. As already indicated, the technical application of polymers classifies these materials as rubbers, plastics, or fibers. Such a classification describes a state of matter but fails to specify the conditions under which the polymer is in the rubbery or plastic state. By inference, the comparison has been made at room temperature and assumes that, as the temperature is lowered or raised, two polymers, one rubber and the other plastic, will maintain that same relation one to the other. Such is not the case, since at very specific temperatures for each polymer, plastics may become rubbers, rubbers may become plastics, and fiber polymers lose part or all of their crystallinity.

The change in non-crystalline polymers from glasslike hardness to rubberlike softness occurs more gradually than it does in crystalline polymers, though there is a well-defined *softening point* which may be used for practical characterization. This softening point is quite close to what is known as the *second-order transition temperature*.

When the primary thermodynamic properties of a polymer are plotted against temperature, a change in the slope of the properties, such as volume or heat content, becomes apparent at some temperature. This is a discontinuity of the first derivative of the property; hence is considered a second-order phase transition. This transition occurs at a characteristic temperature, T_m, °C, for practically all the high polymeric materials that have been studied. In many cases, the transition is well defined. In many polymers, however, the change occurs over a small temperature range. At this temperature a marked change in most physical properties is observed.

A few examples of second-order transition temperatures for a number of high polymers are given in Table 18. All values of T_m were based on thermal expansion measurements.

TABLE 18

Polymer	Structure	T_m, °C	Reference No.
Polyvinyl alcohol	—CH₂—CH— 　　OH	85	68
Polyvinyl acetate	—CH₂—CH— 　　OCOCH₃	28	68
Polyvinyl ethyl ether	—CH₂—CH— 　　OC₂H₅	< −10	68
Polyvinyl isobutyl ether	—CH₂—CH— 　　O 　HC$\diagup$C₂H₅$\diagdown$CH₃	< −10	68
Polyvinyl butyral	—CH₂—CH—CH₂—CH— 　　O　　　O 　　　H 　　　C 　　　C₃H₇	50.1	69
Polyethylene	—CH₂—CH₂—	87	70
Polyacrylic acid	—CH₂—CH— 　　COOH	80–95	71
Polymethyl acrylate	—CH₂—CH— 　　COOCH₃	3	72
Polymethyl methacrylate	CH₃ —CH₂—C— 　　COOCH₃	57–68	73
Polyvinyl chloride	—CH₂—CH 　　Cl	75	69
Polyvinylidene chloride	—CH₂—C— 　Cl　Cl	−18	74
Polystyrene	—CH₂—CH— （ring）	81	75
Polyindene	—CH——CH— CH₂—（ring）	85	68

TABLE 18 *(Continued)*

Polymer	Structure	T_m, °C	Reference No.
Polyvinyl carbazole	$-CH_2-CH-$ N (carbazole ring)	85	68
Nylon	$-OC(CH_2)_4CONH(CH_2)_6NH-$	47	74
Polyisobutylene	$-C-CH_2-$ $CH_3 \quad CH_3$	-74	76

The second-order transition temperature is most readily determined by thermal measurements, whereby a change in the slope of this volume-temperature curve is observed. Boyer and Spencer [77] have defined this transition temperature as follows:

"The second-order transition temperature, (T_m), associated with thermal expansion of polymers, is the lowest temperature at which an observable amount of viscous flow can occur under the thermal expansion forces acting on the molecules, and within the time limits of the experimental technique employed."

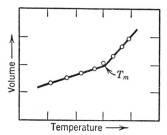

FIGURE 38. Typical volume-temperature relationship.

The second-order transition temperature is a common reference point, therefore, for the comparison of all high polymers since below that temperature all normal rubberlike polymers become hard and stiff, and above that temperature normally rigid polymers begin to acquire rubber characteristics. A typical volume expansion plot, deriving the T_m value, is shown in Figure 38. If the transition temperature occurs over a range of temperatures, the intersection of the two straight line portions of the curve is considered as the second-order phase transition temperature.

The transition temperature appears to be related to the onset of rotation in the solid state,[76, 78, 79] and when associated with thermal expansion, may be defined as the temperature at which sufficient rotation of polymer segments exists "to permit an observable amount of viscous flow within the time scale of the apparatus used and under the thermal expanding forces acting upon the specimen." Expressed differently, the transition temperature represents an isoviscous state, or a state where the viscosity of the polymer is approximately 10^{13} poises.[78] Transition temperatures are observed in a number of other properties, and this transition is manifested by a discontinuity in a plot of the property versus temperature. These properties, including volume relations, are tabulated as follows:

Volume.
Heat capacity.
Compressibility.
Thermal conductivity.
Refractive index.
Dielectric properties.
Modulus of elasticity.
X-ray crystallinity.

Typical literature data exemplifying these transitions were generalized in Figures 39 to 46, inclusive.

Überreiter [85] likens the transition temperature to an internal melting point above which the polymer behaves as a liquid of constant volume, capable of undergoing plastic and elastic deformations of a high order with a Poisson ratio of 0.5, while at the same time preserving the external fixed shape of a solid, capable of supporting shear load.

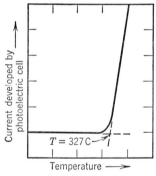

Eyring [86] considers that as the transition temperature is approached from the low temperature end, that segments of long polymer chains gradually move farther apart, resulting in the appearance of new holes, and that the side groups attached to the polymer chain, or whole segments of the chain, can undergo free rotation, to a more or less degree, along the axis of the polymer chain. The Mark [87] mechanism of long-range elasticity in rubber and the Kauzmann-Eyring [88] theory of viscous flow in polymers require, as a condition, the articulate movement of the polymer chain. More recently, the second-order transition has been identified with the temperature in polymers at which rotation of polymer segments begins. These segments may

FIGURE 39. Loss of X-ray crystallinity of tetrafluoroethylene polymer.[80] (Reprinted by permission from the authors and the *Journal of the American Chemical Society*.)

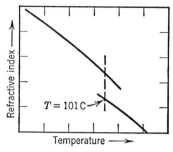

FIGURE 40. Change of refractive index of polyethylene.[70] (Reprinted by permission from *Industrial and Engineering Chemistry*.)

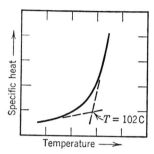

FIGURE 41. Change of specific heat of polyethylene.[70] (Reprinted by permission from *Industrial and Engineering Chemistry*.)

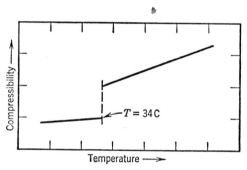

FIGURE 42.   Compressibility curve for rubber sulfur compound (19.5% S).[81]

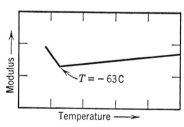

FIGURE 43.   Modulus of elasticity as a function of temperature for rubber containing 8% sulfur.[82]

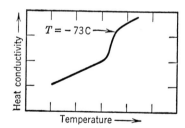

FIGURE 44.   Conductivity of amorphous rubber versus temperature.[83]

contain as many as forty carbon atoms.[68, 89-91] The investigations[92] of solid polyamides also offer convincing evidence for the rotation of segments in polymers.

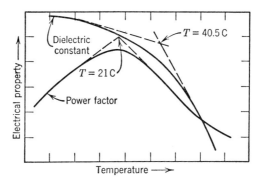

FIGURE 45. Change of electrical properties of polystyrene as a function of temperature.[70] (Reprinted by permission from *Industrial and Engineering Chemistry*.)

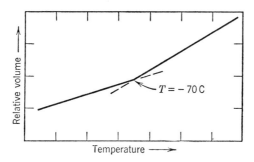

FIGURE 46. Relative volume of amorphous rubber versus temperature.[84]

A number of factors may influence the second-order transition temperature just as they do in the first-order phase transition. These factors are:

Molecular weight.
Crosslinking.
Stress.
Copolymerization.
Plasticizers.
Orientation.
Time.

MOLECULAR WEIGHT

The T_m values for polyisobutylenes of various molecular weights were reported [71,93] as increasing rapidly in the low molecular weight range, and thereafter leveling off as summarized in Figure 47.

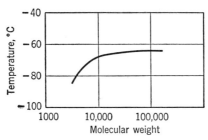

FIGURE 47. T_m as a function of molecular weight for polyisobutylene.

CROSSLINKING

Bekkedahl [94] illustrated the change of T_m on rubber with progressive degrees of vulcanizations, varying from the rubber hydrocarbon to ebonite. It is interesting to note that the curve was S-shaped and that the data of a number of investigations followed the general curve of Figure 48. These data included thermal expansion,[81,84,95] softening point,[95] refractive index,[96] permanent set,[97] yield point,[98] and heat capacity.[84]

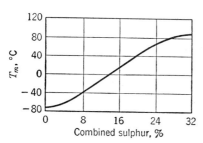

FIGURE 48. Influence of combined sulfur on second-order transition temperature of rubber. (From R. F. Boyer and R. S. Spencer [drawn by N. Bekkedahl], "Second-Order Transition Effects in Rubber and High Polymers," *Advances in Colloid Science*, Vol. II, H. Mark and G. S. Whitby, Editors. Interscience Publishers, Inc., New York, 1946.)

It may be noted in Figure 48 that there is no increase in T_m until about 3 per cent combined sulfur is reached, and that at about 28 per cent combined sulfur, the curve levels off; that is, when the polymer chains are sufficiently crosslinked, rotation of polymer segments is greatly reduced or even eliminated. This is true of the thermosetting resins, such as the phenol-formaldehyde, urea-formaldehyde, and melamine-formaldehyde resins. The crosslinking of unsaturated polyester resins, such as glycol maleate by peroxide catalysts and another vinyl monomer, shows a relation of T_m to the degree of crosslinking similar to a vulcanization.

These data are in accord with the suggestions of Tuckett[91] and Überreiter,[99] that crosslinking would prevent rotation and that a higher temperature would be required to give an equivalent amount of rotation. Boyer and Spencer[100] copolymerized styrene with 0 to 1.5% of divinylbenzene and measured T_m; the cubical coefficient of expansion, $\beta_1{}^a$ below T_m; the cubical coefficient of expansion, $\beta_2{}^b$ above T_m; and the swelling volume in toluene at 23 C. Their data are summarized in Table 19.

TABLE 19

EFFECT OF CROSSLINKING ON T_m OF POLYSTYRENE

Divinyl-benzene, %	T_m, °C	$\beta_1{}^a \times 10^4$	$\beta_2{}^b \times 10^4$	Swelling Volume	Average No. Monomer Units between Crosslinks
0	87	2.33	6.22	....	0
0.2	....	....	....	....	700 *
0.4	....	....	....	....	280 *
0.6	89.5	2.43	6.29	5.80	172
0.8	92	2.38	6.60	5.06	101
1.0	94.5	2.85	7.35	4.59	92
1.5	97	2.30	8.99	3.68	58

* Extrapolated values.

From R. F. Boyer and R. S. Spencer, *Advances in Colloid Science*, Vol. II, p. 25, H. Mark and G. S. Whitby, Editors. Interscience Publishers, Inc., New York, 1946.

These investigators showed that a plot of T_m against percentage divinylbenzene indicated that a minimum concentration of about 0.4% divinylbenzene was needed to effect T_m. Their extrapolation of 0.4% divinylbenzene, in a linear relation of a log-log plot of the number of monomers between crosslinks as a function of percentage divinylbenzene, led them to conclude that about 300 monomer units exist between the points of crosslinkages, thus:

This value of 300 monomer units corresponds roughly to the observations of Jenckel and Braucker,[71] who found that T_m began to level off at a molecular weight of 30,000 to 40,000 for polystyrene and at a molecular weight of about 20,000 for polyisobutylene. For styrene and isobutylene, 300 monomeric units would correspond to 600 carbon atoms in the chain, and, as Spencer and Boyer point out, one cross-linkage point per a few hundred carbon atoms would not be expected to hinder rotation of polymer rotation, in view of the fact that the segment length calculated from viscous flow measurements is about 40 carbon atoms.[88] Crosslinking can also be effected between polymer chains by means other than direct valency bonds. Substituent groups, such as chlorine or nitrile, which exert high secondary valence forces, are also effective, but of a different order of magnitude. Thus the T_m value for parachlorostyrene polymer is higher than that of polystyrene; that of paracyanostyrene polymers are higher than those of the chlorostyrene polymers.

COPOLYMERIZATION

Often copolymerization results in a continuous, non-linear change in T_m, the value of T_m of the copolymer corresponding to a value between

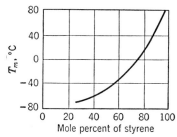

FIGURE 49. T_m values for copolymers as a function of styrene and methyl acrylate concentration.

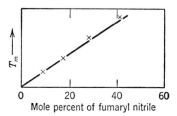

FIGURE 50. T_m values for copolymers as a function of styrene and fumaryl nitrile concentration.

the T_m values of the polymers of the monomers comprising the copolymer. Überreiter[85] measured the T_m values of copolymers of styrene and butadiene from 100 to 100 mole per cent of each component. The curve for the second-order transitions ranged in a continuous non-linear curve from -85 C for polybutadiene to $+80$ C for polystyrene. In some cases, as in the copolymers of styrene and methyl acrylate, Jenckel[72] found a T_m of approximately 80 C for 100 per cent polystyrene, which decreased continuously but not linearly to a value of about -70 C for the copolymer of 25 mole per cent styrene and 75 mole per cent methyl acrylate. The same author indicates T_m for methyl acrylate polymer of 4 C. These data are given in Figure 49.

The generalization may be made that copolymers may have T_m properties which are compromises of the properties of the pure polymers, but that a small amount of certain monomers in a copolymer may exert a disproportionate effect because of a large disrupting effect on the linear and lateral order of the polymer. Certain copolymers may also be prepared with a comonomer, such as styrene, and a comer, such as fumaryl nitrile, which does not undergo vinyl polymerization alone, to produce an increase in T_m proportional to the amount of comer. In such a case the maximum amount of fumaryl nitrile that combines in the copolymer is 50 mole per cent. The results are indicated graphically in Figure 50.

STRESS

If the transition temperatures represent a viscous state condition, the application of force should cause an acceleration of viscous flow to supplement the flow due to thermal energy. Scott [81] has shown that as the external load was increased from one atmosphere to 800 bars on a sample of vulcanized rubber (19.5 per cent combined sulfur), T_m increased from 36 to 45 C.

Müller [101] has shown that the decrease of T_m for polystyrene was proportional to the increase in degree of orientation. The effect of external tension on the T_m value of the copolymer of vinylidene chloride and vinyl chloride has been noted by Boyer and Spencer.[74] As an example of an orientable polymer, Boyer and Spencer [74] prepared a copolymer of vinylidene chloride and vinyl cyanide (Saran F). This copolymer was oriented by stretching, allowed to crystallize, and linear expansion measurements, parallel and perpendicular to the direction of orientation, were determined. Above T_m the linear expansion coefficient was the same in both directions; below T_m the expansion coefficient perpendicular to the direction of orientation was about three times greater than that of the value in the direction of the linear chain. Boyer and Spencer point out that the anisotropic expansion of Saran F, at right angles to the chains, is similar to that in low molecular weight compounds and is relatively free from transition effects. On the other hand, expansion parallel to the chains can occur only by a bulk displacement of chains or chain segments parallel to each other. Therefore, the increased thermal expansion above T_m must depend on some other mechanism, most probably viscous flow. A viscous flow mechanism accounts for the time effects noted in these transitions. The rate of viscous flow below T_m is too small to give an observable effect. These investigators also pointed out that, with the admission of the viscous flow hypothesis,[102] second-order transitions can be treated in terms of melt viscosity behavior of the polymers and time effects, molecular weight, plasticizers, etc., can be interpreted.

TIME EFFECTS

The second-order transition is also characterized by time effects other than the time required to establish thermal equilibrium. These time

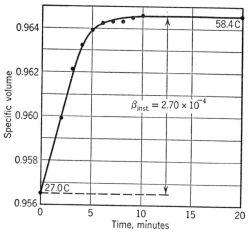

FIGURE 51. Isothermal expansion of polystyrene at 58.4 C. Thermal lag in dilatometer and "instantaneous" expansion. (By permission from the American Institute of Physics, New York.)

effects are noted in the immediate vicinity below T_m. At a few degrees above T_m, rate effects and thermal equilibria are of the same order, hence not observable. At temperatures lower than 10 to 15 C below T_m, the rates of volume change are exceedingly slow. Alfrey, Goldfinger, and Mark [103] emphasize that the transition temperature, which appears to be definite for a given polymer, is simply a consequence of different observers studying the phenomenon at fairly fixed rates; namely, the heat rate, rate of deformation, etc. They refer to the "apparent second-order transition in polystyrene" and emphasize that there is no thermodynamic singularity involved. Richards [104] had previously stressed this view, pointing out that the transition depends on the speed of the test with which it is observed. Boyer and Spencer [102, 105, 106] have obtained equilibrium-volume-temperature curves for polystyrene. These curves

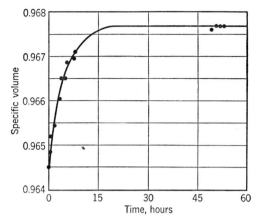

FIGURE 52. Isothermal expansion of polystyrene at 58.4 C. Slow approach to equilibrium. (By permission from the American Institute of Physics, New York.)

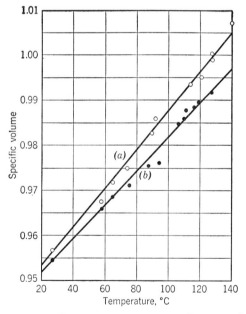

FIGURE 53. Equilibrium volume-temperature curves of two samples of polystyrene. (a) β inst. $= 2.70 \times 10^{-4}$ per °C; β eq. $= 4.53 \times 10^{-4}$ per °C. (b) β inst. $= 2.83 \times 10^{-4}$ per °C; β eq. $= 3.98 \times 10^{-4}$ per °C. (By permission from the American Institute of Physics, New York.)

exhibit no second-order transition in the temperature range of 20 to 150 C. These investigators consider these data as demonstrating that the second-order transition, at least for polystyrene, involves a rate phenomenon, and not a thermodynamic singularity. This is on the assumption that the equilibrium-volume-temperature curve for polystyrene shows no transition at some temperature below 20 C. Such

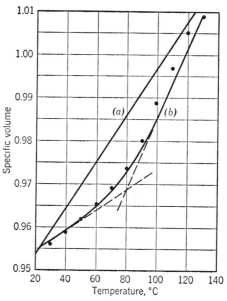

FIGURE 54. Expansion of polystyrene from equilibrium at 23 C, with a heating rate of 0.82 C per minute. The dots are the experimental points. (*a*) Equilibrium curve for comparison. (*b*) Theoretical curve under the above conditions. (By permission from the American Institute of Physics, New York.)

data have not yet been published. The data of Spencer and Boyer are summarized in Figures 51 to 54.[106] These investigators also show that at finite rates of temperature variation, that is, under non-equilibrium conditions, the volume changes by two mechanisms:

$$\frac{d(\Delta\sigma)}{dt} = -\beta\Delta\sigma \tag{59}$$

$$\frac{d(\Delta\sigma)}{dt} = -\frac{\sigma_e(273)(\Delta\beta)\,dt}{dt} \tag{60}$$

where $\Delta\sigma$ is the difference between actual specific volume at time t and temperature T and the equilibrium specific volume at T, β is a quantity of the form $A \exp(-E/RT)$, $\sigma_e(273)$ is the equilibrium specific volume at 0 C, and $\Delta\beta$ is the difference between the equilibrium and the "instantaneous" expansion coefficients. These equations on combination yield the expression:

$$\frac{d(\Delta\sigma)}{dt} = -\frac{\beta\Delta\sigma}{dT/dt} - \sigma_e(273)\Delta\beta \qquad (61)$$

Figure 54 shows the equilibrium volume-temperature curve (*a*), the theoretical curve (*b*) obtained from the above equation, and the observed curve under the same conditions given by the circled points. The agreement between theory and experiment is good, and the observed curve approaches the equilibrium curve asymptotically at the higher temperatures.

PLASTICIZERS

A plasticizer is a substance added to a polymer which is capable of forcing polymer chains apart, and thereby produces the same effect as temperature. However, it has been pointed out [107] that if this were the

TABLE 20

Effect of Plasticizer on T_m of Polymers

A. Ethylcellulose Plasticized by Tricresyl Phosphate

Plasticizer, %	T_m, °C
0	65
20	−2
30	−13
40	−28
50	−40
60	−51
80	−52
100	−53

B. Nitrocellulose Plasticized by Tricresyl Phosphate

0	40
10	3
20	−10
40	−30
60	−43
70	−49
80	−50
100	−52

C. Polystyrene Plasticized by Ethylbenzene

0	82
3	68
5	50
10	22

only effect of plasticizers, a small percentage of plasticizer should lower T_m by as much as 100 C. Since plasticizers will be considered separately, it may be stated at this time that plasticizers do shift [78, 85, 108] the T_m values toward lower temperatures, as indicated in the data of Table 20.

SECOND-ORDER TRANSITIONS AND MOLECULAR STRUCTURE

It has been pointed out [107] that when high polymers are arranged on a T_m scale, the T_m of the important rubbers fall below −40 C, while the plastics have a T_m above +50 C. It was also shown that crystalline polymers, such as polythene, nylon, and Saran, violate this generality. It is apparent that a T_m value alone is insufficient to classify a polymer as a rubber or a plastic or a fiber, since the molecular structure of the polymer, including the nature and quantity of the intermolecular and intramolecular forces as well as the geometry of the polymer chains in relation to a neighboring chain, determine these characteristics. On the other hand, polymers are valued technically for their mechanical and physical properties rather than as chemical entities or complexities. The extent to which these polymers exhibit a rubbery, a plastic, or a fiber state determines the scope of their application as rubbers, plastics, or fibers. The T_m value, therefore, is a consequence of the structure, order, fit, inter- and intramolecular forces in a polymer, and although the T_m value may not be used to classify polymers as rubbers or plastics or fibers, it is exceptionally valuable in comparing the individual members within a group of rubbers or plastics or fibers.

Rubberlike polymers have been called *elastomers*,[109] which is considered a contraction of the term *elastopolymers*. This term embraces all polymers possessing elastic properties, and associates this property with the elasticity of rubber; that is, it recognizes a rubbery state. This rubber state is not necessarily associated with the polymeric hydrocarbon of the rubber-producing *Hevea brasiliensis* tree, or of such plants as *Cryptostegia grandiflora* [110] or of the common milkweed.[111] It has been shown [112] that the rubber obtained from the seed of *Smilax rotundifolia* was a polyester and not a hydrocarbon.

The N-methyl-substituted nylons, such as those prepared from sebacic acid and decamethylenemonomethyldiamine, were shown to be rubbery, whereas the use of unsubstituted diamine resulted in fiber-forming polymers.[49] Plasticized polyvinyl chloride is also rubbery and quite elastic. It should be stressed that rubberlike elasticity involves large deformations at high rates of deformation; that is, rapid elongation and rapid retraction. Many synthetic elastomers have slow retraction rates. High retraction rates are found in those elastomers prepared from suitable dienes alone or as copolymers. Polyisobutylene has a high retraction rate in contrast to plasticized polyvinyl chloride. In polyvinyl chloride, although the plasticizer is efficient in lowering the T_m value and in separating the polymer chains to produce rubberlike compositions, it does not supply the kinetic energy necessary and responsible for rapid retraction. Furthermore, in true rubbers, Eley [113] points out that a small degree of vulcanization or crosslinking tends to suppress viscous flow without affecting the highly elastic behavior. However, high degrees of crosslinking markedly suppress viscous flow and reduce elastic behavior. Any comparison, therefore, relating to structures even within the class of elastomers must be made among those compounds which are related to each other structurally and chemically.

THE EFFECT OF STRUCTURES ON T_m VALUES

The polyprenes are derived as polymerization products of dienes of the general formula, CR_2=CR—CR=CR_2. If the geometric order of the polyprenes is assumed to be constant, substitution of the hydrogen atoms in the parent polybutadiene should produce a change in T_m value, since these substitutions influence segmental rotation in the solid state. This influence depends on:

1. The nature of the substituent group, since the intermolecular force constants along the chain contribute to the extent of crystallinity in the polymer.
2. The bulk of the substituent group which would tend to keep the chain apart and, therefore, permit segmental rotation.

This effect would be counterbalanced, however, by the hindrance of rotation due to the steric effect of the group itself. Copolymerization of butadiene with other monomers should produce effects closely related to the effect produced by substitution. Polybutadiene,[85] —$(CH_2$—CH=CH—$CH_2)_n$—, has a T_m of about -85 C, whereas polymethylbutadiene,[114] —$(CH_2$—C=CH—$CH_2)_n$—,
$$| \atop CH_3$$
has a T_m value of about -73 C, and polydimethylbutadiene, —$(CH_2$—C=C—$CH_2)_n$—, about -60 C.
$$| \quad | \atop CH_3 \ CH_3$$

In view of the effect of methyl group substitution, it would be expected that the polymer of 2-phenylbutadiene would have a higher T_m than even the dimethylbutadiene. No data have been published on this polymer, but it has been described as a poor rubber and quite brittle. The T_m properties of styrene-butadiene copolymers appear to be in harmony with such a description for as the mole percentage of styrene is increased in the copolymer, T_m increases. Überreiter shows a T_m value of about -50 C for 50 mole per cent of styrene in the butadiene copolymer, and about -61 C for the composition containing 25 mole per cent of styrene. In contrast to styrene copolymer, the copolymer of butadiene with acrylonitrile has a T_m value [115] of -23 C.

Because of the lower bulk factor of the nitrile group, as compared to the phenyl group, it would be expected that the T_m of the nitrile copolymer would be lower than that of the styrene copolymer. However, because of the highly polar nature of the nitrile group, which increases the force between chains, the T_m value increases. By this reasoning, it is logical to find [116] that polymers of 2-chlorobutadiene-1,3 (chloroprene) have a higher brittle temperature than polybutadiene, and that polymers of 2,3-dichlorobutadiene-1,3 are more brittle than chloroprene polymers.

Polyisobutylene has become a commercially important elastomer, but is not a polyprene and cannot be compared structurally to butadiene polymers. Rather it should be considered a vinyl compound based on ethylene. The reason for this becomes apparent as we compare polybutadiene with a T_m of about -85 C with a value, as we have already seen, for about $+87$ C for polyethylene. Polyethylene [70] is crystalline at room temperature to an extent of about 75 per cent and has an identity period of 2.5 Å, which corresponds to a fit value of one. Since polyethylene does not contain high polar groups attached to the chain, the inter- and intramolecular forces, tending to prevent segmented rotation, cannot be large if considered locally rather than for large, ordered areas. The intermolecular force per mole of methylene groups is about 1 kilogram calorie per mole.[117]   In contrast to the order found in polyethylene, polybutadiene is not crystalline until highly stretched; and even then the amount of amorphous material is very high. When two methyl groups are substituted on every second carbon atom of polyethylene, polyisobutylene results. These methyl groups force the chains apart so that they can no longer fit into a crystal lattice, and the polymer assumes the shape of a spiral with a fit value of $1/7$; hence it should acquire rubbery properties. Polyisobutylene has a T_m value of -74 C, which is within the range of the polybutadienes. The presence of two methyl groups on the same carbon atom exert mutual repulsion and diminish the hindrance to segmental rotation in the chains. Furthermore, as we have seen in methyl substitution on the polybutadienes, the methyl group has limited effectiveness in hindering rotation because of its small size. A rigid, bulky group, such as a phenyl group, is much more effective. If one of the methyl groups of isobutylene is replaced by a phenyl group, isopropenylbenzene is obtained. Ethylene, isobutylene, and isopropenylbenzene are compared structurally as follows:

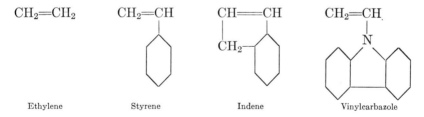

$CH_2{=}CH_2$	$CH_2{=}C$	$CH_2{=}C$
Ethylene	Isobutylene	Isopropenylbenzene

The solid polymers of isopropenylbenzene are not rubbery, indicating that the phenyl group is more effective in preventing the segmental rotation in the chain. Similarly, styrene is effective as a copolymerizing agent in stiffening the polymers of isobutylene. Phenyl substitution exerts an effect on segmental rotation also by intermolecular reaction because of the polarizability of phenyl groups. The calculations by Mark [118] indicate that the molar cohesion of polystyrene is about four times that of polyethylene. This increase in molar cohesion compensates for the loss of crystallinity as is evident from the T_m value of polystyrene of about 81 C contrasted to 87 C for polyethylene. X-ray diffraction studies suggest that polystyrene exists as an irregularly folded amorphous structure lacking crystallinity. It must be assumed, therefore, that the bulk of the phenyl group, as well as the polarization of the phenyl group, exert a steric hindrance on segmental rotation. This same behavior is observed in other aryl-substituted ethylenes, such as polyindene and polyvinylcarbazole. A comparison of their structures with ethylene and styrene would indicate a behavior similar to styrene:

$CH_2{=}CH_2$	$CH_2{=}CH$	$CH{=}CH$	$CH_2{=}CH$
Ethylene	Styrene	Indene	Vinylcarbazole

The T_m value for both polyindene and polyvinylcarbazole is $+85$ C. However, whereas the styrene and indene polymers were amorphous, polyvinylcarbazole does show a crystalline pattern; and, because of the crosslinking action of this crystallinity and reduced viscous flow, it may be used at temperatures in excess of its T_m value. The attachment of methyl groups to the benzene ring of styrene is effective in raising T_m by hindering segmental rotation through a bulk mechanism, and this may be observed in the behavior of 2,5-dimethylstyrene when compared to styrene. The T_m value of styrene may be increased also by an intermolecular interaction between chains by substitution of polar groups on the benzene ring. Thus dichlorostyrene is more heat resistant than monochlorostyrene, whereas the polymer of meta-cyanostyrene is infusible. These same results can be obtained by copolymerization, for example, of styrene with acrylonitrile or with fumaryl dinitrile. If the polar groups, such as the chlorine or nitrile groups, are attached directly to the polyethylene chain, thereby eliminating the bulky phenyl group, the ethylene polymer chain retains a high degree of its crystallinity, and potential fiber-forming polymers are obtained. Such polymers can be cold-drawn, and because of the effective crosslinking of the polar groups coupled with crystallinity, they possess operating temperatures in excess of their T_m values. If the polar group is bulky or has low molar cohesion values, the crystallinity is reduced and the T_m value is a compromise of bulk-factor effects and secondary valence forces. This latter condition is typical of the plastics, which for practical applications should have a T_m value of at least 60 C. Whereas the crystalline polymers may be used both as fibers and as plastics at temperatures in excess of T_m, the plastics are restricted in use, preferably to temperatures below T_m.

If one of the hydrogen atoms on every second carbon atom of the polyethylene chain is substituted by such small, compact, polar groups as the hydroxyl, chlorine, or nitrile groups, so as to maintain the same degree of crystallinity in the polymer, the resulting T_m value will be the consequence of the spreading of the polymer chain compensated by the extent of the binding forces associated with the attached polar groups. However, the degree and type of molecular order are not necessarily maintained as may be observed in the X-ray identity periods and line intensity studies previously mentioned. The identity period of polyethylene is 2.5 Å or a fit value of 1, that of polyvinyl alcohol is 2.5 Å or a fit value of 1, that of polyvinyl chloride is 5.0 Å or a fit value of ½, and that of polyacrylonitrile appears to be 2.5 Å or a fit value of 1. In polyvinyl alcohol and polyacrylonitrile, the substituted groups are located on the same side of the chain, whereas in polyvinyl chloride, the chlorine atoms alternate first to one side then to the other side of the chain. In a comparison of polyethylene, polyvinyl alcohol, polyvinyl chloride, and polyacrylonitrile, the polyvinyl chloride would be expected to have the lowest T_m value if we assumed that all these polymers possessed the same ratio of crystalline to amorphous mass. Of the remaining three polymers, polyacrylonitrile would have the highest T_m value. A comparison of their T_m values is given in Table 21.

TABLE 21

Substance	Repeating Unit	Fit Ratio	T_m, °C
Polyvinyl chloride	—CH$_2$—CH— Cl	0.5	75
Polyethylene	—CH$_2$—CH$_2$—	1	87
Polyvinyl alcohol	—CH$_2$—CH— OH	1	85
Polyacrylonitrile	—CH$_2$—CH— CN	1	>150
Polyvinylidene chloride	Cl —CH$_2$—C— Cl	0.54	−18

It may be observed that if two chlorine atoms are placed on the same carbon atom, as in the case of polyvinylidene chloride, high internal mobility is obtained and the T_m of polyvinyl chloride of 75 C is reduced to −18 C. This effect is similar to that observed with polyisobutylene, and the hindrance to segmental rotation is reduced by the mutual repulsion of two chlorines on the same carbon atom. This repulsion effect was also observed in polyvinyl chloride, whereby the chlorine atoms alternated on either side of the chain. The bonding forces between chains of polyvinylidene chloride is higher than those in vinyl chloride as is evidenced by its relative insolubility in solvents that dissolve polyvinyl chloride, and by the fact that the oriented form of polyvinylidene chloride may be used at considerably higher operating temperatures than oriented polyvinyl chloride.

If the cyano groups of polyacrylonitrile are converted to ester groups, the T_m value changes rapidly. In such a case, the dipole interaction between chains containing ester groups should be of the same order as between chains containing hydroxl groups, whereas the steric effect of the ester group should be larger than that of a cyano group or a hydroxy group. The increased size of these ester groups, however, should space the chains far apart, decreasing both the bulk effect and the interchain reaction. The T_m value of polymethyl acrylate is a compromise of these effects, and has a value of about 3 C. Polyvinyl acetate, as an isomer of polymethyl acrylate, should follow a similar system and should have a T_m considerably lower than polyvinyl alcohol. The T_m value for polyvinyl acetate is 28 C in contrast to 85 C for polyvinyl alcohol. These values of polymethyl acrylate and polyvinyl acetate appear to be consistent with the fact that neither of them has ever been reported to possess crystallinity.

A further consideration of these two esters demonstrates the effect of side chain bulk and dipole interaction. If polymethyl acrylate is hydrolyzed to polyacrylic acid, the side chain bulk is reduced and a carboxyl group, which exerts much stronger bonding forces than an ester group, is formed. Polyacrylic acid is crystalline, and its T_m value increases to 80 to 95 C as compared to 3 C for the methyl ester. If the alpha hydrogen of the methyl acrylate is replaced by a methyl group, polymethyl methacrylate is obtained. In this transition the bonding forces between chains have not been markedly increased, but the side chain bulk factor has increased. The T_m of polymethyl methacrylate is about 60 C as compared to 3 C for the methyl acrylate polymer, and neither polymer is crystalline, which is in accord with expectations. If polyvinyl acetate with a T_m of 28 C is converted to a polyvinyl ether having the same number of carbon atoms in the side chain, T_m would be expected to remain the same unless the dipole effect of the substituent group influences the T_m value. The structures of polyvinyl acetate and polyvinyl ether are represented as follows:

$$-(CH_2-CH)_n-$$
$$|$$
$$O$$
$$|$$
$$C=O$$
$$|$$
$$CH_3$$

Polyvinyl acetate

$$-(CH_2-CH)_n-$$
$$|$$
$$O$$
$$|$$
$$CH_2$$
$$|$$
$$CH_3$$

Polyvinyl ethyl ether

The T_m value of polyvinyl ethyl ether is lower than -10 C as compared to $+28$ C for polyvinyl acetate. The effect of "rigid side group" on polyvinyl ethers may be readily noted with the phenyl ethers, or more dramatically by contrasting polyvinyl isobutyl ether to polyvinyl butyral, whose structures are represented as follows:

$$-(CH_2-CH)_n-CH_2-CH-$$

Polyvinyl isobutyl ether

$$-CH_2-CH-CH_2-CH-$$

Polyvinyl butyral

Since the butyral has its ether linkages common to two carbon atoms in the same chain, the butyral group would have the effect of more rigidity for the same bulk as the butyl groups of the ether, and therefore should have a higher T_m than the ether. The T_m value of polyvinyl butyral is about 50 C; that of polyvinyl ether is lower than -10 C.

PLASTICIZATION

Plasticizers are stable organic compounds usually possessing low volatility, and therefore a relative degree of permanence, and are added to polymers to produce changes in the physical properties of the polymer. For this reason, plasticizers have considerable technical importance. In a practical sense, plasticizers are compatible with the polymer, at least within certain concentrations; that is, plasticizers can be added to polymers without phase separation. The efficiency of the plasticizer is concerned with the amount of plasticizer needed to produce the required change in the desired physical property. Plasticizers produce changes in the physical properties by separating the chains of the polymer, thereby reducing the magnitude of the intermolecular forces. As already indicated, the second-order transition temperature, T_m, is lowered by the addition of plasticizers. Other related phenomena, such as bend-brittle point,[119] T_b; the flex-brittle point,[120] T_f; the dielectric loss factor,[121-123] T_e; and Young's modulus,[121, 124] T_{ym}, are also changed by plasticizers.

Assuming a compatible plasticizer, the degree of retention of a plasticizer by a polymer and, conversely, the loss of plasticizer, is controlled by the vapor pressure of the plasticizer and its rate of diffusion through the plasticized polymer mass. A boiling point of 400 C at atmospheric pressure appears to define the minimum vapor pressure requirements of a desirable plasticizer, since this condition corresponds roughly to a weight loss from a polymer-plasticizer mass in static air of about 5 per cent at 100 C after five hours. The loss of plasticizer is usually measured by the loss of weight of the polymer-plasticizer mixture at 100 C as a function of time. Accelerated testing is performed by displacing the air in the test oven at the rate of several cubic feet per minute.

The efficiencies of a series of plasticizers, therefore, can be correlated by measuring the effects on the second-order transition temperature, the brittle point, the flex point, the dielectric properties, modulus of elasticity, etc. The comparative efficiencies of ethylbenzene and paraffin oil as plasticizers for polystyrene are compared in Table 22 by measurement of the T_m values.[85, 125]

TABLE 22

Ethylbenzene		Paraffin Oil	
%	T_m, °C	%	T_m, °C
0	80–82	0	80–82
3	68	3	75
5	50	..	..
10	22	10	56
..	..	20	49
..	..	50	43

Frith and Tuckett [126, 127] have treated the problem of compatibility of a plasticizer with a polymer in terms of partial molal free energy of dilution, $\overline{\Delta F}_1$, as the plasticizer is added in increasing amounts to the polymer. The limit of compatibility is given by the concentration corresponding to a partial molal free energy of dilution equal to zero, $\overline{\Delta F}_1 = 0$. Boyer and Spencer [128] point out that the partial molal heats of dilution can be related to the cohesive energy densities of polymer and plasticizer, which in turn are equal to the Huggins-Flory empirical constant, μ, which describes solvent-polymer interaction.[129-131]

Boyer and Spencer have generalized the relationships between second-order transition temperature and the other common methods of measuring plasticizer efficiency, as shown in Figure 55.[128] This figure is an idealized correlation between the different tests, showing that the second-order transition is the lowest of several temperature characteristics adapted to study plasticizer action and that all the other tests are inter-related. These investigators also point out that the tests in Figure 55 differ widely in the molecular responses they elicit from the polymer. The second-order transition, T_m, test involves very small deformations of a viscous flow mechanism, whereas the brittle tests involve relatively large and rapid deformation. The mechanism of this deformation

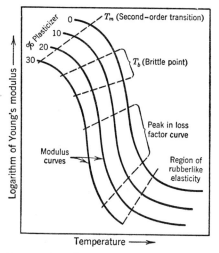

FIGURE 55. Generalized relationships between the second-order transition temperature and other common methods of measuring plasticizer efficiency. (From R. F. Boyer and R. S. Spencer, "Effect of Plasticizers on Second-Order Transition Points of High Polymers," *J. Polymer Sci.*, **2**, 157 [1947]. Interscience Publishers, Inc.)

occurs primarily by chain uncoiling, that is, a high elasticity mechanism. The dielectric test involves the rotation of dipoles, but no gross displacement of the specimen except possibly minor electrostrictive effects. The peak in dielectric loss usually occurs in a temperature range wherein a plastic acquires rubberlike elasticity as the temperature is increased.[132] Large deformation at high rates of deformation characterize rubberlike elasticity. All these phenomena or tests require rotation of chain segments about carbon-carbon bonds, and this segmental rotation permits dipole rotation, viscous flow, and high elastic deformation. Thus the Boyer-Spencer chart encompasses in one figure all the common phenomena that characterize high polymers. Simril [116] points out that if the time dependence of second-order transitions and brittle temperatures are considered, T_m may be considered to be the lower limit of T_b; and that there is a temperature range for each polymer above which internal mobility increases; and T_b and T_m values for comparable time scales are valuable in comparing internal mobility and segmental freedom of structurally different polymers.

It was shown by Flory [93] that the viscosity of concentrated solutions of polyesters in liquids, whose structure is similar to the segmer units of the polymer, is related to the weight average chain length taken over the polymer and the solvent treated as monomer. The weight average chain length is proportional to the weight fraction, W_2, of the polymer in solution and

$$\log \eta = A + B(W_2)^{1/2} \qquad (62)$$

where η is the viscosity and A and B are constants. To express a temperature dependence, Boyer and Spencer [105] modified the Flory equation to give

$$\log \eta = A + B(W_2)^{1/2} + \frac{E}{RT} \qquad (63)$$

where E is the energy of activation for viscous flow, R is the gas constant, and T is absolute temperature. By assuming that the energy of activation, E, is constant, that is, an isoviscous state for the second-order transition temperature, the equation becomes

$$\sqrt{W_2} = D - \frac{E}{BRT} \qquad (64)$$

where B and D are constants. This equation indicates that a linear relation is to be expected between the reciprocal absolute transition temperature and the square root of the weight fraction of the plasticized polymer.

Some experimental data confirmed this equation, but since the data of Kauzmann [133] for dielectric dispersions in plasticized polyvinyl chloride indicated that the energy and entropy of activation decreased rapidly with increased plasticizer content, Boyer and Spencer attempted to confirm the square root relation. Empirically, they found that the energy and entropy of activation listed by Kauzmann were linear functions of the square root of the weight fraction of the plasticizer. These relations may be expressed as

$$\Delta S = \Delta S_0 - K_1 \sqrt{W_1} \qquad (65)$$

$$\Delta H = \Delta H_0 - K_2 \sqrt{W_2} \qquad (66)$$

and are summarized in Figure 56.[128]

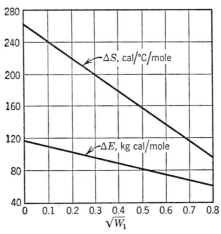

FIGURE 56.   Dependence of entropy and energy of activation on plasticizer content. (From R. F. Boyer and R. S. Spencer, "Effect of Plasticizers on Second-Order Transition Points of High Polymers," *J. Polymer Sci.*, **2**, 157 [1947]. Interscience Publishers, Inc.)

By basing a derivation on the Kauzmann and Eyring entropy relation [88] of viscous flow of large molecules, Flory's work on concentrated solutions,[93] coupled with the square root derivation relating ΔS and ΔH to $\sqrt{W_1}$, and the concept of the isoviscous state,[134]

$$\eta = \text{constant} \qquad (67)$$

the expression

$$\sqrt{W_2} = P' - \frac{Q'}{T} \qquad (68)$$

is obtained, which is of the same form as the original equation

$$W_2 = D - \frac{E}{BRT} \qquad (69)$$

If the weight fraction, W_1, of the plasticizer is small and if the centigrade temperature, t, is small compared with 273, the equation may be transformed by the substitutions

$$W_2 = 1 - W_1 \tag{70}$$

$$T = t + 273 \tag{71}$$

$$\sqrt{1 - W_1} = F - \frac{G}{1 + \dfrac{t}{273}} \tag{72}$$

to

$$t = L - MW_1 \tag{73}$$

where L and M are constants. On expansion, the expression becomes

$$1 - \sqrt{W_1} = H + Jt \tag{74}$$

$$t = L - MW_1 \tag{75}$$

where F, G, H, J, L, and M are constants.

The square root relationship was shown by Boyer and Spencer to give linear plots for polyvinyl chloride plasticized by tricresyl phosphate, as shown in Figure 57,[78] using the data of Davies, Miller, and Busse,[121] for the loss factor at 60 and 1000 cycles, and the data of Wurstlin [135] for the 50-cycle loss factor curve and for the T_m values from thermal expansion data.

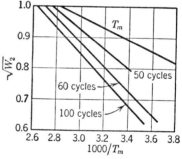

FIGURE 57

(From R. F. Boyer and R. S. Spencer, "Second-Order Transition Effects in Rubber and High Polymers," *Advances in Colloid Science*, Vol. II, H. Mark and G. S. Whitby, Editors. Interscience Publishers, Inc., New York, 1946.)

The effect of styrene monomer on the softening temperature of polystyrene was also shown by Boyer and Spencer [77] in Figure 58,[128] using the data of Aleksandrov and Lazurkin.[136] The softening points are those observed by noting the temperature at which the sample began to deform appreciably under a given load.

The derivation of the square root equation takes no account of differences in the chemical nature and performance of plasticizers, but it has been shown that there is a marked dependence on the nature of the plasticizer. Zhurkov [137] has shown that if the solvent is of such a nature

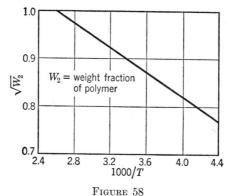

(From R. F. Boyer and R. S. Spencer, "Effect of Plasticizers on Second-Order Transition Points of High Polymers," *J. Polymer Sci.*, **2**, 157 [1947].   Interscience Publishers, Inc.)

that it is attracted to the active or polar groups (nodes) along a polymer chain, the lowering of the solidification temperature is independent of the nature of the solvent and directly proportional to the number of solvent molecules present:

$$T - T_1 = \Delta T = \frac{(2nRT^2)}{uN} \tag{76}$$

where n = number of solvent molecules,
N = number of active groups,
u = binding energy per node,
T = solidification temperature of the unplasticized polymer,
T_1 = solidification temperature of a plasticized polymer.

The linear dependence of softening temperature on solvent concentration was substantiated by experimental data [138] which were replotted by Boyer and Spencer as in Figures 59 and 60.   Figure 59 shows the application of the equation, $\Delta T = (2nRT^2)/uN$ to methyl methacrylate in five different solvents, all of which are fairly good solvents for the polymer.   In contrast, Figure 60 shows that for polyisobutylene and polybutadiene the plasticizing efficiency depends on the chain length of the aliphatic solvent.   This may be explained by the fact that these two hydrocarbon polymers do not contain strong polar or active groups and that the aliphatic solvent hydrocarbon aligns itself with the polymer chain and blocks further attraction at other attraction centers.

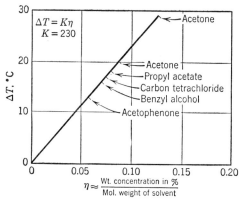

FIGURE 59

(From R. F. Boyer and R. S. Spencer, "Effect of Plasticizer on Second-Order Transition Points of High Polymers," *J. Polymer Sci.*, **2**, 171 [1947]. Interscience Publishers, Inc.)

Boyer and Spencer also considered an empirical approach to explain the variations in the efficiencies of different plasticizers. Four major approaches to plasticizer action were recognized:

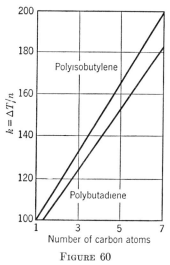

1. The chemical similarity between polymer and plasticizer, and a resulting division between solvent and non-solvent type plasticizers, both classes of which may be satisfactory for a given polymer.
2. The molecular weight, size, and shape of the plasticizer molecule.[122, 138]
3. The viscosity of the plasticizer which indicates that high-viscosity plasticizers are not too desirable for reducing low-temperature brittleness.
4. The temperature coefficient of viscosity of the plasticizer, suggesting that those plasticizers that maintain a high degree of fluidity at low temperatures are preferred for reducing low-temperature brittleness.

FIGURE 60

(From R. F. Boyer and R. S. Spencer, "Effect of Plasticizer on Second-Order Transition Points of High Polymers," *J. Polymer Sci.*, **2**, 171 [1947]. Interscience Publishers, Inc.)

Leilich and Wurstlin [123,139] were among the first to recognize the importance of the viscosity of the plasticizer itself. Jones [140] has reviewed and extended the plasticizer viscosity concept and has presented a number of curves showing how low-temperature flexibility, hardness, tensile strength, etc., depend on the viscosity of the plasticizers. Two curves from his paper are included in Figures 61 and 62.

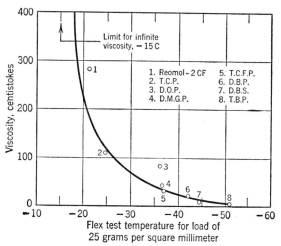

FIGURE 61. Relation between stiffening point of Hycar OR-15 compounds and viscosity of plasticizer. (Reprinted by permission from The Institution of the Rubber Industry, London.)

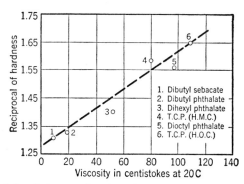

FIGURE 62. Relation between viscosity of plasticizer and hardness of a plastic PVC/100% plasticizer. (Reprinted by permission from The Institution of the Rubber Industry, London.)

Jones' data would indicate polymer-plasticizer interaction and that the correlation of the efficiency of a plasticizer and its viscosity or its viscosity temperature coefficient is related to the attractive forces between plasticizer molecules.

Grunberg and Nissan [141] correlated the energy of activation of viscosity to the viscosity of pure liquids as follows:

$$\log \eta = \log A + \frac{E_{\text{visc}}}{RT} \tag{77}$$

and pointed out that the E_{visc} should be equal to the work of cohesion for unassociated liquids.

Ewell and Eyring [142] derived on a theoretical basis the empirical equation of Friend,[143] relating latent heats of evaporation to viscosities:

$$l = \frac{9.2(R/M)(T_1 T_2)}{(T_2 - T_1) \log_{10} (\eta_1/\eta_2)}$$

where l = latent heat of vaporization,
M = molecular weight,
η_1 = viscosity at absolute temperature, T_1,
η_2 = viscosity at absolute temperature, T_2,
R = gas constant.

This equation has an important bearing on the value of μ, which is the thermodynamic solvent-polymer interaction constant. An empirical correlation between μ and plasticizer efficiency is given in Figure 63 from the publication of Boyer and Spencer.[144]

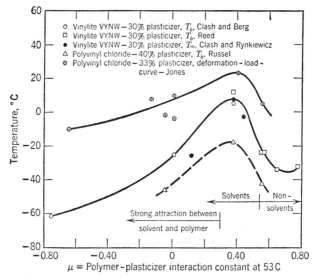

FIGURE 63. Empirical correlation between plasticizer efficiency and the thermodynamic solvent-polymer interaction constant, μ. (From R. F. Boyer and R. S. Spencer, "Effect of Plasticizer on Second-Order Transition Points of High Polymers," *J. Polymer Sci.*, **2**, 171 [1947]. Interscience Publishers, Inc.)

Transition and brittle temperatures were taken from data of Clash and Berg,[145] Reed,[146] Clash and Rynkiewicz,[69] Russell,[147] and Jones.[140] Values of μ were taken from Doty and Zable [148] for polyvinyl chloride at 53 C.

The plotted data are convincing that those plasticizers having a high negative or a high positive value of μ are most efficient in lowering the

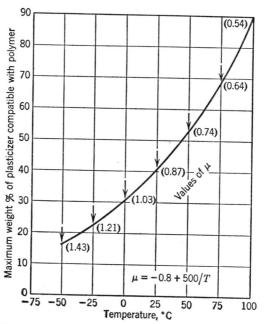

FIGURE 64. Calculated dependence of compatibility on temperature for an oil-type plasticizer. μ values are given at 25° temperature intervals along the curve. (From R. F. Boyer and R. S. Spencer, "Effect of Plasticizer on Second-Order Transition Points of High Polymers," *J. Polymer Sci.*, **2**, 171 [1947]. Interscience Publishers, Inc.)

brittle point. The least efficient are those having a μ of about 0.4. A relation between the volume fraction and the polymer may be expressed for those cases where the molecular weight of the polymer is high and μ is greater than 0.6, that is, in the region of partial miscibility as

$$\mu = \frac{-(\ln v_1 + v_2)}{v_2^2} \qquad (78)$$

where v_2 is the volume fraction of the polymer and v_1 is the volume fraction of the plasticizer.[130, 131, 149]

The value, v_1, defines the critical concentration of plasticizer which can be added to the polymer, and above that concentration the plasti-

cizer will not be compatible. Huggins [129] also showed the temperature
dependence of μ as

$$\mu = \alpha + \beta/T \tag{79}$$

where α and β are constants and T is the absolute temperature. If α
and β are known, it is possible to show the relation between v_1 and
temperature. Figure 64 shows such a relation between percentage
plasticizer and temperature for typically poor solvents having $\alpha =$
-0.80 and $\beta = 500$. This curve shows that about 35 per cent of the
plasticizer which it characterizes can be added at room temperature, but,
as the temperature is lowered, some of the plasticizer will be forced
out either by exuding to the surface or by forming a second phase in the
polymer mass. In contrast to this, for good solvents, that is, $\mu < 0.55$,
μ will remain constant or decrease with temperature.

Boyer and Spencer [128] have tabulated, as in Table 23, the nature of the
solvent for different values of μ.

TABLE 23

GENERAL CHARACTERISTICS OF μ

μ Value	Nature of Solvent	Effect of Temperature on μ
$\mu > 0.55$	Non-solvent—limited miscibility	μ increases with decreasing temperature
$\mu < 0.55$	Solvent—complete miscibility	. . . .
$0.25 < \mu < 0.45$	Good solvent	μ independent of temperature
$\mu < 0.25$	Strong attraction between solvent and polymer	μ decreases with decrease in temperature

From R. F. Boyer and R. S. Spencer, *J. Polym. Sci.* **2**, 171 (1947). Interscience
Publishers, Inc.

The value of μ depends on the latent heat of vaporization as seen
from the Huggins equation: [129]

$$\mu = \frac{1}{\gamma} + \left[\frac{KV_1}{RT}\right]\left[\left(\frac{E_2}{V_2}\right)^{\frac{1}{2}} - \left(\frac{E_1}{V_1}\right)^{\frac{1}{2}}\right]^2 \tag{80}$$

where γ = the coordination number,
$\quad K$ = constant,
$\quad E_1/V_1$ = cohesive energy density of the solvent,
$\quad E_2/V_2$ = cohesive energy density of the polymer,
$\quad E_1$ = approximate latent heat of vaporization of the solvent,
$\quad V_1$ = molar volume of the solvent.

This equation has been criticized [150] as failing to provide for the
specific interaction between solvent and polymer and that it predicts
that μ should always be positive, whereas often it is actually negative.

In any case, it describes a dependence of μ on the latent heat of vaporization, which, as has been shown, is a function of the temperature coefficient of viscosity. Thus μ appears to be a constant that describes both the compatibility and efficiency of a plasticizer.

Since the plasticization of a polymer may be considered as the mixing of two liquids, the thermodynamic relationships in ideal and non-ideal solutions are briefly reviewed, thereby correlating the meaning of μ as relating to plasticizer interaction and to osmotic pressure relationships.

THE THERMODYNAMIC RELATIONSHIPS IN IDEAL SOLUTIONS

The free energy of a system is related to the heat content and entropy according to the second law of thermodynamics by the equation

$$\Delta F = \Delta H - T \, \Delta S \tag{81}$$

where ΔF = total change in free energy,

ΔH = total change in heat content,

ΔS = total change in entropy,

T = absolute temperature.

In an ideal solution $\Delta H = 0$, that is, there is no heat of mixing, and the molecules are essentially of the same shape, size, and flexibility. The change in entropy of an ideal solution represents the increase in randomness over that corresponding to the two unmixed liquids:

$$\Delta S = -R(n_1 \ln N_1 + n_2 \ln N_2) \tag{82}$$

where R = gas constant,

n_1 = concentration of solvent A,

N_1 = mole fraction of solvent A,

n_2 = concentration of solvent B,

N_2 = mole fraction of solvent B,

ΔS = total change in entropy.

By combining equations 81 and 82, the following relationship is established:

$$\Delta F = RT(n_1 \ln N_1 + n_2 \ln N_2) \tag{83}$$

By differentiating with respect to one of the solvent components of the solution, the free energy relationship due to dilution by that component becomes, since

$$N_1 = \frac{n_1}{n_1 + n_2}$$

$$\frac{\partial F}{\partial n_1} = \overline{\Delta F}_1 = RT \ln N_1 \tag{84}$$

which in terms of fugacity relations, since

$$f_1 = f_1^0 N_1$$

$$\frac{\partial F}{\partial n_1} = \overline{\Delta F}_1 = RT \ln \frac{f_1}{f_1^0} \tag{85}$$

This equation shows that the decrease in free energy, when one mole of a component is placed in complete solution in another component, is equivalent to an ideal distillation process, in which the fugacity is the idealized vapor pressure, since the equation $PV = nRT$ deals only with ideal gases. The ratio of fugacities, f_1/f_1^0, is termed activity, a, and in non-ideal solutions, the activity coefficient, a/N, deviates from unity.

The partial molal free energy may be equated to other functions besides activity, for example,

$$\overline{\Delta F}_1 = RT \ln a_1 = -\theta(\overline{\Delta H}_{f,1}/T_{f,1}) = \theta(\overline{\Delta H}_b/T_b) = -\pi \overline{V}_1$$

$$= \overline{\Delta H}_1 + T\overline{\Delta S}_1 = \pi RT \ln (1 - N_2) \tag{86}$$

where $\theta =$ the temperature differential,

$\overline{\Delta H}_f =$ the partial molal heat of fusion of solvent A,

$T_f =$ the absolute temperature of fusion of solvent A,

$\overline{\Delta H}_b =$ the partial molal heat of evaporation of solution A,

$T_b =$ the absolute temperature of fusion of solution A,

$\pi =$ the osmotic pressure of solution A,

$\overline{V} =$ partial molal volume of solution A,

$\overline{\Delta H}_1 =$ partial molal heat of dilution of solution A,

$\overline{\Delta S}_1 =$ partial molal entropy of dilution of solution A.

If $\overline{\Delta F}_1$ is negative, the two liquids are miscible and, if $\overline{\Delta F}_1$ is positive, the liquids will separate out into two phases. At $\overline{\Delta F}_1 = 0$, the system is in equilibrium.

THERMODYNAMIC SYSTEMS INVOLVING POLYMER SOLUTIONS

Polymer solutions deviate greatly from the laws of ideal solutions. According to equation 86, the osmotic pressure equation in dilute solution becomes

$$\frac{\pi}{c} = \frac{RT}{M_2} \tag{87}$$

which is van't Hoff's law.

In the case of high polymers, π/c_2 is not constant, but varies with c approximately linearly. The shape and size of the polymer are distinctly different from those of the solvent, and in fact are many times larger than the solvent molecules. Because of the long chain and the flexible nature of the polymer, it can assume numerous configurations. On the basis of equation 86, and by using the $\overline{\Delta S}_1$ values to account for configurational entropy and neglecting $\overline{\Delta H}_1$ as small compared to $\overline{\Delta S}_1$,[130,131] the following relationship is derived:

$$\frac{\pi}{c_2} = (RT/M_2) + (RT/\overline{V}_1\rho_2{}^2)(1/2 - \mu)c_2$$

where π = osmotic pressure,
c_2 = concentration of solute,
R = gas constant,
T = absolute temperature,
$\overline{V}_1$ = partial molal volume of solvent,
ρ_2 = density of solvent,
μ = constant for a particular monomer-polymer system.

By plotting π/c against c, a straight line is obtained with the intercept RT/M_2 and the slope $(RT/\overline{V}_1\rho_2{}^2)(1 - \mu)c_2$. The slope determines the value of μ, which is a measure of the interaction of polymer and solvent. Since polymers can be considered as liquids, the mixing of plasticizer and polymer follows generally the thermodynamic principles of ordinary liquids. If $\overline{\Delta F}_1$ is negative, the polymer and plasticizer form a single phase. Since $\overline{\Delta H}_1$ is negative in case of a strong solvent, $\overline{\Delta F}_1$ is negative, and a single phase results. If the absorption of heat of mixing, $\overline{H}_1$, is greater than zero, $\overline{\Delta F}_1$ is positive at temperatures below which $\overline{\Delta H}_1 = T\,\overline{\Delta S}_1$, and the plasticizer will separate out from the swollen polymer.

THE TECHNICAL IMPORTANCE OF PLASTICIZERS

Plasticizers have two important functions:

1. They reduce the viscosity of the polymer at processing temperatures, thereby avoiding decomposition.
2. They serve to soften the polymers at normal temperatures to yield flexible or rubbery-type materials.

As an example, cellulose acetate of fairly high molecular weight lacks plasticity, and in certain fabrication processes it cannot be processed without decomposition. Likewise, it cannot be molded. When compounded with plasticizers, it can be satisfactorily molded, extruded, or calendered, and even used in melted form. The rigidity of the plasticized composition will depend on the amount of plasticizer, and rigid-to-flexible products are possible. Stiff and inflexible mixtures have a modulus of about 10^5 pounds per square inch. Polyvinyl chloride can be plasticized in a similar manner to give rigid compounds, but it finds greater application when plasticized to flexible compounds having a modulus of elasticity of about 10^2 to 10^3 pounds per square inch, that is, between 500 to 2000 pounds per square inch.

Reed [151] has listed some of the essential properties of technically important plasticizers in Table 24.

TABLE 24

IMPORTANT PROPERTIES OF PLASTICIZERS

Compatibility	Physiological Properties
	Odor
Ease of Incorporation	Taste
	Toxicity
Permanence	
Volatility	Economic Factors
Water extraction	Cost
Oil extraction	Availability
Migration	
Chemical stability	Special Factors
	Flammability
Plasticizing Efficiency	Electrical properties
At normal temperatures	Color
At subnormal temperatures	Effect on resin stability

THE PROPERTIES OF HIGHLY DISORDERED POLYMERS

The phenol-formaldehyde resins are typical crosslinked resins. Crosslinked resins are considered an extreme case of disordered polymers due to branching. Flory [27] and de Boer [152] calculated that if all the primary valence bonds are formed in the heat-hardened resin, the theoretical strength should be 4000 kilograms per square millimeter, whereas the observed is only about 1/500 of this value (8 kilograms per square millimeter). If the strength is derived from van der Waals' forces, the theoretical value is 35 kilograms per square millimeter. To explain this discrepancy, Houwink [153] proposed his *Lockerstellen theory*, which suggests that the theoretical strength is not obtained because of the presence of flaws in the molecular structure of the resin. He further suggests that these flaws occur because not all the possible methylene bridges between the phenolic groups are formed, and they are not formed because all the phenolic nuclei do not lie in the same plane. These unbridged gaps have a weakening on the strength of the macromolecules, since crosslinking is incomplete, as may be observed in phenol nuclei *a* and *b*, so that further condensation cannot occur. Also the presence of occluded reaction products, such as water, may give rise to holes or flaws.

$$\text{OH} \quad \text{—CH}_2\text{—} \quad \text{OH} \quad \text{—CH}_2\text{—} \quad a \quad \text{—CH}_2\text{—} \quad \text{OH} \quad \text{—CH}_2\text{—} \quad \text{OH}$$

$$\text{OH} \qquad \text{OH}$$

$$\dot{\text{C}}\text{H}_2 \qquad \qquad \dot{\text{C}}\text{H}_2\text{OH} \qquad \qquad \dot{\text{C}}\text{H}_2$$

$$\text{—CH}_2\text{—} \quad \text{OH} \quad \text{—CH}_2\text{—} \quad b \quad \text{—CH}_2\text{—} \quad \text{OH} \quad \text{—CH}_2\text{—}$$

$$\text{OH} \qquad \text{OH} \qquad \text{OH} \qquad \text{OH}$$

It is doubtful if the discrepancy between the theoretical and observed values is primarily due to the failure of formation of bonds or to occluded matter. Rather it appears most probable that the phenol-formaldehyde polymers are of spherocolloidal form which are built up of large regions and are attached to each other by van der Waals' forces. The analogy is to a heap of sponges (phenol-formaldehyde spherocolloids), each sponge being attached to its neighbor sponges by a special adhesive (van der Waals' forces).

This viewpoint differs somewhat from Houwink's suggestions. We have already seen that in linear addition polymers the rupture under stress is due to van der Waals' forces and not to the rupture of a carbon to carbon bond. This viewpoint is justified by the results of studies on insoluble and infusible polystyrene.[30] These products were obtained by copolymerizing styrene with a number of tetrafunctional molecules such as divinylbenzene, glycol dimethacrylate, methallyl methacrylate, etc. All these tetrafunctional monomers polymerize to insoluble infusible polymers whereas styrene by itself produces a linear thermoplastic resin. The copolymers of styrene, with increasing quantities of the tetrafunctional molecules, become increasingly more insoluble and infusible and likewise more rigid. However, the tensile strength and the impact strength correspondingly decrease to exceedingly low values. The insolubility and infusibility prove beyond a doubt that crosslinkages had occurred, and since the molecular weight had become exceedingly high it would be expected that the strength values would increase if the ruptures occur on the primary bonds. It is reasonable to assume that crosslinking produces molecules of such shape that the fit or packing is lowered. It follows that the Lockerstellen flaws also reside in the van der Waals' or secondary valence forces. It may be added at this point that whereas the vulcanization of rubber through sulfur produces profound changes in the polymer, the crosslinking sulfur bridges do not influence the strength values in a properly and carefully prepared rubber latex film.[154] This is so because the rubber molecule is originally linear and possesses, even after careful vulcanization, the inherent properties of a long-chain polymer. Crosslinking does not change its structure into that of a spherocolloid.

SWELLING AND SOLUTION AS A FUNCTION OF BRANCHING AND CROSSLINKING

Certain physical properties are directly attributable to the functionality of the reactants from which the polymer is derived. Monomers with a functionality of 2 produce chain polymers which are soluble and fusible; while monomers of functionality greater than 2 produce insoluble polymers. When a linear high polymer is placed in contact with a suitable solvent, swelling of the polymer occurs as the solvent is imbibed by the polymer. The swelling is in proportion to the amount of solvent present, and, if sufficient solvent is available, complete solution of the polymer occurs. If the polymer contains crosslinkages between the chains, the swelling is reduced in proportion to the number of crosslinkages. In most cases, if the crosslinkages are numerous, no swelling occurs. Often, as in the swelling of a divinylbenzene–styrene copolymer, the swelling may exceed a fiftyfold increase in volume. The most plausible explanation offered for this phenomenon, by Flory,[131-155] is that the absorption of the solvent is essentially an osmotic phenomenon which produces an expansion of the polymer structure. Equilibrium is obtained when the osmotic forces are equally balanced by the elastic forces associated with the expansion of the polymer network. The phenomenon of swelling may likewise be offered as evidence that macromolecules are not always present as free macromolecules but may exist as such only in dilute solutions. Complete insolubility may likewise be considered as primary evidence of crosslinking, though, in some cases, as in polyacrylonitrile, chemical verification should be obtained since other factors, such as high secondary valence bonding, may be responsible for its apparent insolubility.

Crosslinked polymers have been classified as net polymers and space polymers. They represent two basic concepts of the geometry of crosslinked polymers, which, in reality, represent the degree of crosslinking. If a linear polymer is pictured as a bundle of long chains, and only infrequent crosslinkages are distributed along the chain, a net polymer is obtained. The schematic drawing may be represented as:

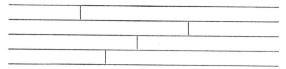

Such compositions are obtained in copolymers of a monomer with functionality of 2, with minor or very small portions of a monomer of functionality greater than 2. Such copolymers will swell and may even dissolve. As the ratio of monomer of functionality 4 is increased, or if a monomer of functionality 3 is used, crosslinkage becomes extensive, and the polymer chain no longer is linear but grows in space to a polymer similar to the sponge analogue of the phenol-formaldehyde resins. It is obvious that the transition from a linear to a net to a space polymer may be gradual, but in all cases the solubility decreases and the X-ray patterns become diffuse as the crosslinkages increase.

BRANCHING AND DISPROPORTIONATION

Staudinger [156] and Schulz [9] have discussed a process similar to cross-linking, and have called it branching. Branching and crosslinking have often been referred to as similar processes, whereas they are different not only as to cause but also as to effect on the solubility and other physical properties of the polymer. Branching refers to long-chain molecules that have an occasional side arm or branch attached to the linear chain which *does not bridge, or cross to, another chain.* Branching may occur in polymerization through a disproportionation reaction with resulting free valencies. The formation of branching may also be represented as occurring in the monomer stage. These processes are indicated in Schemes I and II.

Scheme I.   Branching Due to Initiation Reactions at Monomer Stage

In the thermal polymerization of vinyl compounds, such as styrene, the growth of the polymer is initiated by a bivalent radical of the monomer, for example, $CH_2=CHX \rightarrow -CH_2-CHX-$. Two of these radicals may react by disproportionation to give other radicals:

$$-CH_2CHX- + -CH_2CHX- \quad \begin{array}{l} \nearrow -CH_2CH_2X + \quad \diagdown CHCH-X \\[1em] \text{or} \\[1em] \searrow CH_3CHX + -CH_2-\overset{|}{\underset{|}{C}}-X \end{array}$$

Polymer growth then occurs by addition of monomer to these radicals producing branched structures, as, for example:

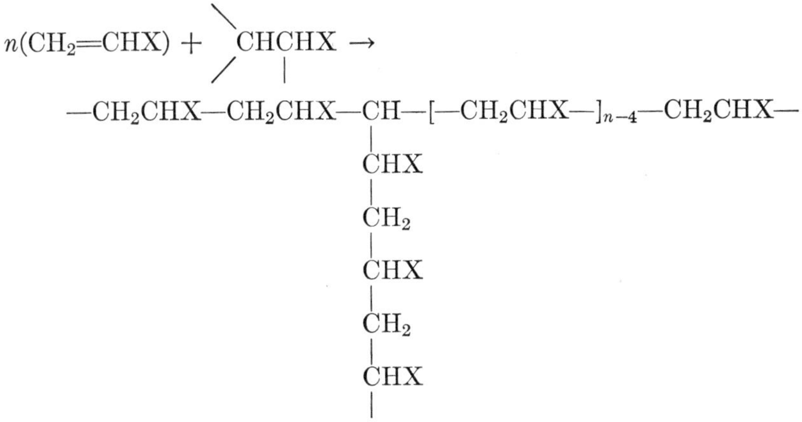

$$n(CH_2\!=\!CHX) + \overset{\diagdown}{\underset{\diagup}{C}}HCHX \rightarrow$$

$$-CH_2CHX-CH_2CHX-CH-[-CH_2CHX-]_{n-4}-CH_2CHX-$$
$$| $$
$$CHX$$
$$|$$
$$CH_2$$
$$|$$
$$CHX$$
$$|$$
$$CH_2$$
$$|$$
$$CHX$$
$$|$$

In a free radical catalyzed polymerization, such as in the peroxide catalysis of a vinyl monomer, the free radical, $R\cdot$, from the catalyst may react with a monomer to produce a center for branching, for example:

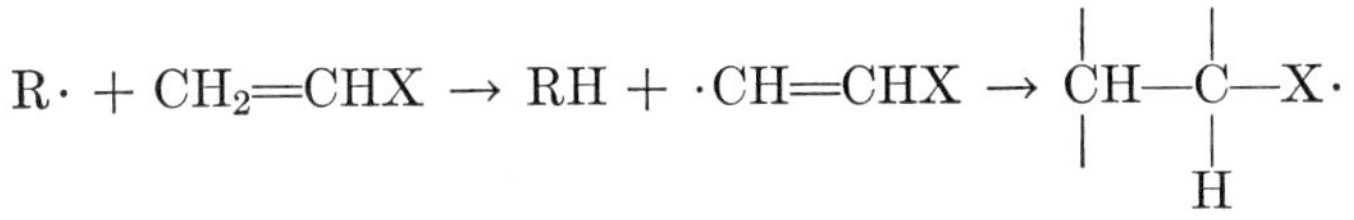

$$R\cdot + CH_2\!=\!CHX \rightarrow RH + \cdot CH\!=\!CHX \rightarrow \overset{|}{C}H\!-\!\overset{|}{\underset{H}{C}}\!-\!X\cdot$$

Scheme II.   Branching in the Polymer Stage

Branching in the polymer stage occurs by migration of the hydrogen atom in a polymer chain when an activated monomer or a free radical collides with the chain.

A thermally activated monomer may collide with a polymeric chain to remove a hydrogen atom, leaving an active center on the chain where branch growth can occur by further addition of monomer:

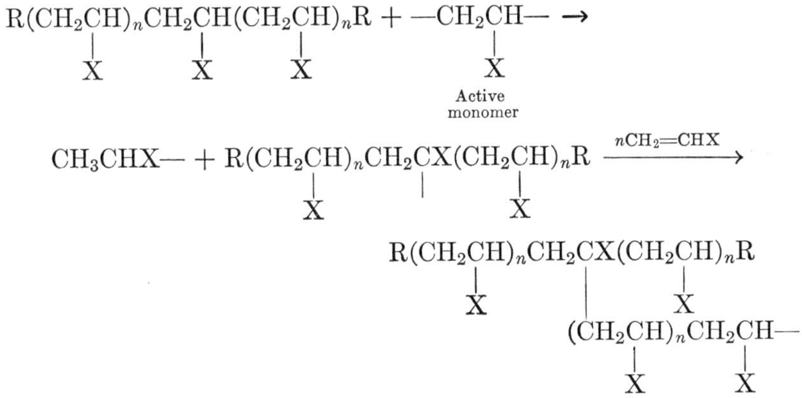

$$R(CH_2CH)_nCH_2CH(CH_2CH)_nR + -CH_2CH- \rightarrow$$
$$\underset{X}{|} \quad \underset{X}{|} \quad \underset{X}{|} \quad \underset{\underset{\text{monomer}}{\text{Active}}}{\underset{X}{|}}$$

$$CH_3CHX- + R(CH_2CH)_nCH_2CX(CH_2CH)_nR \xrightarrow{\; nCH_2=CHX \;}$$
$$\underset{X}{|} \qquad\qquad \underset{X}{|}$$

$$R(CH_2CH)_nCH_2CX(CH_2CH)_nR$$
$$\underset{X}{|} \qquad | \qquad \underset{X}{|}$$
$$(CH_2CH)_nCH_2CH-$$
$$\underset{X}{|} \qquad \underset{X}{|}$$

A free radical, $R\cdot$, from the catalyst, may undergo a chain transfer by the removal of a hydrogen from the polymer chain, producing a polymer radical. Branching occurs by further addition of monomer:

$$R\cdot + R'(CH_2CH)_nCH_2CH(CH_2CH)_nR \rightarrow$$
$$\qquad\qquad\quad | \qquad\quad | \qquad\quad |$$
$$\qquad\qquad\quad X \qquad\quad X \qquad\quad X$$

$$RH + R(CH_2CH)_nCH_2CX(CH_2CH)_nR' \xrightarrow{nCH_2=CHX}$$
$$\qquad\qquad | \qquad\qquad\quad | \qquad\qquad |$$
$$\qquad\qquad X \qquad\qquad\quad\quad X$$

$$R'(CH_2CH)_nCH_2CX(CH_2CH)_nR'$$
$$\qquad\qquad | \qquad\qquad\quad | \qquad\qquad |$$
$$\qquad\qquad X \qquad\qquad\quad\quad X$$
$$\qquad\qquad\qquad\qquad\quad (CH_2CHX)_n{-}$$

Instead of free radical from the catalyst, the radical may even be the polymer radical of a growing chain, $R(CH_2CHX)_n\cdot$, in which case it behaves similarly to the radical $R\cdot$ of the preceding example.

By either scheme, the polymer chain acquires branches that may be represented schematically as:

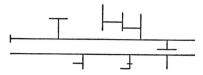

Branching does not produce insolubility, but as the degree of branching increases, the rate, but not the equilibrium, of solubility is affected. Extensive branching produces particles approaching spherical shapes, by changing the axis ratio, and the polymers therefore have viscosities different from those of a linear unbranched polymer of the same molecular weight. In fact, the viscosities will be lower, the higher the branching. The schematic picture of branching indicates that a linear polymer having one or two crosslinks per chain may behave similarly to a branched polymer with the same chain length.

This relation of polymer shape to polyfunctionality is summarized in Figure 65.

The changes in structure and properties of a polymer as it progresses from a linear to a space polymer as a result of increased functionality may be schematically represented as in Figure 66.

Polyfunctional molecule
Cyclic compounds
Chain polymers
Linear
Crosslinked
Unbranched
Branched
Net
Space

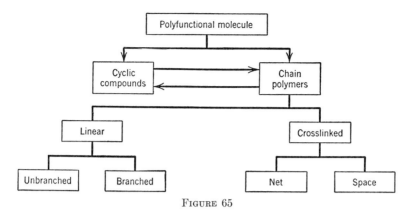

FIGURE 65

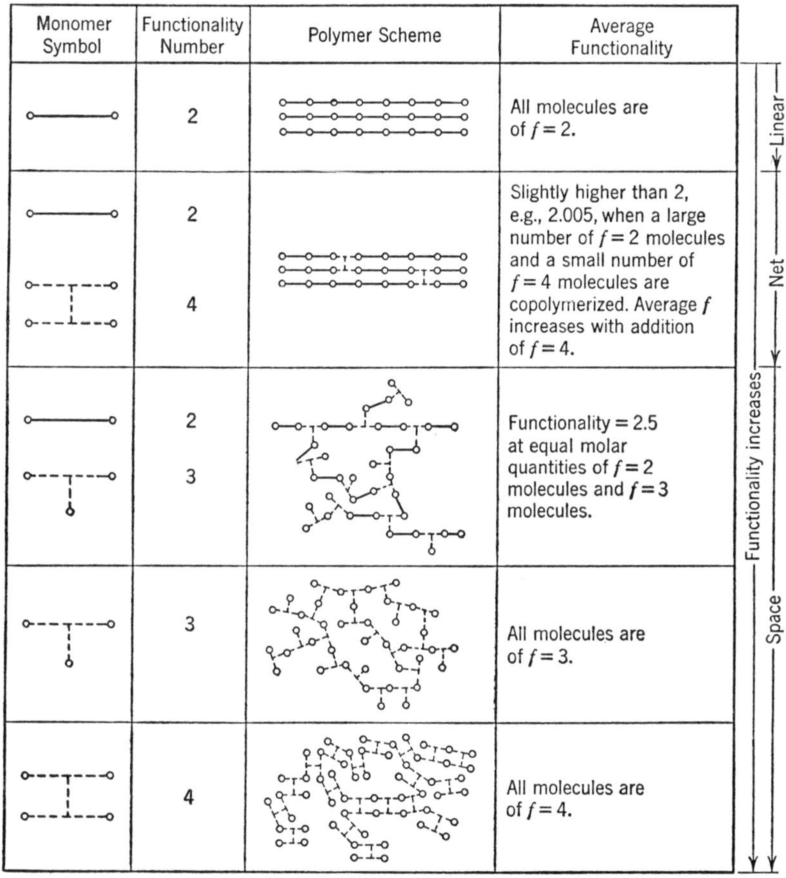

Monomer Symbol
Functionality Number
Polymer Scheme
Average Functionality
2
All molecules are of f = 2.
2
4
Slightly higher than 2, e.g., 2.005, when a large number of f = 2 molecules and a small number of f = 4 molecules are copolymerized. Average f increases with addition of f = 4.
2
3
Functionality = 2.5 at equal molar quantities of f = 2 molecules and f = 3 molecules.
3
All molecules are of f = 3.
4
All molecules are of f = 4.
Linear
Net
Space
Functionality increases

FIGURE 66

CONTRAST OF PROPERTIES OF LINEAR AND
CROSSLINKED POLYMERS

The properties and behavior of linear and crosslinked chains may be contrasted as follows:

LINEAR

Branched and Unbranched

1. Unlimited faculty for swelling and the eventual formation of homogeneous solutions. Every very high polymer is capable of unlimited swelling, and although the rate of solubility is low, the polymers are still capable of being dissolved.

2. In very dilute solutions, as for example in the limiting case of extreme dilution, the dispersed molecules behave as independent kinetic units and exhibit the property of normal viscosity. Solutions of these polymers may be used in the preparation of films or filaments.

3. These polymers have a temperature zone whose sharpness is more or less defined and depends on its chemical and physical nature, for example, the type of atoms in the chain, their molecular weight, cohesive forces, etc. Above this temperature zone the polymer behaves as a viscous fluid, and, below it, the behavior corresponds to an amorphous or semicrystalline solid. Most of these polymers soften without decomposition, and the softening zone is reproducible. Decomposition does occur in some polymers having unstable group in the chain, or when secondary forces along the chain are very high, and decomposition occurs before softening. Polyacrylonitrile, polyvinyl alcohol, certain proteins, and cellulose belong to this class.

4. If not normally so, at least when stretched or otherwise worked as by rolling or cold drawing, many linear

CROSSLINKED

Net and Space

1. These polymers show a limited capacity for swelling, but they do not dissolve. The degree of swelling decreases with crosslinking. Excellent examples are the divinylbenzene–styrene copolymers, glyceryl phthalate, rubber vulcanized to different degrees, etc. Swelling as a function of crosslinking is given [157] in Figure 67.

2. These polymers do not dissolve, but in some cases they may swell. Where solution apparently occurs, it has been accomplished through the destruction of primary chemical bonds, as, for example, insoluble polydiallyl phthalate may be hydrolyzed by concentrated hydrochloric acid.

3. These polymers have no softening zone corresponding to those of the linear polymers since they never really melt. They become soft at very high temperature, at which they usually decompose. If they have a large number of crosslinkages they may not even soften but decompose directly when the temperature becomes sufficiently high. Usually such polymers are brittle. However, they have improved heat distortion values [30] and find wide application in industrial use, and higher crosslinkages show less distortion under load, as in Figure 68.

4. As the number of crosslinkages increase, the sharp X-ray diagrams of linear polymers begin to become

polymers give X-ray crystal diagrams indicating an oriented structure, the intensity of orientation increasing to a maximum with the degree of stretching. Many polymers show liquid diagrams before stretching. If the linear or branch disorder is high, the possibility of orientation decreases.

5. These polymers readily undergo chemical reactions in the dissolved or swollen state without appreciably changing the average chain size. As a rule these reactions are reversible, and the derivatives will be given an X-ray pattern similar to the parent material. Typical examples are (a) the conversion of cellulose to cellulose acetate and its reconversion to cellulose, (b) the reversible conversion of polyvinyl alcohol to acetate, (c) the hydrogenation of polystyrene, etc.

The polymer in some cases does not have to be in a dissolved or swollen state. Polyvinyl alcohol and paraformaldehyde can be made to react in an aliphatic hydrocarbon in which neither the reacting materials nor the product of reaction is soluble.[30]

indistinct. When the crosslinkages are sufficiently numerous only indistinct amorphous ring diagrams are obtained. Working by rolling or stretching does not produce orientation.

5. As crosslinkages increase, permutoid reactivity decreases; and if the crosslinkage is sufficiently high, reactivity eventually disappears. This may be readily observed as the degree of esterification of copolymers of acrylic acid and divinylbenzene is studied. The esterification reactivity decreases with an increase in the ratio of divinylbenzene to acrylic acid. A more startling example is found in attempts to react polymer of polyvinyl alcohol and maleic anhydride with paraform in hexane. Formalization almost completely disappears when more than one hydroxyl in ten of the polyvinyl alcohol is crosslinked.[30]

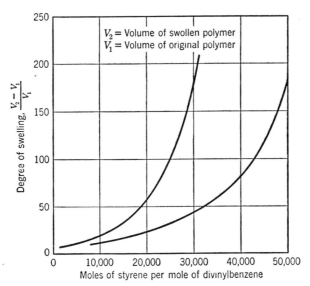

FIGURE 67.   Effect of crosslinkages on swelling.[157]

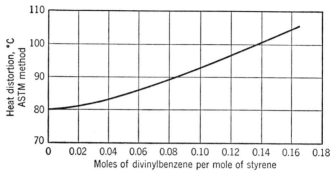

FIGURE 68.   Effect of crosslinkages on heat resistance.[30]

REFERENCES

1. L. H. Cragg and H. Hammerschlag, *Chem. Revs.*, **39**, 82 (1946).
2. S. D. Douglas and W. N. Stoops, *Ind. Eng. Chem.*, **28**, 1152 (1936).
3. J. M. Grim, private communication, Koppers Senior Fellow, Mellon Institute.
4. R. Signer and R. Gross, *Helv. Chim. Acta*, **17**, 59 (1934).
5. R. Signer and R. Gross, *Helv. Chim. Acta*, **17**, 335 (1934).
6. R. Signer and R. Gross, *Helv. Chim. Acta*, **17**, 726 (1934).
7. G. V. Schulz, *Z. physik. Chem.*, **B43**, 25 (1939).
8. G. V. Schulz, A. Dinglinger, and E. Husemann, *Z. physik. Chem.*, **B43**, 385 (1939).
9. G. V. Schulz, *Z. physik. Chem.*, **B44**, 227 (1939).
10. G. V. Schulz, *Z. physik. Chem.*, **B47**, 155 (1940).
11. G. V. Schulz and A. Dinglinger, *Z. physik. Chem.*, **B43**, 47 (1939).
12. W. H. Carothers, *Trans. Faraday Soc.*, **32**, 39 (1936).
13. P. J. Flory, *J. Am. Chem. Soc.*, **62**, 1561 (1940).
14. P. J. Flory, *J. Am. Chem. Soc.*, **58**, 1877 (1936).
15. P. J. Flory, *J. Am. Chem. Soc.*, **61**, 3334 (1939).
16. P. J. Flory, *J. Am. Chem. Soc.*, **62**, 1057 (1940).
17. P. J. Flory, *J. Am. Chem. Soc.*, **62**, 1064 (1940).
18. P. J. Flory, *J. Am. Chem. Soc.*, **62**, 2255 (1940).
19. P. J. Flory, *J. Am. Chem. Soc.*, **62**, 2261 (1940).
20. W. H. Carothers, *Chem. Revs.*, **8**, 353–426 (1931).
21. W. D. Lansing and E. O. Kraemer, *J. Am. Chem. Soc.*, **57**, 1369 (1935).
22. P. J. Flory, *J. Am. Chem. Soc.*, **65**, 372 (1943).
23. P. J. Flory, *J. Am. Chem. Soc.*, **58**, 1881 (1936).
24. G. V. Schulz, *Z. physik. Chem.*, **B30**, 379 (1935).
25. G. V. Schulz, *Z. physik. Chem.*, **B32**, 27 (1936).
26. G. V. Schulz, *Z. physik. Chem.*, **B40**, 319 (1938).
27. P. J. Flory, *J. Am. Chem. Soc.*, **63**, 3083 (1941).
28. R. H. Kienle, P. A. van der Meulen, and F. E. Petke, *J. Am. Chem. Soc.*, **61**, 2258 (1939).
29. C. Walling, *J. Am. Chem. Soc.*, **67**, 441–447 (1945).
30. G. F. D'Alelio, unpublished results.
31. G. F. D'Alelio, U. S. Patent 2,363,836.

32. J. W. Breitenbach and W. Thury, *Experientia*, **3**, 281–282 (1947).
33. A. M. Sookne and M. Harris, *Ind. Eng. Chem.*, **37**, 478–482 (1945).
34. P. J. Flory, *J. Am. Chem. Soc.*, **67**, 2048–2050 (1945).
35. C. W. Bunn, *Research*, **I**, No. 14, 632 (1948).
36. W. H. Keesom, *Physik. Z.*, **22**, 129 (1921).
37. W. H. Keesom, *Physik. Z.*, **23**, 225 (1922).
38. P. Debye, *Physik. Z.*, **21**, 178 (1920).
39. P. Debye, *Physik. Z.*, **22**, 302 (1921).
40. F. London and R. Eisenschitz, *Z. Physik*, **60**, 520 (1930).
41. J. C. Slater and J. G. Kirkwood, *Phys. Rev.*, **37** (2nd Ser.), 682 (1931).
42. M. Dunkel, *Z. physik. Chem.*, **A138**, 42 (1928).
43. M. Dunkel and K. L. Wolf, *Müller-Pouillets Lehrbuch der Physik*, Vol. IV, 3rd part, pp. 579–683.
44. L. Pauling, L. O. Brockway, and J. Y. Beach, *J. Am. Chem. Soc.*, **57**, 2705 (1935).
45. L. Pauling, H. D. Springall, and K. J. Palmer, *J. Am. Chem. Soc.*, **61**, 927 (1939).
46. L. O. Brockway, J. Y. Beach, and L. Pauling, *J. Am. Chem. Soc.*, **57**, 2693 (1935).
47. C. W. Bunn, *Trans. Faraday Soc.*, **35**, 482 (1939).
48. M. L. Huggins, *Rubber Chem. and Technol.*, **18**, 763–771 (1945).
49. W. O. Baker and C. S. Fuller, *J. Am. Chem. Soc.*, **65**, 1120 (1943).
50. C. S. Marvel, *Frontiers of Chemistry*, R. E. Burk, Editor, Vol. 1, p. 219, Interscience Publishers, New York, 1943.
51. W. M. D. Bryant, *J. Polymer Sci.*, **2**, 547 (1947).
52. M. L. Huggins, *J. Am. Chem. Soc.*, **66**, 1991 (1944).
53. S. T. Gross, C. E. Schildknecht, and O. A. Zoss, *Isomerism in Vinyl Polymers*, Division of Cellulose Chemistry, 112th meeting of A.C.S., New York, 1947.
54. J. R. Katz, *Chem.-Ztg.*, **49**, 353 (1925).
55. C. S. Fuller and C. J. Frosch, *J. Phys. Chem.*, **43**, 323 (1939).
56. C. S. Fuller and C. L. Erickson, *J. Am. Chem. Soc.*, **59**, 344 (1937).
57. H. Mark, W. O. Baker, and C. S. Fuller, *Advancing Fronts in Chemistry*, edited by S. B. Twiss, Vol. 1, p. 12, Reinhold Publishing Corp., New York, 1945.
58. C. W. Bunn, *Proc. Roy. Soc. (London)*, **A180**, 40, 67, 82 (1942).
59. C. S. Fuller, *Chem. Revs.*, **26**, 143 (1940).
60. R. C. L. Mooney, *J. Am. Chem. Soc.*, **63**, 2828 (1941).
61. C. W. Bunn, *Nature*, **161**, 929 (1948).
62. C. S. Fuller, C. J. Frosch, and N. R. Pape, *J. Am. Chem. Soc.*, **62**, 1905 (1940).
63. M. L. Huggins, *J. Chem. Phys.*, **13**, 37–42 (1945).
64. L. Misch and L. Picken, *Z. physik. Chem.*, **B36**, 398 (1937).
65. J. Natta and R. Rigamonti, *Atti. accad. sci. Lincei*, **24**, 381 (1936).
66. A. J. Wildschut, *J. Appl. Phys.*, **17**, 51–60 (1946).
67. W. O. Baker, *Advancing Fronts in Chemistry*, edited by S. B. Twiss, Vol. 1, p. 143, Reinhold Publishing Corp., New York, 1945.
68. E. Jenckel, *Kolloid Z.*, **100**, 163 (1942).
69. R. F. Clash, Jr., and L. M. Rynkiewicz, *Ind. Eng. Chem.*, **36**, 279 (1944).
70. F. C. Hahn, M. L. Macht, and D. A. Fletcher, *Ind. Eng. Chem.*, **37**, 526 (1945).
71. E. Jenckel and E. Braucker, *Z. physik. Chem.*, **A185**, 465 (1940).
72. E. Jenckel, *Z. physik. Chem.*, **A190**, 24 (1941).
73. F. E. Wiley, *Ind. Eng. Chem.*, **34**, 1052 (1942).
74. R. F. Boyer and R. S. Spencer, *J. Applied Phys.*, **15**, 398 (1944).
75. W. Patnode and W. J. Scheiber, *J. Am. Chem. Soc.*, **61**, 3449 (1939).
76. J. D. Ferry and G. S. Parks, *J. Chem. Phys.*, **4**, 70 (1936).

77. R. F. Boyer and R. S. Spencer, *J. Applied Phys.*, **16**, 594 (1945).

78. R. F. Boyer and R. S. Spencer, *Advances in Colloid Science*, edited by H. Mark and G. S. Whitby, Vol. II, Interscience Publishers, New York, 1946.

79. R. F. Boyer and R. S Spencer, *J. Polymer Sci.*, **2**, 159 (1947).

80. W. E. Hanford and R. M. Joyce, *J. Am. Chem. Soc.*, **68**, 2082 (1946).

81. A. H. Scott, *J. Research Natl. Bur. Standards*, **14**, 99 (1935).

82. K. H. Meyer and C. Ferri, *Helv. Chim. Acta*, **18**, 570 (1935).

83. A. Schallamach, *Proc. Phys. Soc.* (London), **53**, 214 (1941).

84. N. Bekkedahl, *J. Research Natl. Bur. Standards*, **13**, 411 (1934).

85. K. Überreiter, *Angew. Chem.*, **53**, 247 (1940).

86. H. Eyring, *J. Chem. Phys.*, **4**, 283 (1936).

87. H. Mark, *Chem. Revs.*, **25**, 121 (1939).

88. W. Kauzmann and H. Eyring, *J. Am. Chem. Soc.*, **62**, 3113 (1940).

89. R. M. Fuoss, *J. Am. Chem. Soc.*, **63**, 369 (1941).

90. T. Alfrey, Jr., and H. Mark, *Rubber Chem. and Technol.*, **14**, 525 (1941).

91. R. F. Tuckett, *Trans. Faraday Soc.*, **38**, 310 (1942).

92. C. S. Fuller, W. O. Baker, and N. R. Pape, *J. Am. Chem. Soc.*, **62**, 3275 (1940).

93. P. J. Flory, *J. Phys. Chem.*, **46**, 870 (1942).

94. R. F. Boyer and R. S. Spencer, *Advances in Colloid Science*, edited by H. Mark and G. S. Whitby, Vol. II, p. 8, Interscience Publishers, New York, 1946.

95. S. Kimura and N. Namikawa, *J. Soc. Chem. Ind.* (Japan), **32**, 196 (1929).

96. A. T. McPherson and A. D. Cummings, *J. Research Natl. Bur. Standards*, **14**, 553 (1935).

97. H. F. Church and H. A. Daynes, *Rubber Chem. and Technol.*, **10**, 64 (1937).

98. H. F. Church and H. A. Daynes, *Rubber Chem. and Technol.*, **12**, 826 (1939).

99. K. Überreiter, *Kolloid Z.*, **102**, 272 (1943).

100. R. F. Boyer and R. S. Spencer, *Advances in Colloid Science*, edited by H. Mark and G. S. Whitby, Vol. II, p. 24, Interscience Publishers, New York, 1946.

101. F. H. Müller, *Kolloid Z.*, **95**, 138 (1941).

102. R. F. Boyer and R. S. Spencer, *Advances in Colloid Science*, edited by H. Mark and G. S. Whitby, Vol. II, p. 22, Interscience Publishers, New York, 1946.

103. T. Alfrey, Jr., G. Goldfinger, and H. Mark, *J. Applied Phys.*, **14**, 700 (1943).

104. W. T. Richards, *J. Chem. Phys.*, **4**, 449 (1936).

105. R. F. Boyer and R. S. Spencer, *J. Applied Phys.*, **16**, 594 (1945).

106. R. S. Spencer and R. F. Boyer, *J. Applied Phys.*, **17**, 398 (1946).

107. R. F. Boyer and R. S. Spencer, *Advances in Colloid Science*, edited by H. Mark and G. S. Whitby, Vol. II, p. 27, Interscience Publishers, New York, 1946.

108. K. Überreiter, *Z. physik. Chem.*, **B48**, 197 (1941).

109. H. L. Fisher, *Ind. Eng. Chem.*, **31**, 941 (1939).

110. H. L. Trumbull, *Ind. Eng. Chem.*, **34**, 1328 (1942).

111. E. B. Paul, A. L. Blakers, and R. W. Watson, *Can. J. Research*, **21B**, 219 (1943).

112. A. R. Kemp and H. Peters, *India Rubber World*, **110**, 639 (1944).

113. D. D. Eley, *Trans. Faraday Soc.*, **38**, 299 (1942).

114. M. Ruhemann and F. Simon, *Z. physik. Chem.*, **A138**, 1 (1928).

115. N. Bekkedahl and R. B. Scott, *J. Research Natl. Bur. Standards*, **29**, 87 (1942).

116. V. L. Simril, *J. Polymer Sci.*, **2**, 144 (1947).

117. H. Mark, *Ind. Eng. Chem.*, **34**, 1343 (1942).

118. H. Mark, *Am. Scientist*, **31**, 97 (1943).

119. M. L. Selker, G. G. Winspear, and A. R. Kemp, *Ind. Eng. Chem.*, **34**, 157 (1942).

120. R. F. Clash, Jr., and R. M. Berg, *Ind. Eng. Chem.*, **34**, 1218 (1942).

121. J. M. Davies, R. F. Miller, and W. F. Busse, *J. Am. Chem. Soc.*, **63**, 361 (1941).
122. D. J. Mead, R. L. Tichenor, and R. M. Fuoss, *J. Am. Chem. Soc.*, **64**, 283 (1942).
123. F. Wurstlin, *Kolloid Z.*, **105**, 9 (1943).
124. R. F. Clash, Jr., and R. M. Berg, *Symposium on Plastics*, pp. 54–56, Philadelphia District Meeting A.S.T.M., 1944.
125. E. Jenckel and K. Überreiter, *Z. physik. Chem.*, **A182**, 361 (1938).
126. E. M. Frith, *Trans. Faraday Soc.*, **41**, 90 (1945).
127. E. M. Frith and R. F. Tuckett, *Nature*, **155**, 164 (1945).
128. R. F. Boyer and R. S. Spencer, *J. Polymer Sci.*, **2**, 157 (1947).
129. M. L. Huggins, *Ann. N. Y. Acad. Sci.*, **44**, 431 (1943).
130. M. L. Huggins, *Ann. N. Y. Acad. Sci.*, **43**, 1 (1942).
131. P. J. Flory, *J. Chem. Phys.*, **10**, 51 (1942).
132. R. F. Tuckett, *Trans. Faraday Soc.*, **40**, 448 (1944).
133. W. Kauzmann, *Rev. Modern Phys.*, **14**, 34 (1942).
134. G. S. Parks and W. A. Gilkey, *J. Phys. Chem.*, **33**, 1428 (1929).
135. F. Wurstlin, *Kolloid Z.*, **105**, 15 (1943).
136. A. P. Aleksandrov and Ya S. Lazurkin, *Compt. rend. acad. sci.* (URSS), **43**, 376 (1944).
137. S. N. Zhurkov, *Compt. rend. acad. sci.* (URSS), **47**, 475 (1945).
138. S. N. Zhurkov and R. I. Lerman, *Compt. rend. acad. sci.* (URSS), **47**, 106 (1945).
139. K. Leilich, *Kolloid Z.*, **99**, 107 (1942).
140. H. Jones, *Trans. Inst. Rubber Ind.*, **21**, 298 (1945–1946).
141. L. Grunberg and A. H. Nissan, *Nature*, **154**, 146 (1944).
142. R. H. Ewell and H. Eyring, *J. Chem. Phys.*, **5**, 726 (1937).
143. J. N. Friend, *Trans. Faraday Soc.*, **31**, 542 (1935).
144. R. F. Boyer and R. S. Spencer, *J. Polymer Sci.*, **2**, 171 (1947).
145. *Symposium on Plastics*, p. 54, Philadelphia District Meeting A.S.T.M., 1944.
146. M. C. Reed, *Ind. Eng. Chem.*, **35**, 896 (1943).
147. J. J. Russell, *Ind. Eng. Chem.*, **32**, 509 (1940).
148. P. Doty and H. S. Zable, *J. Polymer Sci.*, **1**, 90 (1946).
149. M. L. Huggins, *J. Am. Chem. Soc.*, **64**, 1715 (1942).
150. R. F. Boyer and R. S. Spencer, *J. Polymer Sci.*, **2**, 172 (1947).
151. M. C. Reed, *J. Polymer Sci.*, **2**, 116 (1947).
152. J. H. de Boer, *Trans. Faraday Soc.*, **32**, 10 (1936).
153. R. Houwink, *Trans. Faraday Soc.*, **32**, 128 (1936).
154. S. S. Kistler, *Advancing Fronts in Chemistry*, Vol. 1, p. 19, edited by S. B. Twiss, Reinhold Publishing Corp., New York, 1945.
155. P. J. Flory, *J. Chem. Phys.*, **9**, 660 (1941).
156. H. Staudinger and G. V. Schulz, *Ber.*, **68**, 2320 (1935).
157. H. Staudinger and E. Huseman, *Ber.*, **68**, 1618 (1935).

CHAPTER 5

Polyreactions

High polymers are prepared only through molecules that are polyfunctional, and the polymerization reactions of these polyfunctional molecules are known as polyreactions. The implied converse, that all polyfunctional molecules will produce high polymers, is not true since polyfunctional molecules may react in either of two ways:

1. Intramolecularly (within itself).
2. Intermolecularly (between different molecules).

In Chapter 4 it was shown that monomers could produce either chains or cyclic compounds. Such a monomer is the polyfunctional molecule aminocaproic acid, $NH_2(CH_2)_5COOH$, which can undergo both intramolecular and intermolecular reactions.

In *intramolecular reaction* the product is a seven-membered ring compound, caprolactam:

Aminocaproic acid	Caprolactam

In *intermolecular reaction,* intermolecular at all stages, the reaction product is an open chain of linear structure:

$$nNH_2(CH_2)_5COOH \rightarrow$$

$$NH_2(CH_2)_5CO[NH(CH_2)_5CO]_{n-4}—NH(CH_2)_5CONH(CH_2)_5CONH(CH_2)_5COOH + (n-1)H_2O$$

Such an intermolecular reaction product may be terminated by an intramolecular reaction, since the polymer chain is considered to be a single polyfunctional molecule, as, for example:

$$NH(CH_2)_5CO[NH(CH_2)_5CO]_{n-4}—NH(CH_2)_5CONH(CH_2)_5CONH(CH_2)_5CO$$

Such cases, however, are not common.

170

RING FORMATION FROM POLYFUNCTIONAL MOLECULES.
THE STABILITY OF RING COMPOUNDS

In condensation reactions, if a five- or a six-membered ring can form, that reaction leads to the formation of ring compounds, even if not exclusively to the formation of a chain. The structure of the reacting molecule or molecules and stereochemical factors control the formation of rings or chains, and where five- or six-membered rings have been excluded by the nature of the reactants, chain reaction occurs intermolecularly.[1]

That rings containing five or six atoms may exist in strainless and non-planar forms was suggested originally by Sachse in 1890, and later by Mohr.[2] Baeyer's strain theory had assumed that the atoms of the chain were all in the same plane. Mohr postulated that decahydronaphthalene (decalin) could exist in *cis* and *trans* forms because of strainless non-planar rings. His predictions were verified by the isolation of stable *cis* and *trans* decalin, shown in Figure 1:

	Cis decalin	*Trans* decalin
M. p., °C	−43.3	−31.5
B. p., °C	194.	185.
Specific gravity, D_4^{20}	0.895	0.870
Heat of combustion, kg/cal	1499.9	1495.2

FIGURE 1

If a chain model of a bifunctional molecule, such as a hydroxy or amino acid having five or six atoms in the chain, is rotated, the end atoms collide and a five- or six-membered ring is obtained. If a chain containing more than six atoms is rotated, the ends can be brought together to form a strainless non-polar ring. The formation is arbitrary, however, and hence not as stable. Hill and Carothers[3] imply a probability factor for the direct formation of a ring structure from such a polyfunctional molecule, for, since the chain can assume a multiplicity of shapes, the particular configurations requisite for the ring closure are relatively few. If such a molecule is placed under conditions of reaction, it is most probable that the reactive group of one molecule will react with the complementary reactive group of another molecule, rather than by itself, and that intermolecular rather than intramolecular products result.

While the Mohr theory explains the existence of large ring molecules, for example, 12, 13, 14, 15, 16 atoms, it does not mean that large rings may be made directly from polyfunctional molecules with the same number of atoms. Carothers' researches have shown that, as a rule, polyfunctional molecules that might lead to large rings almost invariably lead to linear polymers. The large-membered ester rings were usually prepared in very low yields by Ruzicka and Stoll,[4] using the method of Baeyer and Villiger,[5] which consisted of the oxidation of cyclic ketones by Caro's acid:

$$
\begin{array}{ccc}
\mathrm{CH_2\!-\!\!-C\!=\!O} & & \mathrm{CH_2\!-\!\!-C}\!\!\!\diagup^{\displaystyle O} \\
\ \ \ |\qquad\quad | & \xrightarrow{[0]} & \ \ \ \ |\qquad\qquad\diagdown_{\displaystyle O} \\
\mathrm{(CH_2)}_n\!-\!\!\mathrm{CH_2} & & \mathrm{(CH_2)}_n\!-\!\!\mathrm{CH_2}\diagup
\end{array}
$$

$$n = 10\ \text{to}\ 14$$

The starting ketones are obtained by heating the thorium salts of the dibasic acids to 400 to 500 C. The fact that these cyclic esters could not be prepared directly from hydroxy acids led Carothers to believe that the corresponding ketones were not the primary products of reaction of the thorium dicarboxylic salts, but that linear ketones were the primary product and that the cyclic ketones were the result of the depolymerization of the linear ketones.[6] He verified this concept in the preparation of a large number of monomeric and dimeric rings by the depolymerization of linear polymers. The fact that linear polymers may be converted to cyclic monomers or oligomers would indicate that these formations may be reversible, that is, the cyclic compounds may be capable of forming linear compounds. As shall be noted, the conversion of cyclic compounds depends not only on the nature of the compound but also on the type of compound. This may be exemplified by stating that some six-membered rings may be made to polymerize while others are sufficiently stable that the corresponding linear compound is not known.

Ruggli[7] has shown that dilution favors ring formation, that is, intramolecular reaction. Carothers applied the principles of dilution to his studies in preparing large rings from reactants that could produce inter- or intramolecular reaction products and found that if a five- or a six-membered ring was excluded, intermolecular or chain products were obtained.

In the preparation of large rings from polyfunctional molecules, Ruzicka noted a very interesting relationship between the yield and the size of the rings. Calcium oxide is used with the dicarboxylic acid for the lower members of the series, whereas thorium or cerium oxide gives better results with the higher dicarboxylic acids. The cyclization of the dicarboxylic acid to a ketone is equivalent to a dehydration and decarboxylation reaction. In fact, five- and six-membered cyclic ketones may be prepared in high yield by treatment of the dicarboxylic acid with acetic anhydride.

$$\begin{array}{c} COOH \\ / \\ (CH_2)_4 \\ \diagdown \\ COOH \end{array} \xrightarrow{(CH_3CO)_2O} \begin{array}{c} CH_2 \\ / \diagdown \\ CH_2 \quad CO \\ | \qquad | \\ CH_2\!\!-\!\!-CH_2 \end{array} + CO_2 + H_2O$$

The metal oxide method gives yields of 75 to 80 per cent for five- and six-membered rings, becoming less for the seven-membered and only 20 per cent for the eight-membered ketone rings. The yield of ketone in the C_9 to C_{13} series is about 0.5 per cent, and for the C_{13} to C_{18} series, the yield increases again to 5 per cent and then drops again to about 2 per cent.

Spanagel and Carothers [8] observed the dependence of easy ring formation on ring size for cyclic esters and cyclic anhydrides. The studies are summarized in Figure 2.

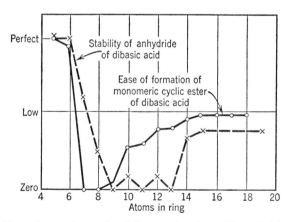

FIGURE 2. Ease of formation and stability vs. ring size. (Reprinted by permission from the authors and the *Journal of the American Chemical Society*.)

Five- and six-membered rings are vertically strainless, and the difficulty with which rings of less than five atoms are formed is understood readily by the strain imposed on the valency angles. The strain in larger rings may be relieved according to the Sachse-Mohr concept, that is, the assumption of non-planar form. In large rings that contain substituent groups, the non-planar form may be prevented by steric interferences.

CONDENSATION POLYREACTIONS. RINGS AND POLYMERS

The hydroxy acids represent polyfunctional molecules that may react intermolecularly as well as intramolecularly. These acids are represented generally by the formula $HO(CR_2)_nCOOH$ and are well suited to show how ring formation occurs as the value of n is increased.

The Reactions of α-Hydroxy Acids

The simplest of the hydroxy acids is glycolic acid, $HOCH_2COOH$. The self-esterification of glycolic acid at 100 to 150 C produces either a linear polymer or a cyclic compound: [9]

$$n HOCH_2COOH \xrightarrow[\text{reaction}]{\text{intermolecular}} H[OCH_2CO]_n OH + (n-1)H_2O$$
$$\underset{\text{Polyglycolide}}{}$$

$$2HOCH_2COOH \xrightarrow[\text{reaction}]{\text{intermolecular}}$$

$$HOCH_2COOCH_2COOH \xrightarrow[\text{reaction}]{\text{intramolecular}} \begin{array}{c} O-CH_2CO \\ | \qquad | \\ OC-CH_2O \end{array}$$

Glycolyl glycolic acid   Diglycolide

The polyglycolide, $H(OCH_2CO)_nOH$, has a melting point of 223 C and is less soluble in chloroform than the diglycolide, which melts at 86 C.[10]

The diglycolide may also be prepared from polyglycolide by distillation under reduced pressure. Similarly, the polyglycolide may be prepared from the cyclic dimeric glycolide by heating or by allowing it to stand at room temperature for a longer time. Thus we see that the reaction is reversible [11] and is probably the first published example of the polymerization of a six-membered ring and the depolymerization of its polymer to the ring.

$$n \begin{array}{c} O-CH_2CO \\ | \qquad | \\ OC-CH_2O \end{array} \rightleftharpoons (C_2H_2O_2)_{2n}$$

Cyclic dimer   Polymer

Lactic acid, α-methylglycolic acid, is a homologue of glycolic acid; and a behavior similar to glycolic acid should be expected. The polymerization of lactic acid by means of distillation is represented by the following:

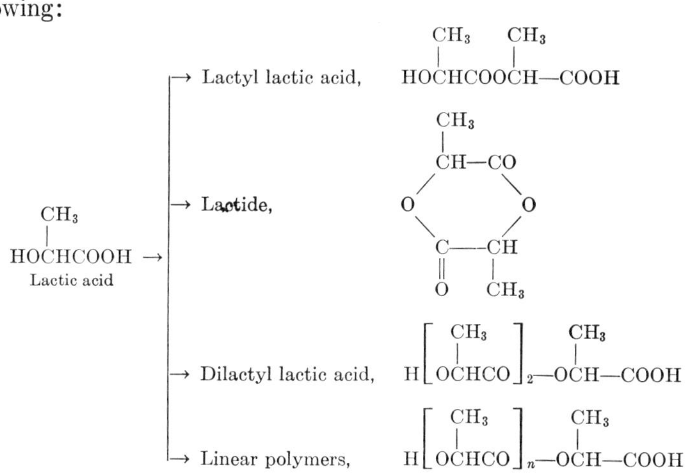

$$\begin{array}{cc} CH_3 & CH_3 \\ | & | \end{array}$$
→ Lactyl lactic acid, $HOCHCOOCH—COOH$

$$CH_3$$
$$|$$
$$CH—CO$$
→ Lactide, $O \diagup \qquad \diagdown O$
$$C——CH$$
$$\| \quad |$$
$$O \quad CH_3$$

$$\begin{array}{c} CH_3 \\ | \end{array}$$
$$HOCHCOOH →$$
Lactic acid

→ Dilactyl lactic acid, $H\left[\begin{array}{c} CH_3 \\ | \\ OCHCO \end{array}\right]_2 —O\overset{\displaystyle CH_3}{\underset{\displaystyle |}{C}H}—COOH$

→ Linear polymers, $H\left[\begin{array}{c} CH_3 \\ | \\ OCHCO \end{array}\right]_n —O\overset{\displaystyle CH_3}{\underset{\displaystyle |}{C}H}—COOH$

Commercial lactic acid usually contains about 8 per cent of lactyl lactic acid and of the lactide.   The lactide differs from glycolide in that it does not polymerize spontaneously but only on being heated or treated catalytically.

Carothers [6] reports that attempts to polymerize some of the homologues of glycolide derived from the higher hydroxy fatty acids have been unsuccessful.   The behavior of glycolide and its homologues with respect to the formation of polymer chains may be represented as follows:

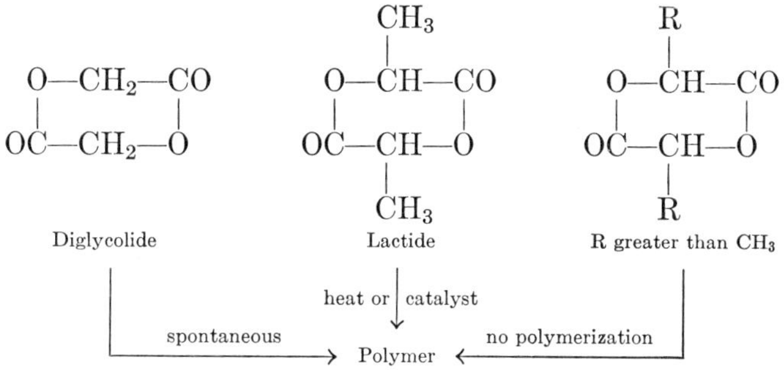

$$O—CH_2—CO$$
$$| \qquad\qquad |$$
$$OC—CH_2—O$$
Diglycolide

$$CH_3$$
$$|$$
$$O—CH—CO$$
$$| \qquad\qquad |$$
$$OC—CH—O$$
$$|$$
$$CH_3$$
Lactide

$$R$$
$$|$$
$$O—CH—CO$$
$$| \qquad\qquad |$$
$$OC—CH—O$$
$$|$$
$$R$$
R greater than CH_3

heat or | catalyst
spontaneous   ↓   no polymerization
→ Polymer ←

The Reactions of β-Hydroxy Acids

The β-hydroxy acids of the formula $HOCR_2CR_2COOH$, are, in general, unsuitable for esterification polymerization.   The simplest member, hydracrylic acid, $HOCH_2CH_2COOH$, dehydrates during heating to acrylic acid.   It is most probable that esterification to hydracrylylhydracrylic acid occurs first, and is followed by a deacylation reaction:

$$2HOCH_2CH_2COOH \rightarrow HOCH_2CH_2COOCH_2CH_2COOH \rightarrow$$

$$CH_2{=}CHCOOH + HOCH_2CH_2COOH$$

Similarly, β-hydroxybutyric acid dehydrates on heating to crotonic acid:

$$\underset{\underset{CH_3}{|}}{HOCHCH_2COOH} \rightarrow CH_3CH{=}CHCOOH$$

In general, the homologues of the β-hydroxy acids dehydrate as follows:

$$\underset{\underset{R}{|}}{HOCHCH_2COOH} \rightarrow RCH{=}CHCOOH$$

In contrast, β-hydroxyisobutyric acid is so unstable that it dehydrates spontaneously to methacrylic acid:

$$\underset{HOCH_2{-}\underset{|}{\overset{|}{C}}HCOOH}{\overset{CH_3}{}} \rightarrow \underset{CH_2{=}\underset{|}{\overset{|}{C}}{-}COOH}{\overset{CH_3}{}}$$

and, in general, its homologues dehydrate as follows:

$$\underset{HOCH_2{-}\underset{|}{\overset{|}{C}}H{-}COOH}{\overset{R}{}} \rightarrow \underset{CH_2{=}\underset{|}{\overset{|}{C}}{-}COOH}{\overset{R}{}}$$

If both α hydrogens are substituted by methyl groups to give β-hydroxypivalic acid, dehydration does not occur and a polyester is formed, thus:

$$n\underset{\underset{CH_3}{|}}{\overset{\overset{CH_3}{|}}{HOCH_2{-}C}}{-}COOH \rightarrow \underset{\underset{CH_3}{|}}{\overset{\overset{CH_3}{|}}{HOCH_2{-}C}}{-}CO{-}\left[{-}O\underset{\underset{CH_3}{|}}{\overset{\overset{CH_3}{|}}{CH_2{-}C}}{-}CO{-} \right]_{n-1}{-}OH$$

or, in general,

$$n\underset{\underset{R}{|}}{\overset{\overset{R}{|}}{HOCH_2{-}C}}{-}COOH \rightarrow \underset{\underset{R}{|}}{\overset{\overset{R}{|}}{HOCH_2{-}C}}{-}CO{-}\left[{-}O\underset{\underset{R}{|}}{\overset{\overset{R}{|}}{CH_2{-}C}}{-}CO{-} \right]_{n-1}{-}OH$$

The possibility of ring formation in the self-esterification of β-hydroxy acid is reduced because of steric considerations and because the ring would be an eight-atom ring.

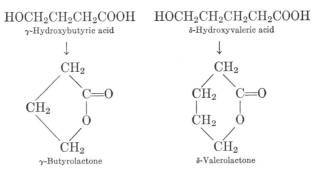

The Reactions of γ- and δ-Hydroxy Acids

The γ-hydroxy acids,

$$\text{HOC}\underset{\underset{\text{R}}{|}}{\overset{\overset{\text{R}}{|}}{\text{C}}}\underset{\underset{\text{R}}{|}}{\overset{\overset{\text{R}}{|}}{\text{C}}}\underset{\underset{\text{R}}{|}}{\overset{\overset{\text{R}}{|}}{\text{C}}}\text{—COOH,}$$

and the δ-hydroxy acids,

$$\text{HOC}\underset{\underset{\text{R}}{|}}{\overset{\overset{\text{R}}{|}}{\text{C}}}\underset{\underset{\text{R}}{|}}{\overset{\overset{\text{R}}{|}}{\text{C}}}\underset{\underset{\text{R}}{|}}{\overset{\overset{\text{R}}{|}}{\text{C}}}\underset{\underset{\text{R}}{|}}{\overset{\overset{\text{R}}{|}}{\text{C}}}\text{—COOH,}$$

differ from the α and β homologues in that they are transformed very readily into a simple monomeric cyclic ester by intramolecular reactions. The γ-hydroxybutyric acid produces γ-butyrolactone, and the δ-hydroxyvaleric acid produces the δ-valerolactone, as follows:

HOCH$_2$CH$_2$CH$_2$COOH   HOCH$_2$CH$_2$CH$_2$CH$_2$COOH
γ-Hydroxybutyric acid δ-Hydroxyvaleric acid

γ-Butyrolactone δ-Valerolactone

The γ-lactones and other five-membered cyclic esters show no tendency to polymerize, even when heated with and without catalysts for 12 months at 80 C.[12]

On the other hand, δ-valerolactone was reported to change spontaneously into a polymer melting at 48 C.[13]

Lactone formation also occurs in the self-esterification of 2,3,4-trimethyl-1-arobanic acid:

$$
\begin{array}{c}
\text{HOCH}_2\text{CH}\underset{|}{\text{---}}\text{CH}\underset{|}{\text{---}}\text{CH---COOH} \\
\overset{|}{\text{OCH}_3}\ \overset{|}{\text{OCH}_3}\ \overset{|}{\text{OCH}_3}
\end{array}
\rightarrow
$$

$$
\begin{array}{c}
\quad\quad\overset{\displaystyle \text{CO}}{\diagup\ \ \diagdown} \\
\text{CH}_3\text{---O---CH}\quad\text{O} \\
\underset{|}{}\quad\quad\underset{|}{} \\
\text{CH}_3\text{---O---CH}\quad\text{CH}_2 \\
\quad\quad\diagdown\ \diagup \\
\quad\quad\text{CH} \\
\quad\quad\overset{|}{\text{OCH}_3}
\end{array}
$$

δ-Lactone

Drew and Haworth [14] observed that this lactone changed spontaneously to a polymer from which the lactone could be regenerated by distillation in vacuum at 175 C. Carothers and his co-workers [12] prepared α-*n*-propyl-δ-valerolactone from α-*n*-propyl-δ-bromovaleric acid and found that it did not polymerize spontaneously in 12 months or after heating at 80 C for one month. When heated in the presence of catalysts, as zinc chloride for one month at 80 C, a polymer was formed with molecular weight of about 1100 to 1200.

The Reactions of ε-Hydroxy Acids and the ω-Homologues

Originally, it was believed [15] that the ε-hydroxy acids did not form lactones but that they dehydrated to olefinic acids on heating. As a rule, the ε-hydroxy acids, or hydroxy acids of chain length greater than six, do not form monomeric cyclic lactones but react to form linear polymers. However, Carothers and co-workers [16] have shown that by heating ε-hydroxycaproic acid at 150 to 210 C, it is possible to isolate a large yield of purified lactone (63 per cent). Small amounts, about 1 per cent, of dimeric cyclic ester were also isolated. The lactone showed no tendency to polymerize when allowed to stand under ordinary conditions, but when it was heated in a sealed tube at 150 C for 12 hours, it solidified to a polymeric mass:

$$
n\text{HO(CH}_2)_5\text{COOH} \rightarrow n
\begin{array}{c}
\quad\quad\overset{\displaystyle \text{CH}_2}{\diagup\ \ \diagdown} \\
\text{CH}_2\quad\ \ \text{CO} \\
\underset{|}{}\quad\quad\underset{|}{} \\
\text{CH}_2\quad\ \ \text{O} \\
\quad\diagdown\ \diagup \\
\quad\text{CH}_2\ \text{CH}_2 \\
\quad\quad\text{CH}_2
\end{array}
\rightarrow (\text{C}_6\text{H}_{10}\text{O}_2)_n
$$

| ε-Hydroxycaproic acid | Lactone | Polymer |

This polymer is depolymerized only with great difficulty.

The series of ω-hydroxy acids, $HO(CH_2)_nCOOH$, where n is 8 to 16, is

$$HO(\overset{\overset{\textstyle R}{|}}{\underset{\underset{\textstyle R}{|}}{C}})_nCOOH,$$

known, and the self-esterification of the hydroxy acids, where n is greater than 5, does not produce lactones but linear polymers. A number of workers [4, 17, 18] have published the preparation of lactones corresponding to the hydroxy acids with n values of 12 to 16. Though all these lactones are stable substances and can be distilled without decomposition, they cannot be prepared directly from the corresponding hydroxy acid, but by the oxidation of cyclic ketones with Caro's acid.

RING AND POLYMER REVERSIBILITY

Carothers [6] describes the polymerization of the lactones which do polymerize as a process of ester exchange, and the depolymerization is the reverse transformation proceeding by a similar mechanism as indicated by the arrows.

Polymerization
$$O-CR_2-\overset{\overset{\textstyle O}{||}}{C} + O-CR_2-\overset{\overset{\textstyle O}{||}}{C} + O-CR_2-\overset{\overset{\textstyle O}{||}}{C} + O-CR_2-\overset{\overset{\textstyle O}{||}}{C}$$

Depolymerization
$$-O-CR_2-\overset{\overset{\textstyle O}{||}}{C}---O-CR_2-\overset{\overset{\textstyle O}{||}}{C}---O-CR_2-\overset{\overset{\textstyle O}{||}}{C}---O-CR_2-\overset{\overset{\textstyle O}{||}}{C}-$$

Although of no direct interest to the present discussion of the actions of polyfunctional molecules in high polymer formation, attention should be called to the studies on depolymerization carried out by Carothers on linear polymers, whereby macrocyclic esters (containing rings larger than 5, 6, or 7 atoms) were prepared. This depolymerization method made possible the synthesis of a large number of cyclic compounds having as many as 24 ring atoms. A number of them are dimeric rings. The general considerations of ring structure as the product of reaction of dihydric alcohols and dibasic acids as well as the depolymerization reactions are known.[3, 8, 19-23]

POLYMERIZABILITY AND THE NATURE OF THE RING

The γ-lactones were shown to be very stable rings with little or no tendency to polymerize. It must not be concluded, however, that all five-membered rings are stable in the polymerization sense. The chemical nature of the ring compound may produce marked changes in this

property, and therefore the behavior of other rings should be considered
in relation to its homologues and isomers.   In contrast to the γ-lactones, the behavior of the carbonic acid anhydride of the α-amino acids
should be mentioned.[24]   These compounds are also five-membered rings

of the generic structure,

$$\begin{array}{c} CR_2-CO \\ | \qquad\qquad\searrow \\ | \qquad\qquad\quad O. \\ | \qquad\qquad\nearrow \\ NR-CO \end{array}$$

The N-carboxyglycine anhydride,

$$\begin{array}{c} CH_2-CO \\ | \qquad\qquad\searrow \\ | \qquad\qquad\quad O, \text{ is soluble in water} \\ | \qquad\qquad\nearrow \\ NH-CO \end{array}$$

at 0 C, and at 15 C, CO_2 is evolved and glycine is formed:

$$\begin{array}{c} CH_2-CO \\ | \qquad\qquad\searrow \\ | \qquad\qquad\quad O + H_2O \rightarrow NH_2CH_2COOH + CO_2 \\ | \qquad\qquad\nearrow \\ NH-CO \end{array}$$

If the anhydride is treated with a little water at room temperature or is
heated, CO_2 is liberated and a protein-type insoluble polymer is obtained.   On hydrolysis of the polymer, glycine is obtained, indicating
that it had the structure

$$H(NHCH_2CO)_n-OH$$

The polymer resembles the hornlike polymer obtained by Balbiano.[25,26]
The anhydrides of the N-substituted N-carboxy-α-amino acids also
polymerize in this fashion.[27]

ADDITION POLYREACTIONS.   FORMATION OF RINGS AND POLYMERS

Reactions of Compounds with Olefinic Unsaturation

Under normal conditions of polymerization, mono-olefinic compounds
do not produce ring structures.   If, in the absence of cracking or rear-
rangements, or of thermal decompositions, ring structures are obtained
during polymerization, these rings contain multiples of two carbon atoms
for the ethylenic compound or its homologues, $R_2C=CR_2$, because the
cyclic oligomers were derived from the bivalent radical, $-CR_2-CR_2-$.

If any rings are formed, they should be cyclobutane, cyclohexane, cyclooctane, etc., derivatives.

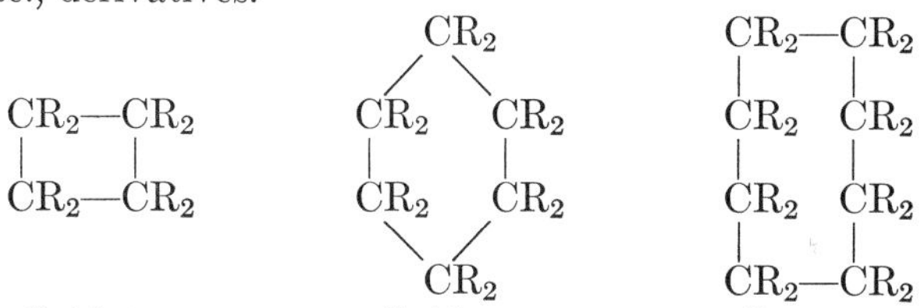

$$CR_2—CR_2 \atop CR_2—CR_2$$

Cyclobutane

$$CR_2 \atop CR_2 \; CR_2 \atop CR_2 \; CR_2 \atop CR_2$$

Cyclohexane

$$CR_2—CR_2 \atop CR_2 \; CR_2 \atop CR_2 \; CR_2 \atop CR_2—CR_2$$

Cyclo-octane

Evidence for the formation of such ring structures from ethylene has not been published,[28] even when ethylene is polymerized under high pressures and below decomposition temperatures (100 to 300 C).[29,30] However, cyclic derivatives have been obtained by subjecting gaseous hydrocarbons to thermal decomposition at 750 to 1050 C, and the following scheme [31] is suggested for the formation of cyclic compounds.

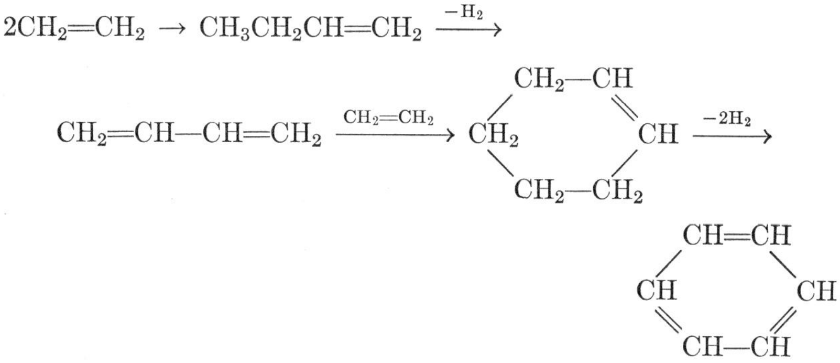

$$2CH_2{=}CH_2 \rightarrow CH_3CH_2CH{=}CH_2 \xrightarrow{-H_2}$$

$$CH_2{=}CH{-}CH{=}CH_2 \xrightarrow{CH_2{=}CH_2} \begin{array}{c} CH_2—CH \\ CH_2 \qquad CH \\ CH_2—CH_2 \end{array} \xrightarrow{-2H_2}$$

$$\begin{array}{c} CH{=}CH \\ CH \qquad CH \\ CH—CH \end{array}$$

Styrene, under the normal conditions of polymerization, such as with peroxide-type catalysts, yields high molecular weight linear polymers and not cyclic compounds, though dimers and trimers have been isolated under special conditions. These dimers and trimers may be either linear or cyclic compounds. Oligomers of this type are usually obtained under ionic catalytic conditions. As an example, the treatment of 100 grams of a mixture of 40 per cent styrene and 60 per cent ethylbenzene at 100 C with 60 grams of a 60 per cent aqueous H_2SO_4 gives the following mixture of products:

Dimers	80 per cent
Linear dimer	76 per cent
Cyclic dimer	4 per cent
Mixed trimers	15 per cent
Higher polymers	5 per cent

The linear dimer has the structure CH_3—CH—CH=CH, and the

cyclic dimer is a saturated diphenylcyclobutane, CH_2—CH—

In contrast to styrene, α-methylstyrene does not readily give high molecular weight polymers with peroxide catalysts, nor does it polymerize spontaneously. It may be polymerized easily with ionic catalysts, such as tin chloride. Staudinger and Breusch [32] isolated a series of dimers, trimers, tetramers, etc., from the polymer mixture and determined that these polymers were saturated. They attributed cyclic structures to these oligomers, for example, the dimer was a cyclobutane derivative, the trimer was a cyclohexane derivative, etc. On the basis

TABLE 1

Sulfuric Acid		Reaction		Conversion, %	Unsaturated Dimer, %	Saturated Dimer, %
Aqueous Concentration, %	Quantity, %	Temperature, °F	Time, Hours			
30	400	170–190	4	40	40	0
40	400	170–190	4	43	43	0
50	400	122–180	6	100	99	1
60	400	122–180	6	100	98	2
60	3	150–180	6	12	12	0
60	6	150–180	6	20	20	0
60	100	150–180	6	77	75	2
70	400	180–190	6	100	10	90
50	400	70– 80	8	20	20	0
60	400	70– 80	8	100	100	0
70	400	75–100	8	100	90	10
80	400	75–100	5	100	0	100

Data from U. S. Patent 2,429,719.

of their physical properties, it was assumed that these polymers were 4, 6, 8, 10, 12, 14, and 16 atom chain rings.

Hersberger, Hill, and Heiligmann [33] have shown the conditions under which substantial yields of linear unsaturated dimers of α-methylstyrene may be obtained and the yield of saturated cyclic dimer reduced.

The properties of the unsaturated linear dimer and the saturated cyclic dimer are contrasted as follows:

	Cyclic Dimer	Linear Dimer
B.p.$_{0.1\ mm}$, °C	117.7–120	117.2–120
N_D^{20}	1.5633	1.5677
Bromine number	0	67
M.p., °C	52.2–53.9	....

As evident from Table 1 the use of the sulfuric acid catalyst in concentrations of 70 per cent or higher produces larger quantities of cyclic dimer.

In contrast to α-methylstyrene, α-chlorostyrene, even though it copolymerizes with other monomers such as styrene, has not been successfully polymerized to high molecular weight compounds either by heat, light, stannic chloride, or BF_3. BF_3 converts this chlorostyrene into triphenylbenzene. The probable intermediates are phenylacetylene and trichlorotriphenylcyclohexane.

As a generalized observation, it may be observed in the system,

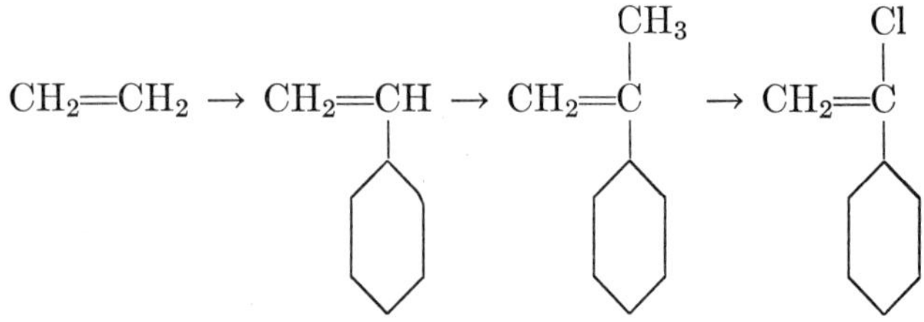

$$CH_2{=}CH_2 \rightarrow CH_2{=}CH \rightarrow CH_2{=}\underset{\displaystyle \bigcirc}{\overset{\displaystyle CH_3}{C}} \rightarrow CH_2{=}\underset{\displaystyle \bigcirc}{\overset{\displaystyle Cl}{C}}$$

that, as substitution of the ethylene becomes complex, spontaneous polymerizability decreases, and that even under ordinary peroxide catalysis high molecular weight polymers are not obtained. With ionic catalysts the yield of cyclic products is greater than with peroxide catalysts, and under specified conditions, may actually favor cyclization exclusively.

In the emulsion polymerization of butadiene, which has been catalyzed with a peroxide type of catalyst, small quantities of vinylcyclohexene are obtained. Butadiene, which may be considered to be a substituted ethylene, namely bivinyl, may polymerize either as a 1,4 monomer, or as a 1,2 monomer, as, for example:

$$CH_2{=}CH{-}CH{=}CH_2 \xrightarrow{1,4} -CH_2{-}CH{=}CH{-}CH_2-$$

$$CH_2{=}CH{-}CH{=}CH_2 \xrightarrow{1,2} -CH_2{-}\underset{\displaystyle CH{=}CH_2}{CH}-$$

In emulsion polymerizations used in the preparation of synthetic rubber, butadiene polymerizes through both mechanisms, and as a result some vinylcyclohexene is found by the following reaction.

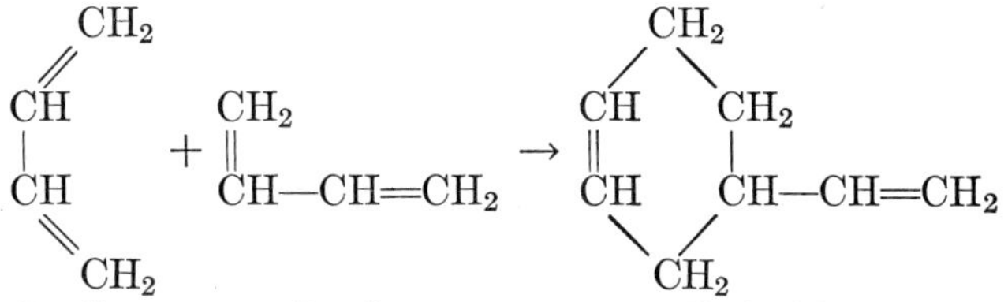

$$
\begin{array}{ccc}
\begin{array}{c} CH_2 \\ \parallel \\ CH \\ | \\ CH \\ \diagdown \\ CH_2 \end{array}
&
+\ \begin{array}{c} CH_2 \\ \parallel \\ CH{-}CH{=}CH_2 \end{array}
& \rightarrow \quad \text{Vinylcyclohexene}
\end{array}
$$

Butadiene   Butadiene   Vinylcyclohexene

In contrast to obtaining vinylcyclohexene as a by-product, the vapor-phase polymerization of butadiene may produce vinylcyclohexene exclusively.

Acetylene has been polymerized by both chemical and physical means. Light and electrical discharges have been extensively investigated.   At elevated temperatures of about 400 C, many chemical bodies have been used as catalysts to produce liquid and tarry substances of an aromatic nature.   Best known among the polymers of acetylene is cuprene or carbene,[34] which was first reported by Erdmann and Köthner.[35-37]   This polymer, prepared by the action of acetylene at 230 C on copper or copper oxide, is a voluminous, yellow-brown solid with an apparent volume of about 40 cubic centimeters per gram.   Cyclic oligomers of acetylene have been prepared by Reppe directly in high yields from acetylene under pressure in the presence of nickel chloride or cyanide as catalyst and tetrahydrofurane as a solvent.[38]   By this synthesis cyclo-octatetraene was obtained.

$$4CH\equiv CH \rightarrow$$

Cyclo-octatetraene

The cyclo-octatetraene is a golden liquid of density 0.938, with a boiling point of 142 to 143 C, a melting point of −7 C, and a density of the solid of 1.04 ± 0.02.[39]

Reactions of Some Compounds having Carbon-Hetero-Atom Structure

Polymers are readily prepared from ethylene oxide.   It has been shown [40] that these polymers are mixtures that can be separated into fractions which range in molecular weights from 400 to 5000.   These polymers are not depolymerized by heat, but yield complicated products including acetaldehyde and acrolein.   Faworski [41] has shown that ethylene oxide may be dimerized to dioxane:

$$2CH_2\text{---}CH_2 \rightarrow$$

which shows no further tendency to polymerize without drastic treatment.   Today it has widespread use as a stable industrial solvent. Formaldehyde, CH_2O, differs from ethylene oxide in that its polymers are reversible to monomers.   Formaldehyde can be cyclized [42] to a stable six-membered ring, trioxane,

Formaldehyde can be regenerated from trioxane with acids. The polymers of formaldehyde, which have been exhaustively studied by Staudinger,[43] have been shown to contain forty to at least one hundred repeating units in the polyoxymethylene chain. Formaldehyde is readily regenerated on heating in the presence of catalysts. It may be possible to explain the difference in the degradative behavior of the polymers of ethylene oxide and of formaldehyde on consideration of their respective chain polymers.

I. In polyoxymethylene, the rupture can occur only between a carbon to oxygen linkage whereas in polyethylene oxide the rupture can occur at a carbon to carbon linkage as well as at a carbon to oxygen linkage.

II. The polyethylene oxide is a true ether compound whereas polyoxymethylene behaves more as an acetal of formaldehyde and methylene glycol, $HOCH_2OH$. Acetals can undergo exchange reactions similar to an ester exchange, as, for example,

$$\underset{\substack{\text{Dimethyl}\\\text{acetal}}}{CH_2\!\!\begin{array}{l}\diagup OCH_3\\[4pt]\diagdown OCH_3\end{array}} + \underset{\substack{\text{Butyl}\\\text{alcohol}}}{2C_4H_9OH} \xrightarrow[\text{exchange}]{\text{acetal}} \underset{\substack{\text{Dibutyl}\\\text{acetal}}}{CH_2\!\!\begin{array}{l}\diagup OC_4H_9\\[4pt]\diagdown OC_4H_9\end{array}} + \underset{\substack{\text{Methyl}\\\text{alcohol}}}{2CH_3OH}$$

and it would be expected that polymers of acetal structure should depolymerize either into monomers or cyclic oligomers. Substantiation of this concept is found in the publication of Hill and Carothers on cyclic and polymeric formals.[21] In their studies on alkylene formals of structural unit, $-(CR_2)_nOCH_2O-$, where n is at least 2, it was demonstrated that if a six-membered ring could form, only a ring was obtained; and if a seven-membered ring could form, both rings and polymers could form, and they were interconvertible.

SUMMARY OF LINEAR INTERMOLECULAR AND INTRAMOLECULAR REACTIONS OF POLYFUNCTIONAL MOLECULES

1. If five- or six-membered rings are possible from polyfunctional molecules, they will form more readily through condensation reactions than through addition reactions.
2. Most five- and six-membered rings are stable and are polymerized with difficulty, even in the presence of catalysts. The chemical nature of the ring compound, however, may increase this reactivity.

3. Addition polymers are reversible with difficulty, and the products of reversible reaction are not homogeneous but correspond to the possible degradation products due to rupture of primary valence bonds and not to the exchange of primary valence bonds.

4. Most linear condensation products obtained by the elimination of a simple molecule of water, or its equivalent, and which can undergo exchange reactions, are reversible and depolymerized to a monomer ring or a ring containing a simple multiple of the segmer. These monomeric or dimeric rings are not necessarily repolymerizable spontaneously but may be relatively stable substances.

5. Ionic catalysts favor ring formation in addition polymerization reactions. The conditions for ring formation in high yields usually are quite specific, and are favored by high temperature and high catalyst concentrations.

REFERENCES

1. W. H. Carothers, *J. Am. Chem. Soc.*, **51**, 2548–2559 (1929).
2. J. Mohr, *J. prakt. Chem.* (2), **98**, 315 (1918).
3. J. W. Hill and W. H. Carothers, *J. Am. Chem. Soc.*, **55**, 5031–5039 (1933).
4. L. Ruzicka and M. Stoll, *Helv. Chim. Acta*, **11**, 1159 (1928).
5. A. Baeyer and V. Villiger, *Ber.*, **32**, 3625 (1899).
6. W. H. Carothers, *Chem. Revs.*, **8**, 353–426 (1931).
7. P. Ruggli, *Ann.*, **392**, 92 (1912).
8. E. W. Spanagel and W. H. Carothers, *J. Am. Chem. Soc.*, **57**, 929–934 (1935).
9. Victor von Richter, *Organic Chemistry*, Vol. I, p. 366, The Blakiston Co., Philadelphia, 1929.
10. Victor von Richter, *Organic Chemistry*, Vol. I, p. 367, The Blakiston Co., Philadelphia, 1929.
11. C. A. Bischoff and P. Walden, *Ber.*, **26**, 262 (1893).
12. W. H. Carothers, G. L. Dorough, and F. J. Van Natta, *J. Am. Chem. Soc.*, **54**, 761–772 (1932).
13. F. Fichter and A. Weisswenger, *Ber.*, **36**, 1200 (1903).
14. H. D. K. Drew and W. N. Haworth, *J. Chem. Soc.* (London), **130**, 775 (1927).
15. Victor von Richter, *Organic Chemistry*, Vol. I, p. 375, The Blakiston Co., Philadelphia, 1929.
16. F. J. Van Natta, J. W. Hill, and W. H. Carothers, *J. Am. Chem. Soc.*, **56**, 455–457 (1934).
17. W. H. Lycan and R. Adams, *J. Am. Chem. Soc.*, **51**, 625 (1929).
18. P. Chuit and J. Hausser, *Helv. Chim. Acta*, **12**, 463 (1929).
19. J. W. Hill and W. H. Carothers, *J. Am. Chem. Soc.*, **55**, 5039–5043 (1933).
20. W. H. Carothers and J. W. Hill, *J. Am. Chem. Soc.*, **55**, 5043–5052 (1933).
21. J. W. Hill and W. H. Carothers, *J. Am. Chem. Soc.*, **57**, 925–928 (1935).
22. E. W. Spanagel and W. H. Carothers, *J. Am. Chem. Soc.*, **58**, 654–656 (1936).
23. J. W. Hill and W. H. Carothers, *J. Am. Chem. Soc.*, **55**, 5023–5031 (1933).
24. H. Leuchs, *Ber.*, **39**, 857 (1906).

25. L. Balbiano, *Ber.*, **34**, 1501 (1901).
26. L. Balbiano and D. Trasciatti, *Ber.*, **33**, 2323 (1900).
27. T. Curtius and W. Sieber, *Ber.*, **55**, 1543 (1922).
28. For review on polymerization of ethylene, see H. M. Stanley, *J. Soc. Chem. Ind.*, **49**, 349T (1930). See also pp. 126–133 and 259–268 in *Polymerization*, by R. E. Burk, H. E. Thompson, A. J. Weith, and I. Williams, ACS Monograph Series 75, Reinhold Publishing Corp., 1937.
29. E. W. Fawcett and R. O. Gibson, *J. Chem. Soc.* (London), **137**, 386 (1934).
30. A. Wachter, *Ind. Eng. Chem.*, **30**, 822 (1938).
31. A. E. Dunstan, E. N. Hague, and R. V. Wheeler, *Ind. Eng. Chem.*, **26**, 307 (1934).
32. H. Staudinger and F. Breusch, *Ber.*, **62**, 442 (1929).
33. A. B. Hersberger, D. Hill, and R. G. Heiligmann, U. S. Patent 2,429,719 (October 28, 1947).
34. W. Herzog, *Chem.-Ztg.*, **55**, 461, 478 (1931).
35. H. Erdmann and P. Köthner, *Z. anorg. Chem.*, **18**, 49 (1898).
36. H. Erdmann and P. Köthner, *Z. anorg. Chem.*, **18**, 57 (1898).
37. H. Erdmann and P. Köthner, *J. Chem. Soc.* (London), **76**, 21 (1899).
38. *British Plastics*, **19**, 258 (June 1947).
39. Report by Walter Reppe on *Cyclopolyolefines*, Ludwigshaven on Rhine, April 28, 1944, B.I.O.S. Final Report 137, London, H.M. Stationery Office.
40. H. Staudinger and O. Schweitzer, *Ber.*, **62**, 2395 (1929).
41. A. Faworski, *Chem. Zentr.*, **78**, 15 (1907).
42. A. Kekule, *Ber.*, **25**, 2435 (1892).
43. H. Staudinger, *Die Hochmolekularen organischen Verbindungen*, J. Springer, Berlin, 1932.

CHAPTER 6

Polymerization Processes

CLASSIFICATION

The manner or means of converting monomers, comonomers, and comers into polymers are many, but these processes which admit of numerous modifications are readily classified into three simple basic

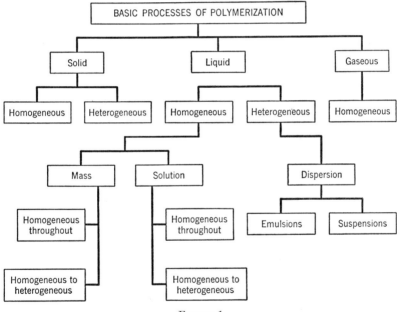

FIGURE 1

processes, according to whether the polymerization reaction occurs in the *gaseous*, *liquid*, or *solid phases*. All three basic processes are of academic interest. However, practically all commercial polymers are prepared, utilizing liquid phase processes. The modifications of the three basic processes are shown in Figure 1. The classification gaseous, liquid, or solid phase polymerization includes both condensation and addition polymerization reactions. As we have already indicated, the mechanism of the reaction as well as the kinetics are not necessarily the same for addition and condensation systems. It is likewise true that if a polymer can be produced from monomers by more than one method of polymerization, the mechanism for the polymerization is not necessarily the same for the different systems.

GASEOUS PHASE POLYMERIZATION

Addition Reactions

Examples of gaseous phase polymerization are not generally known. Some are called gaseous polymerizations but not rightly so; properly, they are oligomerizations since the products of reaction are dimers, trimers, tetramers, etc. For a system to be classified strictly as a gaseous polymerization system, the reactants, as well as the products of reaction, must exist in the gaseous or vapor phase, at least, to the point *where a high polymer is formed. This very condition of definition* excludes the polymers since all high polymers are decomposed before becoming gaseous. Many oligomers, however, have vapor pressures sufficiently high so that they may exist in the vapor phase. Recent polymerization of ethylene to polyethylene [1] has been called *gaseous polymerization.* Gaseous ethylene is polymerized at high temperatures and pressures, and a solid polymer is obtained. Since at high temperatures, but at atmospheric pressure, polyethylene is unstable and is reconverted to gaseous and liquid products, we are justified in assuming that this polymerization of ethylene is gaseous only at the beginning of the reaction to a low degree of polymerization, and that, most probably, the propagation of polymerization occurs in a liquid phase by diffusion of monomeric ethylene, first to oligomeric and later to polymeric ethylene. This is illustrated as follows.

$$CH_2{=}CH_2 \xrightarrow{\text{catalyst}} \underset{\text{Gas}}{RCH_2CH_2 \cdot} \xrightarrow{CH_2=CH_2}$$
$$\underset{\text{Gas or liquid}}{RCH_2CH_2CH_2CH_2 \cdot} \xrightarrow{CH_2=CH_2}$$
$$\underset{\text{Liquid}}{RCH_2CH_2CH_2CH_2CH_2CH_2 \cdot} \xrightarrow{CH_2=CH_2} \text{etc.}$$

If the polymerization of ethylene is performed in a hydrocarbon such as a kerosene fraction, the process is a liquid process since it involves solution. If the ethylene is polymerized while dispersed in water, the system is a liquid heterogeneous system. Gaseous phase reactions of hydrocarbons by the petroleum industry in which both the monomer and the oligomers remain in the gaseous phase during the reaction are gaseous oligomerization systems. The conversions of gaseous acetaldehyde to gaseous paraldehyde, and of gaseous butadiene to gaseous vinylcyclohexene, and of gaseous ketene to gaseous diketene are true gaseous oligomerizations and not polymerizations. The polymerization of gaseous isoprene [2] on an aluminum chloride catalyst, the photopolymerization of butadiene, [3] and the thermal polymerization of gaseous styrene probably involve other than gaseous phases usually a liquid phase and are not true gas polymerizations. The thermal polymerization of gaseous styrene was studied by Breitenbach,[4] who showed that the "polymers" were of low molecular weight with a degree of polymerization between 2 and 6. The temperature range studied was between 249 and 310 C; at 311 C, only dimers were formed. The gaseous polymerization showed measurable velocities only at temperatures not lower than 220 C.

Condensation Reactions

Experimental data for gaseous condensation polymerizations are negligible. It is reasonable to believe that those monomers or comers that undergo liquid condensation reactions to give monomeric or dimeric rings, and are volatile, would also produce rings if condensed in the vapor phase. Thus trimethylene glycol and formaldehyde, which in a condensation reaction produce only a six-membered ring, would be expected to produce the same product if gaseous glycol and gaseous formaldehyde were condensed. On the other hand, tetramethylene glycol and formaldehyde react in the liquid phase to produce a seven-membered alkylene formal ring as well as a polymer. This ring and its polymers are interconvertible at high temperatures.[5] If these same reactants were subjected to the conditions of gaseous condensation, only ring products normally would be expected unless high pressures were used. In such a case, the system becomes analogous to an ethylene polymerization and a gaseous polymerization only at the beginning of the process.

SOLID PHASE POLYMERIZATION PROCESS

Very few examples of polymerization in the solid phase are known. In solid phase polymerization, the monomer or reactants exist in a solid phase, which may be crystalline, and are converted to a polymer which may or may not be crystalline. There is a possibility of solid phase polymerization occurring in both addition and condensation systems whether the phases are homogeneous or heterogeneous.

Addition Polymerization

HOMOGENEOUS SOLID PHASE

Solid phase addition polymerization has been observed in only a few monomers having active terminal vinyl groups. As will be noted from the following, polymerization occurred whether the monomers were initially solid at room temperature or were solidified by freezing.

A sample of pure crystalline 2,5-dichlorostyrene was stored without inhibitor in a refrigerator for a period of six weeks. Macroscopically, there was no apparent change in appearance of the crystals. In a number of chemical reactions, in which the monomer was used, discrepancies were found which warranted an examination of the dichlorostyrene. It was found that 10 per cent of the monomer had become converted to polymer.[6]

Crystalline dimethyl itaconate stored at room temperature for a period of about one year was found to be about 25 per cent polymerized.[6]

A number of divinylbenzene samples which were stored in a frozen condition were found to be polymerized to different degrees. Macroscopically, the appearance of the crystals had not changed.[6] Some of the samples were still soluble; others were insoluble in benzene and acetone. These results indicated that soluble, fusible partial polymers of divinylbenzene could be isolated and used industrially.[7,8]

A more recent publication [9] has shown that crystalline diisopropenyldiphenyl becomes insoluble and infusible on standing. A comparison was made of the crystalline structures of the monomer and polymer. Even though the external structure of the crystals appeared to be the same, X-ray studies showed that the polymer had the pattern typical for a crosslinked polymer.

A large number of samples of solid, fusible polymers, and copolymers of monomers or comers of functionality greater than 2 became insoluble, or infusible, or insoluble and infusible on standing even though they never became liquid. Examples are [6] the solid, soluble fusible polymers and copolymers of such substances as glycol dimethacrylate, styrene and allyl acrylate, and methyl methacrylate and methallyl methacrylate.

HETEROGENEOUS SOLID PHASE PROCESS

The conditions for such a process would be fulfilled by a minimum of:

(1) At least two copolymerizable solids which may be either comonomers, a monomer and comer, or two comers.

(2) A system in which at least one reactant is a solid and at least one

other reactant is a liquid or gas. In such a system, the solid phase must be retained, that is, the components of the system are not soluble in each other.

As far as the author is aware, there are no published data for a heterogeneous solid phase process, but we may speculate that copolymerization will occur in these systems if the components of the system polymerize alone in a solid state and if no inhibiting effect of one component on another exists.

It would be reasonable to expect that, if the melting point of the mixture of solids was not depressed a serious extent, or if no inhibition took place, intimately mixed crystals of divinylbenzene and diisopropenyldiphenyl in a fine state of subdivision would copolymerize. Similarly, we should expect that a solid diisocyanate and a solid dihydric or polyhydric alcohol would react in the solid state to form a polymer.

The field of the polymerization of solids warrants intensive study since it may shed considerable light on the mechanism of polymerization and copolymerization. The implications in this fact, that crystalline bodies such as divinylbenzene and diisopropenyldiphenyl have been observed to polymerize, pose many questions to be answered. Does one monomer leave a crystal lattice to approach another monomer to effect chain growth? In divinyl and diisopropenyldiphenyl crystals, are the double bonds adjacent and so disposed that polymerization can take place without migration? If a monomer is fixed in a crystal lattice, is the chemical structure of the polymer fixed so that inversion of the repeating units in the polymer may occur and so that in a solid phase polymerization a head-to-head polymer may be formed whereas a head-to-tail polymerization may occur in a liquid system? Are the monomers in an emulsion lattice oriented in some fashion similar to crystalline monomers? How and why is the external crystal form maintained in the polymerization of crystalline monomers while the X-ray pattern changes?

Solid Phase Condensation Polymers

HOMOGENEOUS SYSTEM

Such a system would be represented by solid or crystalline hydroxy acids, for example, hydroxyundecylenic acid, undergoing condensation with the elimination of by-product water. For such a system to remain in the solid phase, it must exist below its melting point, and practically no evidence exists of polymer formation by such a reaction since the rate of esterification is quite low.

HETEROGENEOUS SYSTEMS

Such a system would be represented by a crystalline or solid dicarboxylic acid such as adipic acid and a crystalline polyhydric alcohol such as pentaerythritol or sorbitol. In this case also practically no evidence exists that polymer formation occurs due to the extremely low rate of esterification.

In contrast to additional polymerizations, solid phase condensation polymerizations are complicated by equilibrium conditions between the reactants and the product of reaction and its by-products·

$$\text{Reactants} \rightleftharpoons \text{products} + \text{by-products}$$

Undoubtedly evidence of solid phase condensation polymerization would be found if the by-product were an easily removed product such as a gas. Such a system might comprise a solid dicarboxylic acid chloride and a solid polyhydric alcohol. Such a field warrants further investigation.

LIQUID PHASE PROCESSES

Most polymerization processes involve liquid phase reactions. Practically all the condensation and addition reactions are carried out above the melting point of the monomer or mixture of monomers, comonomers, or comers and are therefore liquid phase processes. In some cases, the liquid phase is obtained by the use of solvents. The wide variation possible in liquid phase polymerization is of extreme technical importance in addition polymers since practically all such polymers are prepared in that manner.

In gaseous polymerization, the limitation was expressed that in such a gaseous polymerization system it was necessary not only that the monomer but also that the products of reaction must exist in the gaseous phase at least to the point where high polymers formed. Analogously, limitations must likewise be placed on a liquid phase process. To be classified as a liquid phase process, not only must the monomer exist in a liquid phase, but the reaction product must also exist in a liquid phase, at least to the point where high polymers are formed.

Liquid phase processes may be subdivided into numerous modifications, as indicated in Figure 1, and the major basic separation is made between homogeneous and heterogeneous systems.

A homogeneous system is defined as one in which there is no separation of either monomer, polymer, or intermediate phase during the polymerization process. A heterogeneous system is defined as a system in which more than one phase exists at any stage of the process. Thus a homogeneous monomer system may become heterogeneous as polymerization progresses. It is even possible for a heterogeneous monomer system to become homogeneous with polymerization. Specific examples for such systems are discussed with each classification. The classification of a system as heterogeneous solely because there were different phases in some stage of its process is not an arbitrary one but is based on the reasoning that the kinetics of a heterogeneous system are much more complicated than homogeneous systems, and that such a system warrants special attention.

Mass Polymerization

Mass polymerization is also called "block" polymerization. This process is called mass polymerization because the monomer in a liquid form is polymerized in "mass," whereby (1) the monomer acts as solvent for the monomer and in most cases for the polymer and (2) the polymer acts as solvent for the polymer. The polymer is usually obtained as a solid casting or "block" from which the process derived its alternate name. Mass polymerization may be homogeneous or heterogeneous. When styrene is polymerized in mass, the solution gradually increases in viscosity until a solid polymer is obtained without the separation of phases. Such a system is a homogeneous mass polymerization system. In contrast, liquid vinyl chloride polymerizes to produce a polyvinyl chloride which precipitates as a fine powder insoluble in the monomer until substantially all the monomer is converted to polymer. Acrylonitrile and acrylic acid behave in the same manner. Likewise, a copolymer of styrene and maleic anhydride precipitates from a homogeneous solution of styrene and maleic anhydride.

ADDITION POLYMERIZATION

Homogeneous system. In general, mass polymerization methods are not used widely industrially for addition polymers because of the large free energy change that occurs with the disappearance of olefinic bonds (20,000 calories per mole). Laboratory samples of polymers are conveniently prepared in this manner because, as a rule, the mass used is small, and a rather uniform temperature may be maintained throughout the mass. In industrial processes special precautions must be used since heat transfer problems are complicated by large masses. Usually the monomer is polymerized to 25 to 35 per cent conversion or to such a stage of viscosity that it can be readily agitated and heat removed during polymerizations, and still be pourable into containers or forms for further polymerization under controlled conditions. Continuous polymerization systems have been developed for styrene and some monomers.

Heterogeneous system. Such a system is represented by a mixture of incompatible monomers. All components of the system are polymerizable, but separate phases exist in which at least one of the polymerizable components is in a liquid phase. Such a system is represented by a mixture of styrene and fumaric dianilide or styrene and fumaryl nitrile within certain concentrations. Both fumaric dianilide and fumaryl nitrile are solids. In the styrene and fumaryl nitrile system the phases, within certain limits, have a tendency to disappear as polymerization progresses if the mass is agitated, since the copolymer of styrene and fumaryl nitrile, as formed, acts as a blending agent for the separate monomers. In other cases, even if both monomers are liquid, precipitation of the copolymer will occur if the copolymer is not soluble in either monomer. The system described above is of little technical or academic interest not only because of the uncontrollable variances obtained in finished products prepared in this manner but also because such a system is difficult to study. Copolymers of incompatible monomers are best prepared by solution in mutual solvents or in dispersed systems, as, for example, by emulsion polymerization.

CONDENSATION PROCESS

Such a system would be described by the amidation or esterification of appropriate amino acids or hydroxy acids. These reactions are the normal amide and ester formation processes; they do not involve heats of reaction of the order found in addition polymers, and are carried out at temperatures above the melting points of the reactants. Since these types of reactions are carried out with relative ease, they have found wide industrial application in the preparation of numerous polymers, particularly among the nylons and a group of polyester resins such as a number of alkyd resins. These reactions are more readily controlled and are prepared in larger batches than for the addition polymers. Sometimes the weight of the finished polymer exceeds 10,000 pounds per batch.

Solution Processes

The solution process is distinguished from liquid mass polymerization by the addition of solvents. The added non-polymerizable component may be an active solvent or a partial solvent. An active solvent is a true solvent for both monomer and polymer, whereas a partial solvent is an active solvent for the monomer and not for the polymer. The partial solvent may be chosen so that all polymers precipitate regardless of molecular weight, or only polymers of definite minimum or higher molecular weight will precipitate. This may be accomplished by selection of solvents or by a mixture of them. Partial solvents obviously result in a heterogeneous system. An example of homogeneous solution of the addition polymerization type may be found in the polymerization of styrene in xylene, methyl methacrylate in ethyl acetate, vinyl acetate in acetone, etc. The polymerization of vinyl chloride in hexane represents a heterogeneous system in which the monomer is soluble but the polymer is insoluble.

Solution polymerization is used industrially for a number of reasons. It offers a more positive temperature control over the polymerization since the solvent, particularly under reflux, can act as a heat-transfer medium. Solution polymerizations are, as a rule, more uniform than mass polymerizations since the presence of the solvent permits agitation during polymerization and thereby eliminates "local" reactions and overheating. Likewise, since many polymers are used in solution for impregnation and coatings, there is great economy in preparing the polymer in a one-stage process.

The use of partial solvents is determined by several considerations. Where the polymer is desired in a fine state of subdivision, partial solvents may be used effectively to accomplish that objective. Partial solvents seem to be effective in producing isolable polymers having a certain minimum degree of polymerization. This is because the solubility of any certain polymer decreases with degree of polymerization and at a certain chain length precipitation will occur. As an example, the low molecular weight polyvinyl chlorides are dissolved in a host of solvents, whereas the high molecular weight polymers have little or no solubility in the same solvents. In a selected solvent all the high polymers will precipitate, leaving the low polymers in solution. Such a system is expected to produce a more homogeneous polymer than one prepared in a mass polymerization system. Such a principle has been applied to the preparation of copolymers of vinyl chloride and vinyl acetate in hexane.[10] In Chapter 9, such a system is considered in more detail under diffusion propagation. Solution processes are more often applied to addition polymerization than to condensation polymers.

Dispersions in General

PARTICLE SIZE AND SETTLING

Dispersion systems involve two components, a dispersion medium and a dispersed phase. When dispersion systems are used in polymerizations, the polymerizable components comprise the dispersed phase, and the dispersion phase is non-polymerizable. Dispersed systems can be prepared in which the dispersed particle size can vary from atomic to visible dimensions. Dispersions in which the particle size exists in the lower end of the scale are called solutions. Such a system has already been discussed. Between the lower limits called solutions and the upper limit of large settling particles, a large number of dispersed systems exist which are relatively stable. The particle dimensions of such relatively stable systems lie between 1 millimicron as a lower limit and 1 micron as an upper limit. Such dispersed systems are divided into suspensoids and emulsoids. No sharp transition boundary can be made in the particle sizes of solutions, emulsions, or suspensions, but it is generally agreed as a result of observation that a transition from solution to emulsion occurs at an approximate particle size of 1 millimicron and from emulsoids to suspensoids at 1 micron. Suspensoids are relatively inert suspended solids. Above 1 micron the particles do not disperse easily and settle readily if not agitated. Some of the differences between emulsoids and suspensoids are:

(1) Emulsoids have electrical charges and are irreversibly precipitated by electrolytes whereas suspensoids may or may not be charged.
(2) Emulsions have an observable Brownian movement under a microscope whereas suspensoids are devoid of such movement.
(3) The viscosity of an emulsion is not much greater or only slightly greater than that of the dispersion medium, but much less than that of a solution of the same polymer. Suspensoids do not change the viscosity of the medium.

Dispersed polymerization systems are concerned with monomers insoluble in a dispersing medium. The conditions of such a system are the same as for any other dispersed particles, with the exception that, since the particle comprises polymerizable materials, polymerization will occur if the conditions are appropriate.

VISCOSITY

Any insoluble particle of a substance, liquid or solid, in contact with another liquid will sink or float, depending on the relative densities of the substance and the liquid. As the particle size decreases, the settling velocity of the particle becomes constant, and when the particle becomes very small, viscous flow becomes evident. Robinson[11] has modified Stokes' equation on settling and has related the settling factor (phase separation, breaking power) of emulsion to particle size and density as follows:

$$C = \frac{d^2(S - S_1)_g}{18\eta} \tag{1}$$

where C = rate of dispersion separation in centimeters per second,

d = diameter of the spherical particles in centimeters,

S = density of the emulsified particles in grams per cubic centimeters,

S_1 = density of the whole emulsion in grams per cubic centimeters,

g = gravity constant (981 centimeters per second ^{2}),

η = viscosity of the emulsion in poises.

This equation shows that C is directly proportional to d, the size of the particle, which, if made smaller, produces a more stable dispersion. As the particle size decreases, those particles that fall within the colloidal range of 1 to 500 millimicrons begin to exhibit the oscillatory or zig-zag motion known as Brownian movement. Likewise, since settling or separation is due to density differences, those systems in which the dispersed phase and the dispersion medium approach each other in density represent the more stable dispersions.

Robinson's equation also indicates that the higher the viscosity of a given emulsion, the more stable the dispersion. However, in many practical applications of dispersions, such as emulsions, very high viscosities are undesirable, and a compromise is usually made between viscosity and stability. Finally, stable systems can be prepared only by preventing the finer droplets of the dispersion from reuniting into coarser droplets.

THE WORK OF DISPERSION

The preparation of a dispersed system, for example, an emulsion, requires work. Thomas defines the amount of work required [12] on the systems as equal to the product of the interfacial tension and the increase in surface as a result of preparing the emulsions.

$$W = \gamma \, \Delta S \qquad (2)$$

where W = work in ergs per square centimeter,

γ = interfacial tensions in ergs per square centimeter,

ΔS = the increase in square centimeters of the surface of the dispersed phase.

Since the original surface of the dispersed phase is small compared to the surface of the dispersed phase in emulsified form, ΔS may be considered to be related to the volume of the emulsion droplets and to their diameters as $\Delta S = 6V/d$, and the total work required is

$$W = \gamma \frac{V}{d} \qquad (3)$$

where V = total volume of the emulsified internal phase in cubic centimeters,

d = diameter of the emulsified drops in centimeters.

This equation shows that more work is required to produce an emulsion of finer particles than one of coarse particles, and that if the particle size is kept constant, less work is required if the interfacial tension is reduced or, conversely, the same amount of work will produce a finer particle size as the surface tension is reduced.

Dispersion agents—emulsifying agents. Although it is possible to produce a dispersion that consists primarily of two components, the dispersed phase and the dispersion phase, such dispersions as mercury in water, whose particle size ranges from 0.5 to 1.5 microns, are relatively unstable and require considerable work for their preparation. This consideration has led to the introduction of a third body, which can lower the interfacial tension, into such a system. Such bodies, called emulsifying agents, are capable of sufficiently reducing the interfacial tension so as to produce emulsions. If a colloidal mill is used in the preparation of an emulsion, the interfacial tension must be reduced by means of emulsifying agents to 10 dynes or less; if the emulsion is to be prepared spontaneously such as by simple paddling or stirring, the interfacial tension should be reduced to 1 dyne or less.[13]

Protective colloids. The main factors in the preparation of a dispersed system, such as an emulsoid or a suspensoid, already considered, do not necessarily prevent coalescence of the particles. The sensitivity to coalescence may be decreased by protective colloids. This protective action is similar to the phenomenon resulting from the addition of gelatin to a silver sol. When gelatin is added to such a sol, larger quantities of electrolyte are required to precipitate the gold or silver colloid than in the absence of the gelatin. In the preparation of polymers from monomers, particularly in those containing $CH_2{=}C\diagup^{\diagdown}$ groups, another complication exists not normally found in the preparation of emulsion colloids. Many monomers, when polymerized in dispersions, progress from a liquid to a highly viscous mass with great adhesive and cohesive properties. In such cases, protective colloids are sometimes used. This protective film itself must be non-adherent so that, if two dispersed particles come into contact with each other, there will be no coalescence and little or no resistance to separation. In polymerization processes, dispersion systems may be summarized as in Table 1.

TABLE 1

	Stability of System	Particle Dimension	Dispersion Medium
1. Solution	Non-settling	Atomic	Solvent
2. Emulsoid	Relatively non-settling	Greater than atomic from about 1 millimicron to a micron	Non-solvent
3. Suspensoid	Settling	A micron or greater	Non-solvent

Solution polymerization has already been considered; and emulsoids and suspensoids remain to be considered.

The general concept of emulsion covers a large number of products that, under a microscope, appear to be a liquid medium in which are suspended minute droplets of a second liquid. As a rule, the liquid in liquid dispersions is known as an emulsion, but by common consent the term has been extended to include dispersions of molten or solid materials such as a wax or a resin in a liquid, even if the dispersed phase becomes solid on cooling.

Polymer Dispersions—Emulsoids and Suspensoids

As a process of preparing polymers, this system is not concerned with the preparation of dispersed systems from preformed polymers. Dispersion polymerization refers to the process of preparing polymers directly from monomers in a dispersed system and polymerizing the dispersed monomer. The particle size of the dispersed phase of the polymer, which is the desired final form, determines whether emulsoids (1 millimicron to 1 micron) or dispersoids (>1 micron) are obtained. Since dispersoids are considered to be systems containing relatively inert suspended solids of particle size, so that their stability is poor, they find little or no technical importance as such, though the suspension process is used industrially to prepare the polymer and the polymer product isolated from the dispersing phase. The dispersed products of industry are as a rule very stable emulsions in which the dispersion phase is, in most cases, substantially water. Most of these emulsions are the products of addition polymerizations.

EMULSION POLYMERIZATIONS

In an emulsion polymerization system there are four basic components:

The dispersion medium. It is inert to the monomer. In most systems the medium consists of water of a high degree of purity and represents 25 to 85 per cent of the total weight of the system. The density and solubility characteristics of the aqueous phase may be changed by water-soluble monohydric and polyhydric alcohols such as ethyl alcohol, ethylene glycol, glycerin, etc. Such modifiers are used in small quantities, usually less than 10 per cent of the total amount of water.

The dispersed phase. It comprises the polymerizable material. This phase may be a single monomer or a mixture of monomers, comonomers, comers, etc. With mixtures, copolymers are obtained. The polymerizable phase may comprise up to 75 per cent of the total weight of the system, and is insoluble in the dispersion system.

The emulsifying agent. Since most emulsion polymerization systems are carried out with simple agitation, the interfacial tensions between the monomer phase and the water phase must be reduced considerably to produce stable emulsions. Often the choice of the emulsifying agent is a critical one, because sometimes, even if excellent emulsification is obtained, the rates of polymerization and the polymers obtained may vary rather greatly with a series of emulsifying agents. Typical emulsifying agents that may be mentioned are the sodium, potassium, ammonium, and alkyl ammonium salts of the long-chain carboxylic, sulfinic, and sulfonic acids; the alkylated aromatic sulfonic acids, etc., as well as some of the acid salts of long-chain primary, secondary, and tertiary amines. In conjunction with emulsifying agents, surface tension regulators, protective colloids, and buffers are often used. Though not essential to all emulsion polymerizations, they lend uniformity and control to such processes.

Surface Tension Regulators. As polymerization occurs, the emulsion system changes from a monomer emulsion system to a polymer emulsion system, accompanied by a change in the interfacial tension between the dispersed phase and the dispersion phase. In many emulsion systems, certain substances, when added to the emulsion system, have been found to maintain a favorable particle size condition. Such substances are usually aliphatic alcohol with a chain length of five to ten carbon atoms. They have been called surface tension regulators and are effective at less than 0.5 per cent of the monomer weight.

Buffers. Most emulsion polymerization systems are very critical to hydrogen ion conditions which must be maintained throughout the process. In some systems, because of the hydrolysis or changes in the monomer, the emulsifying agents, the catalyst, large changes in pH result, and the polymerization may become inhibited or retarded. The standard buffers, such as the phosphates, borates, and acetates, are used in required amounts, usually less than 3 per cent.

Protective Colloids. They are used not only to prevent premature precipitation of either the monomer or the polymer emulsion but also to prevent the coalescence of the viscous cohesive and adhesive particles that exist as an intermediate form in many polymerizations. Hydroxyethylcellulose, methylcellulose, sodium carboxymethylcellulose, polyvinyl alcohol, gelatin, starch, casein, the alginates, and related substances are widely used as protective colloids. Some protective colloids, such as polyvinyl alcohol or sodium polyacrylate, may also function as dispersion agents in certain emulsoid and suspensoid polymer systems.

The catalyst. Its function is to accelerate the rate of polymerization. In emulsions the catalyst behaves as it does in mass or solution polymerization, that is, although it increases the rate of polymerization, it decreases the molecular weight of the polymer. Water-soluble catalysts are preferred in emulsion systems, but water-insoluble catalysts may be used either alone or in conjunction with the water-soluble ones. Some catalysts such as ammonium persulfate may also act as emulsifying agents. The vinyl acetate–water and ammonium persulfate system produces excellent emulsions in the absence of added emulsifying agents. Many emulsion systems polymerize readily without catalyst, though it is an economic advantage to use 0.05 to 1 per cent of catalyst. The water-soluble peracids or their compounds are effective catalysts, such as hydrogen peroxide, and urea peroxide; the inorganic perborates, persulfates, and percarbonates are effective catalysts as well as the ozonides, ozone and oxygen. In many polymerization systems, oxygen may act as an inhibitor rather than an accelerator, and then the system must be purged of oxygen.

Catalyst Activator. Most catalysts such as are used in vinyl addition polymerization are oxidizing agents. In many cases, when such a polymerization is carried out in the presence of a reducing substance capable of reacting with the oxidizing agent, the reaction proceeds at a much higher rate. Such systems are called reduction activated polymerizations since they are initiated by free radicals which are the reactive intermediate products of the oxidation-reduction process. In these systems the period of inhibition is likewise reduced. A number of oxidizable salts, metals, organic and inorganic compounds have been found to act as reduction activating agents. Some of them are iron, copper, sulfurous acid, sulfites, bisulfites, metabisulfites, hydrosulfites, sulfoxylates, thiosulfates, and hydroquinone.[14-20]

Polymerization Regulators. In many systems a polymerization regulator is used in conjunction with the catalyst. These compounds appear to have a direct influence on the course of the polymerization, particularly in reducing branching or crosslinking, or even the molecular weight. Certain mercaptans, like dodecyl mercaptan, which is used in emulsion polymerization of butadiene copolymers, may be mentioned as an example. Its direct action appears to favor the 1,4 addition of butadiene instead of the 1,2 and 3,4 addition which produces cross-linking:

$$-CH_2-CH=CH-CH_2-$$

1,4 addition—
results in a chain

$$-CH_2-CH-$$
$$\quad\quad\quad |$$
$$-CH_2-CH-$$

1,2 and 3,4 addition—
results in crosslinking

The mercaptan may also act as a catalyst activator in a reduction activation system.[21-23] In emulsion polymerization of monomers containing a single $CH_2=C$ grouping, the aliphatic chlorinated compounds, such as carbon tetrachloride, hexachloroethane, chloroacetamide,[6] chloroacetonitrile,[6] seem to have a beneficial influence on the polymerization by acting as telomers or chain transfer agents. The catalyst regulator is used in concentrations of 1 to 5 per cent, depending on its efficiency and the system in which it is used.

THE ADVANTAGES OF EMULSION POLYMERIZATION

Most polymerization emulsions use water as the dispersing phase, and in such a system many advantages may be found that more than outweigh the disadvantages. The extensive use of natural rubber latex as a technical product indicated the obvious advantages that would be gained in use of emulsions of synthetic polymers. Other values are found in economies and improvements in manufacturing processes. The advantages of emulsion polymers may be listed as follows:

(1) The polymerization reaction admits of a high degree of control. The heat liberated during polymerization is easily dissipated by transfer to the aqueous dispersing medium, and the temperature of the polymerizing mass is thereby readily controlled.

(2) There is greater uniformity of end product from batch to batch than can be obtained in mass polymerization.

(3) There is an absence of organic solvents that may be inflammable or toxic. At any rate, they are more expensive than water, and many of the synthetic latices may be used without the addition of organic solvents.

(4) The solid polymers may be easily isolated in a finely divided form by precipitation, and readily washed free of impurities. The processing and compounding of the precipitated polymer are facilitated by the fine particle size.

(5) The viscosity of a polymer in an aqueous emulsion is much lower than an equivalent solution of the same polymer in an organic solvent, and impregnating processes are more readily accomplished by use of the emulsion. It is interesting to compare the low viscosity of a synthetic rubber latex emulsion containing 35 to 40 per cent polymer with the very high viscosity of a solution in benzene of the same polymer after it has been isolated from the aqueous emulsion. It is obvious that the viscosity values do not measure the same values for the emulsion-dispersed phase and for the solvent-dispersed phase.

(6) The rate of polymerization is much faster in emulsion than in mass or solution polymerization. Months are required to polymerize butadiene by itself and without a catalyst, whereas in the emulsion process without catalyst the polymerization is completed in about 15 days and in the presence of catalyst within 24 hours or less.

(7) The emulsion process is easily interrupted at any stage of the polymerization and thereby lends itself to the addition of other materials, either coreactive substances such as other monomers, or nonreactive components which may facilitate the polymerization or subsequently modify the properties of the polymer.

(8) In many instances emulsion polymerization reduces the degree of undesirable side reactions. Less branching is found in vinyl polymers thus prepared, and, as a rule, the molecular weight is higher. In the butadiene polymers cyclization is reduced.[24]

(9) Many monomers that copolymerize poorly in mass, copolymerize readily in emulsion.[25]

These particular advantages have been the main reason for the adoption of emulsion polymerization not only to vinyl and acrylic polymers, but also to the preparation of synthetic rubbers from butadiene and other comonomers.

In final form the emulsion usually has the appearance of a milklike latex, though often translucent and transparent emulsions are obtained. The particle sizes of the dispersed polymers in commercial emulsion range from 0.1 micron (100 millimicrons) to 0.5 micron. The emulsion may be precipitated by electrolytes such as aluminum sulfate solutions and sodium chloride–sulfuric acid solutions, or by organic substances which are soluble in the dispersing phase but non-solvents for the polymer.

SUSPENSOID POLYMERIZATIONS—BEADS OR PEARLS

In a suspension polymerization process, the dispersed phase exists as discrete macroscopic beads during the monomer phase, during polymerization, and after polymerization is completed. This system represents particles of dimensions larger than emulsoids and therefore is a suspensoid. Basically the process is related to the emulsion system in that the dispersion agents function as suspension stabilizers, because of particle size of the dispersed phase, rather than as emulsifying agents. In suspension polymerization there are four basic components.

The dispersion medium. The dispersion medium is a liquid which is chemically inert to the monomer or the polymerizable components. In most industrial applications the medium used is water, though it may be a non-reactive organic liquid in which the monomers and polymers are insoluble. The dispersion medium may comprise as little as 40 per cent of the polymerization system.

The suspended phase. This phase, which comprises the polymerizable materials, may be a single monomer or a plurality of monomers, as comonomers or comers. Where a plurality of polymerizable components are used, copolymers are obtained only if the monomer components are copolymerizable in bulk or mass polymerization. Dispersion polymerization differs from emulsion polymerization in that many copolymerizations that occur in emulsion do not occur in mass polymerization. Furthermore, if mutual inhibition by a pair of monomers occurs in mass polymerization, similar inhibitions are found in suspension polymerization. In suspension polymerization the polymerizable components may be as high as 60 per cent of the system. The dispersed monomer phase may also contain dissolved or absorbed plasticizers, lubricants, dyes, etc. Kinetic studies indicate that suspension polymerizations are essentially bulk or mass polymerizations in bead form effectively controlled thermally by the dispersing medium.

Catalyst. Many suspension polymerizations may be performed in the absence of catalysts. Then the rate of polymerization corresponds to that of a thermally initiated mass or bulk polymerization. A catalyst may be used to accelerate the polymerization and the catalyst functions as it does in other systems, where simultaneously with the acceleration of the polymerization rate, there is a decrease in the molecular weight of the polymer. Two types of catalysts may be used in suspension polymerizations, depending on the phase in which the catalyst is soluble. Since water is the most common dispersion medium, ionic catalysts like $AlCl_3$, BF_3, which react with the medium, are not used. In suspension polymerizations these catalysts may be used.

1. *Monomer-soluble catalysts.* They are usually insoluble in water or are so much less soluble in water than in the monomer that, owing to the distribution coefficient, they are concentrated in the monomer phase.

2. *Dispersion-phase soluble catalysts.* In general, it may be stated that monomer-soluble catalysts are more effective than the water-

soluble catalysts. In the water-suspension polymerization of styrene at 90 C, using 1 per cent of catalyst as calculated on the weight of the monomer, the initial rate of polymerization using benzoyl peroxide is eight to ten times greater, in terms of moles of polymer per liter per hour, than the rate produced by ammonium persulfate.

THE NEED OF SUSPENSION STABILIZERS

The dispersion agent in a suspension system is known as a suspension stabilizer in contrast to an emulsion polymerization wherein the dispersion agent is called an emulsion agent. In a suspension polymerization system which involves only water, catalyst, and polymerizable monomers, dispersion is accomplished by agitation, usually in the form of stirring or shaking. The agitated system consists of catalyzed beads of monomer dispersed in water. If agitation is stopped, the monomer beads, depending on the relative density of the monomer to water, will rise or sink, and then coalesce to a homogeneous liquid layer. The beads of monomer will be reformed on stirring if the mechanical work supplied is sufficient to prevent agglomeration. The average size of these beads depends on a dynamic and not a statistical phenomenon, that is, globules collide, agglomerate, and are mechanically redispersed. The stability of these beads appears to be related to an interfacial property between the dispersed and the dispersing phase.

Once polymerization is initiated, the nature of the bead must necessarily change as it consists of polymer dissolved in monomer. As the concentration of the polymer increases with greater degrees of conversion, the viscosity of the bead first increases, then the bead becomes quite gummy and tacky, and finally becomes hard and smooth. In general, most polymers progress through a viscous to a gummy stage before the final degree of polymerization is attained. The point or percentage of conversion at which the viscous stage becomes evident depends on the specific monomer or mixture of monomers used; but, as a rule, this point ranges between 10 and 30 per cent. Similarly, most polymers become hard and lose their tacky condition between 70 to 90 per cent conversion. If the beads in the viscous or tacky stage come into contact with each other, agglomeration occurs. Whereas the original monomer droplets were easily redispersed, the viscous agglomerated monomer-polymer bead cannot, now, be redispersed readily. In most cases, if the conversion has proceeded to a considerable extent, there can be no redispersion regardless of the intensity of agitation. The effects, in that case, are similar to beating an insoluble dough. Only a few monomers such as vinyl chloride, vinylidene chloride, and acrylonitrile are free of a troublesome viscous or tacky stage during polymerizations, primarily because these polymers are insoluble in or only slightly swollen by monomer.

Since the particle sizes in a suspensoid polymerization are much larger than those in an emulsion system and since the suspensoids cream rapidly in the absence of agitation, the polymerization must be carried out under continuous agitation, at least to the point where a solid non-tacky product is obtained. The fundamental principles of dispersions which have been considered earlier apply to the preparation of suspension polymers. This process, however, is not concerned with the preparation of suspensoids from preformed polymers, but rather with the preparation of polymers themselves by suspensoid processes. The application of these principles to an addition polymerization system of an ethylenic type monomer is indicated in a consideration of the factors affecting dispersion systems.

Density. As previously noted, Robinson related the settling factor of dispersed particles to the densities of the dispersed and dispersion phases, respectively. A dispersion system, in which the densities of the dispersed and dispersion phases are identical or approach each other, has a relatively high degree of stability. For the same reason, the beads have little or no tendency to accumulate at the bottom of the reactor or on the surface of the medium. With adjusted or controlled densities, the beads are suspended uniformly throughout the mass. The density of the dispersion medium may be adjusted as required by the addition of substances of higher or lower density than the dispersion medium. These additives may be organic or inorganic, liquid or solid substances soluble in the dispersing medium. It is obvious that additives which produce secondary undesirable effects, such as inhibition, cannot be used.

Viscosity. Robinson's relation has also shown that the higher the viscosity of the dispersion medium, the higher the stability of the dispersion. The viscosity of the dispersion medium may be increased by the addition of viscosity controlling substances soluble in the dispersion medium, as, for example, glycerin, glycol, diethylene glycol, to water. In general, polymerization inhibitors or monomer-solubilizing substances in high concentrations should be avoided.

Interfacial agents. The work of dispersion was already shown to be the product of the interfacial tension and the increase in the surface of the dispersed phase.

$$W = \gamma \, \Delta S \tag{4}$$

or

$$\Delta S = \frac{W}{\gamma} \tag{5}$$

If the work value is maintained as a constant, the relation becomes

$$\Delta S = \frac{K}{\gamma} \tag{6}$$

that is, as the surface tension is lowered, the change in surface area becomes larger, and consequently, the particles become smaller. Obviously, a large decrease in surface tension produces emulsions and not suspensions. The corollary then is that only a slight change in surface tension is necessary to produce marked improvements in the stability of a suspension system. Many substances are effective in accomplishing this change in surface tension, some more effectively than others when used at the same concentration. The quantities to be used depend on the product desired as well as on the nature of the polymerizable phase, the concentration of the medium, the nature of the medium, the conditions of polymerization, the presence of other active substances, and the deliberate or accidental presence of impurities. However, in general, any substance capable of producing a change in the interfacial tension between the dispersion medium and the dispersed phase may be satisfactory. Cautious use must be made of very active substances such as effective emulsifying agents, when used as dispersion agents, because often, even with small concentration, part of the system is obtained as an emulsion system. Some of the reagents that may be used in the preparation of suspension polymers are:

Electrolytes. A solution of electrolyte in water will increase the interfacial tension between the water and the dispersed polymerizable phase due to a concentration of ionic charges at the interface.

Surface Active Agents. Although, in the broadest sense, electrolytes are surface active agents as indicated above, this terminology has been reserved for molecules possessing a hydrocarbon group which is hydrophobic and a soluble group which is hydrophylic. Both groups greatly influence the nature and the property of the agent. The nature and the length of the hydrocarbon group, whether alkyl, aryl, alkaryl, aralkyl, whether linear or branched, bear directly on the properties and uses of the surface active agents. Flett [26] has indicated the utility of a number of soaps and sodium alkyl sulfonates, varying in classification from dispersion agents to washing agents in accordance with the hydrocarbon chain length as shown in Table 2.

The nature of the solubilizing group determines the classification of the surface active agent as anionic, cationic, and non-ionic. The sodium salts of the fatty acids (soaps) and the corresponding alcohol sulfonates, sulfates, phosphates, and thiosulfates are typical of the anionic class whose aqueous dispersions are negatively charged. Surface active

TABLE 2

Properties of Surface Active Agent	Number of Carbon Atoms in Chain	Soaps	Sodium Alkyl Sulfonates
Surface active in concentrated solutions	1	Sodium formate	Sodium methyl sulfate
	2	Sodium acetate	Sodium ethyl sulfate
	3	Sodium propionate	Sodium propyl sulfate
Solubilizers	4	Sodium butyrate	Sodium butyl sulfate
	5	Sodium valerate	Sodium amyl sulfate
	6	Sodium caproate	Sodium hexyl sulfate
	8	Sodium caprylate	Sodium capryl sulfate
Wetting and foaming	10	Sodium caprate	Sodium decyl sulfate
	12	Sodium laurate	Sodium lauryl sulfate
	14	Sodium myristate	Sodium myristyl sulfate
Washing	16	Sodium palinitate	Sodium cetyl sulfate
	18	Sodium stearate	Sodium stearyl sulfate

agents in which cations act as the solubilizing groups are also known, in which the solubilizing action depends on amino or ammonium groups. Cetyl pyridinium chloride is a typical example of a cationic surface active agent, the aqueous dispersions of which are positively charged.

The non-ionic surface agents do not form salts with acids or bases, and, under normal conditions, their dispersions do not carry electrical or ionic charges. Solubilization of this class of agents is achieved by a series of hydroxyl ether groups, and the hydroxy polyethylene ether of diamylphenol, $(C_5H_{11})_2$—⟨⟩—$O(CH_2CH_2O)_{11}H$, is a commercial example of a non-ionic surface active agent. In a suspension system, these substances are concentrated at the interface of the dispersed and dispersing phases.

Insoluble Inorganic Dispersion Agents. A large number of water-insoluble inorganic oxides, hydroxides, and salts, when very finely divided, are concentrated at the interface of an aqueous dispersion system and thereby improve the stability of the system. Röhm and Trommsdorff [27] were among the first to show that solid dispersion agents which are insoluble in water could be used in the suspension polymerization of bead polymers. These authors showed that kaolin, talc, barium sulfate, kieselguhr, aluminum oxide, and ferric oxide could be used. A typical example of their formulation was given as

Ethyl acrylate	95 parts
Water	400 parts
Talc	5 parts
Benzoyl peroxide	0.1 part

The mixture was polymerized with agitation at 70 C for 3 hours to produce fine beads. A suspension of very fine magnesium carbonate has been the commercial preparation of methyl methacrylate pearls for a number of years.[28] The insoluble carbonates, sulfates, phosphates, or silicates of aluminum, calcium, barium, or magnesium may be used in a similar manner.

The particle size of the finely divided pigments which have been found to give satisfactory dispersions have a diameter of less than a micron. Some satisfactory ranges for stable dispersions have been indicated by Fischer and Gans [29] as:

Zinc oxide (rubber grade)	0.10 to 0.12 micron
Titanium dioxide (anatase)	0.20 to 0.35 micron
Whiting (calcium carbonate)	0.85 micron

For the preparation of good dispersions, the inorganic solids should be deflocculated, that is, each solid particle should remain geometrically independent and unassociated with adjacent particles. Such deflocculated suspensions show low yield values approaching zero.[30]

Surface active agents may be used to facilitate pigment dispersions in water systems, and water-soluble reagents are particularly effective. These surface active agents deflocculate the pigment particles by forming a monomolecular layer on the pigment. For many pigments less than 1 per cent is needed, and as the size of the pigment becomes smaller 2 to 3 per cent is required.[31]

Polymeric Water-Soluble Organic Suspension Agents. These substances are polymeric and of high molecular weight. They differ in molecular weight from the surface active agents such as the soaps whose molecular weights are less than one thousand. Furthermore, these polymeric substances contain a multiplicity of solubilizing groups along the polymeric chain, usually one group per polymer or copolymer segmer unit. In low concentrations they dissolve in water to form colloidal solutions, and in a dispersion system are concentrated at the interface. These polymeric dispersion agents may be natural or synthetic and may be classified further as non-ionic, anionic, and cationic.

Among the non-ionic types are such compounds as methylcellulose, hydroxyethylcellulose, and polyvinyl alcohol.[17] Polysodium acrylate, sodium alginate, carboxymethylcellulose and its soluble salts, and the acid and the water-soluble salts of polymerized ethylenic polycarboxylic acids [32, 33] have been successfully used as anionic suspension agents in the preparation of polymeric beads.

Water-dispersible salts of chitin and of polymeric compounds having amino or ammonium substitution are typical of cationic suspension agents but, to date, have found no application for that purpose.

Although most of the suspension stabilizers function by an interface mechanism, many exert a secondary effect by the formation of a thin organic or inorganic layer on the dispersed bead, thereby functioning as a protective colloid and diminishing or eliminating the tendency of the globules to coalesce on contact with each other. If the dispersed beads do not coalesce on contact, the particle size distribution is a statistical and not a dynamic phenomenon, and the distribution is determined by the summation of all the physical factors of the system.

It becomes apparent that many suspension stabilizers may perform more than one function. Sodium chloride may be added to increase simultaneously the interfacial tension and the density. Sodium polyacrylate may be added as an electrolyte as well as a surface active agent. By analogous reasoning, stabilization of the suspension may be achieved by the combination of two or more methods. As previously indicated, an insoluble organic dispersion agent may be used in the presence of a surface active agent. If the surface active agent is of the non-ionic type, a suitable electrolyte may be added. As a further example, a non-ionic polymeric water-soluble organic suspension agent may be used in the presence of one of its anionic derivatives or homologues.

No generalized condition can be formulated for the preparation of dispersion polymers. Each polymer system must be considered separately since the conditions for the preparation of a definite polymer may be unsatisfactory even for a copolymer based on the same parent monomer as the major polymerizable component. A number of factors affect the successful preparation of polymer beads. The first of them is the monomer itself. It must be borne in mind that no monomer is completely insoluble in water, if water is used as the dispersing phase. In fact, some monomers such as acrylonitrile, methacrylonitrile, and vinyl acetate are quite soluble in water. The quantities of monomer that dissolve in the water phase may undergo solution polymerization. The initiation of polymerization in the aqueous phase, however, is somewhat retarded because of the use of water-insoluble catalyst. Furthermore, as polymerization progresses, the monomer finally is absorbed or dissolved in polymer and removed from the aqueous phase. Since solution polymerizations tend to produce polymers of low molecular weight, high solubilizing conditions should be avoided in suspension polymerizations. If the monomer is relatively water soluble, the solubility may be reduced by the addition of salt. If the monomer is relatively or only slightly insoluble, care must be used in the selection of viscosity-controlling ingredients, since they may increase the solubility of the monomer.

The ratio of monomer to dispersion phase, the reactive nature of the monomers, the presence of comonomers and comers, the nature and type of dispersion agents, the type of catalyst, the temperature of polymerization, the rate of stirring, and the adhesive nature of the swollen intermediate monomer-polymer bead are among the factors to be considered in the preparation of suspension polymers.

The polymeric beads prepared by suspension polymerization range in size from microscopic beads, which appear macroscopically as a fine powder, to pearls which the author has prepared in sizes as large as one-quarter inch in diameter. Such beads have considerable resiliency, and beads of polystyrene or acrylonitrile-ethyl acrylate copolymer exhibit bouncing properties similar to those of rubber balls. Large mass castings of polystyrene or of the copolymer showed no such physical properties. This property may be attributed not only to the physical shape of the particle but probably also to a "polymer skin" on the bead where the molecular weight of the skin may be of a slightly different order of magnitude from that of the core of the bead. When properly prepared the beads are clear and internally free, as determined by X-rays, of the suspension agents used in the polymerization system.

Bead polymerization is advantageous in that it produces a polymer, which after being washed and dried is in condition for processing. Bead polymers are rarely used directly. In most applications they are processed with dyes, lubricants, etc., prior to use. Divinylbenzene cross-linked styrene beads may be sulfonated and used directly as one of the most effective cation exchange resins known.[34, 35]

CONDENSATION DISPERSION POLYMERIZATIONS

Dispersion systems are not generally used for the preparation of condensation polymers. Such a system requires that the monomer or comers as well as the derived polymers are insoluble in the dispersion medium. In most cases, not water, but an inert high boiling organic liquid is used as the dispersion medium. Such a system would be represented by the preparation of polyamides from aminocaproic acid or hexamethylene diamine and adipic acid in a mineral oil at a temperature in which the reactants and the product of the reactants are in a liquid condition so that agitation can disperse the insoluble polymerizable phase. The system is so constructed that by-products of the condensation, such as water, are removed as formed, thereby favoring the formation of polymers of high molecular weight. On completion of polymerization, the temperature of the system is lowered at least to a point where solidification of the polymer occurs. The polymer is then removed by filtration and washed free of surface contaminants.

In the preparation of polyesters, such as polyethylene succinate from ethylene glycol and succinic acid, such esterification catalysts as small quantities of zinc chloride, lead oxide, or toluene sulfonic acid may be used.

REFERENCES

1. E. W. Fawcett *et al.*, U. S. Patent 2,153,553 (April 11, 1939); British Patent 471,590 (Feb. 4, 1936).
2. W. H. Carmody and M. O. Carmody, *J. Am. Chem. Soc.*, **59**, 2073 (1937).
3. G. Gee, *Trans. Faraday Soc.*, **34**, 712 (1938).
4. J. W. Breitenbach, *Oesterr. Chem. Ztg.*, **42**, 232 (1939).
5. J. W. Hill and W. H. Carothers, *J. Am. Chem. Soc.*, **57**, 925 (1935).
6. G. F. D'Alelio, Unpublished results.
7. G. F. D'Alelio, U. S. Patent 2,405,817.
8. G. F. D'Alelio, U. S. Patent 2,378,195.
9. I. Valyi, A. G. Janssen, and H. Mark, *J. Phys. Chem.*, **49**, 461 (1945).
10. E. W. Reid, U. S. Patent 2,064,565 (Dec. 15, 1936).
11. C. S. Robinson, *Ind. Eng. Chem.*, **18**, 869 (1926).
12. A. W. Thomas, *J. Am. Leather Chem. Assoc.*, **22**, 171 (1927).
13. P. Finkle, H. D. Draper, and J. H. Hildebrand, *J. Am. Chem. Soc.*, **45**, 2780 (1923).
14. R. G. R. Bacon, *Trans. Faraday Soc.*, **42**, 140–155 (1946).
15. J. H. Baxendale, M. G. Evans, and G. S. Park, *Trans. Faraday Soc.*, **42**, 155–169 (1946).
16. L. B. Morgan, *Trans. Faraday Soc.*, **42**, 169–183 (1946).
17. G. F. D'Alelio, *A Laboratory Manual of Plastics and Synthetic Resins*, p. 95, John Wiley and Sons, New York, 1943.
18. French Patent 812,267 (Aug. 4, 1937).
19. C. F. Fryling, U. S. Patent 2,379,431.
20. E. C. Britton and W. J. Le Fevre, U. S. Patent 2,333,633.
21. I. M. Kolthoff and W. E. Harris, *J. Polymer Sci.*, **2**, 41–48 (1947).
22. I. M. Kolthoff and W. E. Harris, *J. Polymer Sci.*, **2**, 49–71 (1947).
23. I. M. Kolthoff and W. E. Harris, *J. Polymer Sci.*, **2**, 72–81 (1947).
24. P. Stöcklin, *Trans. Inst. Rubber Ind.*, **15**, 51 (1939–1940).
25. H. Hopff, *Angew. Chem.*, **51**, 432 (1938).
26. Lawrence H. Flett, Vol. VI, p. 243, *Colloid Chemistry*, Jerome Alexander (Editor), Reinhold Publishing Corp., New York, 1946.
27. Otto Röhm and Ernest Trommsdorff, U. S. Patent 2,171,765.
28. British Intelligence Objectives Sub-Committee Final Report No. 363, p. 9, Röhm und Haas, A. G. Darmstadt, London, H. M. Stationery Office.
29. Earl K. Fischer and David M. Gans, Vol. VI, p. 291, *Colloid Chemistry*, Jerome Alexander (Editor), Reinhold Publishing Corp., New York, 1946.
30. H. Green, *Ind. Eng. Chem.*, **15**, 123 (1923).
31. E. K. Fischer and David M. Gans, Vol. VI, pp. 316–326, *Colloid Chemistry*, Jerome Alexander (Editor), Reinhold Publishing Corp., New York, 1946.
32. G. F. D'Alelio, U. S. Patent 2,294,226.
33. H. W. Arnold and G. L. Dorough, U. S. Patent 2,232,515.
34. G. F. D'Alelio, U. S. Patent 2,366,007.
35. W. C. Bauman and J. Eichhorn, *J. Am. Chem. Soc.*, **69**, 2830 (1947).

CHAPTER 7

Molecular Weight Determinations

The non-homogeneity of polymers was discussed in Chapter 4, and it was shown by fractionation methods that polymers consist of a mixture of molecules differing in molecular weights. The molecular weights assigned to a polymer were shown to be an average value, and it has been the custom to designate these average values by an overline over the value considered. Thus the average values of the number average molecular weights, weight average molecular weights, and sedimentation average molecular weights are designated, respectively, as $\overline{M}_n$, $\overline{M}_w$, and $\overline{M}_z$. Similarly, the average degree of polymerization may be indicated by $\overline{DP}$, the average osmotic pressure as $\overline{\pi}$, etc.

The methods or means of determining the molecular weights of either the unfractionated polymer, or of its fractions, are considered in this chapter. The methods of measurement may be divided into the physical methods and the chemical methods.

MOLECULAR WEIGHTS BY PHYSICAL METHODS

Molecular Weights from Osmotic Pressure

The existence of a pressure when a solution is separated from the solvent by a semipermeable membrane is due thermodynamically to the differences of the fugacity [1] of either the solute or solvent in the solution phase and in the solvent phase. It can be shown that through osmotic pressure and fugacity relations, by means of partial molal free energy, partial molal volume, partial molal heat content, and partial molal entropy changes, the osmotic pressure can be directly related to molecular weight.[2]

The relationship of molecular weight to osmotic pressure is given by the van't Hoff equation:

$$M = \frac{RT}{(\pi/C)} \tag{1}$$

or

$$\pi = \frac{RT}{M} \cdot C$$

215

The equation $M = RT/\pi/C$, has been shown to be applicable to dilute solutions of low molecular weight polymers. If the van't Hoff equation is valid, the value of π/C would be a constant and independent of concentration. This value is not verified in a plot of π/C against C for high molecular weight polymers. This is shown in Figure 1 for a number of polymers investigated by Flory.[3]

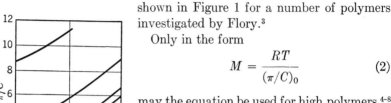

Only in the form

$$M = \frac{RT}{(\pi/C)_0} \qquad (2)$$

may the equation be used for high polymers.[4-8] The value $(\pi/C)_0$ represents the reduced osmotic pressure and is obtained by extrapolating the osmotic pressure concentration ratio, π/C, to zero concentration. The reduced osmotic pressure molecular weight relation becomes

FIGURE 1. π/C as a function of C. (Reprinted by permission from the authors and the *Journal of the American Chemical Society.*)

$$\bar{M}_n = \frac{RT}{(\pi/C)_0} \qquad (3)$$

where R represents the gas constant, T the absolute temperature, π the osmotic pressure expressed in grams per square centimeter, C the concentration expressed in grams per 100 cubic centimeters, and $\bar{M}_n$ the number average molecular weight since the osmotic pressure depends on the number of particles. A typical example of such calculations is shown in the work of Flory.[3] In his work the polymer was polyisobutylene dissolved in cyclohexane, and the specific polymer was a well-fractionated sample. The data are summarized in Table 1.[3]

TABLE 1

Polymer Sample	C in grams/100 cc Solvent	π in grams/sq cm	π/C
1	2.04	10.82	5.31
2	2.00	10.58	5.29
3	1.50	5.73	3.82
4	1.02	2.57	2.52
5	1.00	2.42	2.42
6	0.76	1.32	1.74
7	0.51	0.65	1.28
8	0.34	0.30	0.88

Reprinted by permission from the authors and the *Journal of the American Chemical Society.*

Most osmotic measurements are made at 25 C, and for this particular sample the molecular weight becomes

$$M_n = \frac{2.53 \times 10^5}{(\pi/C)_0} = \frac{2.53 \times 10^5}{0.30} = 8.1 \times 10^5 = 810{,}000$$

The value of $(\pi/C)_0 = 0.30$ was obtained by extrapolation of curve B of Figure 1.

This method, using the reduced osmotic pressure, was used extensively by Dorby.[9]

Mark and his co-worker [10,11] used this method in a study of the osmotic pressure–viscosity molecular weight relationship of a number of fractionated samples of cellulose acetate which were characterized and reported by Sookne et al. in a previous paper.[12]

The data in Figure 1 show that the value (π/C) increases rapidly with concentration and they show a curved relationship. In a good solvent in which the partial molal heat of solution is zero, the relationship may be linear or only slightly curved. Flory,[4] Huggins,[8] and Miller [13] have obtained a linear relationship derived on thermodynamic and statistical studies, indicating the need for corrective terms in the osmotic pressure equation. Thermodynamically, the osmotic pressure and the partial molal volume of the solvent are related to the partial molal free energy of dilution by the equation:

$$\pi \overline{V}_1 = -\overline{\Delta F}_1 = T \overline{\Delta S}_1 - \overline{\Delta H}_1 \tag{4}$$

where $\overline{V}_1$ is the partial molal volume of the solvent; $\overline{\Delta F}_1$ is the partial molal free energy of dilution.

Huggins,[14,15] using statistical mechanics, derived the equation for the partial molal entropy of solution as

$$\overline{\Delta S}_1 = -R \left[\ln(1 - V_2) + \left(1 - \frac{\overline{V}_1}{\overline{V}_2}\right) V_2 + \frac{1}{Z'} V_2 + \frac{4}{3(Z')^2} V_2{}^3 + \cdots \right] \tag{5}$$

or

$$\frac{\overline{\Delta S}_1}{R} = \frac{\overline{V}_1}{\overline{V}_2} V_2 + \left(\frac{1}{2} - \frac{1}{Z'}\right) V_2{}^2 + \cdots \tag{6}$$

The value of $\overline{\Delta H}_1$ has been given by Scatchard [16] and Hildebrand [17] in the expression

$$\overline{\Delta H}_1 = K_{1,2} \overline{V}_1 V_2{}^2 \tag{7}$$

In equations 6 and 7:

$Z' =$ the effective average coordination number of the solvent molecules and solute submolecules,

$V_2 =$ the volume fraction of the solute,

$\overline{V}_2$ = the partial molal volume of the solute,

$\overline{V}_1$ = the partial molal volume of the solvent,

$K_{1,2}$ = constant, depending on the interaction of solvent and solute.

If the volume fractions are converted to grams per cubic centimeter, the osmotic pressure equation 4 becomes

$$\frac{\pi}{C_0} = RT\left[\frac{1}{M_2} + \frac{1}{d_2{}^2\overline{V}_1}\left(\frac{1}{2} - \frac{1}{Z'} - \frac{K_{1,2}}{RT}\right)C_0 + \cdots\right] \tag{8}$$

Huggins considers the coefficient of C_0 as an empirical constant, μ_1, and expresses the relation as

$$\frac{\pi}{C_0} = RT\left[\frac{1}{M_2} + \frac{1}{d_2{}^2\overline{V}_1}\left(\frac{1}{2} - \mu_1\right)C_0 + \cdots\right] \tag{9}$$

The above equation may be expressed in the following form, and includes the deviation from so-called ideal behavior, heat of mixing, etc.

$$\frac{\pi}{C_2} = \left[\frac{RT}{M_2} + \frac{RTd_1}{M_1d_2{}^2}\left(\frac{1}{2} - \mu\right)C_2 + \cdots\right] \tag{10}$$

where C_2 is concentration of solute in grams per millimeter, d_1 and d_2 are the densities of the solvent and solute respectively, M_1 and M_2 are the molecular weights of solvent and solute respectively, R is the gas constant, T is the absolute temperature, π is osmotic pressure, and μ_1 is a constant which characterizes the components of a system and is considered to be constant only at low concentrations of polymer (25 grams per liter or less).

Huggins [14] has tabulated a number of values of μ_1 for certain polymers, and the data for a few selected polymers are given below in Table 2.

TABLE 2

Polymer	Solvent	μ_1	Temperature, °C
Cellulose triacetate	Tetrachloroethane	−1.8	24.4
Cellulose tributyrate	Acetone	0.36	25
Cellulose nitrate	Cyclohexanone	0.15	27
Cellulose nitrate	Acetone	0.30	25
Polystyrene	Toluene	0.44	27
Polystyrene	Benzene	0.20	5
Polyvinyl chloride	Tetrahydrofurane	0.14	27
Polyvinyl chloride	1,4-dioxane	0.52	27
Rubber	Benzene	0.44	25
Rubber	Ether	0.55	15–20
Rubber	Carbon tetrachloride	0.28	15–20

The use of an added term [19] in equation 10 is found to be important sometimes for the calculation of molecular weights using osmotic pressure data. At other times it is negligible. This can be demonstrated by plotting the values of

$$\frac{\pi}{C_2} \quad \text{and} \quad \left[\frac{\pi}{C_2} - \frac{RTd_1C_2{}^2}{3M_1d_2{}^3} \right]$$

against C_2, in which case the value of the intercept, at which $C_2 = 0$, is inversely proportional to the molecular weight:

$$\frac{RT}{M_2} = \left(\frac{\pi}{C_2} - \frac{RTd_1C_2{}^2}{3M_1d_2{}^3} \right)_{C=0} \tag{11}$$

In a specific case, Huggins, using data of Table 3 obtained by Caspari,[18] showed that a molecular weight of 94,000 was obtained for a sample of rubber when the third term was included, whereas a molecular weight of 102,000 was indicated when the term was excluded. This difference in molecular weights is shown graphically in Figure 2.[19]

TABLE 3

OSMOTIC PRESSURE OF RUBBER IN LIGHT PETROLEUM

$M_1 = 93$ $T = 298$ K
$d_1 = 0.68$ $R = 82.07$ ml atm per degree
$d_2 = 0.92$ $\pi = \dfrac{hd_s}{1033}$

d_s = density of solution = 0.74 gram per ml

C_2, grams per ml	h, cm	π/C_2, ml atm per gram	$\dfrac{RTd_2C_2{}^2}{3M_1d_2{}^3}$	$\left(\dfrac{\pi}{C_2} - \dfrac{RTd_1C_2{}^2}{3M_1d_2{}^3} \right)$
0.0354	39.4	0.796	0.096	0.700
0.0267	24.6	0.659	0.055	0.604
0.0179	13.0	0.520	0.025	0.495
0.0050	2.2	0.320	0.002	0.318
0	....	0.240[*a]		0.260[*b]

* Extrapolated value, a = molecular weight of 102,000 and b = molecular weight of 94,000.

OSMOTIC MEASUREMENTS

The static method and the dynamic method of measurement may be used to determine the osmotic pressure of a solution.

The static method. In the static method, the osmotic pressure of the solution is balanced by the liquid column or head that develops by the influx of solvent into the solution. The system is simple, and the

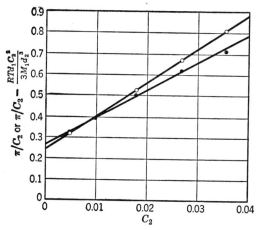

FIGURE 2. Osmotic pressure of rubber in light petroleum with (black dots) and without (white dots) the third term, $\dfrac{\pi}{C_2} - \dfrac{RTd_1C_2^2}{3M_1d_2^3}$. (Reprinted by permission from *Industrial and Engineering Chemistry*.)

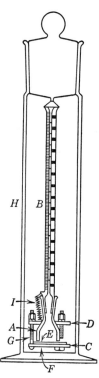

A = heavy glass cell
B = capillary tube of approximately
     0.7 mm bore and 300 mm scale
C = clamp base
D = clamp yoke
E = membrane
F = perforated membrane support
G = yoke bolts
H = outer cylinder
I = spring

FIGURE 3. Modified Schulz osmometer.

equipment is easily constructed. Basically, it consists of a membrane separating a tube containing the solution and an attached calibrated capillary, and a container for the solvent. The static method is described by Herzog and Spurlin,[20] and Meyer and Boissonnas.[21]

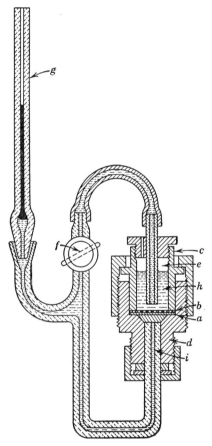

FIGURE 4. The Bourdillon osmometer.

a = membrane
b = perforated supporting plate for membrane
c = upper section of chamber
d = lower section of membrane

e = cell chamber
f = stopcock
g = manometer
h = outer fluid
i = inner fluid

The basic principles of the static-elevation osmometer were adopted by Schulz [22] (Figure 3) for general use and by Bourdillon [23] (Figure 4) for micro-quantities of solution since it uses 0.2 milliliter of solution and is effective at concentrations as low as 0.25 millimole per liter.

The operation of any osmotic pressure measurement depends primarily on the performance of the membrane used. Not only must the membrane be semipermeable, but for the practical operation it should also have a high rate of solvent transfer. Regenerated cellulose that has never been dried appears to be the best general-purpose membrane.[24]

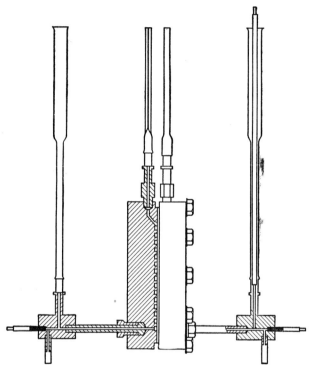

FIGURE 5a. Fuoss-Mead dynamic-equilibrium osmometer (complete). (From R. M. Fuoss and D. J. Mead, "Osmotic Pressures of Polyvinyl Chloride Solutions by a Dynamic Method," *J. Phys. Chem.*, **47**, 59 [1943]. The Williams and Wilkins Company, Baltimore, publishers.)

The dynamic method. The dynamic method depends upon counterbalancing the osmotic pressure by an externally applied pressure of known magnitude. The external pressure required to prevent the flow of solvent, at zero instrument head, in or out of the solution is equal to the osmotic pressure of this solution. This system was introduced by Berkeley and Hartley[25] and has had many modifications. The dynamic method, as applied by van Campen[26] and Obogi and Broda,[24] was substantially improved by Fuoss and Mead.[27] The vertical capillary type of Fuoss and Mead appears to be the best form[27] (Figure 5a) of osmometer to use for the molecular weight determination of polymers.

Goldblum has shown [28] some of the sources of error in the Fuoss-Mead osmometer and has suggested certain improvements in its design and operation. The design of the osmometer plate is shown in Figure 5*b*,

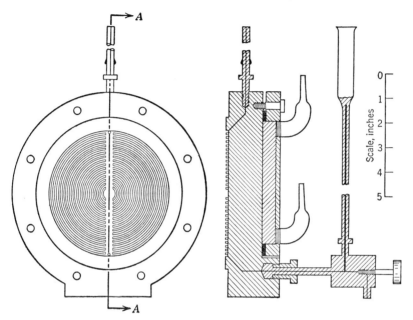

FIGURE 5*b*. Osmometer plate.   FIGURE 5*c*. Section of osmometer plate through *A–A*.

and a cross section is shown in Figure 5*c*. He also points out that a temperature control within 0.004 C is desirable for accurate measurements.

Molecular Weight from Viscosity Measurements

VISCOSITY OF LIQUIDS

Solutions or melts of high polymers exhibit flow characteristics which are very different from those of ordinary liquids. Not only are the viscosities of the melts high, but the viscosities of their solutions are also large compared to that of the solvent, even when very dilute solutions are used. The viscosity of a 50 per cent sucrose solution in water will be about 1.5 poises at room temperature, whereas a 10 per cent solution of medium high molecular weight polystyrene will be in excess of 50 poises. The poise, the absolute unit of viscosity, is defined as the viscosity of a material which requires a shearing force of 1 dyne per square centimeter to maintain a velocity gradient of 1 centimeter per second between two planes 1 centimeter apart. The relation is expressed mathematically as

$$\eta = \frac{\tau}{dv/dx} \qquad (12)$$

where η = viscosity in grams per centimeter per second,
   τ = shearing force in dynes per square centimeter,
   dv/dx = velocity gradient perpendicular to the plates in centimeters per second.

The term *poise* was first used in a series of researches performed by J. L. M. Poiseuille in 1846.[29, 30]

Viscosity may be considered a phenomenon of internal friction which regulates the motion of adjacent portions of liquid, and its reciprocal is defined as fluidity, ϕ. The units of measurement of fluidity are *rhes*, centimeter seconds per gram,

$$\phi = \frac{1}{\eta}$$

NEWTONIAN AND NON-NEWTONIAN LIQUIDS

If the shearing stress, τ, of a simple low molecular weight liquid is plotted against its velocity gradient, dv/dx, a linear relationship is found as shown in curve A of Figure 6. Such a linear relation shows that the viscosity is independent of the rate of shear. Such liquids are known as Newtonian liquids. Many high molecular weight liquids, or solutions of high molecular weight substances, do not exhibit this simple linear relation and are known as non-Newtonian liquids. This may be observed in curve B, and means that the viscosity of the liquid decreases with increasing stress. Solutions of high molecular weight polymers are non-Newtonian liquids if concentrated solutions are used for measurement. If the viscosity of the solution is several times that of the solvent, large variations in the viscosity values are obtained. However, if the relative viscosity of the solution is less than 1.5, the change in viscosity produced by variations in shear stress is probably not large.

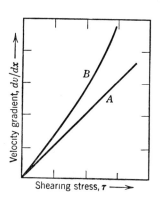

FIGURE 6. Velocity gradient as a function of shearing stress.

Staudinger [31] studied the variations of specific viscosity as a function of velocity gradient for solution in tetralin at 20 C for a polystyrene of 600,000 molecular weight. Figure 7 summarizes these studies for various concentrations:

Curve A	0.40 per cent
Curve B	0.20
Curve C	0.10
Curve D	0.05
Curve E	0.01

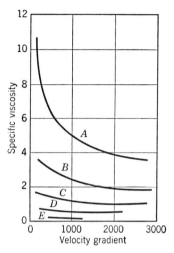

FIGURE 7. The relation of specific viscosity to velocity gradient.

In these curves, it will be observed that not only the concentration but also the specific viscosity of the solution is a factor in determining the change in viscosity.

In their studies on polyvinyl chloride in different solvents, Mead and Fuoss [32] corrected their viscosities to zero rate of shear. In other studies, Baker, Fuller, and Heiss [33] showed that capillary size caused a variation in the viscosities of the concentrated solutions of ω-hydroxyundecanoic polymers, but, for dilute solutions, the viscosities did not vary with capillary size.

A complicating factor in the use of viscosity-molecular weight measurements is that the polymers are characterized by having one dimension great in comparison to the other dimensions. Staudinger [34-36] rationalized to a proportionality between the length of a molecule, and therefore its molecular weight, and its effect on viscosity by starting with Einstein's equation

$$\eta^* = \eta(1 + \phi) \tag{13}$$

relating the effect of a colloidal particle on the viscosity of the liquid in which it is suspended, wherein η^* is the viscosity coefficient of the suspension, η is viscosity of the solvent, and ϕ is the fraction of the volume occupied by the suspended particle. In this equation, the conditions must be such [37] that the particles are spheres uniformly distributed at random in such a concentration that the mean distance between suspended molecules is large compared to their radii, and the radii of the suspended molecules are large compared to the radii of the solvent molecules. The Einstein equation can be written as:

$$\frac{\eta^*}{\eta} - 1 = K\phi \tag{14}$$

The ratio η^*/η is known as the relative viscosity η_r, and the value $\eta_r - 1$ as the specific viscosity, sp, so that equation 14 becomes

$$\eta_{sp} = K\phi \qquad (15)$$

For higher concentrations this relationship is no longer linear but is expressed as a power series expansion as

$$\eta_{sp} = K_1\phi + K_2\phi^2 + K_3\phi^3 + \cdots \qquad (16)$$

The value of the coefficient $K_1 = 2.5$, whereas the value of the second coefficient, K_2, which is of value in the explanation of the change of intrinsic viscosity with concentration of polymers in solution, is not known with the same certitude.

This problem has been studied by Guth et al.,[38, 39] Eilers,[40, 41] and Simha.[42] As an example, Eilers correlated specific viscosity in the form of a power series expansion in this expression:

$$\eta_{sp} = 2.5\phi + 4.94\phi^2 + 8.78\phi^3 + \cdots \qquad (17)$$

Staudinger,[31] recognizing that polymers were not spherical particles as was assumed in the derivation, calculated the volume swept out by a molecule spinning about an axis perpendicular to its length as $(l/2)^2\pi d$, where l is the length of the molecule and d is its thickness. Staudinger next assumed that, for molecules of linear structure, the molecular weight is proportional to the length of the polymer. He obtained the equations

$$\eta_{sp} = K_m M C_{gm} \qquad (18)$$

$$\frac{\eta_{sp}}{C_{gm}} = K_m M = \frac{\eta - \eta_0}{\eta_0} \qquad (19)$$

where K_m = a characteristic constant,

C_{gm} = concentration in gram unit group (primary moles) per liter, that is, weight of polymer in grams equal to the molecular weight of the monomer (for example, 104 for polystyrene),

M = molecular weight of polymer,

η = viscosity of the solution,

η_0 = viscosity of the solvent.

Staudinger[31] demonstrated that the specific viscosity of carbon tetrachloride solutions of paraffins, aliphatic esters, and ketones was given by the equation

$$\frac{\eta_{sp}}{C_{gm}} = ny + x = K_m M \qquad (20)$$

where C_{gm} is given in grams per liter divided by 14 for each —CH_2—group, n equals the number of carbon atoms in the molecule, and y and x are constants. For the equation to be valid, the value of n must be greater than 9. Once the constants are known, the equation for molecular weight becomes

$$M = \frac{K_m}{\eta_{sp}/C_{gm}} = \frac{K_m}{\text{reduced viscosity}} \qquad (21)$$

where η_{sp}/C_{gm} is the reduced viscosity, that is, the viscosity increase per unit concentration. In this case Staudinger and his co-workers determined the constant K from viscosities of polymers in a relatively low molecular weight range, and by extrapolating K_m far beyond the range for which it was determined, he obtained molecular weights up to and higher than 100,000 for polystyrene, rubber, cellulose derivatives, etc.

It must be noted that the value η_{sp}/C as a function of C is not necessarily constant. Daneš [43] has taken very careful measurements on polystyrene in benzene solution, and the plot of data is shown in Figure 8. The limiting viscosity is obtained by extrapolation to zero concentration.

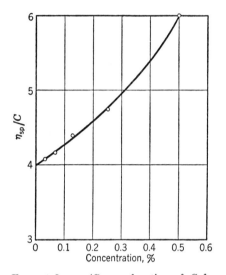

FIGURE 8. η_{sp}/C as a function of C for polystyrene in benzene solution.

To compensate for this variation, Staudinger defined the proportionality in terms of the limit approached by the reduced viscosity at infinite dilution, thus

$$K_m M = \left(\frac{\eta_{sp}}{C_{gm}}\right)_0 = \left(\frac{\eta_{sp}}{C_{gm}}\right)_{\lim C \to 0} \qquad (22)$$

Staudinger also expressed a logarithmic relation between viscosity and molecular weight as

$$K_m M = \left[\frac{\log_{10} \eta_r}{C_{gm}}\right]_0 = \left[\frac{\log_{10} \eta_r}{C_{gm}}\right]_{\lim C \to 0} \qquad (23)$$

wherein $(\log_{10} \eta_r)/C_{gm}$ is the inherent viscosity. Hess and Sakurada [44] showed that the inherent viscosity form of equation 23 varies less with concentration than the reduced viscosity form [45,46] of equation 22. They showed also that, if natural logarithms are used, the two forms approach each other at infinite dilution,

$$\lim_{C \to 0} \left(\frac{\eta_{sp}}{C} \right) = \lim_{C \to 0} \left(\frac{\ln \eta_r}{C} \right) \tag{24}$$

wherein C is grams of polymer per 1000 cubic centimeters of solution and not to be confused with C_{gm}. The relationship in equation 24 is illustrated in Figure 9.[45]

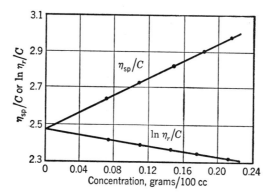

FIGURE 9. Relation of η_{sp}/C to $\ln \eta_r/C$ as a function of concentration.

Kraemer and Van Natta [47] reaffirmed the findings of Hess and Sakurada and introduced the term intrinsic viscosity symbolized by $[\eta]$:

$$[\eta] = \lim_{C \to 0} \left(\frac{\eta_{sp}}{C} \right) = \lim_{C \to 0} \left(\frac{\ln \eta_r}{C} \right) \tag{25}$$

and therefore an appropriate revision [48,49] of the Staudinger equation becomes

$$[\eta] = K_v M \tag{26}$$

Since the value of $[\eta]$ is based on C and not on C_{gm}, the value of the K_v constant in the equation is proportional to, *but not equal to*, the K_m of the Staudinger equation.

Since viscosities are very easily measured and the relationship appears to offer a suitable method for measuring molecular weights, the equation $[\eta] = KM$ was readily accepted and proved to be useful often. For polymers with molecular weights ranging up to 8000 a number of investigators have shown that a small additive term must be added to Staudinger's equation:

$$[\eta] = K_v M + K_0 \tag{27}$$

Meyer and van der Wyk [50] have shown that at 20 C the relationship in equation 27 for normal paraffins in carbon tetrachloride is expressed with the given values for K_v and K_0 as follows:

$$[\eta] = 10.4 \times 10^{-5}M + 0.011 \tag{28}$$

Hibbert and his co-workers [51,52] studied the viscosity-molecular weight relationship of the polyoxyethylene glycols at a number of temperatures in two different solvents. Since the specific viscosities were measured at only one concentration, the intrinsic viscosity relation is not given. The specific viscosity relation, however, follows the form

$$\eta_{sp} = K_m M + B_0 \tag{29}$$

The values of K_m and B_0 are given in Table 4.[51]

TABLE 4

K_m AND B_0 CONSTANTS FOR POLYOXYETHYLENE GLYCOL

Solvent	Temperature, °C	K_m	B_0
Carbon tetrachloride	20	5.7×10^{-5}	0.187
	30	4.8×10^{-5}	0.159
	40	3.4×10^{-5}	0.121
Dioxane	20	6.2×10^{-5}	0.128
	30	5.6×10^{-5}	0.119
	40	5.3×10^{-5}	0.095

Expressed in values of the terms of equation 27, at 20 C, the equation using carbon tetrachloride as a solvent for the polyoxyethylene glycol is given as

$$[\eta] = 0.83 \times 10^{-5}M + 0.034 \tag{30}$$

Flory and Stickney [45] also found a linear relation between viscosity and molecular weight according to the relationship

$$\left(\frac{\ln \eta_r}{C_{gm}}\right)_0 = K_m M + y' \tag{31}$$

for polydecamethylene glycol adipate. Their data are given in Table 5.[45]

TABLE 5

K_m AND y' CONSTANTS FOR POLYDECAMETHYLENE GLYCOL ADIPATE

Solvent	Temperature, °C	K_m	y'
Chlorobenzene	25	3.35×10^{-5}	0.094
	79	2.94×10^{-5}	0.051
Diethyl succinate	79	1.97×10^{-5}	0.067

Expressed in values of the terms of equation 27, the equations become

At 25 C in chlorobenzene: $[\eta] = 2.2 \times 10^{-5}M + 0.060$

At 79 C in chlorobenzene: $[\eta] = 1.87 \times 10^{-5}M + 0.032$

At 79 C in diethyl succinate: $[\eta] = 1.25 \times 10^{-5}M + 0.042$

It should be mentioned that Staudinger appreciated that an additive term was required in the linear relationship of equation 26. As originally proposed by Staudinger,[31] the relationship between molecular weight and viscosity was expressed by the equation

$$[\eta_{sp}/C_{gm}]_0 = K_m(\text{D.P.}) + y \tag{32}$$

where D.P. is the degree of polymerization. It was reasoned that in a low molecular weight polymer, $A—(R)_{\text{D.P.}}—B$, the ratio of end groups A and B to the structural repeating unit, R, is high, producing large changes in polarity and solvent interactions and therefore requiring an additive term, y. As the D.P. value increases, the effect of A and B decreases, the viscosity depends strictly on the degree of polymerization, and the value of y may be neglected. Staudinger used the equation

$$[\eta_{sp}/C_{gm}]_0 = K_m M \tag{33}$$

because, by utilizing the concentration in basal moles, he attempted to express the results of viscosity measurements on different polymers in units which might have about the same proportionality constant with molecular weight. According to Kraemer,[49] equation 34 gives a weight average molecular weight:

$$[\eta] = K_v \bar{M}_w + K_0 \tag{34}$$

NON-LINEAR RELATIONSHIPS. THE KM^a EQUATION

In the domain of high polymers, that is, polymer in excess of 10,000 molecular weight, the original Staudinger equation was subjected to the question of validity. The idea that as a carbon chain is lengthened it remains extended to maximum length was not accepted without question. Meyer and van der Wyk[53] studied the changes in viscosity of the normal paraffins from C_{17} to C_{30} on the viscosity of carbon tetrachloride and found that the viscosity increased more rapidly than the molecular weight.

Carothers and Van Natta[54] studied the viscosity values of high molecular weight polyesters of polyoxydecanoic acid, and found that the molecular weight of the polymers could be obtained by titration up to values of about 25,000. This value was found to be in agreement with molecular weight values obtained in ultracentrifuge determinations. The viscosity method gave reliable and comparable results[47] up to molecular weight values of 16,000, but from this point on, for example, up to 25,000, the discrepancies became greater. This divergence was confirmed by other experimenters.[45, 55]

Staudinger and some of his collaborators [56-60] have shown that the constant K appears to decrease as molecular weight increases. Staudinger attempts to explain this as being due to some peculiarity of the chain configuration or to a branched chain structure rather than to the failure of the law. Meyer [61] insists that such discrepancies cannot, without proof of branching, be interpreted as due to branching, since the quantitative validity of Staudinger's equation, to a given linear polymer, had not been proved. Some of the discrepancies summarized by Meyer, showing a decrease of K_m with molecular weight increase, are given in Table 6.[61]

TABLE 6

Polymer	Molecular Weight	$K_m \times 10^4$	Solvent
Polystyrene	438	7.0	Benzene
	193,000	1.25	Benzene
Polyvinyl chloride	60,000	1.05	Tetrahydrofurane
	150,000	0.54	Tetrahydrofurane
Polyvinyl alcohol	40,000	0.68	Water
	108,000	0.43	Water
Cellulose acetate	678	16.6	m-Cresol
	272,000	3.6	m-Cresol
Polymethylacrylate	74,500	0.45	Acetone
	321,000	0.31	Acetone
Polyvinyl acetate	75,000	0.52	Acetone
	640,000	0.25	Acetone

Mark [62, 63] proposed the form

$$[\eta] = KM^a \quad \text{or} \quad K_m M^a \tag{35}$$

where K and a are two characteristic constants. Houwink [64] established the relationship $[\eta] = KM^a$ for the polymers of methyl acrylate, methyl methacrylate, vinyl alcohol and vinyl acetate on an analysis of results published by Staudinger and Warth [59] and found a to be less than one in some instances. Houwink showed that the value $a = 0.6$ is in agreement with the theoretical calculation of Kuhn,[65, 66] who predicted that for randomly coiled molecules a might be as low as 0.5. Equation 35 expresses a non-linear relation, and a, in many cases, is not 1.0. Those polymers which exhibit a linear reaction are considered special cases in which the exponent, a, is unity or nearly so. Schulz and Dinglinger [67]

illustrated this by their careful study of polymethylmethacrylate polymers. The intrinsic viscosities of eighteen fractions were measured in
chloroform solution at 20 C and the relationship expressed as

$$[\eta_{sp}/C_{gm}]_0 = 0.47 \times 10^{-4}(\text{D.P.}) + 95 \times 10^{-4} \qquad (36)$$

and they show that it is in excellent agreement with the equation

$$[\eta] = KM^a \quad \text{or} \quad [\eta] = 3.3 \times 10^{-5}M^{0.85} \qquad (37)$$

The excellent work of Flory [68] is probably best suited for determining
the validity of the non-linear equation $[\eta] = KM^a$.

Flory [68] examined the relationship between intrinsic viscosity and
the molecular weight of carefully fractionated polyisobutylene. The
intrinsic viscosity was compared with their absolute number average
molecular weight determined by the osmotic pressure method. In this
case, by osmotic pressure measurements, satisfactory precision was
obtained to permit absolute weight determinations of about 1,000,000.
In the equation,

$$\overline{M}_n = \frac{RT}{(\pi/C)_0}$$

where $\overline{M}_n$ is the number average molecular weight, π is expressed in
grams per square centimeter, C in grams per 100 cubic centimeters, and
the value $(\pi/C)_0$ is obtained by the extrapolation of the known values
of π/C to zero concentration. Typical data from these experiments are
shown in Table 7.[68]

TABLE 7

Polymer Designation	Intrinsic Viscosity	$(\pi/C)_0$	Osmotic Molecular Weight
A(7–8)	0.866	1.25	202,000
A(8–9)	0.698	1.86	136,000
A(10–12)	0.495	3.19	79,300
A(12–14)	0.370	4.97	50,900
A(14–17)	0.303	6.38	39,700
A(17–20)	0.260	8.94	28,300
A(24–30)	0.203	12.77	19,800
A(30–40)	0.165	18.11	13,970
A(40–55)	0.137	22.70	11,130

Reprinted by permission from the authors and the *Journal of the American Chemical Society.*

These data may be expressed in the equation

$$[\eta] = KM^a \qquad (38)$$

where the equation for the straight line drawn through a plot of $\overline{M}_n$

versus $[\eta]$ is given as $\log M = 5.378 + 1.56 \log [\eta]$ and where $K = 3.60 \times 10^{-4}$ and $a = 0.64$. The value a is a constant for the specific solvent–solute system.

It becomes apparent that in the equation $[\eta] = KM^a$, when a equals 1, it becomes identical with Staudinger's equation. The equation $[\eta] = KM^a$ seems to hold over a large range of molecular weights, and it has been experimentally proved. The following values tabulate a number of experimental determinations for K and a.

1. For polyhydroxyundecanoic acid in chloroform [33] at 25 C:

$$K = 3.2 \times 10^{-5} \quad \text{and} \quad a = 1$$

2. For polyvinyl alcohol in water [69] at 30 C:

$$K = 5.9 \times 10^{-4} \quad \text{and} \quad a = 0.67$$

3. Polyvinyl chloride in cyclohexanone [32] at 25 C:

$$K = 7.0 \times 10^{-5} \quad \text{and} \quad a = 1$$

4. Polyisobutylene in diisobutylene [68] at 20 C:

$$K = 3.60 \times 10^{-4} \quad \text{and} \quad a = 0.64$$

5. Cellulose acetate in acetone [10] at 25 C:

$$K = 9.1 \times 10^{-4} \quad \text{and} \quad a = 0.67$$

6. Polycaprolactam in 40 per cent sulfuric acid [69] at 20 C:

$$K = 2.4 \times 10^{-4} \quad \text{and} \quad a = 0.51$$

From these examples it may be noted that the a value may vary for different polymers. It may sometimes be one, whereas at other times it is nearly as low as 0.5.

INTRINSIC VISCOSITY IN CONCENTRATED SOLUTION

Huggins[70] indicated a proportionality between the reduced specific viscosity and the concentration of the solution according to the equation

$$\frac{\eta_{sp}}{C} = [\eta] + k[\eta]^2 C + k'[\eta]^3 C^2 \cdots \tag{39}$$

Govaerts and Smets [71] have derived an empirical equation,

$$[\eta] = \frac{\eta_{sp}}{C} [1 + (K - \eta_{sp}/150)\eta_{sp}] \tag{40}$$

or

$$\frac{\eta_{sp}}{C} = [\eta][1 + K\eta_{sp} - \eta^2_{sp}/150] \tag{41}$$

The constant K was determined for a number of polymers and was found to be remarkably constant, as indicated in Table 8.[71]

TABLE 8

Polymer	Solvent	Average Value of K
Polystyrene	Benzene	0.25
Polystyrene	Toluene	0.21
Polystyrene	Tetralin	0.20
Polymethylmethacrylate	Chloroform	0.20
Polyisobutylene	Chloroform	0.27
Polymethacrylonitrile	Acetone	0.27
Polyvinyl alcohol	Water	0.32
Polyvinyl acetate	Benzene	0.25
Polyvinyl acetate	Acetone	0.27

From R. Govaerts and G. Smets, "Determination of Intrinsic Viscosity of Linear Polymers in Concentrated Solution," *J. Polym. Sci.*, **2**, 612 (1947). Interscience Publishers.

These investigators show that if $[\eta]$ is computed by extrapolation of η_{sp}/C as a function of C, many errors are introduced in the values. The Schulz formula,[72]

$$\frac{\eta_{sp}}{C} = [\eta] + k'[\eta]\eta_{sp} \tag{42}$$

also gives variable results. By using the modified equations of Govaerts and Smets,[71] a remarkable consistency is found in the value of $[\eta]$ over a wide range of concentrations, as indicated in the data in Table 9.

It was also observed that with an increase in intrinsic viscosity the calculated values of K decrease. For example, with polystyrenes of increasing molecular weights, the values of K found were

$$[\eta] = 1.37 \times 10^{-2} \quad \text{and} \quad K = 0.32$$

$$[\eta] = 4.88 \times 10^{-2} \quad \text{and} \quad K = 0.21$$

This would indicate that K is a constant describing the shape of the molecule in solution as its molecular weight changes, and that molecules of low and high molecular weight are not extended to the same degree in solution

TABLE 9

POLYVINYL ACETATE

$K = 0.26$ and $[\eta] = 2.19 \times 10^{-2}$

Concentration in grams/liter	η_{sp}	$(\eta_{\mathrm{sp}}/C) \times 10^3$	$[\eta]_{\text{calc.}} \times 10^3$ Modified Equation	$[\eta]_{\text{calc.}} \times 10^3$ Schulz Equation
200	14.85	74.3	21.9	14.4
193	14.13	73.3	21.9	14.8
190	13.80	72.6	21.9	14.9
185	13.18	71.2	21.8	15.2
182	12.75	70.1	21.7	15.3
177	12.60	71.2	22.1	15.7
173	12.00	69.4	22.0	15.9
170	11.51	67.7	21.8	16.0
158	10.46	66.2	22.1	16.8
27	0.67	25.0	21.3	21.0
20	0.49	24.4	21.6	21.5
15	0.37	24.5	22.3	22.2
10	0.23	22.9	21.6	21.5
5	0.11	22.0	21.4	21.3
4	0.09	22.0	21.5	21.5
3	0.07	23.0	22.6	22.6
2	0.04	22.5	22.2	22.2
1	0.02	23.0	22.8	22.8
0.5	0.01	22.0	21.9	21.9

From R. Govaerts and G. Smets, "Determination of Intrinsic Viscosity of Linear Polymers in Concentrated Solution," *J. Polym. Sci.*, **2**, 612 (1947). Interscience Publishers.

VISCOSITY AVERAGE MOLECULAR WEIGHT

In a previous discussion of molecular weight values, in Chapter 4, the number average molecular weight, $\bar{M}_n$, the weight average molecular weight, $\bar{M}_w$, and the sedimentation average molecular weight, $\bar{M}_z$ were discussed and correlated. In the equation

$$[\eta] = KM^a \tag{43}$$

if a equals one, the molecular weight is the weight average molecular weight, $\bar{M}_w$. If, however, a is not one, the definition of viscosity average molecular weight is more complex and is expressed as [70]

$$[\eta] = KM_\eta^{-a} \tag{44}$$

and

$$\bar{M}_\eta = [M_i^a x_i]^{1/a} \tag{45}$$

which is derived as follows.

The intrinsic viscosity on the whole polymer, $[\eta]_T$, in relation to a series of fractions obtained from it is given as

$$[\eta]_T = \sum_1^n [\eta]_i x_i \tag{46}$$

where x_i is the weight fraction of the fraction having a viscosity of $[\eta]_i$. In a relationship involving the following variables, if η_0 is the viscosity of the solvent, $\eta_1 \cdots \eta_i \cdots \eta_n$ are the viscosities of the solutions, including that of the ith fraction, $C_1, C_2 \cdots C_i \cdots C_n$ are the concentrations of the corresponding fractions, $X_1, X_2 \cdots X_n$ are the weight fractions of the fractions in the whole polymer, and C_T is the total concentration of all fractions, then

$$\ln \frac{\eta_1}{\eta_0} = [\eta]_1 C_1 = C_T [\eta]_1 X_1 \tag{47}$$

$$\ln \frac{\eta_2}{\eta_1} = [\eta]_2 C_2 = C_T [\eta]_2 X_2 \tag{48}$$

etc. for $\ln \dfrac{\eta_3}{\eta_2} \cdots$, then

$$\sum_1^n \ln \frac{\eta_i}{\eta_{i-1}} = C_T \sum_1^n [\eta]_i X_i \tag{49}$$

but, since $\eta_n = \eta_T$,

$$\sum_1^n \ln \frac{\eta_i}{\eta_{i-1}} = \ln \frac{\eta_T}{\eta_0} = C_T \sum_1^n [\eta]_i X_i \tag{50}$$

so

$$[\eta]_T = \frac{\ln (\eta_T/\eta_0)}{C_T} = \sum_1^n [\eta]_i X_i \tag{51}$$

but, since

$$[\eta]_i = K \bar{M}_i{}^a \tag{52}$$

then

$$[\eta]_T = K \Sigma M_i{}^a X_i = K \bar{M}_n{}^a \tag{53}$$

or

$$\bar{M}_n = [\Sigma M_i{}^a X_i]^{1/a}$$

Huggins,[8,70,73–75] Flory,[4] Simha,[42,76] Fuoss and Mead,[27] Eyring et al.,[77] Houwink,[64] Kuhn,[78] Mark et al.[79] have shown by theoretical treatment that the value of the exponent a depends on the average shape of the particles of high polymer in the particular solution. They have shown also that if all the particles were in the shape of rigid compact spheres, the value of a would be zero and the intrinsic viscosity would not depend on particle size, a fact which is in conformity with Einstein's law. If the particles were of the shape and characteristics of rigid rods, a would be two. For particles intermediate in shape between rigid compact spheres and rigid rods, such as a long, kinked, soft filament, the value of a would lie between zero and two; but if the filament had shrunk to its most probable length, the value of a would be 0.5. Most polymers when dissolved in a solvent of good solution characteristics show a value for

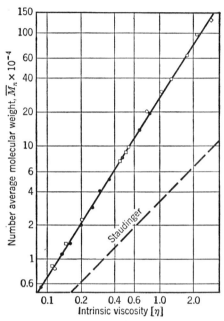

FIGURE 10.   Log $\overline{M}_n$ vs. log (η) for polyisobutylene fractions from polymer A ($\bullet$), polymer C ($\circ$), polymer D ($\square$), and from polymer B ($\diamondsuit$). Molecular weights calculated from Staudinger's relationship are shown by the broken line. (Reprinted by permission from the authors and the *Journal of the American Chemical Society*.)

a between 0.6 and 1.0. It may be readily appreciated that if such a system is disturbed, as for example adding poor solvents or precipitants, the value of a may be changed. If a precipitant is added to a solution of a polymer, the value of a decreases and approaches 0.5 as the system approaches the precipitation point. If the solvent added to a polymer solution favors gel formation instead of precipitation, the value of a becomes greater than one, which means the polymer molecules approach a form of a rigid rod, that is, orientation.

As Flory [80] has already indicated in his criticism of other experimental work, osmotic pressure molecular weight determinations which are correlated to the intrinsic viscosity value for the determination of K and a

must be obtained from well-fractionated samples or with polymers whose molecular size distribution curves are reasonably well known.

Flory's work also illustrates (Figure 10) the discrepancies between the two equations, that is, Staudinger's original equation and the modified equation, for viscosity-molecular weight relation, $[\eta] = KM^a$.

Figure 10 [80] shows that Staudinger's method of measuring the K value for a few substances of low molecular weight and then calculating the viscosities for higher molecular weight was not justified. This extrapolation was far too daring, as shown by Signer and Gross [81-84] who made osmotic pressure measurements on polystyrene and showed that Staudinger's values of molecular weight represent one-half to one-third of the actual values and are correct only to order of magnitude.

Several other authors [32, 68, 85] have also carried out measurements of high polymers and have shown the discrepancies or correlations between cryoscopic viscosity and osmotic values.

Staudinger and Schulz [57, 86] had observed discrepancies between osmotic pressure measurements and molecular weight and interpreted the discrepancies caused by branching. Typical data obtained by Schulz are given here. According to Staudinger's original equation the K_m constant for unbranched polystyrene is 1.8×10^{-4}, and the corresponding values for the K_m constant for polymers prepared at a series of temperatures are shown in Table 10.[80]

TABLE 10

Temperature, °C	K_m
20	1.18×10^{-4}
60	0.79×10^{-4}
100	0.57×10^{-4}
132	0.51×10^{-4}
220	0.42×10^{-4}

With the introduction of the a value, Alfrey, Bartovics, and Mark [87] showed that samples of polystyrene prepared at different temperatures have different values of K and a. Data were obtained by determining osmotic pressure molecular weight and equating $[\eta] = KM^a$. The data are shown in Table 11.

If the log $\bar{M}$ is plotted against log $[\eta]$ for the foregoing data, the points characteristic for the fractions of each sample fall on a straight line, but a different straight line for each sample prepared at different temperatures. This appears to be an indication of different internal structure for the various polystyrenes, that is, they are branched to different degrees.

TABLE 11

Fraction No.	$\overline{M}$	$[\eta]$		
	Sample Polymerized at 60 C			
60–1	2,050,000	355		
60–2	1,580,000	295	$K_\eta = 1.6 \times 10^{-2}$	
60–3	890,000	200	$a = 0.70$	
60–4	550,000	140		
	Sample Polymerized at 120 C			
120–1	340,000	155		
120–2	240,000	118	$K_\eta = 6.6 \times 10^{-3}$	
120–3	167,000	86	$a = 0.80$	
120–4	108,000	62		
	Sample Polymerized at 180 C			
180–1	169,000	73		
180–2	145,000	59	$K_\eta = 4.0 \times 10^{-4}$	
180–3	132,000	53	$a = 1.10$	
180–4	110,000	45		

Reprinted by permission from the authors and the *Journal of the American Chemical Society.*

The calculations by Spencer and Drake [88] show the data for polystyrene in Table 12.

TABLE 12

Temperature of Preparation °C	Solvent in Which Viscosity Was Measured	Temperature, °C	K_η	a
60	Toluene	30	1.2×10^{-4}	0.71
120	Toluene	30	5.4×10^{-4}	0.81
180	Toluene	30	9.8×10^{-4}	1.1

VISCOSITY OF MELTS OR LIQUID POLYMERS

The preceding discussion relating viscosity to molecular weight was concerned primarily with polymers in solution. Molecular weights are susceptible to calculation by measurement of the viscosity of the polymer in the form of a liquid. Since, at normal temperature, only the low molecular weight products such as the oligomers are liquid, most polymers are not adapted to such measurements. At higher than room temperature, a number of polymers melt sharply without decomposition or degradation. Such polymers can be studied by melt viscosity measurements. Generally, a number of "crystalline" polymers, such as polyethylene and the linear polyesters, have melting points sufficiently low and sharp that they can be studied in a melt condition. Most polymers, however, such as polystyrene, polyvinyl chloride, and cellulose acetate, are difficult to treat in this manner. Properly, melt viscosities refer to the liquid viscosity at appropriate temperatures of polymers which at normal temperatures, for example, at 25 C, are solids.

Bingham and a number of other investigators [89-94] sought to correlate the viscosity of a liquid with its molecular structure. A number of homologous series were first investigated in an attempt to locate an "atomic" or "group" viscosity value for certain atoms or atomic groups. The sum of these group values would give the viscosity values of the whole molecule. Analogously, certain values have been assigned to atomic and group refraction and to atomic or group polarization. Within certain limits their additive behaviors are satisfactory as indicated by such values as molar refraction, molar sound velocity, parachor, and molar magnetic rotation. Thorpe and Rodger [94] found that each additional $-CH_2-$ group in an homologous series contributes a viscosity increment, but that these increments are not constant; and each increment depends on the temperature, the number of $-CH_2-$ groups already present, as well as on the terminal groups in the molecule. Bingham [89, 90] later studied the correlation between viscosity and molecular constitution, and he pointed out that (1) the fluidity (ϕ) was better suited for the correlation and (2) the increments for the $-CH_2-$ group in an homologous series were more regular than previously realized, if the different members of the series were compared at constant fluidity rather than at constant temperature.

However, attempts to correlate viscosity or fluidity with chemical constitution in compounds not members of an homologous series have been unsuccessful, probably because viscosity depends not only on the size and shape of the molecules of the liquid, but also on the van der Waals' forces in a particular class of molecules.

However, Eyring and his collaborators [77, 95] have proved that no fundamental relationship has been shown between viscosity and the chemical constitution of organic compounds, even though viscosity of liquids can be very successfully correlated with other physical properties such as compressibility, heat of fusion, and entropy of fusion. In a number of polymers, Flory [96] has shown that the molecular weights of linear polyesters can be correlated with their melt viscosities by the following equation:

$$\log_\eta = A + BM^{\frac{1}{2}} - \frac{C}{T} \qquad (54)$$

where η is viscosity in poises at temperature T; M is weight average molecular weight; and A, B, and C are constants characteristic for a given polymer homologous series.

Figure 11[96] illustrates how closely Flory's relationships in equation 54 represent the molecular weights of polyhexamethyleneglycol adipates

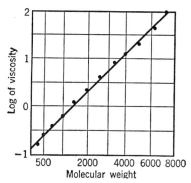

FIGURE 11. Viscosity-molecular weight relationship of polyhexamethyleneglycol adipates. (Reprinted by permission from the authors and the *Journal of the American Chemical Society*.)

over a range of 200 to 8000. Table 13[96] tabulates his values for the three constants A, B, and C in a number of polyesters.

TABLE 13

VALUES OF A, B, AND C IN EQUATION 54 FOR A FEW HIGH POLYMERS MEASURED AT 109 C

Polymers	A	B	C
Decamethylene sebacate	-1.429	1760	0.1108
Decamethylene adipate	-1.435	1800	0.1144
Decamethylene succinate	-1.37	1870	0.112
Diethylene adipate	-1.213	1840	0.0992

Flory called attention to the fact that his empirical relationships confirm Eyring's theory of viscosity, which was based on the assumption of linear, flexible, randomly kinked macromolecules.

Spencer and Dillon [97] have investigated the viscous flow of molten polystyrene of a weight average molecular weight of 360,000 and have determined the effects of temperature and shearing stress in a capillary viscometer. On the assumption that capillary flow is laminar and that the pressure is uniform over a cross section normal to the capillary axis, the rate of shear, D, was expressed by the relation,

$$D = F(\tau)$$

where τ is the shearing stress. The function, F, was related to the volume velocity of flow, Q, by the expression,

$$\eta_0 F(\tau_w) = (\tau_w)\left(\frac{d}{d\tau_w}\right)\left(\frac{\eta_0 Q}{\pi R^3}\right) + 3\left(\frac{\eta_0 Q}{\pi R^3}\right) \tag{55}$$

where η_0 is the limiting viscosity at zero shearing stress, τ_w is the shearing stress at the wall of the capillary, and R is the radius of the capillary. The value of η_0 was calculated according to Poiseuille's law,

$$\frac{1}{4\eta_0} = \frac{Q}{\pi R^3 \tau_w}$$

using extrapolated values of zero shearing stress. Plots of $\log Q/(\pi R^3 \tau_w)$ against τ, which were taken from experimental data, were found to be linear in most cases, so that the extrapolation to zero shearing stress was justified and η_0 could be calculated. For the relation of rate of shear to shearing stress, the approximate relationship was expressed as

$$\eta_0 D = \tau + (7.404 \times 10^{-13})(\tau^{3.268}) \tag{56}$$

In capillary flow, polymer molecules tend to stretch out and to become oriented along the major axis in the direction of flow. When the polymer emerges from the capillary orifice, the molecules tend to return to their original configuration, resulting in a radial expansion of the filament. These authors [97] considered these effects and concluded that their data are in accord with the Eyring theory [98] of viscosity if the changes in the effective areas of the flow units, as the result of flow orientation, are taken into account.

Related studies [99] on the viscous flow of molten polystyrene, using a a parallel plate plastometer, were found to be in excellent agreement with the viscometer studies of Spencer and Dillon.

VISCOSITY MEASUREMENTS

Usually the measurement of viscosities of pure liquids or molten solids is made relative to the viscosity of a known standard substance. The procedures have been standardized by the capillary viscometers of Ostwald and Ubbelohde.

In the Ostwald viscometer the viscosity of the standard substance is given by

$$\eta_0 = C \cdot \rho_0 \cdot t_0 \tag{57}$$

where η_0 is viscosity of the standard substance, at a definite temperature $T \pm 0.1$ C, ρ_0 is the density of the substance at temperature T_0,

C is the viscometer calibration constant, and t_0 is the flow time for the meniscus to fall from A to B in the Ostwald viscometer of Figure 12.

The viscosity, η_x, of the unknown sample is represented by the equation

$$\eta_x = C \cdot \rho_x \cdot t_x \qquad (58)$$

where ρ_x is the density of the unknown at temperature, T_k; t_x is the time of flow at temperature, T_k; and C is the constant in equation 57, since

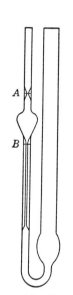

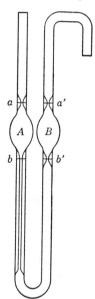

FIGURE 12. Ostwald
viscometer.

FIGURE 13. Ubbelohde
viscometer.

the same viscometer was used. Dividing equation 58 by equation 57 gives

$$\eta_x = \eta_0 \frac{\rho_x t_x}{\rho_0 t_0} \qquad (59)$$

This equation requires a standard material of known viscosity, and the density of both solutions known. Such measurements are usually taken in an Ostwald viscometer. For the values to be sufficiently accurate, the flow time, the period of flow between the marks A and B, should be at least between 100 and 200 seconds so that the system will fulfill the requirements of Newtonian liquid, that is, the rate of shear must be proportional to the shearing stress.

The Ubbelohde viscometer [100] of Figure 13 eliminates the need of density data since the flow occurs under a carefully controlled air pressure. A measured quantity of liquid is used so that while one meniscus is above a, the other is below b'. The liquid is moved by constant pressure from sphere A to sphere B. The time required for the passing of the meniscus between b' and a' is given at t. The viscosity of the unknown at temperature T_k is given as

$$\eta_x = \eta_0 \frac{t_x}{t_0} \tag{60}$$

where η_x, η_0, t_x, and t_0 have the same meanings as in equation 59.

When the viscosity of a pure liquid or melt is measured, a well-known fluid of similar viscosity is used as the standard η_0; but when a solution of a polymer is measured, the solution viscosity is referred to that of the solvent as η_0. For example, the specific viscosity, η_{sp}, of the polymer solution is given by

$$\eta_{sp} = \left[\frac{\text{Time of efflux of polymer solution}}{\text{Time of efflux of solvent}} \right] - 1 \tag{61}$$

The foregoing viscosity equations are based on Poiseuille's relation for Newtonian liquids,

$$\eta = \frac{\pi a^4 P}{8lV} t \tag{62}$$

where a is the radius of the capillary, l is the length, t is the time for V, the volume of the liquid, to pass through the capillary, and P is the driving pressure in dynes per square centimeter. If the same viscometer is used for the standard (solvent) and for the unknown, $\pi a^4/8lV = K$,

$$\eta = KPt \tag{63}$$

and, since the pressure is proportional to density at constant l,

$$\eta_0 = C\rho_0 t_0 \tag{64}$$

Even if the temperature is maintained constant, a number of other sources of error may be found in viscosity measurement. Bingham [101] has considered the problems involved in the determination of viscosity. The shearing stress, σ, exerted on a liquid varies with the distance from the center of the capillary according to the equation

$$\sigma = \frac{Pr}{2l} \tag{65}$$

For liquids or solutions that behave as Newtonian liquids, this variation is not serious. For this reason, only dilute solutions should be used, since, at higher concentrations, viscosity varies with shearing stress.

Also a kinetic energy correction is required [101,102] in the Poiseuille equation, thus

$$\eta = \frac{\pi a^4 P}{8(l + \lambda)V} \cdot t - \frac{m\rho V}{8\pi(l + \lambda)} \cdot \frac{1}{t} \tag{66}$$

where ρ is the density of the liquid, m is a constant of about 1.2, and λ is a correction for l equal in magnitude to a few diameters. Correction is required because not all the potential energy of the liquid is converted by viscous flow to thermal energy. Some of it emerges as kinetic energy. In the Ostwald or Ubbelohde viscometer, because of proper design, the equation is reduced to a simplified form:

$$\eta = A\rho t - \frac{B\rho}{t} \tag{67}$$

where A and B are constants characteristic of the instrument.

In the determination of relative viscosity, Flory [70] used relationships which included corrections of this kind:

$$\eta_r = \left(t - \frac{B}{At} \right) \Big/ \left(t_0 - \frac{B}{At_0} \right) \tag{68}$$

For the determination of $[\eta]$ in the measurement of the molecular weight of a polymer, measurements of η_{sp}/C are made at four or five concentrations, for example, between 0.1 to 8 grams per milliliter. By drawing a straight line through the points, the value of $[\eta]_{C=0}$ is obtained by extrapolation,[72] since

$$\eta_{\mathrm{sp}}C = [\eta] + k'[\eta]_C{}^2 + \cdots \tag{69}$$

However, once the value of k' is known, only one measurement of η_{sp}/C is required. The value of k' is about 0.38 for many polymers in good solvents.[103] Mead and Fuoss [32] have used the equivalent logarithmic form

$$\frac{\ln \eta_r}{C} = [\eta] - \beta[\eta]^2 C \tag{70}$$

wherein $\beta = 0.12$, since mathematically

$$\beta = 0.50 - k'$$

and

$$k' = 0.38$$

which is identical with Tingey's [103] numerical value. However, in the absence of published data on the k' value of other polymers, the value of 0.38 should be used with discretion when only one measurement of η_{sp}/C is made.

Molecular Weight from Ultracentrifuge

The determination of molecular weights by the ultracentrifuge (Figure 14) is due to the developments of Svedberg,[104-106] who used this method in the study of proteins. The principle is based on the facts

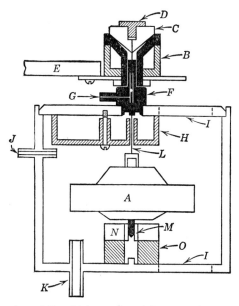

FIGURE 14. Drawing of first high-speed centrifuge of the vacuum type.[136] The turbine is supported and driven by compressed air. The motion is transmitted to the large rotor through a length of piano wire. Absence of air friction against the large rotor prevents heating and permits practical attainment of high speeds.

A = rotor	I = window
B = stator	J = outlet to manometer
C = turbine	K = outlet to vacuum pump
D = friction clutch	L = piano wire
E = supporting arm	M = cork
F = oil bearing (or gland)	N = wood
G = oil inlet	O = metal weight
H = oil collector	

that particles suspended in a liquid distribute themselves so that their concentration diminishes with height due to gravitational influences, the size or weight of the particles, the temperature, etc., and that the vertical distribution of the particles will be proportional to their weights. Under direct gravitational influence it is possible to show changes in concentration if the particles are of enormous size, that is, beyond the size of ordinary molecules. Even with high polymers in solution, it is not possible under gravitational influence to obtain changes in concentration which can be measured with sufficient accuracy to be of value. The concentration difference, however, can be increased by increasing the gravitational force up to one million times its ordinary value by use of a high ultracentrifuge.

Molecular weights are usually determined in an ultracentrifuge by either of two methods: the sedimentation equilibrium method or the sedimentation rate method.

A. THE SEDIMENTATION EQUILIBRIUM METHOD

The actual method consists in subjecting the solution of the polymer to the high gravitational field and measuring the fall in concentration during the course of the centrifuging at definite time intervals. These changes in concentration are followed or recorded by optical changes in refractive index or light absorption. The solution is subjected to centrifuging until an equilibrium between sedimentation resulting from the centrifugal force and diffusion resulting from thermal agitation is reached. This method is based thermodynamically on establishing such a distribution of the solute in the centrifugal field so that the increase in partial molal free energy due to concentration differences along the cell is equal to the decrease in free energy due to the position of the solute molecules.

If concentrations are determined by light absorption methods,[107, 108] the average molecular weight, which varies along the cell, is given by the equation

$$\bar{M}_{wx} = \frac{RT}{(1 - V\rho)\omega^2 x} \cdot \frac{d \ln C}{dx} \tag{71}$$

and the average molecular weight of the whole sample in the cell is given by

$$\bar{M}_w = \frac{\displaystyle\int_{x_0}^{x_n} \bar{M}_{wx} x C_x \, dx}{\displaystyle\int_{x_0}^{x_n} c_x x \, dx} \tag{72}$$

In the foregoing equations, x is the distance from the axis of rotation, R is the gas constant, T is the absolute temperature, V is the partial specific volume of the dissolved polymer, ρ is the density of the solvent, and ω is the angular velocity.

If the line displacement or Schlieren method is used to determine the concentration gradient or refractive index gradient, the average molecular weight is the Z average,[109] $\bar{M}_z$.

These molecular weight relationships are applicable only to dilute solutions of polymers since, in concentrated solutions, deviations increase with increased concentration similarly to the increase of osmotic pressure with concentration. For even dilute polymer solutions that show non-ideal behavior, equation 71 becomes

$$\bar{M}_{wx} = \frac{RT}{(1 - V\rho)\omega^2 x} \cdot \frac{d \ln a_s}{dx} \tag{73}$$

where a_s is the activity, and not the concentration, of the solvent.

Signer has shown that similar discrepancies [81, 83, 110] are found in determining molecular weights by the ultracentrifuge method. His studies on polystyrene in chloroform showed the following results:

Mole Fraction	Molecular Weight
0.00000077	120,000
0.00000024	210,000
0.00000011	270,000
0.00000000	340,000 (extrapolated)

These results show that the molecular weight must, as in the case of the viscosity and osmotic pressure method, be determined at $C = 0$. The extrapolated value, at zero concentration, was obtained by plotting $1/M$ against C.

The ultracentrifuge likewise may be used to advantage to determine the homogeneity or heterogeneity of the sample under study. If the same value of M is obtained at X_1, X_2, X_3, etc., there is only one molecular species in solution. However, if different values of M are obtained

TABLE 14

Percentage of Total	Molecular Weight Range
0.2	25– 35,000
1.7	35– 45,000
3.6	45– 55,000
8.4	55– 65,000
20.0	65– 75,000
23.8	75– 85,000
20.2	85– 95,000
10.4	95–105,000
6.0	105–115,000
3.3	115–125,000
1.7	125–135,000
0.5	135–145,000
0.2	145–155,000

at different distances from the rotational axis, several species of molecules are present. In this method it is possible to obtain molecular weight distribution curves. Signer and Gross [84] obtained the distribution curve of a sample of polystyrene from the centrifugal data tabulated in Table 14.

B. SEDIMENTATION RATE METHOD

Lamm and Poulson [111] have perfected the use of the ultracentrifuge for the determination of molecular weights as based on sedimentation according to the equation:

$$M = \frac{RTS}{[D(1 - V\rho)]} \qquad (74)$$

where R is the gas constant, T is the absolute temperature, ρ is the solvent density, V is the partial specific volume of the solute, S is a characteristic sedimentation coefficient for the dissolved substance at a particular temperature in a particular solvent, and D is the diffusion coefficient.[112] The value of S is obtained by dividing the velocity of displacement of the boundary, dx/dt, by $\omega^2 x$, where x is the point of measurement and ω is the angular velocity, that is,

$$S = \frac{dx/dt}{\omega^2 x} \qquad (75)$$

The diffusion constant, D, is obtained in a centrifuge from the rate of the diffusion of the molecules in solution into pure solvent in contact with the solution. Experimentally the value of the diffusion constant, D, is obtained from Svedberg's expression,

$$\frac{dn}{dz} = \frac{n_1 - n_0}{2\sqrt{\pi Dt}} \cdot e^{-(Z^2/4Dt)} \qquad (76)$$

where dn/dz = change of refractive index in the region of the meniscus,
n_1 = refractive index of the solution,
n_0 = refractive index of pure solvent,
Z = distance of the point of measurement from the point of maximum concentration,
t = time for value of dn/dz.

This determination of D is based on the fact that the sedimentation meniscus spreads as a function of time because of the diffusion of the polymer molecules.

This method is of general validity in very dilute solutions. With polymers of very high molecular weight, the concentration at which these high polymers exist as independent molecules is so low that measurements of sedimentation or diffusion are very difficult. Likewise the hetereogeneity of high polymers causes an indistinct boundary between the solvent and the solution of polymer. This method fails to give a value of homogeneity of the polymer. It also has the disadvantage that it requires higher centrifugal forces than the equilibrium method.

Kraemer and Lansing [49, 113] report the following values of molecular weights of certain high polymers which were determined by the ultracentrifuge method.

Polymer	Molecular Weight Ranges
Cellulose acetate	50,000–250,000
Cellulose nitrate	100,000–160,000
Ethylcellulose	125,000
Polyhydroxydecanoic acid	27,000

Kraemer [113] also compared the molecular weights, obtained by different methods, of fractionated ω-hydroxydecanoic acid polymers. These data are summarized in Table 15.

TABLE 15

Method	Molecular Weight
Viscosity	31,000
End-group titration	25,200
Ultracentrifuge-sedimentation equilibrium	27,000
Ultracentrifuge-sedimentation and diffusion	52,000 *
Ultracentrifuge-sedimentation velocity alone	7,600 †
Ultracentrifuge-diffusion coefficient alone	2,400,000 †

* This value is high most probably because the frictional coefficient at the concentrations used probably is not the same for sedimentation and diffusion.

† These values assumed that the frictional coefficient of a sphere had a volume equal to the molecular volume of the solid polymer.

Molecular Weights from Freezing Points, Boiling Points, and Vapor Pressure

The methods of freezing point lowering, boiling point elevations, and vapor pressure lowering are applicable only to measurements of molecular weights up to about 5000. Even at this limit, the minuteness of the changes in freezing points, boiling points, and vapor pressures precludes their general use because of the limits set by instrumentation.

Under very special conditions, it may be possible to go a little higher than 5000 as Schulz has shown in some instances.[114] However, even these measurements extend to the lower limit of true polymers and, in fact, apply more strictly to oligomers.

It may also be added that these methods, involving ΔT or ΔP changes in a solvent, are of limited value in determining molecular weights of high polymeric substances because, to obtain measurable effects with high molecular weight substances, the concentration required is so high that the relationship of these changes to molecular weight no longer holds.

CRYOSCOPIC METHOD—FREEZING POINT DEPRESSION

This method depends on the lowering of the freezing point of a solvent; the lowering is proportional to the amount and the nature of the substance dissolved in it. The additive properties of two components which form an ideal solution are a linear function of its composition. According to Raoult's law, the partial activity or the vapor pressure of each component is proportional to its mole fraction, N_a:

$$p = N_a p_a \quad \text{or} \quad \frac{p}{p_a} = N_a \qquad (77)$$

According to thermodynamic considerations, the Clausius-Clapeyron equation is given as

$$d \ln p_a = \frac{\Delta H_a}{RT_a^2} dT \qquad (78)$$

where p_a = partial pressure of component a,
ΔH_a = molar heat of fusion of component a,
R = gas constant,
T = the equilibrium temperature in degrees absolute.

The lowering of the melting point or freezing point of component a by the addition of small amounts of another component may be obtained by integrating between the limits of T_a and T, and p_a and p, where T_a and p_a are the freezing points and partial pressures, respectively, of component a.

$$\ln \frac{p}{p_a} = \frac{\Delta H_a}{RT_a} - \frac{\Delta H_a}{RT} = \frac{-\Delta H_a(T_a - T)}{RT_a T} \qquad (79)$$

By substituting equation 77 in equation 79 we obtain

$$\ln N_a = \frac{\Delta H_a(T_a - T)}{RTT_a} \qquad (80)$$

and since $\Delta T = T_a - T$,

$$\Delta T = \frac{-RTT_a}{\Delta H_a} \ln N_a \qquad (81)$$

and since $N_a + N_b = 1$, and

$$N_a = 1 - N_b \tag{82}$$

then

$$\Delta T = \frac{-RTT_a}{\Delta H_a} \ln (1 - N_b) \tag{83}$$

For dilute solutions

$$-\ln (1 - N_b) = N_b \tag{84}$$

and

$$T_a T = T_a^2 \tag{85}$$

then

$$\Delta T = \frac{RT_a^2}{\Delta H} \cdot N_b \tag{86}$$

Since N_b can be expressed in terms of molality, m, that is, in terms of number of moles of solute per 1000 grams of solvent,

$$N_b = \frac{m}{m + \dfrac{1000}{M_a}} \tag{87}$$

where M_a is the molecular weight of the solvent. For dilute solutions m may be neglected in comparison with $1000/M_a$ so that

$$\Delta T = \frac{RT_a^2}{\Delta H_a} \cdot \frac{m}{1000/M_a} = \frac{RT_a^2 \cdot m M_a}{1000 \Delta H_a} = K_F m \tag{88}$$

or

$$K_F = \frac{0.002 T_a^2 M a}{\Delta H_a} \tag{89}$$

Since ΔH_a is the molal heat of fusion and M_a is the molecular weight, the term may be expressed as

$$\frac{M_a}{\Delta H_a} = \frac{1}{L_a} \tag{90}$$

where L_a is the latent heat of fusion of 1 gram of the solvent or

$$K_F = \frac{0.002 T_a^2}{L_a} = \frac{0.002 T_a^2 \cdot M_a}{\Delta H_a} \tag{91}$$

If W_b is the number of grams of solute or polymer per 1000 grams of solvent,

$$m = \frac{W_b}{M_b} \tag{92}$$

and, by substituting in equation 88,

$$\Delta T = \frac{K_F W_b}{M_b} \tag{93}$$

or

$$M_b = \frac{K_F W_b}{\Delta T} \tag{94}$$

which is the well-known van't Hoff's law.[115]
The accuracy of this method of determining molecular weights is dependent on the accuracy with which K_F is known. It can be calculated from equation 91 or from the heat of fusion, or the value may be observed in a compound of known molecular weight by means of equation 93. A comparison of the observed and calculated values [116] for K_F is shown in Table 16.

TABLE 16

Solvent	M.p., °C	K_F Calculated	K_F Observed
Benzene	5.45	5.069	5.7
Borneol	204.0	. . . . . .	35.8
Camphor	178.4	37.7	40.0
Dioxane	11.7	4.71	4.63
Ethylacetanilide	52.0	8.7	8.58
Indene	−1.76	7.35	7.28

Selection of solvent. It must be mentioned that substances with a low molar heat of fusion, for example, 1650 calories for camphor, show a large lowering of the melting point depression with only a small quantity of solute, whereas solvents with a high heat of fusion, such as stearic acid with 13,510 calories, show only a slight change with a high concentration of solute. Also, when two solvents have approximately the same heat of fusion but different melting points, for example, anthracene with m.p. 489 K and $\Delta H = 6890$ calories, and capric acid, with m.p. 305 K and $\Delta H = 6680$ calories, the solvent having the higher melting point will show the greater depression for the same amount of solute.

Even when K_F is accurately determined, not all solutions are ideal. Van't Hoff's equations were derived only for the limiting case of infinitely dilute solutions, and thermodynamics make no predictions as to how their validity is maintained in the range of finite concentrations.[117] Even in infinitely dilute solutions, deviations may be found for other reasons. Such substances as phenol, aniline, or propionic acid associate in benzene and the determined molecular weight may be high, whereas hexaphenylethane, which dissociates into triphenylmethyl, gives low results.[118-121]

Furthermore, such solvents as acetic acid, which associate with themselves or form associated compounds or complexes with the solute, such as dinitrobenzene or picric acid with naphthalene, are to be avoided.

Like viscosity and osmotic pressure molecular measurements of polymers, the ΔT value should be determined, by extrapolation, at $C = 0$.

The two modifications of this method are known as (1) Beckmann's method, using liquid solvents and Beckmann's apparatus, and (2) Rast's method, using camphor. Rast's method [122] takes advantage of the high value of K for camphor, and the depression may be measured in ordinary melting point capillaries if proper precautions are taken. The details of these methods are found in many standard references.[123]

Kemp and Peters [124] compared intrinsic viscosities of polyisobutylenes with molecular weights calculated from cryoscopic measurements at arbitrarily chosen finite concentrations. Their results were criticized by Flory [68] because the sample was not sufficiently fractionated and therefore not sufficiently homogeneous to establish the relationship between the two methods, particularly since the values $(\Delta T/C)$ were used instead of $(\Delta T/C)_{C=0}$, in the region where Raoult's law would be valid.

Too, the results were based on Staudinger's K_m constant,[125] which was determined on low molecular weight polymers and involved an extrapolation beyond the range of cryoscopic measurements.

However, Kemp and Peters [85] have shown that this method is not satisfactory for certain polymers, for example, polystyrenes containing more than twelve segmers could not be measured accurately because of deviation from Raoult's law.

EBULLISCOPIC METHOD—BOILING POINT RISE

This method depends on the lowering of the vapor pressure by a dissolved substance, and the thermodynamic considerations are substantially the same as those considered for melting point depressions. Since the boiling point is defined as the temperature at which the vapor pressure is equal to standard atmospheric pressure, it follows that a solution having a lower vapor pressure than pure solvent must boil at a higher temperature than pure solvent. This increase in temperature is known as ΔT or the boiling point rise. The molecular weight of the dissolved substance is obtained from the equation

$$M_b = \frac{K_B W_B}{\Delta T} \tag{95}$$

where W_B is the concentration of the dissolved substance in grams per 1000 grams of solvent, ΔT is the boiling point increase, and K_B is the boiling point constant of the solvent. The constant K_B may be calculated from the equation $K_B = 0.002T^2/L_a$, where L_a is the latent heat of vaporization of one gram of solvent and T is the boiling point of the pure solvent on the absolute scale. This method likewise is not satisfactory since high polymer solutions are not ideal solutions and the deviations from Raoult's law are large. Raoult's law showed that the relative lowering of the vapor pressure of a given solvent at a fixed temperature is proportional to the concentration of the dissolved substance, provided the solutions are dilute. Freezing point methods are preferred for the molecular weight determinations of oligomers. Both methods are unsatisfactory for high polymers. Deviations from Raoult's law with reference to substances of high molecular weight and for high polymers have been discussed by Meyer [5, 126] and others. They attribute these deviations to entropy considerations.

MOLECULAR WEIGHTS FROM VAPOR PRESSURE LOWERING

Raoult has shown that the relative lowering of the vapor pressure is proportional at a fixed temperature to the concentration of the dissolved substance, provided the solution is dilute.

The molecular weight is given by the equation

$$M_b = \frac{KcP}{\Delta P} = \frac{KW_BP}{\Delta P} \tag{96}$$

where W_B is the concentration of the dissolved substance in grams per 1000 grams of solvent, ΔP is the vapor pressure lowering, P is the vapor pressure of the solvent, and K_B is the boiling point constant of the solvent. Since boiling point elevation and vapor pressure lowering are, as already indicated, related functions, the same considerations hold for molecular weight determination by either method, and neither system is satisfactory for molecular weight determinations of high polymers.

Molecular Weights by Means of an Electron Microscope

The first systematic work of this nature, in which an electron microscope was used, was apparently by Husemann and Ruska.[127] The extensive use of an electron microscope in molecular weight determinations has not yet been achieved. Some preliminary data have already appeared, and the results seem promising. Kropa and his co-workers [128] discussed their results on the studies of polystyrene. They investigated films of polystyrene which were obtained by casting its solution in organic solvents onto water. Electron microscope photographs of these films showed black nodules whose size was in agreement with the molecular weight obtained by viscosity measurements. The film method was not found to be applicable generally to polymers; it did not work well for all polymer species. Boyer and Heidenreich [129] verified the statements that the results obtained from film methods were not very satisfactory and that the preparation of the films was critical. Their method depends on isolating single polymer molecules and relating their physical dimensions to molecular weight. They reasoned that the proper technique should cause the precipitation of long extended molecules existing in the solution in the form of compact coiled-up molecules. By calculation, it is shown that in a polymer of styrene, having a molecular weight of 88,000, its extended length of the form ⋀⋀⋀⋀⋀⋀ will be about 1922 Å, and that in the coiled compact form, it has a diameter of 62 Å. Since it has already been shown that the resolving power of a magnetic electron microscope is at least 10 Å, it is reasonable to expect that, if a polymer could be precipitated from solution in a curled-up state, its molecular weight could be determined. Furthermore, a "colony count" in a specific area should give a distribution curve.

Their technique involved dissolving the polymer in a very dilute solution and then adding a precipitant, causing the molecules to coil and to precipitate. Suspensions of the precipitated mixture were evaporated on a silica screen and examined under the electron microscope. From a dilute solution of polychlorostyrene were obtained circular particles ranging in diameter from 15 to 500 Å, which probably represent single polymer molecules. The measured particle diameter and molecular weights were correlated, and apparently particle diameter varies as the square root of the molecular weight. The molecular weight distribution curves were of the expected shape and extent, although the average molecular weights computed from the distribution curves are four to five times greater than values measured by other methods.

Molecular Weights from Light Scattering

When a beam of light falls upon a liquid, a gas, or a solid, the electrical field of the light induces electronic oscillations in the material. The irradiated materials in turn serve as a secondary source of light and emit scattered radiation with a wavelength equal to that of the incident light. If no fluorescence or absorption occurs when a parallel beam of light is passed through a transparent system such as a gas, a liquid, a solid, or a solution, all the light is lost by scattering and the relation of the intensity of the original light to the scattered light is given as

$$I = I_0 e^{-\tau l} \qquad (97)$$

wherein I_0 = the intensity of the intral beam,
I = the intensity of the transmitted beam,
l = the depth of the solution in centimeters.

The scattering, τ, is called the turbidity.

Lord Rayleigh [130] appears to have been the first to have appreciated the value of light scattering methods, when in 1871 he applied the electromagnetic theory to the problem of light scattering in gases. The first detailed observations on the polarization of scattered light were recorded by Tyndall.[131] Later Rayleigh accounted [132] for the intensity, color, and polarization of light from the sky. Rayleigh's relationship is expressed by the equation

$$\tau = \frac{8\pi}{3} \cdot \left(\frac{2\pi}{\lambda}\right)^4 n\alpha^2 \qquad (98)$$

where α describes the polarizability or the optical properties of the individual molecules or atoms or scattering centers and n is the number of molecules in the gas. Since the polarizability of the isotropic particles immersed in a medium of optical dielectric constant, ϵ_0, is given by Maxwell as

$$\frac{\epsilon - \epsilon_0}{\epsilon_0} = 4\pi n\alpha \qquad (99)$$

equation 98 becomes

$$\tau = \frac{8\pi^3}{3\lambda^4 n} \cdot \left(\frac{\epsilon - \epsilon_0}{\epsilon_0}\right)^2 \qquad (100)$$

The polarizability is also related to the refractive index of the medium, n_r, by the equation

$$n_r - 1 = 2\pi n\alpha \qquad (101)$$

and equation 98 becomes

$$\tau = \frac{32\pi^3}{3} \cdot \frac{1}{\lambda^4} \cdot \frac{1}{n} (n_r - 1)^2 \qquad (102)$$

The relationships of equations 100 and 101, involving the value of n, have been used [133, 134] to determine Avogadro's number since $n = Nc/M$, where N is Avogadro's number, c is the weight concentration, and M represents molecular weight.

Condensed systems [135] such as liquids or solutions do not permit the simple treatment of Rayleigh's gaseous system. In a gas the individual scattering centers are independent molecules; and since this is not true of liquids, we cannot expect that the intensity of scattered light from a liquid will be the mere summation of the intensities from the individual particles. There is a decrease in the intensity of the scattered light because of certain phase relationships. These phase relationships do not reduce the intensity of the scattering parallel to the primary beam, but they sharply reduce the intensity under large angles of incidence.[136, 137]

In condensed systems, the relationship between the polarizability of the individual molecules is complicated, and the refractive index is no longer a simple relation because the neighboring molecules polarize each other. Furthermore, in a condensed system, the molecules not only vibrate under the influence of the light wave but they are subject also to the influence of the field produced by the displaced charges in the rest of the medium. Smoluchowski[138, 139] used the concept of thermodynamic fluctuations to explain the great intensity of scattering observed for pure liquids near their critical temperature. He considered the light scattered from an element of volume ∂v of liquid which is small compared to the wavelength of the incident light, but is, however, large enough to include a great number of molecules. The fluctuations in the number of particles in ∂v will result in a fluctuation in the optical dielectric constant. By relating ∂v to the isothermal compressibility, β, and to the density, σ, the following relationship was expressed

$$\tau = \frac{8\pi^3}{3\lambda^4} \left(\sigma \frac{\partial \epsilon}{\partial \sigma} \right)_T^2 kT\beta \tag{103}$$

which in terms of optical dielectric constant becomes

$$\tau = \frac{8\pi^3}{3\lambda^4} (\epsilon - 1)^2 kT\beta \tag{104}$$

Einstein[140] considered the problem further and pointed out that the scattering in condensed systems is due to thermal density fluctuations, in the absence of which there would be no scattering; an ideal crystal scatters no light. Einstein's extension, which also included liquid mixtures as long as the particles were small as compared to the wavelength of incident light, is given as

$$\tau = \frac{8\pi^3}{3\lambda^4} \frac{RT\overline{V}_0 c}{N \left(\dfrac{-\partial \mu_0}{\partial c} \right)} \left(\frac{\partial \epsilon}{\partial c} \right)^2 \tag{105}$$

where R is the gas constant, $\overline{V}_0$ is the potential molal volume of the solvent, μ_0 is the Gibbs chemical potential of the solvent, c is the average solvent concentration, and N is Avogadro's number. If the solution contains molecules of an order greater than one-tenth of λ, a correction for the dissymmetry factor must be included.

Since the osmotic pressure, P, of a solution is related to the chemical potential of the solvent by the relationship

$$P\overline{V}_0 = -N\mu_0 \qquad (106)$$

Debye,[136, 137, 141] Raman and Ramanathan [142] expressed the relationship as

$$\tau = \frac{8\pi^3}{3\lambda^4} \frac{RTc}{N\left(\frac{\partial P}{\partial c}\right)} \left(\frac{\partial \epsilon}{\partial c}\right)^2 \qquad (107)$$

and if

$$H = \frac{8\pi^3}{3\lambda^4} \left(\frac{\partial \epsilon}{\partial c}\right)^2$$

then

$$\tau = H \frac{RTc}{N\left(\frac{\partial P}{\partial c}\right)} \qquad (108)$$

For dilute solution, the osmotic pressure becomes

$$P = \frac{C}{M} RT + Bc^2 \qquad (109)$$

where B expresses the deviations from ideal solutions, and the equation for light scattering becomes

$$H\left(\frac{c}{\tau}\right) = \frac{1}{M} + \frac{2Bc}{RT} \qquad (110)$$

By a somewhat different manner from Debye's, but on the same basis, Doty et al.[143] related turbidity to molecular weight, and the equation for the relationship is

$$\frac{c}{\tau_2} = \frac{3\lambda^4 N_0}{32\pi^3 n_0^2 (\partial n/\partial c)^2} \left[\frac{1}{M_2} + \frac{2b}{RT} c + \cdots\right] \qquad (111)$$

or

$$\frac{c}{\tau_2} = \frac{1}{H} \left[\frac{1}{M_2} + \frac{2b}{RT} c + \cdots\right] \qquad (112)$$

and if the fourth term is negligible,

$$H\frac{c}{\tau_2} = \frac{1}{M_2} \qquad (113)$$

where $\tau_2 =$ the scattering coefficient,

$H =$ constant for a given polymer-solvent system,

$M_2 =$ molecular weight of the polymer (solute),

$c =$ concentration of the polymer in grams per cubic centimeter of solvent,

$n_0 =$ refractive index of the solvent,

$n =$ refractive index of the solution and $\partial n/\partial c$ is the refractive index increment,

$T =$ absolute temperature,

$R =$ the gas constant,

$N_0 =$ Avogadro's number (6.02×10^{23}),

$b =$ the same coefficient (slope) as that of the osmotic pressure equation, $\pi = (RTc/M_2) + bc^2$, and measures the deviation of the solution from van't Hoff's law,

$\lambda =$ the wavelength of monochromatic light in centimeters.

As with osmotic pressure and the viscosity relationships, the equation to be valid is extrapolated to infinite dilution,

$$\frac{1}{M_2} = H \left(\frac{c}{\tau_2}\right)_{c=0} \tag{114}$$

so that the intercept is the reciprocal of the molecular weight or

$$M_2 = \frac{1}{H} \left(\frac{\tau_2}{c}\right)_{c=0} \tag{115}$$

and thus [144]

$$\lim_{c \to 0} \left(\frac{\tau}{c}\right) = \left(\frac{\tau}{c}\right)_{c=0} = \frac{8\pi^3}{3\lambda^4 N} \left(\frac{\partial \epsilon}{\partial c}\right)^2 = \frac{32\pi^3 n^2}{3\lambda^4 N} \left(\frac{\partial n_r}{\partial c}\right)^2 \tag{116}$$

and

$$H \left(\frac{c}{\tau}\right)_{c=0} = H \left(\frac{c}{\tau_2}\right)_{c=0} = \frac{1}{M_2} \tag{117}$$

The reciprocal of the extrapolated scattering coefficient has also been termed the intrinsic scattering value of the particular polymer in the specific solvent,

$$[\tau_2] = \left(\frac{\tau_2}{c}\right)_{c=0} \tag{118}$$

or

$$M_2 = \frac{1}{H} [\tau_2] \tag{119}$$

which in its rearranged form

$$[\tau_2] = HM_2 \tag{120}$$

may be seen to be related to Staudinger's viscosity equation

$$[\eta] = KM \tag{121}$$

Since light scattering measures the mean weight average molecular weight, $\overline{M}_w$, the expression becomes

$$\frac{1}{\overline{M}_w} = H\left(\frac{c}{\tau_2}\right)_{c=0} \tag{122}$$

This method is extremely sensitive to large molecules and is particularly well adapted to ranges of low concentration where high polymers in solution approach ideal behavior. This method likewise gives an indication of the breadth of the distribution curve.[145, 146] These investigators have shown that low molecular weights, coarse impurities, and color of the polymer or the solvent affect the accuracy of the method. Table 17 [145] gives a comparison of a number of different polymers whose molecular weights were determined by light-scattering methods and by osmotic pressure.

TABLE 17

| | Molecular Weight | |
Polymer	Osmotic Pressure	Light Scattering
Polystyrene 1	172,000	178,000
Polystyrene 2	198,000	182,000
Polystyrene 3	91,000	107,000
Polystyrene 4	....	190,000
Polystyrene 5	....	445,000
Cellulose acetate 1	125,000	123,000
Cellulose acetate 3	75,000	76,000

Dissymmetry and depolarization. In the derivation of equation 108, the assumption was made that the size of the scattering particles was small in comparison to the wavelength of light. If the particles have a linear dimension greater than about one-twentieth of the wavelength, the light scattered from the solution is not symmetrical about 90 degrees. This dissymmetry is the direct result of the extension of the scattering particles beyond a few hundred Ångströms,[147] and the molecule cannot be considered as a point source since the scattering from the different parts of the same molecule may be different. The difference in phase of light scattered from different parts of the molecule is due to difference in path lengths, and a greater difference is produced in the backward than in the forward direction.[148-156]

Stein and Doty [148] have considered this dissymmetry, q, for a number of cellulose acetate [157] fractions and have introduced the correction in the molecular weight values. Likewise, these investigators introduced a correction factor for turbidity due to factors other than concentration, such as turbidities due to fluctuations in concentrations due to orientation. According to the derivation [130] of equation 99, the light scattered

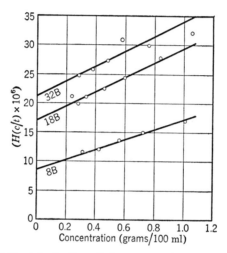

Figure 15. Turbidity data for the cellulose acetate fractions. (Reprinted by permission from the authors and the *Journal of the American Chemical Society*.)

under 90 degrees should be completely polarized, and its electric vector should oscillate in a plane perpendicular to the plane defined by the incident beam and by the direction of observation. Actually, observation shows that the light scattered under 90 degrees has a small horizontal component and the α^2 of equation 99 must be replaced by

$$\alpha \rho^2 = \alpha^2 \frac{6 + 6\rho}{6 - 7\rho}$$

wherein the magnitude of ρ, the depolarization, is of the order of 10^{-2}, thereby reducing the molecular weight values by about 2 to 10 per cent. The value of ρ is independent of concentration [146,158] but dependent on the molecular weight, and is more important in low molecular weight polymers.

By plotting the values of $H(c/t)$ against c, as in Figure 15,[148] an extrapolation to zero concentration was made for $H(c/t)$. Table 18 [148] summarizes the molecular weights as determined by light scattering, that is, uncorrected, then corrected for orientation turbidity, ρ, then corrected for light-scattering dissymmetry. These results were contrasted with the molecular weight values as determined by osmotic pressure measurements.

TABLE 18

Sample Fraction	Intercept $\times 10^6$	Mol. Wt. Uncorrected	ρ	Mol. Wt. Corrected for ρ	q	Dissymmetry Correction Factor	Light-Scattering Mol. Wt. Corrected for ρ and q	Osmotic Pressure Mol. Wt.
8B	8.50	118,000	0.017	114,000	0.60	1.52	173,000	163,000
18B	16.6	60,200	0.037	55,600	0.43	1.38	77,000	75,000
32B	21.2	47,200	0.045	43,000	0.43	1.38	60,000	65,000

Reprinted by permission from the authors and the *Journal of the American Chemical Society*.

LIGHT-SCATTERING APPARATUS

Debye has described [159] a differential refractometer and a photoelectric instrument for the determination of light scattering which permits measuring the scattered intensities between angles of 0 and 125 C. The turbidimeter and dissymmetry apparatus of Doty and his co-workers [148, 156, 157, 160] are shown in Figures 16,[148] 17,[148] and 18.[160]

The turbidity may also be measured by means of the photoelectric turbidimeter,[160] which is shown in Figure 18.

The turbidity of the system is calculated from the equation

$$\tau_0 = K\frac{P_s C_0}{P_0 C_s} \tag{123}$$

where P_s = galvanometer reading for unknown solution,

C_s = photronic cell reading when P_s was measured,

P_0 = galvanometer reading for a standard reference gel,

C_0 = photronic cell reading when P_0 was measured,

K = instrument constant, that is, actual turbidity of the standard gel in this instrument.

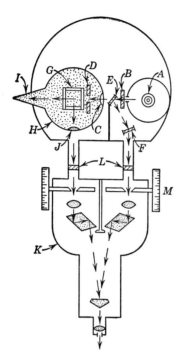

A = mercury arc light source
B = filters to isolate 5461 A line
C = callimating lens
D = diaphragm
E = glass plate to reflect part of light as shown
F = opalescent glass plate
G = square cell containing polymer solution
H = water-filled chamber
I = cone which serves to absorb incident beam through multiple reflection
J = lens
K = Zeiss Pulfrich Photometer
L = removable neutral filters
M = scales indicating slit areas in photometer

FIGURE 16. The turbidimeter. (Reprinted by permission from the authors and the *Journal of the American Chemical Society*.)

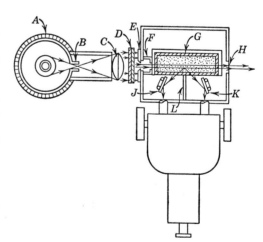

A = lamp housing containing mercury arc
B = slit in front of housing
C = callimating lens
D = light filters
E and F = vertical slits to restrict light beam
G = glass cell containing polymer solution
H = exit hole for light beam
J and K = mirrors
L = barrier to help prevent stray light from striking mirrors

FIGURE 17. Dissymmetry apparatus. (Reprinted by permission from the authors and the *Journal of the American Chemical Society*.)

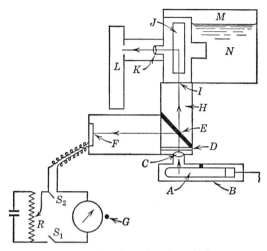

FIGURE 18.   The photoelectric turbidimeter.

A = light source
B = metal housing
C = lens
D = glass filter for monochromatic light 5461 A
E = glass plate, partial reflector to F
F = Weston photronic cell
G = ammeter

H = Wooden case, inside painted dull black
I = aperture
J = cell for solution
K = lens for collecting scattered light
L = light-sensitive phototube
M = metal housing for J
N = thermostat housing for M

(From P. Doty, H. Wagner, and S. Singer, "Association of Polymer Molecules in Solution," *J. Phys. and Colloid Chem.*, **51**, 32 [1947]. The Williams and Wilkins Company, Baltimore, publishers.)

The scattering of the solvent $\tau_{\text{solv.}}$ must be subtracted from τ_0, the scattering of the total system,

$$\tau_2 = \tau_0 - \tau_{\text{solv.}} \tag{124}$$

By measuring τ_2 for various concentrations and plotting Hc/τ as a function of concentration, and setting the intercept at $1/\overline{M}_w$, the turbidity at $[C]_{\to 0}$ is obtained.

Doty and his co-workers used light-scattering methods to determine molecular weights in dioxane solution at various temperatures and for two specific fractions of polyvinyl chloride obtained the data shown in Table 19.[160]

These data would indicate that clusters of high molecular weight components, that is, associate polymers, were breaking down into their lower molecular weight components on heating. The number average molecular weight of these same polymers were investigated using os-

TABLE 19

Fraction	Temperature, °C	Weight Average Molecular Weight
A in dioxane	28.5	16,700,000
	48.0	4,500,000
	63.0	2,040,000
B in dioxane	28.5	12,500,000
	51.0	2,400,000
	62.5	1,780,000

From P. Doty, H. Wagner, and S. Singer, "The Association of Polymer Molecules in Dilute Solution," *J. Phys. and Colloid Chem.*, **51**, 32 (1947). The Williams and Wilkins Company, Baltimore, publishers.

motic measurements, and in both cases no change in molecular weight values occurred until a temperature of about 40 C was reached. At this temperature a sharp drop was observed, and both curves began to level off at 60 C (Figure 19).[160] To verify further the postulate that, even in dilute solutions, polymers are associated, a number of studies were

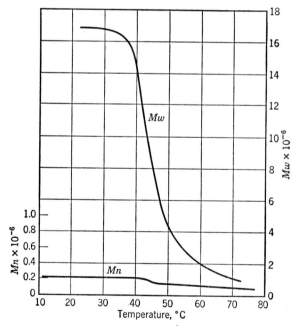

FIGURE 19. Number-average and weight-average molecular weights as a function of temperature. (From P. Doty, H. Wagner, and S. Singer, "Association of Polymer Molecules in Solution," *J. Phys. and Colloid Chem.*, **51**, 32 [1947]. The Williams and Wilkins Company, Baltimore, publishers.)

performed by centrifugal methods. These experiments showed that a definite shift to lower molecules took place on heating when dioxane was used as a solvent for fraction A, and that the change was not marked when butanone was used as the solvent. The clusters of associated polymer molecules were found to reform slowly when the dioxane solution was recooled, and sometimes a month was required before the reassociation was completely reestablished. Similar evidence was obtained but for varying degrees of association for cellulose acetate and for polyvinyl chloride–polyvinyl acetate copolymers.

MOLAR CONSTANTS AND MOLECULAR WEIGHTS

Sound Velocity Method

Weissler, Fitzgerald, and Resnick [161] have presented a method of determining the number average molecular weights of liquid polymers which is based on sound velocities in the polymer. The equation for molecular weight is

$$\overline{M}_n = \frac{Bd}{v^{1/3} - A \frac{(n^2 - 1)}{(n^2 + 2)}} \tag{125}$$

where v = sound velocity,
d = density,
n = refractive index,
A = empirical constant,
B = empirical constant.

In the polyethylene glycol homologous series, an accuracy of 2 per cent was obtained for the lower members, and the method seems suitable for molecular weights up to several thousands.

The method rests on Rao's discovery [162, 163] of the relation of molecular weight to the empirical molar sound velocity R,

$$R = \frac{Mv^{1/3}}{d} \tag{126}$$

where M = molecular weight,
v = sound velocity at temperature, t,
d = density at the same temperature, t.

For each pure liquid, with the exception of water, the molar sound velocity, R, is a constant independent of temperature, the cube root of the velocity and the density varying in such a way that their ratio is constant. The molar sound velocity is an additive property of atoms and bonds similar to molar refraction, even though the velocity of sound in a given homologous series varies. Molar sound velocity can be calculated with reasonable accuracy from published increment values of R, for atoms of carbon, oxygen, hydrogen, etc. Lagemann and Dunbar [164] have shown that, within an homologous series, a linear relationship exists between any two of the following molar constants:

Molar sound velocity:

$$R = \frac{Mv^{\frac{1}{3}}}{d} \qquad (127)$$

Molar refraction:

$$N = \frac{M}{d} \frac{(n^2 - 1)}{(n^2 + 2)} \qquad (128)$$

where n = refractive index.
Molar viscosity:

$$I = (2.9 + \log \log \eta) \frac{M}{d} \qquad (129)$$

where η is the viscosity in millipoises.
Molar magnetic rotation
Parachor
Critical volume
Van der Waals' constant.
The relationship between molar sound velocity and molar refraction is given as

$$R = AN + B \qquad (130)$$

where A is the slope and B the intercept.

By substituting equations 127 and 128 in equation 130 the expression correlating molecular weight to sound velocity and refractive index is obtained.

$$M = \frac{Bd}{v^{\frac{1}{3}} - A \frac{(n^2 - 1)}{(n^2 + 2)}} \qquad (131)$$

Similarly an expression is derived in terms of other pairs of molar constants. In terms of molar viscosity and velocity the equation becomes

$$M = \frac{B'd}{v^{\frac{1}{3}} - A'(2.9 + \log \log \eta)} \qquad (132)$$

and in terms of refractive index and molar viscosity the equation becomes

$$M = \frac{B''d}{\dfrac{(n^2 - 1)}{(n^2 + 2)} - A''(2.9 + \log\log \eta)} \tag{133}$$

These equations should be applicable not only to homologous series, in which each successive member possesses a —CH_2— increment, but also to polymer homologous series, where the increment is a monomer structural unit.

Weissler and his co-workers [161] decided to test the validity of equations 131, 132, and 133 by determining the molecular weights of a series of ethylene glycol polymers using pure members and several commercial mixtures. These polymers, which are represented by the formula $HO(CH_2CH_2O)_nH$, have been previously studied by Staudinger [31] and later by others.[165] The physical properties measured are summarized in Table 20.[161]

TABLE 20

Glycol	Mol. Wt.	Density/cc.	Sound Velocity, m/S	n_D	Viscosity, c.p.	Boiling Point
Ethylene	62.1	1.10689	1642.9	1.4295	13.95	69°/1.2 mm
Diethylene	106.1	1.1094	1567.7	1.4438	22.55	105°/2.0
Triethylene	150.1	1.1158	1593.3	1.4531	29.96	123°/1.2
Tetraethylene	194.2	1.1159	1580.1	1.4567	35.16	138°/0.5
Pentaethylene	238.2	1.1165	1580.0	1.4593	42.37	176°/0.5
Poly-200	200 ± 10	1.1168	1592.2	1.4572	39.71	
Poly-300	300 ± 15	1.1176	1578.0	1.4618	59.02	
Poly-400	400 ± 20	1.1182	1576.0	1.4636	74.70	
Poly-600	600 ± 30	1.1183	1570.0	1.4653	104.62	

The molar constants of these glycols were calculated using published tables [164,166–168] and compared to the observed values. These results are tabulated in Table 21.[161]

TABLE 21

Glycol	Molar Sound Velocity		Molar Refraction		Molar Viscosity	
	Observed	Calc.	Observed	Calc.	Observed	Calc.
Ethylene	661.7	652.0	14.47	14.49	181.2	176.0
Diethylene	1111.2	1106.1	25.40	25.39	312.9	316.9
Triethylene	1571.6	1560.1	36.37	36.31	443.2	457.8
Tetraethylene	2027.1	2014.2	47.36	47.28	575.3	598.7
Pentaethylene	2485.1	2468.2	58.36	58.27	708.3	739.6
Poly-200	2091	2075	48.79	48.87	593.6	617.5
Poly-300	3125	3105	73.71	73.56	897.3	937.5
Poly-400	4163	4135	98.63	98.48	1201.3	1257.5
Poly-600	6236	6195	148.40	148.17	1813.4	1897.5

By permission from the American Institute of Physics, New York.

From these data the existence of a linear relation between molar sound velocity and molar refraction was verified for the five pure compounds shown in Figure 20,[161] in which all the points lie in a straight line and where A is 41.59 and B is 57.7. The slope may also be calculated

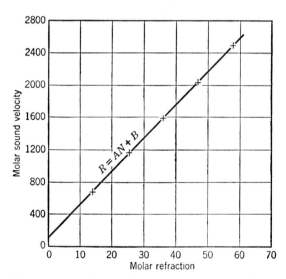

FIGURE 20. Linear relationship of molar sound velocity to molar refraction. (By permission from the American Institute of Physics, New York.)

from the tables of bond increments for each —CH_2CH_2O— segmer, in which the R increment is 454 and the N increment is 10.88. The slope, or R/N, is the quotient 41.73.

After the establishment of the foregoing linear relationship, the molecular weights were calculated and compared to the number average molecular weights obtained by the freezing point depression method in water as a solvent and to the weight average molecular weight determined from the log log plot of bulk viscosity against molecular weight. These lower polyethylene glycols do not appear to conform to the relation $\log \eta = A + BM^{1/2}$ suggested by Flory.[96] These data are summarized in Table 22.[161]

TABLE 22

Glycol	Theoretical Mol. Weight	Sound Velocity Mol. Weight	Number Ave. Mol. Weight	Weight Average Mol. Weight	Mol. Wt. from Viscosity and Velocity	Mol. Wt. from Refraction and Viscosity
Ethylene	62.1	59.9	60.8	62	63.6	62.5
Diethylene	106.1	111.5	101.6	109	131.4	98.2
Triethylene	150.1	147.3	148.5	155	138.0	167.2
Tetraethylene	194.2	195.7	195.4	190	186.0	205.2
Pentaethylene	238.2	237.7	234.5	238	237.9	221.9
Poly-200	200 ± 10	186.2	183	219	187	183
Poly-300	300 ± 15	302.7	315	359	479	185
Poly-400	400 ± 20	381.8	384	480	1677	168
Poly-600	600 ± 30	546.9	561	720	∞	137

By permission from the American Institute of Physics, New York.

The precision of the sound velocity method is estimated to be about 3 per cent, and within experimental error these molecular weights are the same as the number average molecular weights.

Attempts were also made to calculate the molecular weights from other pairs of molar constants, such as (1) velocity and viscosity and (2) refraction and viscosity, as summarized in Table 22. It will be noted that in these values the errors are large, partly because the precision of viscosity measurement is only about one-tenth the precision obtainable in sound velocity or refractive index measurements. With increase in molecular weight, the errors also increase because the numerical values involve a decreasing difference between the two terms in the denominator of the expression:

$$M = \frac{Bd}{v^{\frac{1}{3}} - A \dfrac{(n^2 - 1)}{(n^2 + 2)}} \tag{134}$$

which for the polyethylene glycols is

$$M = \frac{57.7d}{v^{\frac{1}{3}} - 41.59 \dfrac{(n^2 - 1)}{(n^2 + 2)}} \tag{135}$$

MOLECULAR WEIGHTS BY CHEMICAL METHODS

The method of determining molecular weights by chemical analysis depends on the ratio of analyzable end groups to the length of the chain of repeating units. These end groups may represent (1) the normal end group of the polymer, that is, it corresponds to the end group derived from the monomers, or (2) the group or radical of tracer molecules or catalysts. The molecular weights obtained by these methods are the number average, $\overline{M}_n$, since they determine the number of moles of polymer.

Normal End Group Analysis

A number of examples of molecular weights determined by normal end group analysis follow.

Ethylene oxide when polymerized in the presence of an active hydrogen compound, like water, produces a polyethylene oxide containing two terminal hydroxy groups. Thus,

$$n\text{CH}_2\!-\!\!\!-\text{CH}_2 \xrightarrow{\text{H}_2\text{O}} \text{HO[CH}_2\text{CH}_2\text{O]}_n\text{H}$$
$$\diagdown\!\!\diagup$$
$$\text{O}$$

The value of n may be determined by producing the diacetyl ester of the polymer and analyzing for acetyl content. Table 23 [169] presents the molecular weight values obtained by Staudinger,[169] using acetyl end group analysis, and compares these values with those obtained using cryoscopic methods.

Molecular Weights by Chemical Methods 273

In a related manner, Carothers and Dorough [170] prepared a number of ethylene succinates which had a polymerization degree between 6

TABLE 23

D.P. Value	Acetyl Content	Molecular Weight Cryoscopic	Acetyl
5	26.7	220	236
9	17.6	3,415	405
18	9.5	790	820
20	8.4	900	940
27	6.5	1,170	1,240
37	4.6	1,230	1,890
39	4.4	1,610	1,750
59	2.8	2,200	3,000
70	2.6	3,040	3,200
140	1.3	5,900	6,500
145	1.25	5,900	6,800
210	0.92	9,200	9,300
290	0.62	12,000	13,800

and 23. They compared the molecular weights of these polymers obtained by titration of the end acid groups with the molecular weights determined by boiling point methods and found excellent agreement. The data in Table 24 [170] are from their work.

TABLE 24

Sample No.	M.p., °C	Molecular Weight from Neutralization Equivalent	Molecular Weight found in Boiling Ethylene Dichloride	Molecular Weight Calculated from Sodium Salt
VIa	73	1016	1070	1030
VIb	82	1344	1380	1460
VIc	90	1795	1582	2010
IV	98	3417	3110	3740

Reprinted by permission from the authors and the *Journal of the American Chemical Society.*

Carothers and Van Natta [54] prepared a series of polyesters from ω-hydroxydecanoic acid over a very wide range of molecular weights. The titration method was applied first to pure lauric acid (m.w. 200.2), and the values of 200.4, 199.6, and 199.2 were obtained.

Molecular weights then were determined on some of these polymers by other methods and compared to the titration method. The data in Table 25 were obtained.[54]

TABLE 25

Average Value of Molecular Weights Obtained by Titration	Molecular Weight Other Method
780	930 (boiling benzene)
1,720	1,620 (boiling benzene)
25,200	26,700 (ultracentrifuge)

Reprinted by permission from the authors and the *Journal of the American Chemical Society*.

For compounds with molecular weights above 3000, boiling point methods are not consistent within 10 per cent, and above 10,000 these methods are of no value. Lycan and Adams had previously prepared these polyesters of ω-hydroxydecanoic acid,[171] fractionated the polymers, and estimated the molecular weight of the fractions by titration with alkali, in the range of 1000 to 9000.

These same polymers were subjected to study [47] to determine the relation of molecular weight to viscosity. The viscosity of these polymers in very dilute solution of tetrachlorethane was very carefully measured. The results showed that Staudinger's original sample empirical equation relating viscosity to molecular weight was fairly well satisfied until a molecular weight of 16,900 was reached, but beyond that point the viscosities rose more rapidly than the equation required. This condition was taken as proof that Staudinger's assumption that the relation of viscosity to molecular weight established for compounds with molecular weight below 10,000 held for compounds of higher molecular weight was not strictly valid.

The polymers of aminocaproic acid have a terminal amino group which can be analyzed by the Van Slyke method. Matthes [69] determined the degree of polymerization of the caprolactam polymer in this manner. The degree of polymerization, D.P., is given as

$$D.P. = \frac{(1400/p) - 18}{113}$$

where p is the percentage of nitrogen in the polymer $H(NHCH_2CH_2CH_2CH_2CH_2CO)_{D.P.}$—OH.

Tracer Molecule

A typical example of tracer end group analysis may be found in Carothers' data [172] for the polymer of δ-valerolactone prepared in the presence of chloroacetic acid.

$$
\begin{array}{c}
\text{CH}_2 \quad \text{O} \\
\diagup \quad \diagdown \quad \diagup\diagup \\
\text{CH}_2 \quad \text{C} \\
| \qquad\quad | \qquad\qquad \xrightarrow[\substack{0.1 \text{ gram} \\ 150 \text{ to } 160 \text{ C} \\ 15 \text{ hours}}]{\text{ClCH}_2\text{COOH}} \quad \text{ClCH}_2\text{CO}-[\text{O}(\text{CH}_2)_4\text{CO}]_x-\text{OH} \\
\text{CH}_2 \quad \text{O} \\
\diagdown \qquad \diagup \\
\text{CH}_2
\end{array}
$$

δ-Valerolactone
1 gram

The polymer melted at 42 C and contained 3.78 per cent chlorine or a molecular weight of 1008. The polymer was converted to the sodium salt and analyzed for sodium and found to contain 2.3 per cent or a molecular weight of 1000.

Similarly, the nitrogen content of polymeric ethylene oxide catalyzed by dimethylamine or methylamine may be used to evaluate its molecular weight according to the following equations:

$$
n\text{CH}_2\text{---CH}_2 \xrightarrow{(\text{CH}_3)_2\text{NH}} (\text{CH}_3)_2\text{N}-[\text{CH}_2\text{CH}_2\text{O}]_n-\text{H}
$$
$$
\diagdown\text{O}\diagup
$$

or

$$
n\text{CH}_2\text{---CH}_2 \xrightarrow{\text{CH}_3\text{NH}_2} \text{CH}_3\text{NH}-[\text{CH}_2\text{CH}_2\text{O}]_n-\text{H}
$$
$$
\diagdown\text{O}\diagup
$$

Staudinger's data [173] from such experiments shows the comparison in Table 26.

TABLE 26

Catalyst	Viscosity Molecular Weight	Nitrogen in Polymer Theoretical	Found
Methylamine	2000	0.7	0.6
	1500	0.9	0.7
	1400	1.0	0.8
Dimethylamine	2000	0.7	0.7
	1500	0.9	0.4
	1300	1.1	0.6
	1200	1.2	0.6

A tracer molecule may be used in vinyl type polymers to determine molecular weights. For example, Kern and Kämmerer [174] have used tracer substances such as parabromobenzoyl peroxide in the polymerization of styrene for molecular weight determinations. Bartlett and Cohen [175] and Price and his co-workers [176] have shown that the brominated catalysts react with the styrene to initiate the polymerization chain in which one mole of catalyst is combined for each chain. In fractions ranging from 6800 to 109,900 the bromine content was found to increase with decreasing molecular weight.

Of the eight methods described, probably the determination of molecular weights by viscosity measurements is most common. This is so, not only because of the relative ease in performing the measurement but also because of the availability and reasonable cost of the equipment. Osmotic pressure measurements are more exact, but they require considerable skill and are time consuming in contrast to the osmotic measurements. The ultracentrifuge, like the electron microscope, is expensive and requires specialized training for its accurate performance. As has been shown, those methods using van't Hoff's and Raoult's relationships, such as in melting point, boiling point, and vapor pressure changes, are limited in the molecular weight range of application. Light-scattering methods show promise of being inexpensive, simple, and operable, and future developments along this path should be followed. The chemical methods, particularly the "tracer" type of analysis, have been used extensively but usually in conjunction with viscosity or osmotic measurements.

REFERENCES

1. G. N. Lewis and M. Randall, *Thermodynamics*, pp. 190, 213, 235, McGraw-Hill Book Co., New York, 1923.
2. A. Weissberger (Editor), *Physical Methods of Organic Chemistry*, Vol. I, p. 254, Interscience Publishers, New York, 1945.
3. P. J. Flory, *J. Am. Chem. Soc.*, **65**, 376 (1943).
4. P. J. Flory, *J. Chem. Phys.*, **10**, 51 (1942).
5. K. H. Meyer, *Z. physik. Chem.*, **B44**, 383 (1939).
6. K. H. Meyer and A. J. A. van der Wyk, *Helv. Chim. Acta*, **23**, 488 (1940).
7. M. L. Huggins, *J. Phys. Chem.*, **46**, 151 (1942).
8. M. L. Huggins, *J. Am. Chem. Soc.*, **64**, 1712 (1942).
9. A. Dorby, *J. chim. phys.*, **32**, 50 (1935).
10. A. Bartovics and H. Mark, *J. Am. Chem. Soc.*, **65**, 1901 (1943).
11. W. J. Badgley and H. Mark, *J. Phys. Colloid Chem.*, **51**, 58–70 (1947).
12. A. M. Sookne, H. A. Rutherford, H. Mark, and M. Harris, *J. Research Natl. Bur. Standards*, **29**, 123 (1942).
13. A. R. Miller, *Proc. Cambridge Phil. Soc.*, **39**, 54 (1943).
14. M. L. Huggins, *Ann. N. Y. Acad. Sci.*, **44**, 431 (1943).
15. M. L. Huggins, *Ann. N. Y. Acad. Sci.*, **43**, 11 (1942).
16. G. Scatchard, *Chem. Revs.*, **8**, 331 (1931).
17. J. H. Hildebrand, *Chem. Revs.*, **18**, 315 (1936).

18. W. A. Caspari, *J. Chem. Soc.* (London), **105**, 2139 (1914).
19. M. L. Huggins, *Ind. Eng. Chem.*, **35**, 216 (1943).
20. R. O. Herzog and H. M. Spurlin, *Z. physik. Chem.*, Bodenstein-Festband, 239 (1931).
21. C. B. Boissonnas and K. H. Meyer, *Helv. Chim. Acta*, **20**, 783 (1937).
22. G. V. Schulz, *Z. physik. Chem.*, **A176**, 317 (1936); G. V. Schulz and E. Husemann, *ibid.*, **B52**, 1 (1942).
23. J. Bourdillon, *J. Biol. Chem.*, **127**, 617 (1939).
24. R. Obogi and E. Broda, *Kolloid Z.*, **69**, 172 (1934).
25. Earl of Berkeley and E. G. J. Hartley, *Trans. Roy. Soc.* (London), **A206**, 486 (1906).
26. P. van Campen, *Rec. trav. chim.*, **50**, 915 (1931).
27. R. M. Fuoss and D. J. Mead, *J. Phys. Chem.*, **47**, 59 (1943).
28. K. B. Goldblum, *J. Phys. Colloid Chem.*, **51**, 474–479 (1947).
29. E. C. Bingham, *Fluidity and Plasticity*, pp. 331–338, McGraw-Hill Book Co., New York, 1922.
30. J. L. M. Poiseuille, Académie des sciences, Paris, "Memoires présentés par divers savants," *Sciences mathématiques et physiques*, Vol. 9, 433–543 (1846).
31. H. Staudinger, *Die Hochmolekularen organischen Verbindungen*, pp. 28, 199, J. Springer, Berlin, 1932.
32. D. J. Mead and R. M. Fuoss, *J. Am. Chem. Soc.*, **64**, 277 (1942).
33. W. O. Baker, C. S. Fuller, and J. H. Heiss, Jr., *J. Am. Chem. Soc.*, **63**, 2142 (1941).
34. H. Staudinger, *Die Hochmolekularen organischen Verbindungen*, p. 128, J. Springer, Berlin, 1932.
35. H. Staudinger and W. Heuer, *Ber.*, **63**, 222 (1930).
36. H. Staudinger and R. Nodzu, *Ber.*, **63**, 721 (1930).
37. A. Einstein, *Ann. Physik.*, **19**, 300 (1906).
38. E. Guth and O. Gold, *Phys. Rev.*, **53** (2nd Series), 322 (1938).
39. E. Guth and R. Simha, *Kolloid Z.*, **74**, 266 (1936).
40. H. Eilers, *Kolloid Z.*, **97**, 313 (1941).
41. H. Eilers, *Kolloid Z.*, **102**, 154 (1943).
42. R. Simha, *J. Phys. Chem.*, **44**, 25 (1940).
43. V. Z. Daněs, *Kolloid Z.*, **68**, 110 (1934).
44. K. Hess and I. Sakurada, *Ber.*, **64**, 1183 (1931).
45. P. J. Flory and P. B. Stickney, *J. Am. Chem. Soc.*, **62**, 3032 (1940).
46. A. R. Kemp and H. Peters, *J. Phys. Chem.*, **43**, 1063 (1939).
47. E. O. Kraemer and F. J. Van Natta, *J. Phys. Chem.*, **36**, 3175 (1932).
48. E. O. Kraemer and W. D. Lansing, *J. Phys. Chem.*, **39**, 153 (1935).
49. E. O. Kraemer, *Ind. Eng. Chem.*, **30**, 1200 (1938).
50. K. H. Meyer and A. van der Wyk, *Helv. Chim. Acta*, **18**, 1067 (1935).
51. R. Fordyce and H. Hibbert, *J. Am. Chem. Soc.*, **61**, 1912 (1939).
52. E. L. Lovell and H. Hibbert, *J. Am. Chem. Soc.*, **62**, 2140 (1940).
53. K. H. Meyer and A. van der Wyk, *Z. Elektrochem.*, **40**, 446 (1934).
54. W. H. Carothers and F. J. Van Natta, *J. Am. Chem. Soc.*, **55**, 4714 (1933).
55. W. O. Baker, C. S. Fuller, and J. H. Heiss, Jr., *J. Am. Chem. Soc.*, **63**, 3316 (1941).
56. H. Staudinger and E. Husemann, *Ber.*, **68**, 1618 (1935).
57. H. Staudinger and G. V. Schulz, *Ber.*, **68**, 2320 (1935).
58. H. Staudinger and J. Schneiders, *Ann.*, **541**, 151 (1939).

278 Molecular Weight Determinations

59. H. Staudinger and H. Warth, *J. prakt. Chem.*, **155**, 261 (1940).
60. H. Staudinger and K. Fisher, *J. prakt. Chem.*, **157**, 19, 158 (1940–1941).
61. K. H. Meyer, *Kolloid Z.*, **95**, 70 (1941).
62. H. Mark, *Z. Elektrochem.*, **40**, 413 (1934).
63. H. Mark, *Der fester Korper*, p. 103, Hirzel, Leipzig, 1938.
64. R. Houwink, *J. prakt. Chem.*, **157**, 15 (1940).
65. W. Kuhn, *Kolloid Z.*, **62**, 269 (1933).
66. W. Kuhn, *Kolloid Z.*, **68**, 2 (1934).
67. G. V. Schulz and A. Dinglinger, *J. prakt. Chem.*, **158**, 136 (1941).
68. P. J. Flory, *J. Am. Chem. Soc.*, **65**, 372 (1943).
69. A. Matthes, *J. prakt. Chem.*, **162**, 245 (1943).
70. M. L. Huggins, *J. Am. Chem. Soc.*, **64**, 2716 (1942).
71. R. Govaerts and G. Smets, *J. Polymer Sci.*, **2**, 612 (1947).
72. G. V. Schulz, *J. prakt. Chem.*, **159**, 130 (1941).
73. M. L. Huggins, *J. Phys. Chem.*, **42**, 911 (1938).
74. M. L. Huggins, *J. Phys. Chem.*, **43**, 439 (1939).
75. M. L. Huggins, *J. Applied Phys.*, **10**, 700 (1939).
76. R. Simha, *J. Applied Phys.*, **13**, 147 (1942).
77. R. E. Powell, C. R. Clark, and H. Eyring, *J. Chem. Phys.*, **9**, 268 (1941).
78. W. Kuhn, *Z. physik. Chem.*, **A161**, 427 (1932).
79. T. Alfrey, Jr., A. Bartovics, and H. Mark, *J. Am. Chem. Soc.*, **64**, 1557 (1942).
80. P. J. Flory, *J. Am. Chem. Soc.*, **65**, 379 (1943).
81. R. Signer, *Helv. Chim. Acta*, **18**, 701 (1935).
82. R. Signer and R. Gross, *Helv. Chim. Acta*, **17**, 59 (1934).
83. R. Signer and R. Gross, *Helv. Chim. Acta*, **17**, 335 (1934).
84. R. Signer and R. Gross, *Helv. Chim. Acta*, **17**, 726 (1934).
85. A. R. Kemp and H. Peters, *Ind. Eng. Chem.*, **34**, 1097 (1942).
86. G. V. Schulz, *Z. physik. Chem.*, **B44**, 227 (1939).
87. T. Alfrey, Jr., A. Bartovics, and H. Mark, *J. Am. Chem. Soc.*, **65**, 2320 (1943).
88. R. Spencer and L. R. Drake, *Physical Methods of Organic Chemistry*, edited by A. Weissberger, Vol. I, p. 146, Interscience Publishers, New York, 1945.
89. E. C. Bingham, *Am. Chem. J.*, **45**, 264 (1911).
90. E. C. Bingham, *Am. Chem. J.*, **43**, 302 (1910).
91. R. Přibram and A. Handl, *Sitzber. Akad. Wiss. Wien, Math.-naturw. Klasse,* Abt. II, **78**, 113 (1878).
92. R. Přibram and A. Handl, *Sitzber. Akad. Wiss. Wien, Math.-naturw. Klasse,* Abt. II, **80**, 17 (1879).
93. L. Rellstab, *Transpiration homologer Flussigkeiten*, Bonn, 1868.
94. T. E. Thorpe and J. W. Rodger, *Proc. Roy. Soc.* (London), **A60**, 152 (1896).
95. R. E. Powell, E. A. Roseveare, and H. Eyring, *Ind. Eng. Chem.*, **33**, 430 (1941).
96. P. J. Flory, *J. Am. Chem. Soc.*, **62**, 1057 (1940).
97. R. S. Spencer and R. E. Dillon, *J. Colloid Sci.*, **3**, 163–180 (1948).
98. H. Eyring, *J. Chem. Phys.*, **4**, 283 (1936).
99. G. J. Dienes and F. D. Dexter, *J. Colloid Sci.*, **3**, 181–183 (1948).
100. L. Ubbelohde, *Ind. Eng. Chem.*, Anal. Ed., **9**, 85 (1937).
101. E. G. Bingham, *Fluidity and Plasticity*, McGraw-Hill Book Co., New York, 1922.
102. S. B. Stone, *J. Rheol.*, **1**, 240 (1930).
103. H. C. Tingey, *Advances in Colloid Science*, Vol. II, p. 210, Interscience Publishers, New York, 1946.

104. T. Svedberg, *Ind. Eng. Chem.*, Anal. Ed., **10**, 113 (1938).
105. T. Svedberg and K. O. Pedersen, *The Ultracentrifuge*, Oxford, Clarendon Press, 1940.
106. E. G. Pickels, *Chem. Revs.*, **30**, 341 (1942).
107. E. O. Kraemer, *Frontiers in Chemistry*, edited by R. E. Burk, Vol. I, p. 107, Interscience Publishers, New York, 1943.
108. E. O. Kraemer and J. B. Nichols, *The Ultracentrifuge by Svedberg and Pedersen*, p. 423, Oxford, Clarendon Press, 1940.
109. W. D. Lansing and E. O. Kraemer, *J. Am. Chem. Soc.*, **57**, 1369 (1935).
110. R. Signer, *Trans. Faraday Soc.*, **32**, 296 (1936).
111. O. Lamm and A. Poulson, *Biochem. J.*, **30**, 528 (1936).
112. T. Svedberg, *Z. physik. Chem.*, **127**, 51 (1927).
113. E. O. Kraemer and W. D. Lansing, *J. Am. Chem. Soc.*, **55**, 4319 (1933).
114. G. V. Schulz, *Z. physik. Chem.*, **A180**, 1 (1937).
115. J. H. van't Hoff, *Z. physik. Chem.*, **1**, 481 (1887).
116. Landolt-Börnstein, *Physikalisch-Chemische Tabellen*, Erg. IIIc, pp. 2667–2669.
117. G. N. Lewis and M. Randall, *Thermodynamics*, McGraw-Hill Book Co., New York, 1923.
118. M. Gomberg and F. W. Sullivan, Jr., *J. Am. Chem. Soc*, **44**, 1810 (1922).
119. W. E. S. Turner and S. English, *J. Chem. Soc.* (London), **105**, 1786 (1914).
120. C. J. Peddle and W. E. S. Turner, *J. Chem. Soc.* (London), **99**, 685 (1911).
121. E. R. Jones and C. R. Bury, *J. Chem. Soc.* (London), **127**, 1949 (1925).
122. K. Rast, *Ber.*, **55**, 1051, 3727 (1922).
123. A. Findlay, *Practical Physical Chemistry*, 7th Ed., Chapter VIII, Longmans Green & Co., New York, 1941.
124. A. R. Kemp and H. Peters, *Ind. Eng. Chem.*, **34**, 1192 (1942).
125. H. Staudinger and M. Brunner, *Helv. Chim. Acta*, **13**, 1375 (1930).
126. K. H. Meyer and R. Lühdemann, *Helv. Chim. Acta*, **18**, 307 (1935).
127. E. Husemann and H. Ruska, *J. prakt. Chem.*, **156**, 1 (1940).
128. E. L. Kropa, C. J. Burton, and R. B. Barnes, Electron Microscope Society Meeting, New York City, January 11–15, 1944.
129. R. F. Boyer and R. D. Heidenreich, *J. Applied Phys.*, **16**, 621–639 (1945).
130. Lord Rayleigh, *Phil. Mag.*, **41**, 447 (1871).
131. J. Tyndall, *Phil. Mag.*, **37**, 384 (1869).
132. Lord Rayleigh, *Phil. Mag.*, **12**, 81 (1881).
133. J. Cabannes, *Ann. Physik*, **15**, 5 (1921).
134. J. Cabannes, *Diffusion Moleculaire de la Lumière*, Presses Universitaires de France, Paris, 1939.
135. G. Oster, "The Scattering of Light and Its Applications to Chemistry," *Chem. Revs.*, **43**, 319–365 (1948).
136. P. Debye, *J. Applied Phys.*, **15**, 338–342 (1944).
137. P. Debye, *J. Phys. and Colloid Chem.*, **51**, 18 (1947).
138. M. von Smoluchowski, *Ann. Physik*, **25**, 205 (1908).
139. M. von Smoluchowski, *Phil. Mag.*, **23**, 165 (1912).
140. A. Einstein, *Ann. Physik*, **33**, 1275 (1910).
141. P. Debye, Cornell University, *Reports to the Office of Rubber Reserve*, No. CR 103, CR 103A, CR 110, CR 296.
142. C. V. Raman and K. R. Ramanathan, *Phil. Mag.*, **45**, 213 (1923).
143. P. Doty, B. H. Zimm, and H. Mark, *J. Chem. Phys.*, **12**, 144 (1944).
144. P. Debye, *J. Chem. Phys.*, **14**, 687–695 (1946).

145. P. Doty, B. H. Zimm, and H. Mark, *J. Chem. Phys.*, **13**, 159 (1944).
146. P. Doty and H. S. Kaufman, *J. Phys. Chem.*, **49**, 583 (1945).
147. G. Mie, *Ann. Physik*, **25**, 377 (1908).
148. R. S. Stein and P. Doty, *J. Am. Chem. Soc.*, **68**, 159 (1946).
149. P. Debye, *Ann. Physik*, **30**, 59 (1909).
150. Lord Rayleigh, *Phil. Mag.*, **49**, 324 (1900).
151. P. P. Debye, *Lecture at Polytechnic Institute of Brooklyn*, Brooklyn, N. Y., Nov. 25, 1944.
152. P. P. Debye, *Thesis at Cornell University*, 1944.
153. P. P. Debye, *J. Applied Phys.*, **17**, 392 (1946).
154. P. Debye and H. Menke, *Forts Röntgenforschung*, **2**, 1 (1931).
155. V. K. La Mer, *J. Colloid Sci.*, **1**, 71, 79 (1946).
156. K. G. Stern, S. Singer, and S. Davis, *Polymer Bull.*, **1**, 31 (1945).
157. W. J. Badgley, *Polymer Bull.*, **1**, 17 (1945).
158. B. H. Zimm, *J. Chem. Phys.*, **14**, 164 (1946).
159. P. Debye, *J. Applied Phys.*, **17**, 392–398 (1946).
160. P. Doty, H. Wagner, and S. Singer, *J. Phys. and Colloid Chem.*, **51**, 38 (1947).
161. A. Weissler, J. W. Fitzgerald, and I. Resnick, *J. Applied Phys.*, **18**, 434 (1947).
162. M. R. Rao, *Indian J. Phys.*, **14**, 109 (1940).
163. M. R. Rao, *J. Chem. Phys.*, **9**, 682 (1941).
164. R. T. Lagemann and W. S. Dunbar, *J. Phys. Chem.*, **49**, 428 (1945).
165. R. Fordyce and H. Hibbert, *J. Am. Chem. Soc.*, **61**, 1910 (1939).
166. A. Weissberger, Editor, *Physical Methods of Organic Chemistry*, Vol. I, p. 672, Interscience Publishers, New York, 1945.
167. A. Weissberger, Editor, *Physical Methods of Organic Chemistry*, Vol. I, p. 679, Interscience Publishers, New York, 1945.
168. M. Souders, Jr., *J. Am. Chem. Soc.*, **60**, 154 (1938).
169. H. Staudinger, *Die Hochmolekularen organischen Verbindungen*, p. 298, J. Springer, Berlin, 1932.
170. W. H. Carothers and G. L. Dorough, *J. Am. Chem. Soc.*, **52**, 711–721 (1930).
171. W. H. Lycan and Roger Adams, *J. Am. Chem. Soc.*, **51**, 625, 3450 (1929).
172. W. H. Carothers, G. L. Dorough, and F. J. Van Natta, *J. Am. Chem. Soc.*, **54**, 761–762 (1932).
173. H. Staudinger, *Die Hochmolekularen organischen Verbindungen*, p. 299, J. Springer, Berlin, 1932.
174. W. Kern and H. Kämmerer, *J. prakt. Chem.*, **161**, 81–112 (1942).
175. P. D. Bartlett and S. G. Cohen, *J. Am. Chem. Soc.*, **65**, 543–546 (1943).
176. C. C. Price, R. W. Kell, and E. Krebs, *J. Am. Chem. Soc.*, **64**, 1103–1106 (1942).

CHAPTER 8

Kinetics of Polymerizations

KINETIC MEASUREMENTS

The mechanism of any chemical reaction is best derived by the interpretation of kinetic data. In polymerization studies the kinetic data are concerned with the rate of disappearance of monomer and the extent of polymerization. The *degree of polymerization* is not to be confused with the *extent of polymerization*. As has already been pointed out, the degree of polymerization refers to the number of segmers in a specific polymer chain whereas the extent of polymerization refers to the amount of polymer that has been formed in the polymerization reaction at any specific time.

EXTENT OF POLYMERIZATION

The determination of the extent to which monomers have been converted to polymers at any particular moment is essential to a study of the kinetics of polymerization and thereby to the mechanism of polymerization.

The general principles of measuring reaction rates [1-3] apply to polymer systems since the rate of disappearance of the monomers, comers, or comonomers, or the rate of formation of the polymers with time must be determined.

Physical and chemical methods either alone or in conjunction with each other may be used to determine the time rate in polymerization reactions. Some of the methods used to determine the progress of a reaction are described below. The extent of polymerization is usually recorded in percentage or mole fraction. In general the conversion is expressed as $-(dc/dt)$ for monomer since monomers disappear during polymerization.

Physical Methods

In using physical methods, the determinations may be made either by separating the monomer from the polymer or by examining the monomer-polymer mixture without separation.

MONOMER-POLYMER SEPARATION

The first of these methods is by distillation. The first attempts to follow the progress of polymerization of styrene were recorded by Lemoine.[4, 5] He showed that polystyrene is soluble in styrene and that the monomer could be separated from the polymer by fractional vacuum distillation. This distillation method, used widely by a number of investigators, is considered satisfactory under the following conditions.

1. No further polymerization should occur during the distillation. If necessary, the polymerization should be arrested by the addition of weighed amounts of inhibitors.
2. No degradation or cracking of the polymer should occur and the distillate should contain only unpolymerized monomer. The distillate should be refractionated to determine the presence of such oligomers as dimers and trimers.
3. All or a very substantial portion of the polymer must be removed by distillation. Many polymers retain solvent to a tenacious degree, and the values obtained by distillation should be confirmed by another method.

A number of investigators [6-8] used this method in studies on styrene, vinyl acetate, and methyl acrylate, when the monomer was distilled directly from the monomer-polymer mixture.

Sometimes it is advisable to use steam distillation methods to remove unpolymerized monomer. Schmitz-Dumont [9] used steam distillation in the studies on acid-catalyzed indene and skatole polymerization. The acid was neutralized with alkali at the reaction time desired, and the solution distilled to remove unreacted skatole or indene. The polymeric residue was then isolated and dried to constant weight.

Steam distillation is at the present time a current practice in the preparation of or studies on emulsion polymerization systems such as are used in preparing synthetic rubber or polymer latices.

The second method involving monomer-polymer separation utilizes precipitation processes.

The requirements of one precipitation method are that one component of the monomer-polymer mixture be soluble in a specific solvent and the other component be completely or substantially insoluble. This method is well adapted to those systems wherein monomer and polymer are completely compatible with each other at all stages of polymerization. As an example, at early stages of polymerization, that is, at low conversions, the mixture of polystyrene and styrene is still fluid. At this stage the polymer may be isolated by slowly adding the mixture with vigorous agitation to a large volume of methyl alcohol and isolating the precipitated polymer, rewashing or extracting with more methyl alcohol and drying to constant weight. At higher polymer conversions, in which case the polymer solution is very viscous and may even be a solid, the monomer-polymer mixture is first diluted to a low viscosity by benzene, toluene, or styrene and the diluted solution added to the methyl alcohol to effect precipitation of the polymer.[10-12] Since methyl alcohol extracts styrene oligomers, an inhibitor should be added to the methanol solution. The precipitated polymer is removed from the methyl alcohol by filtration. Monomers and any oligomers are isolated from the methyl alcohol filtrates and washings by distillation.

Soluble, fusible partial polymers of divinylbenzene have been isolated by this precipitation method.[13]

The main requirement of another precipitation method is that the polymer be insoluble in the monomer. In certain mass polymerizations, the polymers precipitate during polymerization as soon as formed. These polymers are readily isolated by filtration, dried, weighed, and the percentage conversion determined. Polyacrylonitrile is insoluble in monomeric acrylonitrile and is readily separated by filtration, washed with absolute alcohol, and dried to constant weight. Similarly, polyvinyl chloride is insoluble in vinyl chloride, and the polymer is readily isolated simply by letting the monomer evaporate at room temperature. The polymer is then washed with anhydrous methanol, dried, weighed, and the conversion calculated.

The third method is a modification adapted from the preceding method so that polymer, in those monomer-polymer mixtures normally compatible over wide ranges of conversion, will precipitate as soon as formed. Strain[14] studied the polymerization of methyl methacrylate in mixtures of methanol and water, in which mixture the monomer but not the polymers were soluble. This particular combination of water and methanol did not dissolve the polymer so that once polymerization was started, the polymer precipitated when formed. The extent or the percentage of polymerization was determined with a good degree of accuracy by measuring the amount of precipitated polymer. Similarly, polystyrene will precipitate when styrene is polymerized in methyl alcohol. Reid[15] disclosed that copolymers of vinyl chloride and vinyl acetate precipitate from solution when hexane is used as a solvent for the monomers.

DETERMINATIONS USING MONOMER-POLYMER MIXTURES

The separation or isolation of either the polymer or the monomer offers the best means of determining the extent of the polymerization. Sometimes, however, it is either impractical or impossible to effect such an isolation. Then some of the other methods that can be applied are indicated below.

Refractive index method. This method involves determining the refractive index of the monomer-polymer mixture either directly or with the addition of a solvent, and comparing the refractive index values against standardization curves. The standardization curves are obtained from solutions of known concentrations of polymer *in* monomer. If a solvent is required, a known one is used. Standardization may also be obtained by plotting refractive index of the mixture against polymer concentration; the concentration has been determined previously by precipitation or distillation methods. Stobbe and Reuss [16,17] used this latter method to obtain kinetic data on the polymerization of styrene and cyclopentadiene.

The light activated polymerization of diethyl itaconate was studied by the periodic measurement of the refractive index.[18] The pure ester had a refractive index of 1.43609, which after 65 days of exposure to sunlight became 1.44928.

Refractive index may be used to measure the extent of reaction between phenol and formaldehyde,[19] for which typical data are included in Table 1.[20] The reaction mixture consisted of 1 mole of phenol, 1 mole of formaldehyde as 37.1 per cent formalin, and 0.00588 mole of NaOH.

TABLE 1

Sample Number	Time in Minutes	% Resin	Grams Resin/Mole Phenol	Refractive Index at 25 C	Specific Gravity at 25 C	Viscosity in Centipoises at 25 C	CH_2O moles/liter
0				1.4688			6.30
1	2	31.5	55.4	1.4698	1.081	4.89	5.80
2	6	35.5	62.4	1.4738	1.086	5.50	5.10
3	12	38.9	68.4	1.4790	1.094	6.71	3.90
4	20	43.0	75.6	1.4837	1.103	8.01	2.90
5	30	44.9	78.9	1.4879	1.108	9.24	2.10
6	40	46.7	82.1	1.4923	1.114	10.4	1.70
7	50	47.8	84.1	1.4940	1.117	11.6	1.33
8	60	49.7	87.5	1.4971	1.119	13.0	0.97
9	70	50.6	89.0	1.5009	1.124	15.1	0.93
10	85	52.6	92.5	1.5083	1.130	19.8	0.73
11	90	54.1	95.2	1.5094	1.133	21.2	0.67

The condensation was carried out at reflux temperatures, and a number of other rate values such as per cent resin, specific gravity, viscosity, residual formaldehyde are correlated to time and refractive index.

Optical rotation. Marvel[21] has utilized optically active groups in the monomer to determine the course of polymerization. He followed the polymerization of *d*-*s*-butyl-*α*-chloroacrylate and vinyl *l*-*β*-phenyl butyrate by means of a polarscope.

Viscosity measurements. This method requires the preparation of a standard curve by first preparing solutions of the polymer in monomer and then plotting the viscosity of the solution versus the polymer content. Stobbe and Posnjak[22] applied this method to the polymerization of styrene prepared under a large number of widely varying conditions. Standardization may also be obtained by plotting the viscosity against concentration obtained by an independent source, and then using this curve as a standard. Such data are represented in Table 1, which includes other measurements beside viscosity values.

Density measurements. In this method, the density of periodically extracted samples is compared to previously plotted standardized curves, in a manner similar to that for using refractive index values. This method was used by Breitenbach and Raff[8] in determining the extent of polymerization of vinyl acetate and the acrylic esters. Table 1 correlates density data obtained during the progress of a phenol-formaldehyde reaction to other types of measurements.

Volume contraction—dilatometric measurements. The volume contraction or expansion that occurs during a chemical reaction may be measured by means of a dilatometer. By means of continuous measurements of the volume contraction, Starkweather and Taylor[23] proved that in vinyl acetate polymerization a linear relationship existed between the extent of polymerization and the percentage volume contraction. This method is applicable to those monomer-polymer systems where all the polymers formed are non-volatile and where the density of the polymer does not change during the course of the polymerization.

Absorption spectrum. By means of the analytical extinction coefficient, Goodeve[24] studied the absorption changes that occur during the polymerization of methyl methacrylate. The value of absorption spectrum of methyl methacrylate was compared with the values obtained at intervals during the polymerization until polymerization was complete. Observations on the changes in viscosity that also occurred during polymerization showed that the extinction coefficient was related to the extent of polymerization. Owens[25] developed a photographic spectrophotometric method to follow the progress of a polymerization reaction. His method followed through the quantitative determination of extinction coefficients, and the changes produced in the intensities of the characteristic absorption bands of the monomers or of the polymers having new absorption bands.

Spectra methods showed that monomeric styrene had absorption bands at 2910 Å, at 2830 Å, and complete absorption at wavelengths shorter than 2690 Å. Polystyrene was shown to have a band at 2695 Å and complete absorption below 2400 Å. In mixtures of monomer and polymer, the intensity of the absorption band of the monomer was found to increase regularly as the percentage of monomer increased. From standardized curves, the value or extent of polymerization may be determined readily.

The extinction coefficients are given by A as:

$$A = \frac{\log \dfrac{I_2}{I_0} - \dfrac{I_1}{I_0}}{cl} \qquad (1)$$

where c = concentration of one of the components of the sample, for example, the monomer,

l = thickness of sample,

I_2 = intensity of sample measured at thickness l at an unabsorbed control wavelength,

I_1 = intensity of reference sample at thickness l in an unabsorbed control wavelength,

I_0 = intensity of reference sample at thickness l at an absorbed wavelength.

The spectrophotometric method has been used to determine the residual monomer in polystyrene.[26] Partially polymerized styrene samples were analyzed at two wavelengths with a medium quartz spectrophotometer. The readings were divided by the total sample concentrations, and these values, when plotted against the percentage of monomer in that particular mixture, gave a calibration that could be used for routine analysis.

The monomer content was also calculated from the specific absorption coefficients of pure styrene and polystyrene. By Beer's law, the monomer contents of five synthetic mixtures were calculated from absorption data. The results are shown in Table 2.

TABLE 2

% Monomer Synthetic Mixture	% Monomer at 282 Millimicrons		% Monomer at 291 Millimicrons	
	Uncorrected	Corrected	Uncorrected	Corrected
66.6	67.2	....	66.8	....
50.2	51.0	50.8	51.2	50.9
20.2	20.6	20.4	20.4	20.3
11.2	11.4	11.2	11.3	11.2
2.46	2.65	2.44	2.62	2.46

Vibrational spectrum. Although Raman spectra have been shown to be somewhat adapted to the "fingerprinting" or identification of certain polymers or copolymers, the use of vibrational spectra to determine the extent of polymerization has not been very successful. This method depends on the disappearance of certain frequencies and the appearance of new frequencies formed by new bonds.

The polymerization of chloroprene, CH_2=CH—CCl=CH_2, was examined by Kubota.[27] On polymerization, chloroprene would produce the segmer, —CH_2—CH=CCl—CH_2—, which is quite similar in structure to 2-chlorobutene-2,

$$H_3C—HC=C—CH_3$$
$$|$$
$$Cl$$

It would be expected that polymerized chloroprene would show frequencies similar to the frequency of 2-chlorobutene-2, but different from that of chloroprene. The frequency for the C=C bond in 2-chlorobutene-2 is 1670 centimeters^{-1}. In the polymer a frequency of 1658 centimeters^{-1} was observed, but the intensities of the observed frequency were not proportional to the extent of polymerization.

By Raman spectra methods, polystyrene,[28] methyl methacrylate, methyl crotonate, diethyl maleate, and diethyl fumarate were investigated,[29] and the vibrational frequencies were found to change, but not regularly, as polymerization increased.

The Raman spectra data on acrylic acid, and of monomeric and polymeric methyl and ethyl methacrylates, were recorded by Monnier and others,[30] showing that the intensity of the double bond frequency of the CH_2=C group diminishes with polymerization.

Conductance or resistance. Kienle and Race[31] correlated the changes in conductance during the reaction of a polyhydric alcohol with a polycarboxylic acid with ester values, saponification, and acid numbers. A good correlation was obtained between the various values.

Diamagnetic susceptibility. The polymerization of 2,3-dimethylbutadiene at 146 C and of cyclopentadiene at room temperature was investigated by Farquharson,[32, 33] who showed that the magnetic susceptibility changes during polymerization. This method measures the mass susceptibilities at the initial state and at an intermediate or final state according to the equation

$$F = \tfrac{1}{2}(K_1 - K_2)\Delta H^2 \qquad (2)$$

where K_1 and K_2 are, respectively, the volume susceptibilities of the specimen and of the medium in which the specimen is suspended, A is the cross section of the specimen, H is the field, and F is the force on the specimen. This method has not found wide application in polymerization studies.

Farquharson's data are shown in Figure 1.[32]

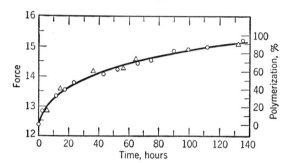

FIGURE 1. Polymerization of dimethylbutadiene. (By permission from The Faraday Society, London.)

Chemical Methods

In general the same methods used to prove the existence of polymers may be used to measure the extent of the polymerization. They were discussed in Chapter 3. Particularly applicable are those methods involving end group analysis, measurements of the disappearance of monomers, comers, etc.

END GROUP ANALYSIS

In condensation reactions reactive groups like hydroxyl, amino, carboxyl, carbalkoxy, halogeno, and nitrilo disappear. The disappearance of these groups is proportional to the extent of polymerization, provided that no side reactions, such as a decarboxylation reaction, have occurred. The acid number of a polyhydric alcohol–polycarboxylic acid measures carboxyl end groups, and this method was used by a number of investigators for polyester reactions.[34–38]

RESIDUAL MONOMER

This method is particularly suited to those processes in which monomers lose very reactive groups by polymerization. A typical example is the polymerization of styrene and vinyl acetate, which lose double bonds on polymerization. The monomer itself readily forms a dibromide:

$$CH_2{=}CHC_6H_5 + Br_2 \rightarrow BrCH_2CHBrC_6H_5$$

The quantity of styrene that disappears may be determined as a difference by bromination of the residual styrene monomer; and since the amount of polymer formed is equivalent to the quantity of styrene that disappears, the extent of the polymerization may be readily calculated.[10, 39] Williams [11, 40] used this bromination method to determine the course of the polymerization of styrene in carbon tetrachloride solution with stannic chloride as a catalyst. A modification of this method involving the disappearance of double bonds was used by Kia-Khwe Jeu and H. N. Alyea,[41] who studied the photopolymerization of vinyl acetate as influenced by various inhibitors. These authors determined the course of the reaction by following the disappearance of vinyl acetate by means of Wij's solution, which gave iodine number values.

KINETICS OF POLYMERIZATION

Condensation Systems

A simple condensation polymerization system is well represented by the polyesterification of a hydroxy acid. It may be written as

$$n[HO(CH_2)_yCOOH] \rightarrow H[O(CH_2)_yCO]_nOH + (n-1)H_2O$$

The condensation of n molecules of hydroxy acids is not accomplished in a single step; rather the polymerization product represents the stepwise reaction of a simple polyesterification. If the conditions are selected so that no cyclization occurs, the reaction may be represented first as

$$HO(CH_2)_yCOOH \xrightarrow{HO(CH_2)_yCOOH}$$

$$H[O(CH_2)_yCO]_2OH \xrightarrow{HO(CH_2)_yCOOH} H[O(CH_2)_yCO]_3OH, \text{ etc.}$$

Simultaneous dimers, trimers, and high n-mers are reacting with each other as well as with monomers, and the reaction is represented as

$$H[O(CH_2)_yCO]_nOH + H[O(CH_2)_yCO]_nOH \rightarrow$$

$$H[O(CH_2)_yCO]_{2n}OH + H_2O$$

If such a mechanism actually occurs then, it should be possible to calculate the molecular weight distribution for such a polymerization. There are two methods of obtaining this distribution, the statistical and the kinetic. In Chapter 4, in the sections dealing with the non-homogeneity of polymers and with the distribution and gelation in condensation polymers, the statistical method was used, and an excellent agreement was obtained with actual experimental values. In the statistical method and in the kinetic method, the assumption was originally made that the reactivity of a particular functional or reactive group (for example, the —OH or —COOH groups) involved in a polyesterification does not change noticeably as the size of the molecule is increased. Actually in non-polymeric esterifications this was found to be true as may be observed in the values obtained by Smith,[42] who studied the HCl catalyzed esterification of methyl alcohol with acids of the formula RCOOH. The activation energy for the reaction

$$RCOOH + CH_3OH \xrightarrow{HCl} H_2O + RCOOCH_3$$

was 10.0 kilocalories per mole. The relative rates as R is increased are given in Table 3.

TABLE 3

R	Actual Rate Constants	Relative Rates at 50 C
CH_3	0.219	100
C_2H_5	0.193	91
nC_3H_7	0.103	48
nC_4H_9	0.101	49
nC_5H_{11}	0.102	50
nC_8H_{17}	0.100	48

Flory's [43] kinetic studies proved that the same consideration is true of polyreactions, that is, that the reactivity of the functional groups does not change noticeably with size. In the kinetic method no use is made of probabilities; rather the integration of a set of differential equations describing the rates of formation of polymer molecules and the rate of consumption of monomer or comer molecules are utilized.

In the presence of an acid catalyst, the esterification is second order. If all functional groups have the same reactivity, there will be only a single reaction constant k; then the differential equation takes the form

$$\frac{dm_1}{dt} = km_1(m_1 + m_2 + m_3 + \cdots) \qquad (3)$$

or

$$\frac{dm_1}{dt} = -km_1 \sum_{n=1}^{\infty} m_n \qquad (4)$$

which means that monomers are consumed by reaction with other molecules of any size at the same specific rate. In the formation of a dimer, reaction occurs between two monomers and they are consumed by reacting with any other molecule. The equation, therefore, becomes

$$\frac{dm_1}{dt} = -\frac{k}{2} m_1 \sum_{n=2}^{\infty} m_n \qquad (5)$$

and enumerates all the possibilities of the disappearance of monomer, which equation when generalized becomes

$$\frac{dm_n}{dt} = \frac{k}{2} \sum_{s=1}^{s=n-1} m_n m_{n-1} - \frac{k}{2} m_n \sum_{s=1}^{s=\infty} m_n \tag{6}$$

This equation describes how a certain n-mer can be formed, and how, in the course of the reaction, it is again used up. The first term comprises all the possibilities for producing an n-mer by reaction of an s-mer with an $(n$-$s)$mer when s goes from 1 to $(n$-$1)$, and the second term, which is minus, enumerates the disappearance of n-mers by condensation with another s-mer from 1 to infinity. The integration of this equation, if we define p as equal to the extent of the reaction, is

$$m_n = p^{n-1}(1 - p)^2 \tag{7}$$

and the weight fraction of m_n-mers is

$$m_n = np^{n-1}(1 - p)^2 = W_n \tag{8}$$

which is identical with the equation derived from statistical considerations. The dependence of p upon time is given by

$$\frac{dp}{dt} = \frac{k}{2}(1 - p)^2 \tag{9}$$

and

$$p = k\frac{t}{2 + kt} \tag{10}$$

and substitution of these values in the previous m_n equation gives

$$\frac{dm_n}{dt} = \left(\frac{kt}{2 + kt}\right)^{n-1} \left(\frac{2}{2 + kt}\right)^2 \tag{11}$$

The maximum concentration for each intermediate is reached at time, t,

$$t = \frac{1 - n}{k} \tag{12}$$

after which the value drops off and becomes zero at time $= \infty$.

The maximum concentration is given by the relation

$$m_n[\text{max}] = \frac{4(1 - n)^{n-1}}{(3 - n)^{n+1}} \tag{13}$$

If the chains are long, that is, n is greater than 20, the equation becomes

$$m_n[\text{max}] = \frac{4}{n^2} \tag{14}$$

It is obvious from this equation that the largest concentration of n-meric molecules decreases in proportion to the square of n. In general it may be stated that distribution data for condensation polymerization can be obtained more directly by the statistical methods discussed in Chapter 4. As will be seen in the following, the kinetic method is more applicable to vinyl polymerizations, and the equations are solved approximately on steady state assumptions.[44-46]

Addition Reactions

KINETIC CHAIN REACTIONS

It has already been pointed out that the mechanism of polymerization for true addition polymerization of the vinyl type is different from that of the condensation type. The distribution curves for condensation polymers, derived by Flory's probability considerations, were shown not to apply unless the initiation, propagation, and termination steps or rates were considered. Obviously, vinyl polymerization is not the result of a single reaction but a composite of series of reactions based on unstable intermediates. Expressed differently, it means that although the whole chemical process in such a polymerization may be expressed by the empirical equation

$$nCH_2{=}CHX \rightarrow -(CH_2CHX)_n-$$

it is not reasonable in the light of present kinetic knowledge to consider that n molecules of the monomer associate in a single complicated collision and that a large number of primary bonds corresponding to n are formed:

$$nCH_2{=}CHX \rightarrow -CH_2CH-CH_2CH- \left(\begin{array}{c}CH_2CH\\ |\\ X\end{array}\right)_{n-3} -CH_2CH- \\ \qquad\qquad\qquad\qquad\quad \underset{X}{|} \quad\;\; \underset{X}{|} \qquad\qquad\qquad\quad\; \underset{X}{|}$$

As in condensation reactions, the polymerization is a result of a growth process. Vinyl polymerizations have been shown to be a series of reactions involving a primary process which is followed by a rapid sequence of reactions, each of which is unstable and will therefore eventually terminate, and in which the primary process is fundamentally different from the secondary step. Such reactions have been termed chain reactions, but only in a kinetic sense. The term *chain* refers strictly to the *kinetic* processes, and these processes have been exhaustively studied by Polanyi and Semenov [47, 48] for systems where polymerizations were not involved.

Since vinyl polymerizations appear to follow this series of steps, they have been called chain polymerizations, that is, vinyl polymerizations occur through a *kinetic chain reaction* to produce polymer chains. The different stages in the process [49, 50] may be referred to as:

Stage I.   The activation or initiation stage.

Stage II.   The propagation stage.

Stage III. The termination stage.

They correspond to the birth, growth, and death of a polymer molecule.

Initiation stage. At this stage a particularly reactive nucleus is first formed. This reactive nucleus may be brought about by a catalyst, by heat, by light, or by other processes. In all cases an active center is produced which possesses great reactivity. If the initiation occurs under the influence of a radical from a catalyst or any other source, the reaction is indicated by the following equation:

$$\text{Catalyst} \rightarrow \text{radical (R·)} \xrightarrow{\text{monomer}} \underset{\text{Reactive nucleus}}{\text{RM·}}$$

or

$$\text{Monomer} \xrightarrow{\text{energy}} \text{radical (·R·)} \xrightarrow{\text{monomer}} \underset{\text{Reactive nucleus}}{\text{·RM·}}$$

Propagation stage. Because of its high reactivity, the nucleus formed in the initiation stage can add on other monomers in rapid sequence, always regenerating a reactive nucleus at the end of the chain, thereby preserving the reactivity of the chain. In this process great amounts of energy are liberated. The steps in the propagation stage may be represented by the equations

$$\text{RM·} + \text{M} \rightarrow \text{RMM·} \xrightarrow{\text{M}} \text{RMMM·} \xrightarrow{\text{M}} \text{RMMMM·} \xrightarrow{\text{M}} \text{etc.}$$

The growth reaction requires much lower energies than the initiating step and therefore can occur more rapidly and lead to the development of long chains.

The termination stage. Since the terminal end of the growing chain is very reactive, it would be possible for the growing chain to add more monomers until the monomers are exhausted. Actually and even on a probability basis, this does not occur. The reactive end of a growing chain may collide with another reactive radical, or growing chain, or with solvent or an impurity to terminate the growth, thus

$$\text{R(M)}_n\text{M·} + \text{R(M)}_m\text{M·} \rightarrow \underset{\text{Terminated chain}}{\text{RM(M)}_{m+n}\text{MR}}$$

$$\underset{\substack{\text{Chloroform}\\\text{impurity or}\\\text{solvent}}}{\text{R(M)}_n\text{M·} + \text{HCCl}_3} \rightarrow \text{Cl}_3\text{C·} + \underset{\substack{\text{Terminated}\\\text{chain}}}{\text{R(M)}_n\text{MH}}$$

Any process by which one polymer chain is terminated and another free radical generated is known as a chain transfer because the new radical can propagate a new chain.

The interrelation of the three individual steps of initiation, propagation, and termination may be understood by comparing the kinetics obtained experimentally with this theoretically formulated process.

At this point we should recall that the order of a reaction is given generally by the following equations in terms of half life:

$$\text{For a zero-order reaction, } t(\tfrac{1}{2}) = \frac{C_0}{2K_0} \tag{15}$$

$$\text{For a first-order reaction, } t(\tfrac{1}{2}) = \frac{\ln C_0}{k_2} \tag{16}$$

$$\text{For a second-order reaction, } t(\tfrac{1}{2}) = \frac{1}{2C_0 k_2} \tag{17}$$

$$\text{For a third-order reaction, } t(\tfrac{1}{2}) = \frac{3}{2C_0{}^2 k_3} \tag{18}$$

or, in general, for an

$$n\text{-order reaction, } t(\tfrac{1}{2}) = \frac{1}{k_n} C_0{}^{n-1} \tag{19}$$

and the temperature dependence generally of reaction velocity constants, regardless of order, may be expressed [51] by

$$\frac{d \ln k}{dT} = \frac{E}{RT^2} \tag{20}$$

or

$$\ln \frac{k_2}{k_1} = \frac{E}{R}\left[\frac{1}{T_1} - \frac{1}{T_2}\right] \tag{21}$$

where E is the activation energy and a straight line is obtained if $\ln k$ is plotted against $1/T$. Furthermore, while the polymerization of a vinyl compound may be considered as an equilibrium between monomer and polymer,

$$\text{Monomer} \rightleftharpoons \text{polymer}$$

practically all polymers are sufficiently stable at ordinary temperatures so that the reaction may be considered as

$$\text{Monomer} \rightarrow \text{polymer}$$

EXPERIMENTAL DATA

In studying the rates of polymerizations, the interpretation of the data is complicated when high concentrations of monomers are used because of the effects of the changing solvent medium on the kinetics.[52] In dilute solution, the rates of the benzoyl-peroxide catalyzed polymerization of vinyl-*l*-β-phenyl butyrate and *d*-*s*-butyl-α-chloroacrylate were found [21, 53] to be first order with respect to monomer concentration and one-half order with respect to the catalyst. Similarly, kinetic studies on styrene,[54, 55] methyl methacrylate, and vinyl acetate [56] have shown this relation between rate and the square root of the catalyst concentration. In general, it may be stated that in *homogeneous systems*, the rate of peroxide-catalyzed vinyl polymerization is proportional to the square root of the catalyst concentration.[53, 57, 58] A number of investigators [56, 59–61, 63, 64] found that vinyl monomers and other substances accelerate the decomposition of peroxides and thereby contribute to the rate of radical production. Kinetically, the square root polymerization law may be derived in the following manner.

DERIVATION OF SQUARE ROOT LAW

Initiation

$$(C_6H_5COO)_2 \xrightarrow{k_i} C_6H_5COO \cdot \xrightarrow{M} C_6H_5COOM \cdot$$

Catalyst

or

$$C_6H_5COO \cdot \rightarrow CO_2 + C_6H_5 \cdot \xrightarrow{M} C_6H_5M \cdot = RM \cdot$$

where the $C_6H_5CO_2 \cdot$ and $C_6H_5 \cdot$ radicals are represented by $R\cdot$, and M is a monomer or another radical which influences the decomposition.[63]

Propagation

$$RM \cdot + M \xrightarrow{k_p} RMM \cdot \xrightarrow[M]{k_p} + \xrightarrow[M]{k_p} + \xrightarrow[M]{k_p} RM_n \cdot$$

Cessation

$$RM_n \cdot + RM_m \cdot \xrightarrow{k_t} RM_mM_nR$$

The rate of disappearance of monomer is

$$- \frac{d[M]}{dt} = k_p[RM_n \cdot][M] \tag{22}$$

A steady state with respect to the formation and destruction of radicals will be reached if the rate constants of the reactions of the radicals

$(k_p$ and $k_t)$ are large compared to their rate of initiation k_i, thus

$$\frac{d[\mathrm{RM}_n \cdot]}{dt} = k_i[\mathrm{Cat}] = -\frac{d[\mathrm{RM}_n]}{dt} = k_t[\mathrm{RM}_n \cdot]^2 \tag{23}$$

and

$$[\mathrm{RM}_n \cdot] = \sqrt{k_i[\mathrm{Cat}]k_t} \tag{24}$$

which when substituted in equation 22 for the value of $[\mathrm{RM}_n \cdot]$ becomes

$$\frac{-d[\mathrm{M}]}{dt} = k_p[\mathrm{M}]\sqrt{k_i[\mathrm{Cat}]/k_t} = K^1[\mathrm{Cat}]^{\frac{1}{2}}[\mathrm{M}] \tag{25}$$

Equation 25 is interpreted to mean that the rate of polymerization is proportional to the square root of the catalyst concentration and directly proportional to the monomer concentration. Attention should be given to the fact that there is no true rate-controlling step since the rate constant, K^1, for the overall process is a composite of the rate constants of the three steps in the process, that is,

$$K^1 = \frac{k_p\sqrt{k_i}}{\sqrt{k_t}} \tag{26}$$

And in the three individual steps the rates were:
First order with respect to radicals initiation, k_i.
Second order with respect to propagation, k_p.
Second order with respect to termination, k_t.
Substantiation may be considered sufficiently conclusive in this catalyzed polymerization for a free radical mechanism, since, in the absence of inhibitors, destruction of free radical activity can occur only by the reaction of two active radicals.

SECOND-ORDER INITIATION

In the preceding analysis the radical was shown to have its origin in a catalyst, and the origin rate of the radicals was first order. "Uncatalyzed" reactions have been studied, and the nature of the initiation appears to be different from the catalyzed initiation of the previous example. The kinetic data presented by a number of investigators [54, 65] indicate that the uncatalyzed initiation is second order between two styrene molecules to form a diradical, thus

$$\mathrm{CH_2}{=}\mathrm{CH} + \mathrm{CH_2}{=}\mathrm{CH} \rightarrow -\mathrm{CH_2CH}-\mathrm{CH_2CH}-$$
$$\ \ \ \ \ \ |\ \ \ \ \ \ \ \ \ \ \ \ \ \ \ \ \ |\ \ \ \ \ \ \ \ \ \ \ \ \ \ \ \ \ \ \ |\ \ \ \ \ \ \ \ \ \ \ \ |$$
$$\ \ \ \ \ \ \mathrm{X}\ \ \ \ \ \ \ \ \ \ \ \ \ \ \ \mathrm{X}\ \ \ \ \ \ \ \ \ \ \ \ \ \ \ \ \mathrm{X}\ \ \ \ \ \ \ \ \ \ \mathrm{X}$$

This mechanism was somewhat strengthened by Kern's [66] isolation of an addition product of quinone with two molecules of styrene:

$$2C_6H_5CH{=}CH_2 \rightarrow$$

$$\underset{\substack{| \\ C_6H_5}}{-CHCH_2}-\underset{\substack{| \\ C_6H_5}}{CH_2CH-} \quad \xrightarrow{\quad O{=}\langle\ \rangle{=}O \quad}$$

In a paper on inhibition and retardation in polymerization, Melville and Watson [67] also conclude that two moles of styrene form a diradical, which, in turn, reacts with the quinone to give the substituted quinone of Kern.

KINETIC SYSTEMS

The distribution of the molecular weights in a polymer is determined by the kinetics of the polymerization process. We can best visualize this relation of kinetics to distribution in the following analysis.

If we confine Avogadro's mole number of molecules, N, in a reaction chamber so that they all become available for a reaction at will by the introduction of a single nucleus of reaction at time zero, the following kinetic system will be observed. Through collision the reaction will start, and if the molecules are monomers, polymerization will occur. The amount of polymer formed per unit time will be greater at the beginning of the reaction than at any time during the reaction because, as the reaction proceeds, the concentration of the monomers drops off and the number of collisions are thereby lowered. The course of such a reaction or polymerization is monomolecular, and since only one nucleus is present the rate is slow, only one polymer chain is formed, and the single polymer chain has N monomers reacted to each other. The reaction is indicated graphically in Figure 2.

If instead of introducing one nucleus, we introduce 2, 3, 4 or n number of nuclei, under conditions wherein we assume that they do not disturb each other and they all react at the same time, the rate will be 2, 3, 4 or n times faster than with one nucleus. Instead of having one chain containing N monomers, we have n chains each containing N/n monomers. Thus with 3 nuclei we have 3 chains, each consisting of $N/3$ number of monomers in each chain, and the polymerization is thrice as rapid. The reaction, still monomolecular, is represented graphically by Figure 3.

Figure 3 indicates that the shorter the time of the reaction, that is, the greater the number of nuclei, the shorter the length of chains. Actually, if more than one nucleus is used, they do not, as in the system just considered, enter into the polymerization simultaneously. They

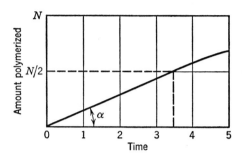

FIGURE 2.   Monomolecular reaction with one nucleus.

do so at different times, so that the second nucleus begins after the first one has started. That is, if the first nucleus starts at t_0, the second one starts at t_1, the value of t being the reciprocal of the rate of the nucleus formation. If the assumption is made that there is no interference between growing chains, the graphic representation is shown as Figure 4a, and the polymerization is summarized in Figure 4b.

The time for $\frac{1}{2} N$ polymerization is longer than if the three nuclei had started at zero. The nature of the curve, however, has changed considerably over Figure 3, and no longer is typical of a monomolecular

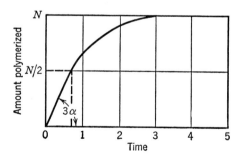

FIGURE 3.   Monomolecular reaction with three nuclei.

reaction. The reaction proceeds, slowly in the initial stages (inhibition period), then as a second nucleus is formed, the reaction becomes accelerated and eventually drops off as monomer is consumed. Furthermore, the two chains will not be of the same length. The chain that started at t_0 has been growing for a longer time than the chain that started at $t_{\frac{1}{2}}$, that is, the chain that started at t_0 has had full time for growth whereas $t_{\frac{1}{2}}$ has had only a fraction of t_0. Thus, as the time interval between t_0 and $t_{\frac{1}{2}}$ is increased, the difference in the length of chains increases. Thus in comparing Figures 2, 3, and 4, we may see that the length of the chain and the distribution of chain length are related to the rate of nuclei formation and their rate of growth.

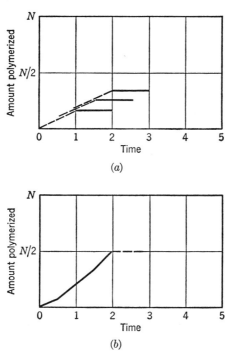

FIGURE 4. (a) Reaction with three nuclei at consecutive times with slow termination. (b) Summary reaction with consecutive nuclei.

In the examples considered so far we have assumed that the death or termination of the chains occurred by exhaustion of the monomer. If for the present we assume that interruption can occur by other means, and that theoretically we can introduce *an interruption substance* at will, the systems will change as indicated in the following examples.

If we consider the example of Figure 2 and introduce an interrupter at any time unit, for example, $t = 1, 2, 3$, etc., the reaction will be monomolecular to that point. Then no further growth will occur, and the reaction will not reflect an asymptotic relation, as in Figure 5.

Thus if the interruption is fast and is comparable to the rate of growth, practically no chain will form at all. If the interruption rate is rapid but much less than the growth rate, the length of the chain will be in proportion to the difference in the rates. If the interruption is extremely slow, a fairly long chain will form. If no interruption occurs, a chain of N molecules will be formed. The reciprocal rate of interruption is

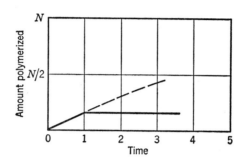

FIGURE 5. Interrupted first order reaction.

obviously proportional to the resulting length of chain, that is, to the life of the individual chain. Similar reasoning may be applied to the conditions of Figure 3, where three chains are being formed at the same time.

In the conditions of Figure 4, where the chains start successively and then are terminated, a number of situations are possible. If the termination of the chain which started at t_0 occurs before the initiation of chain at t_2, the resulting system corresponds to a series of systems

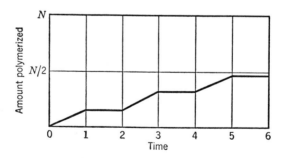

FIGURE 6. Consecutive reactions with rapid terminations.

already represented by Figure 5, but following consecutively over a definite time interval. The summary of this system is represented in Figure 6.

If, on the other hand, the chain formed at time t_0 is terminated only after the chain at t_1 or t_2, etc., is formed, a graph is obtained, as in

Figure 7, which may be drawn to a smooth curve. The graph begins linearly from zero, and nuclear formation and interruption are the limiting factors. The system in Figure 7 is decided by the interaction or relation of chain initiation to chain interruption, and the number of chains growing in the mixture at any moment is given by the ratio of the rates, k_1/k_t.

The initiation, propagation, and termination reactions may be of different orders and may be expressed in the following ways, where

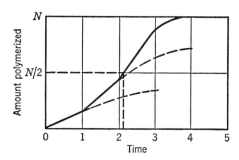

FIGURE 7. System wherein consecutive reactions begin before the termination of the previous reaction.

$K_1 = k_i$, $K_2 = k_p$, and $K_t = k_t$. C is monomer concentration and C^* is the concentration of active molecules.

For the initiation reaction,

$$+ \frac{dC^*}{dt} = K_{11}C \text{ represents a first-order initiation} \qquad (27)$$

$$+ \frac{dC^*}{dt} = K_{12}C^2 \text{ represents a second-order initiation} \qquad (28)$$

$$+ \frac{dC^*}{dt} = K_{13}C^3 \text{ represents a third-order initiation} \qquad (29)$$

For the propagation reaction,

$$- \frac{dC}{dt} = K_{22}CC^* \text{ represents a second-order propagation} \qquad (30)$$

as, for example, by the reaction of a monomer with a polymer radical.

302 Kinetics of Polymerizations

For the termination reaction,

$$-\frac{dC^*}{dt} = K_{31}C^* \text{ represents a first-order termination} \qquad (31)$$

as, for example, by rearrangement,

$$-\frac{dC^*}{dt} = K_{32}C^{*2} \text{ represents a second-order termination} \qquad (32)$$

as by reaction of two polymer chain radicals,

$$-\frac{dC^*}{dt} = K_{32}C^*C \text{ represents a second-order termination} \qquad (33)$$

as by reaction of a polymer chain radical with a monomer.

In these symbols, such as $K_{11}C$, the first index, or 1, indicates the initiation step, and the second index indicates the order of the reaction. Thus K_{22} represents a propagation reaction of second order.

If propagation reaction is high compared with the initiation and termination, the reaction is determined by the step alone:

$$-\frac{dC}{dt} = K_{22}CC^* \qquad (34)$$

Since we assumed that active molecules are produced only by the initiation reaction and destroyed by the terminating reaction, a stationary concentration (steady state) will set in after a short induction period, and the value of C^* is obtained by equating a K_1 to a K_3 equation, as, for example, by equating equation 28 to equation 32.

$$K_{12}C^2 = K_{32}C^{*2} \qquad (35)$$

$$C^{*2} = \frac{K_{12}C^2}{K_{32}} \qquad (36)$$

$$C^* = C\sqrt{K_{12}/K_{32}} \qquad (37)$$

In such a case the empirical rate of reaction is

$$-\frac{dC}{dt} = K_{22}CC\sqrt{K_{12}/K_{32}} = \left(\frac{K_{12}}{K_{32}}\right)^{\frac{1}{2}} K_{22}C^2 \qquad (38)$$

Since the rate of the entire reaction, $-dC/dt$, is obtained by multiplying the start of the reaction by the average number of molecules that are bound in each chain, which is the mean degree of polymerization, $\overline{DP}$, we obtain

$$\frac{dC}{dt} = \frac{dC^*}{dt}\overline{DP} \tag{39}$$

which for different orders have the following values:

$$\text{First order} \quad \overline{DP} = \frac{dC/dt}{-dC^*/dt} \tag{40}$$

$$\text{Second order} \quad \overline{DP} = \frac{2dC/dt}{dC^*/dt} \tag{41}$$

$$\text{Third order} \quad \overline{DP} = \frac{3dC/dt}{dC^*/dt} \tag{42}$$

In second-order polymerization, the degree of polymerization may be expressed as

$$\overline{DP} = \frac{2\left(\dfrac{K_{12}}{K_{32}}\right)^{\frac{1}{2}}K_{22}C^2}{K_{12}C^2} = 2\left(\frac{K_{22}}{K_{12}}\right)\left(\frac{K_{12}}{K_{32}}\right)^{\frac{1}{2}} = \frac{2K_{22}}{(K_{12}/K_{32})^{\frac{1}{2}}} \tag{43}$$

$$\overline{DP} = \frac{2K_{22}}{\sqrt{K_{12}/K_{32}}} \tag{44}$$

In the example just considered the three stages of initiation, K_1 or K_i, the propagation, K_2 or K_p, and the termination, K_3 or K_t, were treated as bimolecular or second order, that is, K_{12}, K_{22}, and K_{32}, and a steady state was formed between K_1 and K_3, that is, $K_{12}C^2$ and $K_{32}C^{*2}$. Other systems can be formed, and they were considered and tabulated by Breitenbach.[68]

These systems leave much to be learned about the nature of the reactive nucleus which is present in all vinyl polymerization systems. These highly reactive radicals have a very short life, and in the case of polystyrene, an individual polymer chain is completed in 10^{-2} to 10^{-6} second.

Melville and Jones,[69, 70] investigating the photopolymerization of gaseous methyl methacrylate, found that the rate of formation of active nuclei was proportional to the pressure or concentration, C, and to the square root of the intensity of radiation

$$\frac{dC^*}{dt} = K_{11}C\sqrt{I} \tag{45}$$

and that the rate of growth was proportional to the pressure and to the concentration of the nuclei

$$-\frac{dC}{dt} = K_{22}CC^* \qquad (46)$$

He found that the average life of the growing chain was very long in terms of days and that oxygen did not act as an inhibitor. If, on the other hand, the reaction was sensitized by hydrogen atoms, the life time dropped to 10^{-2} second. The difference in the polymerization of the methacrylate without and with hydrogen atom sensitization indicates that in the first case a reactive molecule is formed through a double bond mechanism, whereby the double bond is always terminal in the polymer chain, thus:

$$CH_2{=}C\begin{matrix}\diagup CH_3\\ \diagdown COOR\end{matrix} \xrightarrow{h\nu}$$

$$CH_2{}^*{=}C\begin{matrix}\diagup CH_3\\ \diagdown COOR\end{matrix} \xrightarrow[\quad]{nCH_2{=}C\begin{smallmatrix}\diagup CH_3\\ \diagdown COOR\end{smallmatrix}} H\left[\begin{matrix}CH_3\\ CH_2{-}C{-}\\ COOR\end{matrix}\right]_n \begin{matrix}H & CH_3\\ {-}C^*{=}C\\ COOR\end{matrix}$$

With hydrogen atom sensitization, a radical mechanism occurs, thus:

$$H_2 \xrightarrow{h\nu} H\cdot + H\cdot$$

$$H\cdot + CH_2{=}\overset{CH_3}{\underset{COOR}{C}} \rightarrow$$

$$CH_3{-}\overset{CH_3}{\underset{COOR}{C}}\cdot \xrightarrow[\quad]{nCH_2{=}\overset{CH_3}{\underset{COOR}{C}}} H\left[\begin{matrix}CH_3\\ CH_2{-}C{-}\\ COOR\end{matrix}\right]_n {-}CH_2{-}\overset{CH_3}{\underset{COOR}{C}}\cdot \;, \text{etc.}$$

Since radicals are highly reactive intermediates, they are very sensitive to termination. In contrast, the double bond is rather insensitive to impurities, temperature variations, etc., and the result is that long chains are formed with a slow growth.

In the catalyzed polymerization of styrene and methyl methacrylate by benzoyl peroxide or by the methyl methacrylate ozonide, Norrish and Brockman [55] found that the number of active centers formed, n, were proportional to the concentration of the catalyst and that they remained constant over the period of the reaction. These active centers grow at a zero order reaction, and the amount of polymer (dP) formed during dt is

$$dP = K_{22} n \, dt \, e^{-E_2/RT} \tag{47}$$

At time t, the mole per cent of monomer, α, which has undergone polymerization is

$$\alpha = K_{22} t n e^{-E_2/RT} \tag{48}$$

It is reasoned that once a center is started it continues to grow until it stops, and then transfers its energy of activation, E_2, to another monomer, which begins to grow into another chain. In this manner the number of growing chains, n, remains constant, and although an individual chain may stop growing, another chain is started by transfer (chain transfer). If E' is the energy of activation of this transfer and q is its coefficient, the number of terminated chains per unit time is given by

$$qne^{-E'/RT} \tag{49}$$

and the number of molecules (N) present at any particular time is given as

$$N = n + qne^{-E'/RT} \tag{50}$$

where n is the number of molecules that are growing and $qne^{-E'/RT}$ are the number that have terminated.

At any time t, the average degree of polymerization, $\overline{DP}$, is obviously given by

$$\overline{DP} = \frac{\alpha}{N} = \frac{K_{22} n e^{-E_2/RT}}{n + nqe^{-E'/RT}} \tag{51}$$

that is, the ratio of total number of monomers that have undergone polymerization to the total number present at time t.

If we assume that the number of active centers is proportional to the concentration of the catalyst,

$$n \propto c \tag{52}$$

and

$$n = jc \tag{53}$$

$$\overline{P} = \frac{\alpha}{N} = \frac{\alpha}{jc + \dfrac{q\alpha}{K_{22}} e^{-E_1 - E_2/RT}} \tag{54}$$

In a high catalyst concentration the term $q = \dfrac{\alpha}{K_{22}} e^{-E_1-E_2/RT}$ is small because of the small probability of chain transfer, and the equation becomes

$$\bar{P} = \frac{\alpha}{jc} \qquad (55)$$

This equation means that the molecular weight of the polymer will be proportional to the time of the reaction and inversely proportional to the catalyst concentration. If, however, the first term jc becomes negligible to the second term, that is, when there are no catalyst and frequent chain transfer, the molecular weight will be constant throughout the polymerization. This has been observed for styrene and vinyl acetate. If E_1 is greater than E_2, an increase in temperature will decrease the average molecular weight, and this has been found to be true. If the two terms of the denominator are of approximately the same value, the molecular weight will rise at the first part of the reaction; towards the end of the reaction, the molecular weight approaches a constant value. In this derivation, the controlling factor for the overall rate of reaction is not the nucleus formation but the propagation and termination rates, and on this basis Norrish favors the conception of a stepwise addition to an activated double bond rather than the growth of a free radical.

The kinetics of the polymerization of vinyl monomers has been shown to conform to the scheme involving free radical formation, and these radicals initiate polymerization by attacking a monomer, giving rise to another free radical which can add more monomer, etc. The size of the polymer then becomes limited by the termination of the growing chain, that is, by the ratio K_t/K_p, the ratio of the termination, and propagation rate constants. This has been considered by Schulz and others [71-76] in statistical studies to obtain a mathematical expression for the distribution curves. If in a growing chain we call the probability of propagation W_p and that of the probability of termination W_t, then

$$W_p + W_t = 1 \qquad (56)$$

or

$$W_p = 1 - W_t \qquad (57)$$

If the ratio

$$\frac{W_t}{W_p} = K_x \qquad (58)$$

then

$$W_p = \frac{1}{1 + K_x} = 1 - K_x = 1 - \frac{W_t}{W_p} \qquad (59)$$

Then probability of obtaining a chain of degree of polymerization P equals

$$W(P) = (1 - K_x)^P \qquad (60)$$

and if,

$$(1 - K_x) = \alpha \qquad (61)$$

then

$$W(P) = \alpha^P \qquad (62)$$

If the chain is terminated at both ends by reaction, the probability for a terminated chain is

$$W(P) = \alpha^P(1 - \alpha)^2 \qquad (63)$$

which corresponds to Flory's equation for distribution in condensation reactions (see Chapter 4)

$$m_x = p^{x-1}(1 - p)^2 \qquad (64)$$

except that the extent of the reaction is replaced by the ratio of the termination and propagation rates.

The number of chains with P links will be proportional to the probability of formation of such chains:

$$N(P)\, dP = C(1 - \alpha)^2 \alpha^P\, dP \qquad (65)$$

Since in most cases W_t is small compared to W_p, α will be nearly one, and we can replace $(1 - \alpha)^2$ by $\ln^2 \alpha$, and the equation becomes

$$N(P)\, dP = C \ln^2 \alpha \alpha^P\, dP \qquad (66)$$

and the weight distribution curve becomes

$$M(P)\, dP = C \ln^2 \alpha P M_0 \alpha^P\, dP \qquad (67)$$

where M_0 is the molecular weight of the monomer, and the proportionality factor C is

$$C = \frac{M}{\displaystyle\int_0^\infty P M_0 \ln^2 \alpha \alpha^P\, dP} \qquad (68)$$

since the integral over the weight distribution from zero to infinity must give the total amount of material under consideration. A comparison of an actual and theoretical distribution curve of polystyrene according to Schulz [73] is given in Figure 8.

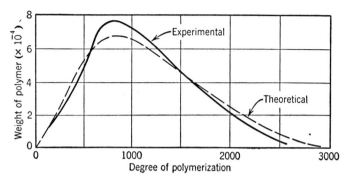

FIGURE 8.   Differential weight distribution curve of polystyrene.

FATE OF THE INITIATING CATALYST

The free radical originally initiating the kinetic chain remains attached to the polymer chains, as has been verified by a number of investigators.[56, 57, 77-84] The reaction may be illustrated by the equation

$$\text{Catalyst} \rightarrow \text{Radical } (R\cdot) \xrightarrow{n \text{ monomers}} R(M)_n\cdot$$

whereafter termination may be represented by the reaction between two such chains

$$R(M)_n\cdot + R(M)_n\cdot \rightarrow R(M)_n(M)_nR$$

The nature of the radical $R\cdot$ depends on the nature of the original catalyst. In vinyl polymerizations, the diacyl peroxides are most commonly used. Studies on the decomposition of diacyl [85-88] indicate a scission to produce two carboxy radicals,

$$\begin{matrix} & O \\ & \| \\ & RC{-}O \\ & \qquad | \quad \rightarrow 2R\overset{\displaystyle O}{\overset{\displaystyle \|}{C}}{-}O\cdot \\ & RC{-}O \\ & \| \\ & O \end{matrix}$$

These carboxy radicals may decarboxylate also to hydrocarbon radicals,

$$R\overset{\displaystyle O}{\overset{\displaystyle \|}{C}}{-}O\cdot \rightarrow R\cdot + CO_2\uparrow$$

Monomers can react with either radical to initiate the polymer chain

$$R\overset{\displaystyle O}{\overset{\displaystyle \|}{C}}{-}O\cdot + M \rightarrow R\overset{\displaystyle O}{\overset{\displaystyle \|}{C}}OM\cdot$$

$$R\cdot + M \rightarrow RM\cdot$$

Since decarboxylation is lower at low temperature, we should expect that polymers prepared at low temperatures would have a higher concentration of the ester groups, $RC\overset{O}{\underset{\|}{}}{-}O(M)_n$ type than the hydrocarbon type $R(M)_n\cdot$, and such has been observed to be the case.

The radicals of the formulas, $RC\overset{O}{\underset{\|}{}}{-}O\cdot$ and $R\cdot$, are obviously monoradical, and since they are capable of propagating the reaction in only one direction, should be found attached terminally to a chain. However, polyradicals, for example, $\cdot R\cdot$ or $\cdot MRM\cdot$ or $\cdot M{-}R{-}M\cdot$, are
$$\underset{\underset{M\cdot}{|}}{}$$
capable of growth in more than one direction. Therefore, by the addition of monomers, they will be located as members of a primary chain. Polyradicals of this kind have already been indicated by Staudinger[89] in explaining the reaction of asymmetrical diphenylethylene with oxygen. The polyradical obtained from the polymeric asymmetrical diphenylethylene peroxide is given as

$$\cdot O{-}\overset{\overset{C_6H_5}{|}}{\underset{\underset{C_6H_5}{|}}{C}}{-}CH_2O\cdot$$

Polyradicals are readily prepared and utilized in polymerizations by the decomposition, in the presence of monomer, of the polymeric peroxides obtained by the reactions of an alkaline peroxide and a halogenated aliphatic acid chloride, for example, chloroacetyl chloride or chloropropionyl chloride [20]

$$mNa_2O_2 + mCl(CR_2)_y{-}COCl \rightarrow \left[{-}(CR_2)_y{-}\overset{O}{\underset{\|}{C}}{-}OO{-}\right]_m$$

In the presence of monomer the polyradical reaction is represented as follows:

$$\left[{-}CH_2\overset{O}{\underset{\|}{C}}{-}OO{-}\right]_m \longrightarrow {-}OCH_2\overset{O}{\underset{\|}{C}}{-}O{-} \overset{2M}{\longrightarrow} \cdot MOCH_2\overset{O}{\underset{\|}{C}}{-}OM\cdot$$

$$\cdot MOCH_2\overset{O}{\underset{\|}{C}}{-}OM\cdot \overset{2nM}{\longrightarrow} \cdot M(M)_nOCH_2\overset{O}{\underset{\|}{C}}{-}O(M)_nM\cdot$$

Moreover, termination may occur in the normal manner as indicated later. However, if two active polyradicals combine, molecular weight will increase without termination:

$$\cdot MRM \cdot + \cdot MRM \cdot \rightarrow \cdot MRMMRM \cdot \xrightarrow{\text{etc.}}$$

If the polyradical has more than two reactive positions, the functionality of each initiating radical is at least three, and crosslinking will result:

$$
\begin{array}{cc}
\overset{\displaystyle\cdot}{M} & \overset{\displaystyle\cdot}{M} \\
| & | \\
\end{array}
$$

$$\cdot MRM \cdot + n(\cdot MRM \cdot) \rightarrow \text{Crosslinked polymer}$$

Polymerizations performed with polymeric phthalyl peroxides have been described.[90] Styrene was used as the monomer and polymerized at 150 C in evacuated sealed tubes. The results are summarized as follows:

1. The degree of polymerization for the uncatalyzed reaction, as measured by intrinsic viscosity, did not vary with percentage conversion. The intrinsic viscosity had a value of 0.82 over the conversion range.
2. The intrinsic viscosity, with benzoyl peroxide used as a catalyst, remained constant with conversion at an intrinsic viscosity value of 0.40.
3. The intrinsic viscosity, with phthalyl peroxide used as a catalyst, increased with conversion from 0.5 to 0.8 at 70 per cent conversion, after which a slight drop in viscosity occurred.
4. The rates of conversion, benzoyl and phthalyl peroxides being used, are higher than the thermally uncatalyzed polymerizations.
5. A comparison of the rate curves of benzoyl and phthalyl peroxides show that the rates when benzoyl peroxide is used are greater at the beginning of the reaction, but that the same time is required (6 hours) for both systems to reach 90 per cent conversion.

Obviously, polyradicals may be considered as an efficient method of producing polymers of molecular weight (that is, of the same intrinsic viscosity) comparable to the uncatalyzed polymerizations. However, if the polyradical is derived from a peroxide type catalyst, the resulting radical which initiates the polymerization becomes an integral part of the polymer chain, since growth occurs in two directions. The stability of these polymers is comparable to those prepared in the presence of O_2 or with polymeric styrene peroxide.[91] Such polymers yellow and degrade with the mechanical processing necessary for industrial utiliza-tion [20] and are inferior in electric properties.[92] Table 4 [92] shows the change in the power factor, tan δ, of polymers containing oxygen as a comer.

TABLE 4

DIELECTRIC LOSS OF POLYSTYRENE PREPARED UNDER VARIOUS CONDITIONS

	Tan δ at 3 × 10⁹ Cycles and 25 C
A. Polymerized in evacuated and sealed tube 4 days at 90 C, 2 days at 120 C, 1 day at 150 C	0.00041
B. Same as A but tube sealed at 1 atm. of oxygen-free N_2	0.00049
C. Same as A but tube sealed at 1 atm. of air	0.00095
D. Same as A but tube sealed at 1 atm. of O_2	0.00161
E. Polymerized in evacuated and sealed tube 4 days at 110 C	0.00089
F. Same as E but resealed in vacuo and further heated 4 days at 150 C	0.00064
G. From styrene prepared from β-phenethyl alcohol, poly-merized as A	0.00053
H. Same as G, reheated 24 hr at 100 C under continuous Hg pump vacuum	0.00027

Reprinted by permission from *Industrial and Engineering Chemistry*.

The ideal catalyst for the production of a thermoplastic high polymer with properties similar to an uncatalyzed polymer, but with the rate of a catalyzed reaction, obviously is a material which would produce a hydrocarbon diradical: $\cdot CH_2 \cdot$, $\cdot \langle \hspace{0.5cm} \rangle \cdot$, $\cdot CH_2 \langle \hspace{0.5cm} \rangle \cdot$, $\cdot CH_2 \langle \hspace{0.5cm} \rangle CH_2 \cdot$, etc.

OXYGEN INHIBITION

Benzoyl peroxide, under certain conditions, also liberates free oxygen. Under such conditions, oxygen is not primarily a catalyst or an initia-tor. In fact, it may act as an inhibitor. Staudinger obse rved the effect of oxygen on the mechanism of a free radical polymerization, and he [89] reported the reaction of asymmetrical diphenylethylene with oxygen as follows:

$$nCH_2{=}C(C_6H_5)_2 + nO_2 \xrightarrow{\text{light}} \left[\begin{array}{c} C_6H_5 \\ | \\ -C-CH_2-O-O- \\ | \\ C_6H_5 \end{array} \right]_n$$

And the polymeric peroxide under heat degraded to diphenyl ketone and formaldehyde

$$\left[\begin{array}{c} C_6H_5 \\ | \\ -C-CH_2-O-O- \\ | \\ C_6H_5 \end{array}\right]_n \xrightarrow{\Delta} n(C_6H_5)_2CO + nCH_2O$$

Since the polymeric polyperoxide gave no test for peroxide, a free radical scission was indicated as an intermediate

$$\left[\begin{array}{c} C_6H_5 \\ | \\ \cdot O-C-CH_2-O\cdot \\ | \\ C_6H_5 \end{array}\right]$$

In the case of styrene [93] a pure polyperoxide was not obtained since oxygen tended to enter the chain at different stages of growth, thus:

$$yCH_2=CHC_6H_5 \rightarrow \left[\begin{array}{c} -CH_2CH- \\ | \\ C_6H_5 \end{array}\right]_y \xrightarrow{2O_2} -O-O-(CH_2CH)_y-O-O- \underset{C_6H_5}{\longrightarrow}$$

$$\xrightarrow{CH_2=CHC_6H_5} -O-O-\left[\begin{array}{c} -CH_2CH- \\ | \\ C_6H_5 \end{array}\right]_y -O-O-\left[\begin{array}{c} -CH_2CH- \\ | \\ C_6H_5 \end{array}\right]_x$$

With methyl methacrylate not only a polyperoxide but also a hydroperoxide [94, 95] is obtained.

$$R\cdot + CH_2=\underset{\underset{COOCH_3}{|}}{\overset{\overset{CH_3}{|}}{C}} \rightarrow RCH_2\underset{\underset{COOCH_3}{|}}{\overset{\overset{CH_3}{|}}{C}}\cdot \xrightarrow{O_2}$$

$$RCH_2\underset{\underset{COOCH_3}{|}}{\overset{\overset{CH_3}{|}}{C}}-O-O\cdot \xrightarrow{CH_2=\overset{CH_3}{\underset{|}{C}}-COOCH_3}$$

$$CH_2=\underset{\underset{COOCH_3}{|}}{\overset{\overset{CH_2\cdot}{|}}{C}} + RCH_2\underset{\underset{COOCH_3}{|}}{\overset{\overset{CH_3}{|}}{C}}-O-O-H \xrightarrow{O_2} CH_2=\underset{\underset{CH_3}{|}}{\overset{\overset{CH_2OO\cdot}{|}}{C}}$$

The peroxide radical is stable against the addition of methacrylate. It accounts for the marked retarding influence of oxygen on the polymerization and for the presence of a hydroperoxide rather than a polyperoxide in the polymer. It is obvious that oxygen may influence a polymerization in more than one way, and it may sometimes act as a catalyst and sometimes as an inhibitor in ethylenic type polymerizations. A number of investigators [96-98] found that oxygen retarded the photopolymerization of vinyl acetate and acrylic acid, but accelerated the photopolymerization of styrene. In the thermal polymerization of styrene, oxygen was found [99] to accelerate slightly the polymerization

TABLE 5

Inhibition by Oxygen

Polymerization Conditions (Reactant Weights in Grams)	Induction Period (Minutes)	Extent of Polymerization *
Water 100. Acrylonitrile 5.0 $K_2S_2O_3$ 0.5 at 50 C		
(a) Stirred under nitrogen	3	43% in 1 hr
(b) Stirred slowly under air	7	37% in 1 hr
(c) Stirred under oxygen; oxygen bubbling through solution	64	0.1% in 1 hr
Water 100. Acrylonitrile 5.0 $K_2S_2O_8$ 0.2 $NaHSO_3$ 0.077 at 30 C		
(a) Stirred under nitrogen	0	86% in 1 hr
(b) Stirred slowly under air	1	83% in 1 hr
(c) Stirred under oxygen; oxygen bubbling through solution	12	13% in 1 hr
Water 100. Acrylonitrile 6.45 $(NH_4)_2S_2O_8$ 1.0 at 20 C		
(a) De-aerated reagents; static system under purified nitrogen	3	60% in 24 hr
(b) Stirred under nitrogen	29	. . . .
(c) Static under air	Long and variable, e.g., 7 hr	70% in 24 hr

* The times given in this column are measured from the end of the induction period. By permission from The Faraday Society, London.

in the early stages but to retard it in the last stages. Melville and Bolland [100] found that oxygen greatly retarded the "dark growth" of chloroprene which was initiated by ultraviolet light; Carothers and others [101] found that oxygen was a powerful catalyst for the polymerization of liquid chloroprene.

Schoenfeld [102] has shown that the polymerization of vinyl chloride proceeds at a faster rate in an oxygen-free system, such as may be accomplished by sweeping out the polymerization system with oxygen-free nitrogen.

In the course of other studies Bacon [103] investigated the polymerization of acrylonitrile in aqueous solution and found that the polymeriza-

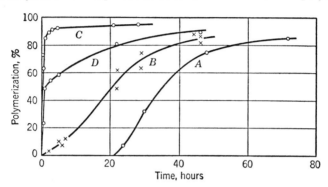

Figure 9. Inhibition by oxygen. (By permission from The Faraday Society, London.)

$$A = \text{Water} \qquad 100 \text{ g}$$
$$(NH_4)_2S_2O_8 \qquad 1.0$$
$$\text{Acrylonitrile} \qquad 6.45$$
$$\text{Under air at} \qquad 20 \text{ C}$$

B = Same as A but in the absence of oxygen
C = Same as A + 0.05 g $Na_2S_2O_4$
D = Same as A + 0.05 g hydroquinone

tion was greatly retarded by the presence of oxygen even when persulfate catalysts were used. The retardation was observed by the occurrence of an induction period depending on the oxygen content of the system, the temperature, and the nature and concentration of the catalyst. His data are summarized in Table 5. [103]

It was also noted, in the cases studied that once polymerization had started, it was not greatly retarded except where undiluted oxygen was in good contact with the system. Bacon also studied the addition of reducing agents to systems containing air. The results are shown in Figure 9. [103] The removal of oxygen reduced the induction period from several hours to 1 to 4 minutes, as may be seen when curves A and B are compared. However, it must be noted that oxygen removal had no effect on the rate of polymerization. The effect of adding a reducing agent was quite different from simply removing oxygen, as may be noted in curves C and D. Not only was the induction period reduced

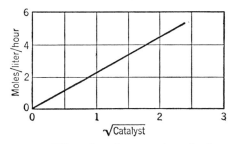

FIGURE 10.   Effect of catalyst on polymerization rate.

but the polymerization rate was increased about fortyfold. This secondary effect, that is, of increasing the rate, has been called *reduction activation*, and these systems which are known as Redox systems are also considered in this chapter.

It may be concluded generally that oxygen may act as an inhibitor, that is, delay the reaction, and in this respect it seems to behave similarly to p-benzoquinone in the thermal polymerization of styrene.[104] In other cases it may also act as a catalyst by an entirely different mechanism.

In homogeneous solution, involving peroxide type catalyst, it was observed that the initial rate of monomer consumption is proportional to the square root of the catalyst concentration, as in Figure 10, and that the conversion of the monomer against time may be represented generally as a straight

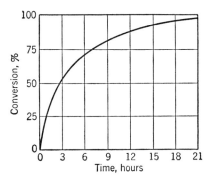

FIGURE 11.   Conversion as a function of time.

line at the beginning of the reaction. As monomer is consumed, the straight line curves off, as in Figure 11.

"Pearl" or bead polymerization represents a heterogeneous system in which the polymer is dispersed in a non-soluble medium, as, for example, styrene in water. In such a system either a water-soluble or an organic-soluble catalyst can be used. In either case the square root law of the catalyst concentration is found to be valid. However, the organic-soluble type is found often to be more effective than the water-soluble type, up to a tenfold effect. Dispersion systems of this type seem to behave as bulk polymerizations dispersed as small particles.

Emulsion systems represent an excessive change in a system as compared to bulk or pearl polymers. The use of soap in polymerization systems appeared about 1927.[105, 106]

Polymerization emulsion systems using styrene as the monomer and potassium persulfate as the catalyst have been the subject of kinetic investigations.[107, 108] In these studies the temperature ranged between 30 and 50 C, and the polymerizations were performed with a number of emulsifying agents in the presence and absence of oxygen. These studies showed that after the inhibition period, the rate of monomer disappearance was proportional to the square root of the catalyst concentration. It was also evident that emulsion polymerization changes the conditions in such a way that the induction or inhibition period exhibits a less irregular character; nevertheless the square root dependence becomes evident after the induction period has passed. The effect of oxygen as observed by Bacon has already been mentioned. His observations supported the evidence of long and erratic inhibition periods recorded by King and Steinbach.[109] The mechanism of growth, that is, the addition of a monomer to an initiating radical to form the chain, appears to be the same for an emulsion system as for homogeneous systems. In emulsion systems the question for study is the location of the initiation, and growth. This phase of the problem will be discussed shortly, not only for emulsion systems but also for all polymerization systems. Similarly, the termination reaction, whereby nuclei are destroyed, appears to be of second order and follows the original concept of termination. In emulsion systems the termination occurs by the mutual chain reaction of two growing chains.[110] The kinetic studies showed that the presence of the emulsifying agent did not change the kinetics of the reaction, but it did increase both the rate and extent of the polymerization.

In a paper, Bovey and Kolthoff [91] reported studies on the influence of oxygen on the emulsion polymerization of styrene. Previous studies [111] had shown that (1) the induction period found in the emulsion polymerization of styrene was approximately inversely proportional to the concentration of the catalyst, (2) the length of the induction period was almost independent of the amount of emulsifying agent, and (3) the induction period was proportional to the amount of oxygen present, provided the initial oxygen pressure was constant. The authors postulated that the initiation reaction was

$$K_2S_2O_8 + M \rightarrow M^* \text{ (activated styrene molecule)}$$

and the oxygen consumption was described by the reaction

$$M^* + O_2 \rightarrow M(O_2)^* \rightarrow \text{Reaction product}$$

The initiation reaction was presumed to be slow, and therefore is the rate-determining step, in contrast to the oxygen reaction, which was very rapid. The mechanism required that the rate of disappearance of oxygen should be independent of oxygen pressure. From experiments carried out at different partial pressures of oxygen, it was found that the induction period was somewhat dependent on the partial pressure of the oxygen, and that the rate of disappearance of oxygen was not independent of oxygen partial pressure. Since the apparent failure of the oxygen disappearance to follow a zero order reaction could be due to an ineffective mixing of the liquid and the gas (oxygen) phase, the study of the effect of oxygen was continued. Bovey and Kolthoff [91] made direct measurements of the rate of oxygen consumption during the induction period caused by oxygen in the emulsion polymerization of styrene and found that the reaction of oxygen during the induction period was (1) essentially zero order with respect to oxygen pressure, (2) nearly independent of the emulsifier, and (3) directly proportional to the concentration of the persulfate catalyst.

The formation of a polymeric styrene peroxide accounted for the oxygen consumed during the induction period, according to the steps:

(Step A) $HO\cdot$ (from $K_2S_2O_8$) $+ CH_2{=}CHC_6H_5 \rightarrow C_6H_5\overset{\cdot}{C}HCH_2OH$

(Step B) $C_6H_5\overset{\cdot}{C}HCH_2OH + O_2 \rightarrow \underset{\underset{C_6H_5}{|}}{HOCH_2CHOO}\cdot$

(Step C) $\underset{\underset{C_6H_5}{|}}{HOCH_2CHOO}\cdot + C_6H_5CH{=}CH_2 \rightarrow$

$\underset{\underset{C_6H_5}{|}\underset{C_6H_5}{|}}{HOCH_2CHOO{-}CH_2CH}\cdot$

(Step D) $\underset{\underset{C_6H_5}{|}\underset{C_6H_5}{|}}{HOCH_2CHOO{-}CH_2CH}\cdot + O_2 \rightarrow$

$\underset{\underset{C_6H_5}{|}\underset{C_6H_5}{|}}{HOCH_2CH{-}CH_2CHOO}\cdot$

(Step E) $\underset{\overset{|}{C_6H_5}}{HOCH_2CH}$—$\underset{\overset{|}{C_6H_5}}{CH_2CHOO}\cdot$ $\xrightarrow{\;n[C_6H_5CH=CH_2 + O_2]\;}$

$$\underset{\overset{|}{C_6H_5}}{HOCH_2CHOO}—\left[\underset{\overset{|}{C_6H_5}}{CH_2CHOO}\right]_n \cdot$$

A polymeric peroxide was isolated corresponding to a 1:1 polymer of styrene and oxygen, wherein styrene was a comonomer and oxygen a comer. The copolymer corresponded to 40 styrene peroxide units and, when heated rapidly to 100 C, exploded with benzaldehyde and formaldehyde as the main decomposition products. Confirmation of the peroxide nature of the polymer was confirmed by a study of its reduction at the dropping mercury cathode and its use as a catalyst for the bulk polymerization of styrene. In the bulk polymerization of styrene by polymeric styrene peroxides, the initiation of the polymerization must occur by means of a polyvalent radical in contrast to the usual monovalent radical obtained from benzoyl peroxide, etc.

$$\underset{\overset{|}{C_6H_5}}{HOCH_2CH}—\left[\underset{\overset{|}{C_6H_5}}{OOCH_2CH}—\right]_n —\rightarrow$$

$$\underset{\overset{|}{C_6H_5}}{HOCH_2CH}—\left[\underset{\overset{|}{C_6H_5}}{OOCH_2CH}—\right]_{n-1} —+ \cdot \underset{\overset{|}{C_6H_5}}{OOCH_2CH}\cdot$$

The behavior of this catalyst is similar to that of polymeric phthalyl peroxide or of the polymeric peroxide [20] obtained by reacting chloroacetyl chloride with sodium peroxide:

$$ClCH_2COCl + Na_2O_2 \rightarrow —(CH_2\overset{\overset{O}{||}}{C}OO)_n—$$

The studies of Bovey and Kolthoff are interesting in explaining certain apparent discrepancies in the early literature on the effect of oxygen on the polymerization system. It becomes obvious, however, that for styrene systems at least, in the early stages of reaction oxygen acts as an inhibitor, during which period (induction) the oxygen is consumed to form a polymeric peroxide. Later, in the course of the polymerization, the polymeric peroxide may liberate polyradicals which could accelerate the polymerization.

CHAIN TERMINATION AND CHAIN TRANSFER

A growing polymer chain may be deactivated by a number of means. In all cases the deactivation occurs by interaction between the growing chain and another molecule.

Chain deactivation or termination can occur between a growing chain and (1) another active chain, (2) a catalyst radical, (3) an inactivated monomer, (4) an inactivated polymer, (5) a solvent molecule, (6) an inhibitor or retarder, and (7) an impurity. It must also be borne in mind that *initial destruction* can occur by reaction between two original radicals, so that a polymer is never obtained, thus: $R \cdot + R \cdot \rightarrow RR$.

The deactivation of a chain by another growing chain to terminate growth has already been considered by the equation

$$R(M)_n \cdot + R(M)_m \cdot \rightarrow R(M)_n(M)_m R$$

In this case, $R(M)_m \cdot$ may also represent any radical, including a catalyst radical, and it may be generalized by $R \cdot$. Thus the growing chain is terminated as expressed by the equation $R(M)_m \cdot + R \cdot \rightarrow R(M)_m R$.

If the chain is deactivated by an inactive monomer, the growth of the chain is terminated and the monomer is converted to another radical. In this case the monomer is represented by MH, and involves a kinetic chain transfer, thus:

$$R(M)_n \cdot + MH \rightarrow R(M)_n H + M \cdot$$

$$R(CH_2CH)_n \cdot + CH_2{=}CH \rightarrow$$
$$\qquad | \qquad\qquad\quad |$$
$$\quad C_6H_5 \qquad\qquad C_6H_5$$

$$R \begin{bmatrix} CH_2CH \\ | \\ C_6H_5 \end{bmatrix}_{n-1} -CH_2CH_2 + CH_2{=}CH$$
$$\qquad\qquad\qquad\qquad\quad | \qquad\qquad\quad |$$
$$\qquad\qquad\qquad\qquad C_6H_5 \qquad\quad C_6H_4 \cdot$$

The radical generated by the chain transfer can react with more monomers and thereby form another polymer chain.

A growing polymer chain can also be terminated and deactivated by an inactive or dead polymer chain which has already been formed. This reaction may be represented by the equation

$$\underset{\text{Growing chain}}{R(M)_n \cdot} + \underset{\text{Dead polymer}}{RM(M)_n R} \rightarrow R(M)_n H + R\overset{\cdot}{M}(M)_n R$$

and a free radical generated along some point of the once dead polymer. This polymer then becomes active and may react further with more monomers to form branches along the original chain. This process is known as branching and will be discussed in more detail later.

The mechanism is substantially the same for all terminations, that is, by reaction with another molecule. The final products may be entirely different, and a number of these will be considered. However, in emulsion systems, even though the chain may exist in a swollen micelle containing other active chains, monomer and dead polymer, the kinetics will remain the same, that is, it will be a second-order reaction.[112] Dostal [113-115] considered a monomolecular chain-breaking reaction in his studies of chain polymerization. Such a monomolecular reaction [116] would be represented by ring closure in a polymer chain. Under ordinary conditions, however, ring closure would not be expected in a polymer chain except in extremely dilute solutions.

Termination and reactivation of growing polymer chains occur readily in solution polymerizations. When an ethylenic monomer such as styrene is polymerized in a solvent, the kinetics, that is, the rates of polymerization, follow the expected behavior, but the average molecular weight of the resulting polymer is lower than that obtained in the absence of a solvent. This may be readily explained by a kinetic chain transfer with the solvent which may be represented as follows:

$$R(M)_n \cdot + SX \rightarrow R(M)_n X + S \cdot$$

where $S \cdot$ is the solvent radical and X is the substituent removed from the solvent. Thus in the polymerization of styrene in benzene and carbon tetrachloride, respectively, the reactions are

$$R(M)_n \cdot + C_6H_6 \rightarrow R(M)_n \cdot H + C_6H_5 \cdot$$

$$R(M)_n \cdot + CCl_4 \rightarrow R(M)_n \cdot Cl + Cl_3C \cdot$$

If these equations are correct, more frequent chain termination should occur in dilute solutions. Schulz [73, 117] and Suess [118, 119] have studied the polymerization of styrene in several solvents and compared the rates and degree of polymerization of the polymers obtained. The data are shown in Figure 12.[119]

It will be noted that pure styrene corresponds to about 8.7 molar, and the polymer produced at 100 C has a $\overline{DP}$ value of 1900. As the concentration of styrene approaches zero, the degree of polymerization approaches zero. It will also be noted that each solvent has a different curve. These authors derive the equation relating degree of polymerization to solvent concentration as

$$\frac{1}{\overline{DP}} = C \frac{[S]}{[M]} + \frac{1}{\overline{DP^0}} \tag{69}$$

where $\overline{DP}$ = the average degree of polymerization in the solution,
$\overline{DP^0}$ = the average degree of polymerization in absence of solvent,
[S] = concentration of solvent,
C = transfer constant or the probability that a radical will unite with a solvent molecule rather than with the monomer,
[M] = concentration of styrene monomer.

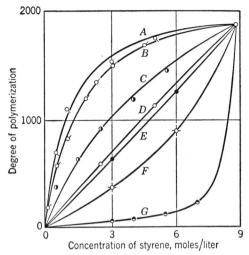

FIGURE 12. Effect of solvents on the degree of polymerization of styrene at 100 C, where the solvent in

Curve A = C_6H_6 Curve E = $ClCH_2CH_2Cl$
Curve B = $C_6H_5CH_3$ Curve F = $Cl_2CHCHCl_2$
Curve C = $C_6H_5C_2H_5$ Curve G = CCl_4
Curve D = $C_6H_4(C_2H_5)_2$

The value of C is readily calculated. If $1/\overline{DP}$ is plotted against [S]/[M], the points for each solvent will fall on a straight line of slope C, and the lines for all solvents will have the intercept $1/\overline{DP}^0$ in common. The slopes of the lines will depend on the nature of the solvent and the temperature. Figure 13 [73] shows the experimental data of Schulz, and Figure 14 [119] shows the experimental data of Suess. The agreement with the theoretically derived equation is excellent.

The data in Table 6, taken from the work [73, 119] of these authors, tabulates a number of transfer constants, the upper and lower limits representing the high and low values of their combined results.

TABLE 6

Solvent	C at 100 C
Toluene	0.000053–0.000072
Chlorobenzene	0.000054
Benzene	0.000031–0.000042
Cyclohexane	0.000031
Ethylene chloride	0.00038
Diethylbenzene	0.00033–0.00063
Ethylbenzene	0.00014–0.00023
Sym. tetrachloroethane	0.0011
Carbon tetrachloride	0.011

322 Kinetics of Polymerizations

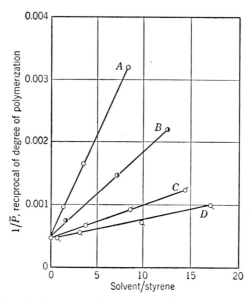

FIGURE 13. Effect of solvents on the degree of polymerization of styrene at 100 C,
where the solvent in

Curve A = $C_6H_4(C_2H_5)_2$ Curve C = $C_6H_5CH_3$
Curve B = $C_6H_5C_2H_5$ Curve D = C_6H_6

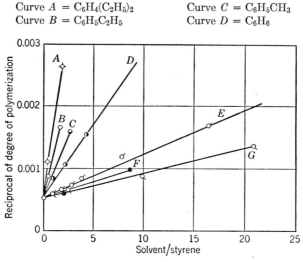

FIGURE 14. Effect of solvents on the degree of polymerization of styrene at 100 C,
where the solvent in

Curve A = $Cl_2CHCHCl_2$ Curve E = $C_6H_5CH_3$
Curve B = $C_6H_4(C_2H_5)_2$ Curve F = C_6H_5Cl
Curve C = $ClCH_2CH_2Cl$ Curve G = C_6H_6
Curve D = $C_6H_5C_2H_5$

The energy of activation of a chain transfer reaction involving a solvent is between 10 and 15 kilocalories per mole, and the solvent with the lowest reactivity has the highest activation constant.

Inhibitors and retarders. Inhibitors are chemical substances present in a polymerization process which cause a well-defined induction period, after which period the polymerization proceeds at its normal rate. The induction period is a result of the reaction of the inhibitor with free radicals, thereby producing a reaction product which is slow in further propagation of the chain or unreactive to further chain propagation.

The rate of reaction of an ideal inhibitor must be high enough to inactivate all the free radicals as soon as they are produced. The induction period represents, therefore, the period during which free radicals have reacted with inhibitor, until the inhibitor is consumed. Inhibitors, therefore, are consumed before true polymerization occurs.

Retarders are chemical substances which retard the polymerization throughout the whole polymerization process. The ideal retarder does not give rise to an induction period. Retarders, similar to inhibitors, also react with free radicals, but at a much slower rate than inhibitors. The rate of reaction of retarders is sufficiently slow that only a fraction of the free radicals produced can initiate or propagate the polymerization. In contrast to inhibitors, retarders can react with growing polymer chains and act as chain breakers. Fragments of retarder molecules, therefore, may be found attached to polymer chains. If added to a polymerizing mixture, retarders will prevent further polymerization. If added to a polymerizable mixture before polymerization, the retarder will prevent polymerization if used in sufficient quantity. If less retarder is used, the polymerization rate will be extremely slow at the initiation and remain slow throughout the reaction. On the other hand, if a small amount of an inhibitor is added to a polymerizing system, polymerization will be stopped only temporarily, until the inhibitor is consumed. In contrast to organic compounds, which act exclusively as either inhibitors or retarders, there are a large number of substances that behave both as inhibitors and retarders, and, in activity, are intermediate to inhibitors and retarders. Where such intermediate compounds are used in a system, a small initial rate of polymerization is observed, this rate increasing continually as a function of time as more of the substance is consumed.

Sometimes the reaction product of an inhibitor and a free radical may act as a retarder, whereby a noticeable induction, followed by a retardation, is observed.

Kolthoff and Bovey [120] summarized the difference in behavior of retarders and inhibitors graphically as in Figure 15.

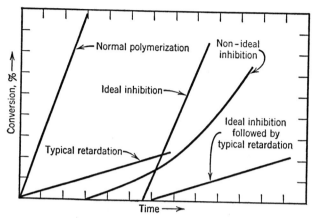

FIGURE 15. Typical time-conversion curves for various inhibitory and retarding effects. (Reprinted by permission of the authors and the *Journal of the American Chemical Society*.)

Breitenbach and others [121] observed the formation of hydroquinone when a mixture of styrene and quinone, which is a strong inhibitor, was heated to 120 C.   On the basis of the known reactions of quinones, Price gives the following hypothesis for the formation of hydroquinone by assuming the initial reaction to be between quinone and the initiating radical, thus:

$$R \cdot \; + \; O{=}\!\!\left\langle \overline{} \right\rangle\!\!{=}O \;\rightarrow\; O{=}\!\!\left\langle \overline{} \right\rangle\!\!{=}O \;\rightarrow$$

and the hydroquinone radical reacts with itself to give hydroquinone and quinone:

$$2\,HO{-}\!\!\left\langle \overline{} \right\rangle\!\!{-}O \cdot \;\rightarrow\; HO{-}\!\!\left\langle \overline{} \right\rangle\!\!{-}OH \; + \; O{=}\!\!\left\langle \overline{} \right\rangle\!\!{=}O$$

That a stoichiometric chemical reaction actually occurs is also indicated by the fact that the induction period in such a polymerization is proportional directly to the amount of inhibitor added.[104]   This observation is confirmed by Bacon,[103] who showed that the induction period in the polymerization of acrylonitrile was dependent on the oxygen content of the system, even when the system was operated as a redox system in the presence of a reducing agent.

It is interesting to note that hydroquinone does not act as an inhibitor for the polymerization of styrene in the absence of oxygen. However, in the presence of oxygen, whereby quinone is first formed, an induction period is observed, and the mechanism postulated by Price, which assumes an initial reaction between quinone and the initiating radical, seems to apply.

Breitenbach and Renner[122] investigated the inhibiting effect of chloranil on the polymerization of styrene in the presence of benzoyl peroxide and determined the molecular weight and composition of the resulting polymer. In previous studies, Price[79] had concluded that the product of this polymerization had the structure

$$\text{Cl}-(\underset{\underset{\displaystyle C_6H_5}{|}}{\text{CH}}-\text{CH}_2)_n-\underset{\displaystyle O}{\overset{\displaystyle O}{\underset{\|}{\overset{\|}{\underset{\text{Cl}}{\overset{\text{Cl}}{\bigcirc}}}}}}-\text{Cl}$$

and that the chloranil was attached terminally to the polystyrene chain· The recent work of Breitenbach[122] offers evidence to prove that styrene and chloranil polymerize to give copolymers whose molecular weights, as determined by osmotic pressure methods, were found to be between 9,000 and 30,000. The chloride content of the copolymers ranged between 37 and 38.2 per cent, with an average mole ratio of chloranil to styrene of 0.80. The structure assignable to these copolymers is

$$-\left[\underset{\underset{\displaystyle C_6H_5}{|}}{\text{CH}}-\text{CH}_2-\text{O}-\overset{\overset{\text{Cl}\quad\text{Cl}}{|\quad\ \ |}}{\underset{\underset{\text{Cl}\quad\text{Cl}}{|\quad\ \ |}}{\bigcirc}}-\text{O}-\right]_n$$

This investigation also shows that such high molecular weight copolymers are formed by the polymerization of certain benzoquinone derivatives such as chloranil, bromanil, trichloromethylquinone, etc., with phenyl-substituted vinyl compounds such as styrene, anathole, and indene. Neither vinyl chloride nor vinyl acetate copolymerizes with chloranil. The copolymer of styrene and chloranil is obtained in the presence of benzoyl peroxide, but not with decalin hydroperoxide or tetra-decalin hydroperoxide. The halogen substitution in the quinone nucleus seems to be essential for the copolymerization. The copolymerization of the chloranil with another monomer occurs through the carbonyl oxygens with a resulting shift of the bonds in the ring. This is analogous to the polymerization of dimethylenequinone and monomethylenequinone, as, for example,

$$CH_2{=}\!\!\left\langle\;\;\;\right\rangle\!\!{=}CH_2 \;\rightarrow\; {-}CH_2{-}\!\!\left\langle\;\;\;\right\rangle\!\!{-}CH_2{-}$$

Dimethylenequinone

$$O{=}\!\!\left\langle\;\;\;\right\rangle\!\!{=}CH_2 \;\rightarrow\; {-}O{-}\!\!\left\langle\;\;\;\right\rangle\!\!{-}CH_2{-}$$

Monomethylenequinone

$$O{=}\!\!\left\langle\;\;\;\right\rangle\!\!{=}O \;\rightarrow\; {-}O{-}\!\!\left\langle\;\;\;\right\rangle\!\!{-}O{-}$$

Quinone

In contrast to inhibitors, retarders deactivate the active chains, $R(M)_n\cdot$, in the growth process, reduce the overall rate of polymerization, and lower the molecular weight of the polymer formed.

Aromatic nitrohydrocarbons are excellent retarders of polymerization. Price and Durham [78] have shown that nitromethane does not retard the polymerization of styrene, and they conclude that the retarding effect [104] of aromatic nitro compounds is due to their reaction with growing radicals to give a radical relatively stable to the further addition of monomer. This conclusion is substantiated by the fact that nitro groups strongly activate the aromatic nucleus toward free radical substitution and that styrene polymerized in the presence of nitrobenzene, nitrothiophene, or 2,4-dinitrochlorobenzene contained one fragment of the retarding substance per polymer molecule.[78, 79] Thus,

$$R(M)_n\cdot \,+\, \overset{\displaystyle Cl}{\underset{\displaystyle NO_2}{\left\langle\;\;\;\right\rangle}}\!\!{-}NO_2 \;\rightarrow\; R(M)_n\!{-}\overset{\displaystyle H\;\cdot\;Cl}{\underset{\displaystyle NO_2}{\left\langle\;\;\;\right\rangle}}\!\!{-}NO_2 \overset{R\cdot}{\longrightarrow}$$

$$R(M)_n\!{-}\overset{\displaystyle Cl}{\underset{\displaystyle NO_2}{\left\langle\;\;\;\right\rangle}}\!\!{-}NO_2 \,+\, RH$$

It may be observed that retarders function by a mechanism similar to that considered for termination by solvent molecules. To the present time, no definite rule has been derived which will permit the prediction of the behavior of any specific substance either as an inhibitor or as a retarder. In fact, many substances behave both as an inhibitor and as a retarder simultaneously. A number of inhibitors or retarders have been studied for styrene, and, industrially, they are called stabilizers. In general, they are aromatic compounds containing quinoid, nitro, nitroso, amino, or phenolic structures.

Quinonoid compounds generally are very effective inhibitors which do not show much retarding effect when used in low concentrations. Benzoquinone is effective. As the molecule becomes more complex, however, its effectiveness decreases so that acenaphthenequinone has only a low inhibitor effect whereas anthroquinone is ineffective; the lower non-alkyl benzoquinones have an efficiency comparable to benzoquinone.

Monophenols, in general, are weak stabilizers. For styrene, phenol is ineffective and the cresols are only slightly better. The effectiveness of phenol increases with an increase in the number of hydroxyl groups, but the efficiency depends on the relative positions of these groups. Catechol is considered to be more effective than resorcinol or hydroquinone, and tertiary-butyl catechol more efficient than catechol. Nitroaromatic hydrocarbons produce strong retardation without complete inhibition. The retarding effect is noticeably increased with an increase in the number of nitro groups, and dinitrobenzene is more effective than nitrobenzene. Aromatic amines behave as inhibitors and increase the induction period without materially reducing the rate of polymerization or of the molecular weight. Substitution of the amino hydrogens has anomalous effects. The amino groups seem to be more effective when attached to an aryl nucleus in the presence of another active group. Thus, nitrodimethylaniline, hydroxydimethylaniline, nitrosodimethylaniline, etc., seem to be especially effective as inhibitors. No stabilizing effect, however, becomes apparent when the amino group is converted to an amide of the structure RCONR-aryl. Tertiary bases, such as pyridine, quinoline, and isoquinoline, are also ineffective. Though it may be stated that the effect of several active groups on a benzene or aromatic nucleus is additive, the effect is qualitative and not necessarily quantitative.

Among other stabilizers for styrene may be mentioned sulfur, paraformaldehyde, phenylacetylene, and the condensation products of aliphatic aldehydes with aromatic amines.

Foord shows the course of the polymerization of styrene at 120 C in the presence of benzoquinone (Figure 16)[104] and phenanthroquinone (Figure 17)[104] by measuring the viscosity of the polymer ($\log_{10} \eta_r$) formed

328   Kinetics of Polymerizations

as a function of time.   Curves A and A' in these figures refer to the
polymerization of styrene in the absence of inhibitors and show that,
after a very short induction period, possibly because of traces of impurities, the polymerization rate increases rapidly to a maximum; thereafter it gradually decreases.   The remaining curves show that the

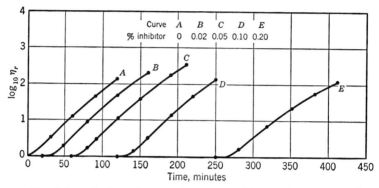

FIGURE 16.   Polymerization of styrene in presence of benzoquinone at 120 C.   (Reprinted by permission from The Chemical Society, London.)

induction period is lengthened with the increased concentration of
either benzoquinone or phenanthroquinone, and that after the induction
period the curves follow a similar course to those of curves A and A'.
For those curves having the highest concentrations of the quinones,
some falling off of the maximum slope may be noticed; this decrease in
slope is more marked with phenanthroquinone than with benzoquinone.

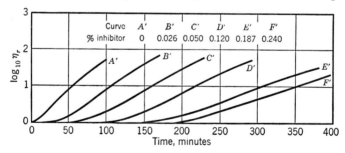

FIGURE 17.   Polymerization of styrene in presence of phenanthraquinone at 120 C.
(Reprinted by permission from The Chemical Society, London.)

Figure 18 [104] shows the dependence of the induction period on the polymerization of styrene at 120 C as a function of the amount of benzoquinone and phenanthroquinone used as a stabilizer.   It may be observed that the increase in the induction period is a linear function of
the concentration of the inhibitor.

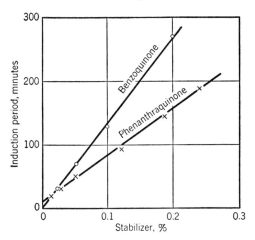

FIGURE 18. Induction period as a function of concentration of stabilizer. (Reprinted by permission from The Chemical Society, London.)

In Table 7 [104] the values of the maximum slope of the $\log_{10} \eta_r$–time curve (A') and the degree of polymerization at a constant viscosity (B') are summarized. The product of these values, $A' \times B'$, gives an approximate value for the true rate of polymerization, C'.

TABLE 7

POLYMERIZATION OF STYRENE AT 120 C IN THE PRESENCE OF PHENANTHROQUINONE

Phenanthro-quinone, %	Induction Period in Minutes	A'	B'	$C' \times 10^4$
0.000	5	0.0230	12.56	8.4
0.012	20	0.0162	18.00	8.5
0.026	30	0.0148	19.34	8.3
0.050	50	0.0134	20.16	7.8
0.120	95	0.0114	21.17	6.7
0.187	145	0.0086	24.47	6.1
0.240	190	0.0077	25.95	5.8

A' = maximum value of $d \log_{10} \eta_r/dt$ (min^{-1}).
B' = percentage polymer at $\log_{10} \eta_r = 1.8$.
C' = maximum polymerization rate (gram mole/cc/hr).

Reprinted by permission from The Chemical Society, London.

Chain termination, inhibition, and retardation in a polymerizing system may be caused by impurities in such a system. Often the impurities are introduced by careless operations or by the use of contaminated equipment. In many systems, impurities are unavoidable.

They may be contained in the monomer in minor quantities as insep-
arable materials. In other cases, the cost of removing the impurities is
too high. In solution polymerization, the impurity might be contained
in the solvent used in the process. The extent to which the impurity
modifies the course of the polymerization depends on the nature of the
impurity. Usually the molecular weight of the polymer is reduced by
the presence of active impurities, as a result of a telomerization process.

BRANCHING

Branching in an ethylenic polymerization is not to be confused with
crosslinking. In the normal polymerization of a monovinyl monomer,
a straight chain polymer should be obtained. Branching will occur, if
during the formation of the linear chain, some elementary step produces
two or more free valencies or radical loci.

Schulz and Staudinger [74, 123] consider that it is probable that the collision of two nuclei may lead to a branching center according to the
following reactions thermally activated:

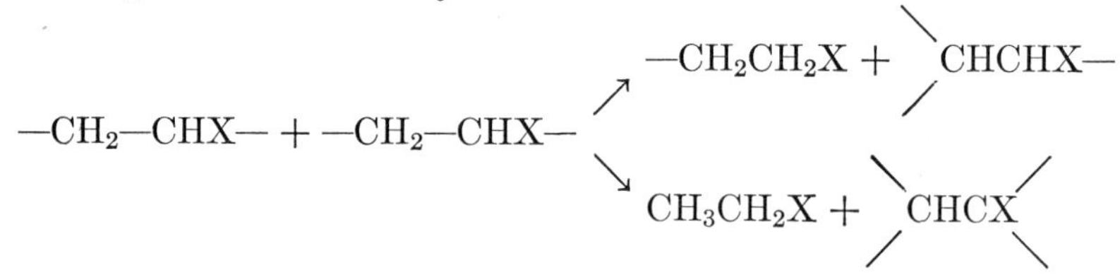

$$-CH_2-CHX- + -CH_2-CHX- \nearrow \begin{array}{l} -CH_2CH_2X + \diagdown CHCHX- \diagup \\ \\ \searrow CH_3CH_2X + \diagdown CHCX \diagup \diagdown \end{array}$$

Also the collision of a short active chain with the body of a long chain
may cause branches to be produced, thus:

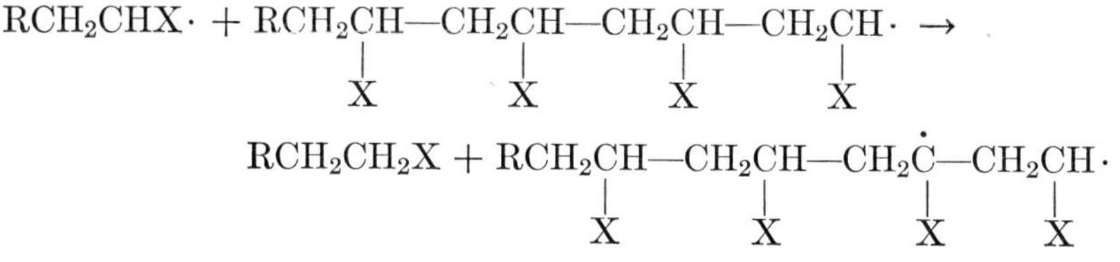

$$RCH_2CHX \cdot + RCH_2CH-CH_2CH-CH_2CH-CH_2CH \cdot \rightarrow$$
$$\qquad\qquad\qquad\quad | \qquad\quad | \qquad\quad | \qquad\quad |$$
$$\qquad\qquad\qquad\quad X \qquad\;\; X \qquad\;\; X \qquad\;\; X$$

$$RCH_2CH_2X + RCH_2CH-CH_2CH-CH_2\overset{.}{C}-CH_2CH \cdot$$
$$\qquad\qquad\qquad\quad | \qquad\quad | \qquad\quad | \qquad\quad |$$
$$\qquad\qquad\qquad\quad X \qquad\;\; X \qquad\;\; X \qquad\;\; X$$

and further growth will occur at the $\overset{.}{C}X$ branches.

If termination of a chain occurs by collision of a large active chain
with the body of a dead chain, branching may also follow by the same
mechanism, thus:

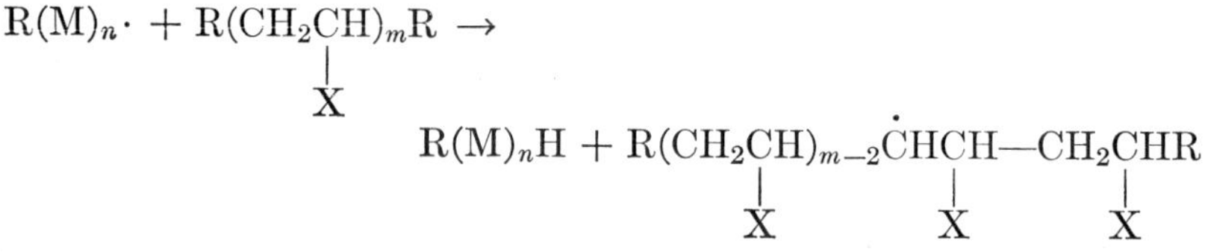

$$R(M)_n \cdot + R(CH_2CH)_mR \rightarrow$$
$$\qquad\qquad\quad\; |$$
$$\qquad\qquad\quad\; X$$

$$R(M)_nH + R(CH_2CH)_{m-2}\overset{.}{C}HCH-CH_2CHR$$
$$\qquad\qquad\qquad\qquad\quad | \qquad\quad | \qquad\quad |$$
$$\qquad\qquad\qquad\qquad\quad X \qquad\;\; X \qquad\;\; X$$

Carlin and Shakespeare [124] have offered convincing experimental proof that branching occurs. Polymethylacrylate was dissolved in monomeric p-chlorostyrene, and the mixture was subjected to thermal polymerization in the absence of catalysts. The polymerized mixture was found to contain (1) poly-p-chlorostyrene and (2) polymer molecules that contained both chlorine and acrylate groups. This investigation also showed that as the percentage of chlorostyrene which polymerized was increased, a larger amount of chlorine was found in the acrylate polymer. The derived data are readily explained by branching of the polyacrylate chain on collision either with active monomeric chlorostyrene or active polymerized chlorostyrene of low molecular weights.

Branching can occur also by the introduction of an initiating catalyst which generates a polyradical, whose functionality is greater than two. Such a catalyst is represented by the acyl peroxide of a tricarboxylic acid, for example, the per-derivatives of mellitic acid, $C_6H_3(COOOR)_3$.

Schulz developed a theory of branching which he treated mathematically:

$\bar{P}_t$ = total average polymerization degree of sample, that is, number of total segmers,

$\bar{P}_m$ = polymerization degree, or number of segmers in main chain,

n_1, n_2 = number of branches of first, second, etc., orders,

$\bar{p}_1, \bar{p}_2$ = length of branches of first, second, etc., orders,

δ = probability that next step in a growing process will lead to branching.

Then

$$n_1 = n\bar{P}_m\delta \qquad (70)$$

The intrinsic cessation probability for such branches is W_c and

$$\bar{p}_1 = \frac{1}{W_c} \qquad (71)$$

The total degree of polymerization including only branches of the first order is

$$\bar{P}_t = \bar{P}_m + n_1\bar{p}_1 \qquad (72)$$

which, on substitution by equation 70 plus equation 71, becomes

$$\bar{P}_t = \bar{P}_m\left(1 + \frac{n\delta}{W_c}\right) \qquad (73)$$

If the assumption is made that branching on the branches of the first order has the same probability as branching on the main chain, then

$$n_2 = n\delta \, n_1 \bar{p}_1 \tag{74}$$

And substituting equation 70 and equation 71, the equation becomes

$$n_2 = n^2 \bar{P}_m \frac{\delta^2}{W_c{}^2} \tag{75}$$

If the average length of the branches of the first order and the second order are regulated by the same cessation probability, the total degree of polymerization, including the first and second order branches, is

$$\bar{P}_t = \bar{P}_m \left[1 + \frac{n\delta}{W_c} + \frac{n^2 \delta^2}{W_c{}^2} \right] \tag{76}$$

and, if the calculations are continued for an infinite number of branches,

$$\bar{P}_t = \bar{P}_m \cdot \left[\frac{1}{1 - \dfrac{n\delta}{W_c}} \right] \tag{77}$$

only if $n\delta < W_c$, that is, the branching probability must not be too high.

$$\frac{\bar{P}_t}{\bar{P}_m} = \left[\frac{1}{1 - \dfrac{n\delta}{W_c}} \right] = b = \text{average degree of branching} \tag{78}$$

The picture of branching may be represented by Figure 19, where P_m represents the main chain, $P_m = 60$, $n_1 = 3$ and represents branching

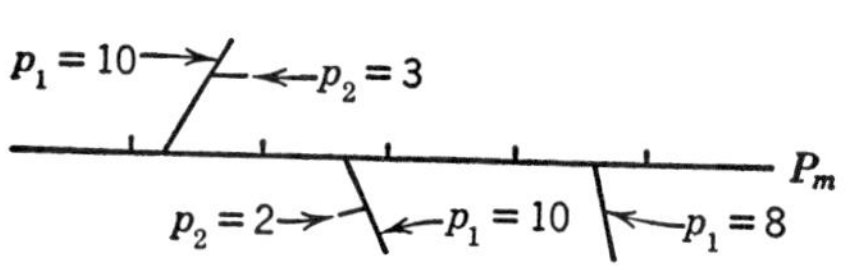

FIGURE 19. Linear chain with a number of branches.

of the first order with $\bar{p}_1 = 9$, and $n_2 = 2$ and represents branching of the second order with $\bar{p}_2 = 2.5$ and $\bar{P}_t = 60 + 27 + 5 = 92$.

Schulz polymerized styrene at increasingly higher temperatures. He compared their K_m constant and determined their average degree of branching. The K_m constant for unbranched polystyrene is 1.8×10^{-4}. The data are summarized in Table 8.

TABLE 8

DEGREE OF BRANCHING

Temperature of Polymerization, °C	$K_m \times 10^{-4}$	Degree of Branching
20	1.18	1.5
60	0.79	2.3
100.5	0.57	3.15
132	0.51	3.5
220	0.42	4.3

These data are consistent with the fact that the K_m constant is closely related to the axis ratio of the polymer and that long chains produce a higher viscosity than branched chain particles. As mentioned in Chapter 7, the presently modified Staudinger viscosity equation, $[\eta_1] = KM^a$, reflects the shape of the polymer particle in the value of a in a particular solvent, and K is a constant depending on the temperature at which the polymer was prepared. In Chapter 7 are the more recent data of K and a obtained by Spencer and Drake.[125]

REDOX SYSTEM

Initiation comes from radicals, and the polymer chain grows in a kinetic chain fashion by addition of monomers to radical. Since the radical originally comes from the catalyst, and since it has been shown that monomers accelerate the decomposition of catalyst, it should be possible to use another molecule instead of the monomer to react with the catalyst to generate radicals. Kharasch and his co-workers [126, 127] have proved by extensive experiments that peroxides produce radicals with ease by reaction with carbon tetrachloride, sodium bisulfite, mercaptans, etc. In view of this, it would be expected that polymerizations carried out in the presence of a small amount of catalyst, which can react with an activator for that specific catalyst to produce radicals, will accelerate the polymerization.[128, 129] Such systems have been called redox systems. This has been determined experimentally, and has been discussed quantitatively by Baxendale, Evans, and Park,[130] who studied the polymerization of acrylonitrile with hydrogen peroxide catalysts and ferrous ion activators. Haber and Weiss [131] have showed the formation and existence of hydroxyl radicals in the oxidation of ferrous ions by hydrogen peroxide in the absence of any monomers.

$$Fe^{++} + H_2O_2 \rightarrow Fe^{+++} + HO^- + HO\cdot \tag{79}$$

Since the hydroxyl radical is the most reactive product, it can react with the initial components of the polymerizable system.

$$CH_2=CHCN + HO\cdot \rightarrow HOCH_2CHCN\cdot \quad (k_{init.}) \quad (80)$$

$$HO\cdot + Fe^{++} \rightarrow Fe^{+++} + OH^- \quad (k_2) \quad (81)$$

$$HO\cdot + H_2O_2 \rightarrow H_2O + HO_2\cdot \quad (82)$$

Equation 80 represents the initiation reaction ($k_{init.}$), the reaction represented by 82 is negligible, and under the molar ratio conditions normally used in polymerization (for example, monomer 100: catalyst 0.5 to 2: activator 1 to 4), equation 81 is about 20 per cent of the initiation reaction of 80.

The propagation step (k_p) is represented by the rapid and successive addition of monomers to the active end of the radical:

$$HOCH_2CHCN\cdot + nCH_2=CHCN \rightarrow$$

$$HO-\left(\begin{array}{c}CH_2CH\\ |\\ CN\end{array}\right)_n-CH_2CHCN\cdot \quad (83)$$

and termination occurs by either of two collision reactions.

$$HO-\left(\begin{array}{c}CH_2CH\\ |\\ CN\end{array}\right)_n\cdot + \cdot OH \rightarrow HO-\left(\begin{array}{c}CH_2CH\\ |\\ CN\end{array}\right)_n-OH \quad (k_t) \quad (84)$$

$$HO-\left(\begin{array}{c}CH_2CH\\ |\\ CN\end{array}\right)_m\cdot + HO-\left(\begin{array}{c}CH_2CH\\ |\\ CN\end{array}\right)_n\cdot \rightarrow$$

$$HO-\left(\begin{array}{c}CH_2CH\\ |\\ CN\end{array}\right)_{m+n}-OH \quad (k_m) \quad (85)$$

Baxendale and co-workers assumed a steady-state approximation for [HO·] and active chain ends [A·] and expressed the steady-state concentration for [HO·] as

$$[HO\cdot] = \frac{k_1ac}{(k_im + k_2a + k_t[A\cdot])} \quad (86)$$

where m = concentration of monomer,
c = concentration of catalyst,
a = concentration of activator.

In this equation the term $k_t[A\cdot]$ can be neglected by choosing suitable reaction conditions, and the equation becomes

$$[HO\cdot] = \frac{k_1ac}{k_im + k_2a} \quad (87)$$

which indicates that the monomer and the ferrous ions are competing for ·OH radicals. The ratio of these two steps can be calculated by introducing equation 87 into the kinetic relations of equations 80 and 81 to obtain

$$\frac{R_{(80)}}{R_{(81)}} = \frac{k_1 m}{k_2 a} \tag{88}$$

Since the ferric ions are readily titratable, the values of a and m may be determined. These authors found that about 20 per cent of the hydroxyl radicals were lost in the side reaction represented by equation 81 and that k_i/k_2 was about 5. They also determined the absolute rate of hydroxyl radical formation from hydrogen peroxide and ferrous ions in the absence of monomer and derived

$$k_1 = 1.78 \times 10^{9-10,100/RT} \tag{89}$$

The energy of activation of 10,000 calories per mole is much lower than the activation energies for thermal radical formation from such catalysts as acetyl and benzoyl peroxide, which have values between 26,000 and 33,000 calories per mole, respectively, depending on the solvent used in the determination.[62, 84, 95, 104] Since the redox system is more efficient in producing radicals at low temperatures, many polymerizations using a redox system may be actually performed at room temperature and even as low as ice water temperature, thereby suppressing chain transfer, branching, crosslinking, or, in general, undesirable side reactions which are dependent on or are increased by temperature increases. However, in certain systems wherein a monomer has a potential functionality greater than 2, crosslinking occurs more readily in redox systems than in normally catalyzed systems. With soap as an emulsifying agent and ammonium persulfate as a catalyst, it is possible to prepare a copolymer of 90 parts of acrylonitrile and 10 parts of butadiene which is soluble in dimethylacetamide. The corresponding copolymer produced under identical conditions, but in the presence of sodium bisulfite as a redox system, produces an insoluble, infusible copolymer.[20] Furthermore, in a redox system, in which catalysts and activator are in the aqueous phase, the initial rate of monomer consumption is directly proportional to the first power of the catalyst concentration, whereas the initial rate of polymerization of styrene, acrylonitrile, etc., in solution is proportional to the square root of the catalyst concentration.

Since the activators are reducing agents, they function in two ways:

1. They facilitate the production of radicals by acting as electron donors, thereby promoting the initiation step.

2. They likewise remove oxygen from the system. This oxygen may be found there as a natural contaminant. Oxygen may also be formed as a by-product of catalytic compositions.

As has already been noted, the inhibition period is reduced, and the presence of a reducing agent may also retard termination.

It is interesting to note that Baxendale and others [110] in a study of the kinetics of an aqueous solution polymerization of methyl methacrylate by a redox system of Fe^{++} and H_2O_2 showed that termination occurs by mutual chain reaction of growing polymer chains. The addition of an emulsifying agent such as cetyltrimethyl ammonium bromide did not change the kinetics of the reaction, but it did have the effect of increasing both the rate and the extent of the polymerization. In these studies, the quantities k_p and k_t appeared to be independent of chain length.

Promoter action of ions. King and Steinbach [109] had observed that the reaction between a persulfate and a thiosulfate is very sensitive to traces of heavy metal ions, such as silver, cuprous, and ferrous ions.

The original reaction between persulfate and thiosulfate may be represented as

$$S_2O_8^= + S_2O_3^= \rightarrow SO_4^= + SO_4 \cdot ^- + S_2O_3 \cdot ^-$$

where the thiosulfate ion donates one electron to the persulfate ion and is oxidized to a thiosulfate radical. Since two radicals are formed, they can both react with another $S_2O_3^=$ ion.

$$SO_4 \cdot ^- + S_2O_3 \cdot ^- + S_2O_3^= \rightarrow SO_4^= + S_4O_6^=$$

In contrast to the hydrogen peroxide ferrous ion system, this system is more complex and more difficult to study since both the electron donor and the electron acceptor produce radicals which in a polymer system can react with monomer, catalyst (persulfate), and activator (thiosulfate), and thereby also produce oxygen as a by-product of these reactions.[130] Morgan [128] has investigated such a polymerization system. He investigated a saturated aqueous solution of acrylonitrile at room temperature, using stoichiometric amounts of persulfate and thiosulfate with 5×10^{-5} to 5×10^{-4} mole of cupric ions, and he discovered a tenfold increase in rate as indicated in Figure 20.[128]

The curves in this figure indicate that the rate of monomer conversion is equal to m^2, rather than to $m^{3/2}$. The increase in conversion rate is roughly proportional to the square root of the promoter concentration, which indicates that the rate of production of initiating radical is directly proportional to the cupric ion concentration.

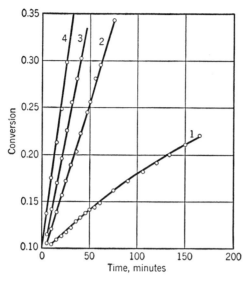

FIGURE 20. Effect of cupric ions on polymerization of acrylonitrile. (1) With no Cu^{++} added. (2) With 0.00005 M Cu^{++} added. (3) With 0.00015 M Cu^{++} added. (4) With 0.0005 M Cu^{++} added. (By permission from The Faraday Society, London.)

Modifiers. Early production of GRS and nitrile rubber, that is, copolymers of dienes and monenes, led to the formation of insoluble polymers and the insolubility was attributed to crosslinking. It was found experimentally that certain organic molecules like the halogenated hydrocarbons, mercaptans,[132-134] and other sulfur derivatives reduced the quantity of crosslinking to produce a technically better polymer.

The compounds are considered to act as chain-transfer agents and thereby reduce branching.[71, 102, 135, 136]. Mayo [65] has shown that the influence of chloroform on the molecular weight of polystyrene can be explained by assuming that the active chain end reacts with chloroform and removes the hydrogen atom, leaving a $CCl_3 \cdot$ radical which can start a new chain, thus:

$$R(CH_2CH)_nCH_2CH \cdot + HCCl_3 \rightarrow R(CH_2CH)_nCH_2CH_2 + \cdot CCl_3$$
$$\quad\;\; | \qquad\quad | \qquad\qquad\qquad\qquad | \qquad\qquad |$$
$$\quad\;\; X \qquad\quad X \qquad\qquad\qquad\qquad X \qquad\qquad X$$

It has also been shown [137] that mercaptans react with radicals to form the $RS \cdot$ radical similar to chloroform and that, furthermore, the $RS \cdot$ radical can react with a double bond. In acting as chain-transfer agents, they retard the excessive growth of a chain, including the branches. Therefore, in the case of monomers of functionality greater than 2, they prevent crosslinking. If these moderators act as chain-transfer agents, they should be found in the polymer. Snyder and others [138] and Wall and others [139] have examined the influence of mercaptans and other modifiers on styrene and styrene-butadiene polymers, respectively. In both experiments, sulfur was found to be an integral part of the polymer. In the butadiene-styrene copolymer prepared in the presence of dodecyl mercaptan, the assumption of chain-transfer action of the modifier requires that each polymer molecule contain one atom of sulfur. Wall studied certain fractions of these copolymers and determined molecular weights and sulfur contents. The values obtained are shown in Table 9.[139]

TABLE 9

MOLECULAR WEIGHT AND SULFUR CONTENT OF STYRENE-BUTADIENE COPOLYMER

Sample	Molecular Weight	Sulfur Atoms per Molecule
A1	33,330 ⎱	0.73
A2	32,600 ⎰	
B1	34,800 ⎱	0.69
B2	34,600 ⎰	
C	49,740	1.13

Reprinted by permission from the authors and the *Journal of the American Chemical Society.*

Beside the experimental limitations of determining molecular weight and sulfur content, numerous other factors can account for the deviation from the theoretical one-one ratio of sulfur to polymer molecule. Mutual termination of two chains by disproportion or combination, as well as chain transfer with monomer, would lower the sulfur content to below unity. Branching explains values higher than one, since more than one polymer molecule can add by this mechanism to a polymer chain. In view of these considerations, the results shown in Table 9 can be considered excellent experimental proof that modifiers act as chain-transfer agents. Modifiers which become attached terminally to a chain are properly called telomers.

Types of Initiation

In the preceding discussion reference was made to a number of means of achieving initiation of ethylenic polymerization reactions. These methods as well as others are summarized in Table 10.

TABLE 10

Types of Initiation

I. Thermal
II. Photochemical
III. Catalytic
    A. Free Radical Type
       1. Normal
       2. Redox
          a. Promoted
    B. Ionic Types
       1. Carbonium
          a. Cationic
       2. Carbanion
          a. Anionic

I. THERMAL INITIATION

Thermal initiation was considered as apparently involving collision between two monomers to give a diradical:

$$CH_2{=}CH + CH_2{=}CH \xrightarrow{K_{12}} -CHCH_2CH_2CH-$$
$$\quad\; | \qquad\quad | \qquad\qquad | \qquad\quad |$$
$$\quad\; X \qquad\quad X \qquad\qquad X \qquad\quad X$$

Involved in this collision reaction there exists (1) a collision factor, which also implies a steric factor depending on the type of monomer, and (2) an energy of activation which is about 25,000 to 35,000 calories per mole.

II. PHOTOCHEMICAL INITIATION

Studies on the photopolymerization of the acrylic and methacrylic esters indicate that the initiation is of first order by double bond activation and that the terminal double bond is progressively activated.

$$CH_2{=}CH + h\nu \xrightarrow{K_{11}} CH_2{=}\overset{*}{C}H \xrightarrow{\quad CH_2{=}CH, X \quad} CH_3CHCH{=}\overset{*}{C}H$$

Thus K_{11} is a measure of active radiation and of the quantum yield. In methyl methacrylate the quantum yield is 0.5, and the initiation is proportional to the concentration of monomer and to the square root of light intensity, $\sqrt{I}$.

III. CATALYTIC INITIATION

Free radical. The thermal and photochemical types of initiation are distinguished from the catalytic initiations in that, in the latter types, a distinct chemical substance is added to the monomeric material. In the normal free radical type as, for example, in a vinyl polymerization initiated by an organic peroxide, a free radical, $R\cdot$, is formed by the catalyst. Initiation involves its reaction with a monomer molecule, thereby generating a new radical. This radical is progressively generated terminally by the further addition of new monomer molecules, thus:

$$[\text{Catalyst}] \rightarrow [R\cdot] + \underset{\underset{X}{|}}{CH_2}{=}CH \xrightarrow{K_{12}}$$

$$\underset{\underset{X}{|}}{R CH_2 CH}\cdot \xrightarrow{\quad \underset{\underset{X}{|}}{CH_2{=}CH} \quad} \text{etc., polymer}$$

The radical, $R\cdot$, thus becomes attached to the polymer chain. Catalysts which have been used in this radical type of initiation include, beside benzoyl peroxide, p-bromobenzoyl peroxide, anisoyl peroxide, chloroacetyl peroxide, $tert$-butyl hydroperoxide, di-$tert$-butyl peroxide, $tert$-butyl perbenzoate, di-$tert$-butyl diperphthalate, 1-hydroxycyclohexyl hydroperoxide-1, p-bromobenzene diazonium hydroxide, N-nitroso-p-bromoacetanilide, triphenylmethyl, diazoaminobenzene, tetraphenyl succino-nitrile, tetrachloro-tetraphenylsuccino-nitrile, etc.

In the redox type of catalysis, the decomposition of the catalyst, normally an oxidizing agent, occurs under the influence of a reducing agent to produce a free radical.

In contrast to free radicals initiated by the decomposition of organic compounds, the free radicals generated by a redox system are derived perferably by the reaction of inorganic materials in ionic form in an aqueous system.

(*A*) By the reaction of ferrous ions with water-soluble peroxides:

$$Fe^{++} + H_2O_2 \rightarrow Fe^{+++} + HO^- + HO\cdot$$

(*B*) By the reaction of a thiosulfate with a persulfate:

$$S_2O_8^= + S_2O_3^= \rightarrow SO_4^= + SO_4\cdot^- + S_2O_3\cdot^-$$

These reactions are extremely sensitive to and promoted by traces of heavy metals such as silver, cuprous, and ferrous ions. Iodide ions also have been found to provide promotion. In the reaction between hydrogen peroxide and ferrous ions, the ferrous ion has a twofold function in that it supplies a reactant for the hydroxyl radical formation, as well as acts as a promoter.

Ionic. The ionic type catalysts used in ethylenic polymerization are represented by such compounds as aluminum chloride, boron trifluoride, sulfuric acid, phosphoric acid, hydrogen fluoride, and stannic chloride. Hunter and Yohe [140] based their theory of polymerization of olefins by aluminum chloride on an electronic structure whereby the aluminum chloride combines with the ionic activated state of the olefin in which two electrons of the unsaturated double bond occupy the same orbital: [141]

$$R':\overset{..}{C}::\overset{..}{C}:R + \overset{..}{Al}:Cl \rightarrow \overset{R'\ R\ Cl}{\underset{R'R\ Cl}{\overset{..\ ..\ ..}{C}:\overset{..}{C}:\overset{..}{Al}:Cl}}$$

This complex is a highly activated molecule because of the terminal structure

$$\overset{R'}{\underset{R'}{\overset{..}{C}:}}$$

which can add another olefin producing a reaction product that would still be in an active state:

$$\overset{R'\ R\ Cl}{\underset{R'\ R\ Cl}{\overset{..\ ..\ ..}{C}:\overset{..}{C}:\overset{..}{Al}:Cl}} \xrightarrow{CR'_2=CR_2} \overset{R'\ R\ R'\ R\ Cl}{\underset{R'\ R\ R'\ R\ Cl}{\overset{..\ ..\ ..\ ..\ ..}{C}:\overset{..}{C}:\overset{..}{C}:\overset{..}{C}:\overset{..}{Al}:Cl}} \xrightarrow{etc.}$$

As a typical example, Hunter mentioned the polymerization products of isobutylene with aluminum chloride at very low temperatures, and these polymers were described as hemicolloids with molecular weights up to 10,000. However, boron trifluoride at a temperature of −80 C or lower gives extremely high molecular weights. [142, 143]

α-Methylstyrene has been polymerized [144] by AlCl$_3$ at −60 to −65 C to high molecular weight products in spite of the fact that α-methylstyrene, unlike styrene, is not polymerized by heating. Either no polymer or only low molecular weight polymers were obtained when this monomer was treated with benzoyl peroxide, zinc chloride, stannic chloride, at room temperature, etc.

All substances which cause ionic polymerization are characterized by strong affinity for an electron pair, and undoubtedly initiate polymerization by polarization of the double bond of the monomer. [145] Substituent groups such as alkyl, aryl, or ether groups promote the release of electrons, and those monomers that contain such groups are most readily polymerized by ionic or electrophilic catalysts.

The kinetics of the ionic reactions are different from the free radical initiated vinyl type of polymerization. The stannic chloride polymerization of styrene was studied by Williams.[12] For monomer concentration, the order was found to be higher than the solution polymerization of styrene in thymol, whereas for catalyst concentration the polymerization was first order and the degree of polymerization was independent of catalyst concentration. These observations appear to be in agreement with the following course of reaction.

Initiation:

$$H^+ + CH_2{=}CH \underset{}{\overset{rapid}{\rightleftharpoons}} HCH_2CH^+ \overset{k_i}{\longrightarrow} HCH_2CHCH_2CH^+$$
$$\qquad\qquad \underset{C_6H_5}{|} \qquad\qquad \underset{C_6H_5}{|} \qquad\quad \underset{C_6H_5}{|}\; \underset{C_6H_5}{|}$$

Propagation:

$$HCH_2CHCH_2CH + nCH_2{=}CH \overset{k_p}{\longrightarrow}$$
$$\underset{C_6H_5}{|}\;\underset{C_6H_5}{|} \qquad\quad \underset{C_6H_5}{|}$$

$$H{-}\left(\underset{C_6H_5}{\underset{|}{CH_2CH{-}}}\right)_n {-}CH_2CHCH_2CH^+$$
$$\qquad\qquad\qquad\qquad \underset{C_6H_5}{|}\;\underset{C_6H_5}{|}$$

Termination:

$$H{-}\left(\underset{C_6H_5}{\underset{|}{CH_2CH{-}}}\right)_n {-}CH_2CHCH_2CH^+ \overset{k_t}{\longrightarrow}$$
$$\qquad\qquad\qquad\qquad \underset{C_6H_5}{|}\;\underset{C_6H_5}{|}$$

$$H{-}\left(\underset{C_6H_5}{\underset{|}{CH_2CH{-}}}\right)_n CH_2CHCH{=}CH + H^+$$
$$\qquad\qquad\qquad\qquad \underset{C_6H_5}{|}\;\underset{C_6H_5}{|}$$

This termination step is monomolecular, and the presence of a double bond per polymer molecule can be explained by the loss of a proton by a first-order process for active centers.

Price and Meister [146] have shown that the process in the polymerization of ethylene in the presence of boron trifluoride does not involve the reaction of the fluoride but of a hydrogen ion. It is known that, in the absolute absence of moisture, no polymerization occurs. In the presence of moisture, a proton is formed:

$$\underset{\ddot{F}}{\overset{F}{F{:}\ddot{B}}} + HOH \rightarrow \left[\underset{\ddot{F}}{\overset{F}{F{:}\ddot{B}{:}\ddot{O}{:}H}}\right]^- + H^+$$

The primary process of the polymerization of the ethylene is probably

$$\underset{\overset{\cdot\cdot}{H}\ \overset{\cdot\cdot}{H}}{H:C::C:H} + H^+ \rightarrow \underset{\overset{\cdot\cdot}{H}\ \overset{\cdot\cdot}{H}}{H:\overset{\cdot\cdot}{C}:C:^+H} \xrightarrow{\ CH_2=CH_2\ } \text{etc.}$$

which appears to be in accord with the fact that the reaction is not inhibited by phenols, oxygen, or the like, but by amines, which can act as proton acceptors:

$$\underset{\overset{\cdot\cdot}{R}}{R:\overset{\overset{\displaystyle R}{}}{\underset{\cdot\cdot}{N}}} + H^+ \rightarrow \left[\underset{\overset{\cdot\cdot}{R}}{R:\overset{\overset{\displaystyle R}{}}{\underset{\cdot\cdot}{N}}:H}\right]^+$$

and thereby inhibit or retard the polymerization by removal of the initiating substance. Anionic initiations of polymerization are known, and the base catalyzed polymerization of methacrylonitrile has been studied.[147] In these studies in which A:⁻ was used to indicate the initiating anionic fragment, the probable course of the polymerization was indicated as follows:

Initiation:

$$A:^- + CH_2 = \underset{\overset{|}{R^1}}{\overset{\overset{\displaystyle R}{|}}{C}} \rightarrow A - CH_2 - \underset{\overset{|}{R^1}}{\overset{\overset{\displaystyle R}{|}}{C}}:^-$$

Propagation:

$$A - CH_2 - \underset{\overset{|}{R^1}}{\overset{\overset{\displaystyle R}{|}}{C}}:^- + nCH_2 = \underset{\overset{|}{R^1}}{\overset{\overset{\displaystyle R}{|}}{C}} \rightarrow A - \left[-CH_2 - \underset{\overset{|}{R^1}}{\overset{\overset{\displaystyle R}{|}}{C}}-\right]_n -CH_2 - \underset{\overset{|}{R^1}}{\overset{\overset{\displaystyle R}{|}}{C}}:^-$$

Termination:

$$A - \left[-CH_2 - \underset{\overset{|}{R^1}}{\overset{\overset{\displaystyle R}{|}}{C}}-\right]_n -CH_2 - \underset{\overset{|}{R^1}}{\overset{\overset{\displaystyle R}{|}}{C}}:^- + H^+ \rightarrow A - \left[-CH_2 - \underset{\overset{|}{R^1}}{\overset{\overset{\displaystyle R}{|}}{C}}-\right]_{n+1} -H$$

The termination may also occur by elimination of A:⁻. Ionic initiations, therefore, may be generalized as follows:

Cationic:

$$Z^+ + CH_2 = CH \rightarrow Z - \underset{\overset{|}{X}}{\overset{\overset{\displaystyle H}{|}}{C}} - \underset{\overset{|}{X}}{\overset{\overset{\displaystyle H}{|}}{C}}^+ \xrightarrow{\ CH_2=CH_x\ } Z - \underset{\overset{|}{H}}{\overset{\overset{\displaystyle H}{|}}{C}} - \underset{\overset{|}{X}}{\overset{\overset{\displaystyle H}{|}}{C}} - \underset{\overset{|}{H}}{\overset{\overset{\displaystyle H}{|}}{C}} - \underset{\overset{|}{X}}{\overset{\overset{\displaystyle H}{|}}{C}}^+ \xrightarrow{\ \text{etc.}\ }$$

Anionic:

$$Z^- + CH_2{=}CH \longrightarrow \underset{\displaystyle X}{\overset{\displaystyle H\ \ H}{Z{-}C{-}C}}\ \overset{CH_2{=}CH_x}{\longrightarrow}\ \underset{\displaystyle H\ X\ H\ X}{\overset{\displaystyle H\ H\ H\ H}{Z{-}C{-}C{-}C{-}C}}\ \overset{etc.}{\longrightarrow}$$

In cationic polymerizations termination occurs by loss of a proton, H^+, which reacts with the negative catalyst complex to reform water and the catalyst:

$$H^+ + \begin{bmatrix} F \\ \overset{\cdot\cdot}{F{:}\overset{\cdot\cdot}{B}{:}O{:}H} \\ \underset{\cdot\cdot}{F} \end{bmatrix}^- \rightarrow BF_3 + H_2O$$

Ionic polymerization may also be applied to the preparation of a number of polymers normally prepared by condensation reactions.

The polyamide of aminocaproic acid is an example of a polymer which may be prepared by a condensation mechanism:

$$NH_2(CH_2)_5COOH \xrightarrow{NH_2(CH_2)_5COOH}$$
$$NH_2(CH_2)_5CONH(CH_2)_5COOH \xrightarrow{nNH_2(CH_2)_5COOH} etc.$$

It can also be prepared by polymerizing caprolactam. However, in the complete absence of water or of acids or basic materials, caprolactam may be heated at 200 C continuously for one to two weeks in the absence of oxygen, without trace of polymerization.[20] In the presence of oxygen, acid products are obtained as a result of oxidation, and polymerization occurs. However, in the presence of acids or of bases or of salts possessing even feeble acidic or basic properties, polymerization occurs.[148] Water is ionic and will also catalyze the polymerization, especially at temperatures at which the hydrolysis of caprolactam to aminocaproic acid occurs.[148] At 220 to 250 C, caprolactam polymerizes because of the presence of ammonia as a result of thermal decomposition.[149] These processes are undoubtedly ionic and may be referred to as an ionic mechanism which is illustrated by the use of HCl as the catalyst:

$$HCl \rightarrow H^+ + Cl^-$$

$$\underset{\displaystyle (CH_2)_4{-}CO}{\overset{\displaystyle CH_2{-}NH}{CH_2{-}NH}} + H^+ \rightarrow \underset{\displaystyle (CH_2){-}(CH_2)_4}{\overset{\displaystyle H}{H{:}N{-}\overset{+}{C}O}} \rightarrow$$

$$NH_2(CH_2)_5\overset{+}{C}O \xrightarrow{\underset{(CH_2)_4{-}CO}{\overset{CH_2{-}NH}{}}} NH_2(CH_2)_5CONH{-}\underset{\displaystyle (CH_2)_4{-}CH_2}{\overset{+}{C}O} \rightarrow$$

$$NH_2(CH_2)_5CONH(CH_2)_5\overset{+}{C}O \overset{etc.}{\longrightarrow}$$

In the presence of bases, a similar mechanism may be postulated.

$$HO^- + (CH_2)_5 \underset{CO}{\overset{NH}{\diagup}} \rightarrow HOOC(CH_2)_5NH^- \xrightarrow{\underset{(CH_2)_4 \text{---}CO}{CH_2 \text{------} NH}}$$

$$HOO(CH_2)_5HNOC(CH_2)_5NH^- \xrightarrow{etc.}$$

The polymerization of the α-amino acid carbonic acid anhydrides of Leuchs [150] probably follows the same type of mechanism.

$$\underset{\underset{O}{\overset{|}{CO}\text{------}}}{\overset{R}{\underset{|}{N}}}\text{---}CR_2\text{---}CO \xrightarrow{H^+} H:\underset{\underset{O}{\overset{|}{CO}\text{------}}}{\overset{R}{\underset{|}{N}}}\text{---}CR_2\text{---}\overset{+}{CO} \rightarrow CO_2 + H\overset{R}{\underset{|}{N}}\text{---}CR_2\overset{+}{CO} \text{------}$$

$$\underset{\underset{R}{\overset{|}{R}} \; etc.}{\overset{H}{\underset{|}{N}}}\text{---}CR_2CO\overset{R}{\underset{|}{N}}\text{---}CR_2\overset{+}{CO} + CO_2 \leftarrow H\overset{R}{\underset{|}{N}}\text{---}CR_2CO\underset{\underset{O}{\overset{|}{CO}\text{------}}}{\overset{R}{\underset{|}{N}}}\text{---}CR_2\text{---}\overset{+}{CO} \leftarrow \underset{\underset{O}{\overset{|}{CO}\text{------}}}{\overset{RN\text{---}CR_2\text{---}CO}{}}$$

Undoubtedly, a similar mechanism is followed in the polymerization of lactones, $(CH_2)_m \underset{O}{\overset{CO}{\diagup}}$, and especially the lactone of β-hydroxypropionic acid, which can be readily prepared from ketone and formaldehyde:

$$CH_2{=}CO + CH_2O \rightarrow \underset{CH_2\text{---}O}{\overset{O}{CH_2\text{---}C{\diagup}{\diagup}}}$$

Through an ionic mechanism it is possible to prepare copolymers comprising components of such diversified monomers as cyclic lactams and vinyl compounds.

A copolymer of caprolactam,[20] $\underset{CO\text{------}NH}{\overset{(CH_2)_4\text{---}CH_2}{}}$, and styrene, $CH_2{=}\underset{C_6H_5}{\overset{H}{\underset{|}{C}}}$,

whose structure may be represented as

$$H[NH(CH_2)_5CO]_x\text{---}\left[\underset{C_6H_5}{\overset{H}{CH_2\text{---}\underset{|}{C}\text{---}}}\right]_y\text{---}NH(CH_2)_5COCH_2\text{---}\underset{C_6H_5}{\overset{H}{\underset{|}{C}}}\text{---}OH$$

where the values of x and y depend on the reactivity and selectivity constants of the two monomers.

Ionizing radiation may also initiate a polymerization by an ionic mechanism. It has been shown that α particles, that is, ionizing radiation,[151, 152] cause the oligomerization of acetylene and that the initiation is due to the reactions:

$$C_2H_2^+ + h\nu \longrightarrow C_2H_2^+ + e^-$$

$$C_2H_2^+ + nC_2H_2 \longrightarrow (C_2H_2)_nC_2H_2^+$$

$$(C_2H_2)_nC_2H_2^+ \xrightarrow{e^-} (C_2H_2)_{n+1}$$

The value of n in the above reactions is approximately nineteen molecules, which are removed from the gas phase per ion pair formed. Lind and Bardwell [152] postulated an ion cluster theory involving about twenty acetylene molecules about a positive nucleus, thus:

$$CH_2{=}CH \rightarrow C_2H_2^+ + e^-$$

$$C_2H_2^+ + 19C_2H_2 \rightarrow (C_2H_2)_{20}^+$$

$$(C_2H_2)_{20}^+ + e^- \rightarrow (C_2H_2)_{20}$$

However, Garrison [153] points out that the polymerization of acetylene by ionizing radiation may be explained both by a free radical mechanism as well as by an ionic mechanism similar to an aluminum chloride mechanism once initiation by the $C_2H_2^+$ ions has occurred. It has been shown [141] that in the aluminum chloride or ionic polymerization the energy of activation is lowered by the combination of the catalyst with the ionic activated state in which two electrons of the unsaturated bond occupy the same orbital. The polymerization of ethylene has been explained [146] on the basis of the primary process:

$$\text{H:C::C:H} + \text{H}^+ \rightarrow \text{H:}\overset{+}{\text{C}}\text{:C:H}$$
$$\overset{\cdot\cdot}{\text{H}}\ \ \overset{\cdot\cdot}{\text{H}} \qquad\qquad \overset{\cdot\cdot}{\text{H}}\ \text{H}$$

Garrison suggests that the $C_2H_2^+$ ion may act as an acid catalyst [154] by combining with the negative carbon atom of the ionic resonance form of the acetylene, thus:

$$\overset{+}{\text{H:C}}\text{::}\overset{-}{\text{C:H}} + \text{H:}\overset{+}{\text{C}}\text{::}\overset{\cdot}{\text{C:H}} \rightarrow \text{H:}\overset{+}{\text{C}}\text{::C:C::}\overset{\cdot}{\text{C:H}}$$

The free radical polymerization would be explained by the presence of an unshared electron in $C_2H_2^+$, thus:

$$H:\overset{.}{\underset{..}{C}}::\overset{.}{C}:H + H:\overset{.}{C}::\overset{.}{\underset{..}{C}}:H \rightarrow H:\overset{.}{C}::C:\overset{..}{\underset{\underset{H}{..}}{C}}::\overset{+}{C}:H$$

In both cases polymerization would occur by further addition of acetylene to the growing active centers.

Sources of Carbonium Ions

Whitmore [155] has summarized the methods of formation of carbonium ions, as follows.

1. From alkyl halides:

$$(C_6H_5)_3CCl + SnCl_4 \rightleftharpoons SnCl_5^- + (CH_3)_3C^+$$
$$RCl + AlCl_3 \rightleftharpoons AlCl_4^- + R^+$$

2. From alcohols by acid reagents or catalysts:

$$R:\overset{..}{\underset{..}{O}}:H + \text{acid reagent} \rightleftharpoons R^+ + H_2O$$

3. From primary amines by the action of nitrous acid:

$$R:\overset{}{\underset{H}{\overset{..}{N}}}:H + H^+ + H:\overset{..}{\underset{..}{O}}:\overset{..}{N}::\overset{..}{\underset{..}{O}} \rightarrow :N:::N: + 2H:\overset{..}{\underset{..}{O}}:H + R^+$$

4. By the addition of a proton to an olefin:

$$:\overset{H\ H}{\underset{\overset{..}{H}\ \overset{..}{H}}{\overset{..}{C}:\overset{..}{C}}}: \xrightarrow{H^+} H:\overset{H\ H}{\underset{\overset{..}{H}\ \overset{..}{H}}{\overset{..}{C}:\overset{..}{C}}}^+$$

5. By the addition of an electronic deficient molecule to an olefin:

$$:\overset{\overset{..}{F}}{\underset{\overset{..}{F}}{\overset{..}{F}:B}} + :CH_2:C(CH_3)_2 \rightleftharpoons F_3B:CH_2:C\overset{+}{\underset{CH_3}{\overset{CH_3}{<}}}$$

6. By the addition of an olefin to the "atomic oxygen" from an oxidizing agent:

$$:\overset{..}{\underset{..}{O}} + :CH_2:C(CH_3)_2 \rightarrow :\overset{..}{\underset{..}{O}}:CH_2:C\overset{+}{\underset{CH_3}{\overset{CH_3}{<}}}$$

348   Kinetics of Polymerizations

7. By the addition of a proton from a suitable reagent to a carbonyl group:

$$C_6H_5:\overset{..}{C}::\overset{..}{C} + H_2SO_4 \rightleftharpoons C_6H_5:\overset{+}{\overset{..}{C}}:\overset{..}{O}:H$$
$$\underset{\overset{|}{H}}{:\overset{..}{O}:} \qquad\qquad \underset{\overset{|}{H}}{:\overset{..}{O}:}$$

REFERENCES

1. F. O. Rice, *Homogeneous Organic Reactions*, Chemical Catalog Co., New York, 1928.
2. C. N. Hinshelwood, *The Kinetics of Chemical Change in Gaseous Systems*, Oxford, Clarendon Press, 1939.
3. A. Farkas and H. W. Melville, *Gas Reactions*, Macmillan and Co., London, 1939.
4. G. Lemoine, *Compt. rend.*, **125**, 530 (1897).
5. G. Lemoine, *Compt. rend.*, **129**, 719 (1899).
6. H. Mark and R. Raff, *Z. physik. Chem.*, **B31**, 275 (1936).
7. H. Dostal and R. Raff, *Z. physik. Chem.*, **B32**, 417 (1936).
8. J. W. Breitenbach and R. Raff, *Ber.*, **69**, 1107 (1936).
9. O. Schmitz-Dumont, K. Hamann, and A. Diebold, *Ber.*, **71**, 205 (1938).
10. G. F. D'Alelio, *Experimental Plastics and Synthetic Resins*, pp. 69–71, J. Wiley and Sons, New York, 1946.
11. G. Williams, *J. Chem. Soc.* (London), **141**, 1046 (1938).
12. G. Williams, *J. Chem. Soc.* (London), **143**, 775 (1940).
13. G. F. D'Alelio, U. S. Patent 2,363,836.
14. D. E. Strain, *Ind. Eng. Chem.*, **30**, 345 (1938).
15. E. W. Reid, U. S. Patent 2,064,565.
16. H. Stobbe and F. Reuss, *Ann.*, **391**, 151 (1912).
17. H. Stobbe, *Ann.*, **409**, 1 (1915).
18. H. Stobbe and A. Lippold, *J. prakt. Chem.*, (2), **90**, 336 (1914).
19. G. F. D'Alelio, *Experimental Plastics and Synthetic Resins*, p. 10, J. Wiley and Sons, New York, 1946.
20. G. F. D'Alelio, Unpublished results.
21. C. S. Marvel, J. Dec, and H. G. Cooke, Jr., *J. Am. Chem. Soc.*, **62**, 3499 (1940).
22. H. Stobbe and G. Posnjak, *Ann.*, **371**, 259 (1909).
23. H. W. Starkweather and G. B. Taylor, *J. Am. Chem. Soc.*, **52**, 4708 (1930).
24. J. W. Goodeve, *Trans. Faraday Soc.*, **34**, 1239 (1938).
25. J. S. Owens, *Ind. Eng. Chem.*, Anal. Ed., **11**, 643 (1939).
26. J. J. McGovern, J. M. Grim, and W. C. Teach, *Anal. Chem.*, **20**, 312 (1948).
27. H. Kubota, *Bull. Chem. Soc.* (Japan), **13**, 678 (1939).
28. R. Signer and J. Weiler, *Helv. Chim. Acta*, **15**, 649 (1932).
29. J. H. Hibben, *J. Chem. Phys.*, **5**, 706 (1937).
30. D. Monnier, B. Susz, and E. Briner, *Helv. Chim. Acta*, **21**, 1349 (1938).
31. R. H. Kienle and H. H. Race, *Trans. Am. Electrochemical Soc.*, **65**, 87 (1934).
32. J. Farquharson, *Trans. Faraday Soc.*, **32**, 219 (1936).
33. J. Farquharson, *Trans. Faraday Soc.*, **33**, 824 (1937).
34. G. Bozza, *Giorn. chim. ind. applicata*, **14**, 294 (1932).
35. J. Savard and S. Diner, *Bull. soc. chim.*, **51**, (4), 597 (1932).
36. R. H. Kienle and F. E. Petke, *J. Am. Chem. Soc.*, **62**, 1053 (1940).

37. G. Bozza, *Giorn. chim. ind. applicata*, **14**, 400 (1932).
38. J. Savard and S. Diner, *Bull. soc. chim.*, **51**, (4), 597 (1932).
39. G. F. D'Alelio, *Experimental Plastics and Synthetic Resins*, p. 177, J. Wiley and Sons, New York, 1946.
40. G. Williams, *J. Chem. Soc.* (London), **141**, 246 (1938).
41. Kia-Khwe Jeu and H. N. Alyea, *J. Am. Chem. Soc.*, **55**, 575 (1933).
42. H. A. Smith, *J. Am. Chem. Soc.*, **61**, 254 (1939).
43. P. J. Flory, *J. Am. Chem. Soc.*, **61**, 3334 (1939).
44. P. J. Flory, *J. Am. Chem. Soc.*, **58**, 1877 (1936).
45. J. Abere, G. Goldfinger, H. Mark, and H. Maidus, *Ann. N. Y. Acad. Sci.*, **44**, 267 (1943).
46. H. M. Hulburt, R. A. Harman, A. V. Tobolsky, and H. Eyring, *Ann. N. Y. Acad. Sci.*, **44**, 371 (1943).
47. M. Polanyi, *Atomic Reactions*, Williams and Norgate, Ltd., London, 1932.
48. N. Semenov, *Chemical Kinetics and Chain Reactions*, Oxford, Clarendon Press, 1935.
49. W. Chalmers, *Can. J. Research*, **7**, 113 (1932).
50. W. Chalmers, *Can. J. Research*, **7**, 472 (1932).
51. S. Arrhenius, *Z. physik. Chem.*, **4**, 226 (1889).
52. J. W. Breitenbach, *Z. physik. Chem.*, **B45**, 101 (1939).
53. C. C. Price and R. W. Kell, *J. Am. Chem. Soc.*, **63**, 2798 (1941).
54. G. V. Schulz and E. Husemann, *Z. physik. Chem.*, **B39**, 246 (1938).
55. R. G. W. Norrish and E. F. Brockman, *Proc. Roy. Soc.* (London), **171A**, 147 (1939).
56. S. Kamenskaya and S. Medvedev, *Acta Physicochim.* (U.R.S.S.), **13**, 565 (1940).
57. C. C. Price, R. W. Kell, and E. Krebs, *J. Am. Chem. Soc.*, **64**, 1103 (1942).
58. C. C. Price, *Ann. N. Y. Acad. Sci.*, **44**, 351 (1943).
59. G. V. Schulz and F. Blaschke, *Z. physik Chem.*, **B51**, 75 (1942).
60. M. S. Matheson, *J. Chem. Phys.*, **13**, 584 (1945).
61. D. Josefowitz and H. Mark, *Polymer Bull.*, **1**, 140 (1945).
62. K. Nozaki and P. D. Bartlett, *J. Am. Chem. Soc.*, **68**, 1686 (1946).
63. P. D. Bartlett and K. Nozaki, *J. Am. Chem. Soc.*, **69**, 2299 (1947).
64. P. F. Hartman, H. G. Sellers, and D. Turnbull, *J. Am. Chem. Soc.*, **69**, 2416 (1947).
65. F. R. Mayo, *J. Am. Chem. Soc.*, **65**, 2324 (1943).
66. W. Kern and K. Feuerstein, *J. prakt. Chem.*, **158**, 186 (1941).
67. H. W. Melville and W. F. Watson, *Trans. Faraday Soc.*, **44**, 887–905 (1948).
68. J. W. Breitenbach, *Monatsh.*, **71**, 275 (1938).
69. H. W. Melville, *Proc. Roy. Soc.* (London), **A163**, 511 (1937).
70. T. T. Jones and H. W. Melville, *Proc. Roy. Soc.* (London), **A175**, 392 (1940).
71. G. V. Schulz, *Z. physik. Chem.*, **B30**, 379 (1935).
72. G. V. Schulz, *Z. physik. Chem.*, **B43**, 25 (1939).
73. G. V. Schulz, A. Dinglinger, and E. Husemann, *Z. physik. Chem.*, **B43**, 385 (1939).
74. G. V. Schulz, *Z. physik. Chem.*, **B44**, 227 (1939).
75. G. V. Schulz, *Z. physik. Chem.*, **B47**, 155 (1940).
76. G. V. Schulz and A. Dinglinger, *Z. physik. Chem.*, **B43**, 49 (1939).
77. C. C. Price, R. W. Kell, and E. Krebs, *J. Am. Chem. Soc.*, **64**, 2508 (1942).
78. C. C. Price and D. A. Durham, *J. Am. Chem. Soc.*, **65**, 757 (1943).
79. C. C. Price, *J. Am. Chem. Soc.*, **65**, 2380 (1943).

80. W. Kern and H. Kammerer, *J. prakt. Chem.*, **161**, 81 (1942).
81. W. Kern and H. Kammerer, *J. prakt. Chem.*, **161**, 289 (1943).
82. A. T. Blomquist, J. R. Johnson, and H. J. Sykes, *J. Am. Chem. Soc.*, **65**, 2446 (1943).
83. P. D. Bartlett and S. G. Cohen, *J. Am. Chem. Soc.*, **65**, 543 (1943).
84. P. D. Bartlett and R. Altschul, *J. Am. Chem. Soc.*, **67**, 812 (1945).
85. J. H. McClure, R. E. Robertson, and A. C. Cuthbertson, *Can. J. Research*, **20B**, 103 (1942).
86. O. J. Walker and G. L. E. Wild, *J. Chem. Soc.* (London), **140**, 1132 (1937).
87. M. S. Kharasch, F. Engelmann, and W. H. Urry, *J. Am. Chem. Soc.*, **65**, 2428 (1943).
88. J. Franck and E. Rabinowitsch, *Trans. Faraday Soc.*, **30**, 120 (1934).
89. H. Staudinger, *Ber.*, **58**, 1075 (1925).
90. H. A. Shah, F. Leonard, and A. V. Tobolsky, *Abstracts of Papers Presented at 114th Meeting of American Chemical Society*, New York, 1947.
91. F. A. Bovey and I. M. Kolthoff, *J. Am. Chem. Soc.*, **69**, 2143 (1947).
92. A. von Hippel and L. G. Wesson, *Ind. Eng. Chem.*, **38**, 1121–1129(1946).
93. H. Staudinger and L. Lautenschläger, *Ann.*, **488**, 1 (1931).
94. E. H. Farmer, *Rubber Chem. and Technol.*, **15**, 765 (1942).
95. C. E. Barnes, *J. Am. Chem. Soc.*, **67**, 217 (1945).
96. H. S. Taylor and A. A. Vernon, *J. Am. Chem. Soc.*, **53**, 2527 (1931).
97. H. Staudinger and H. W. Kohlschütter, *Ber.*, **64**, 2091 (1931).
98. H. Staudinger and A. Schwalbach, *Ann.*, **488**, 8 (1931).
99. G. V. Schulz and E. Husemann, *Z. physik. Chem.*, **B36**, 184 (1937).
100. J. L. Bolland and H. W. Melville, *Proceedings of Rubber Technology Conference*, p. 239, 1938, London.
101. H. Carothers, I. Williams, A. M. Collins, and J. E. Kirby, *J. Am. Chem. Soc.*, **53**, 4203 (1931).
102. F. K. Schoenfeld, U. S. Patent 2,168,808.
103. R. G. R. Bacon, *Trans. Faraday Soc.*, **42**, 144 (1946).
104. S. G. Foord, *J. Chem. Soc.* (London), **143**, 48 (1940).
105. R. P. Dinsmore, U. S. Patent 1,732,795.
106. M. Luther and C. Heuck, U. S. Patent 1,864,078.
107. C. C. Price and C. E. Adams, *J. Am. Chem. Soc.*, **67**, 1674 (1945).
108. I. M. Kolthoff and W. J. Dale, *J. Am. Chem. Soc.*, **67**, 1672 (1945).
109. C. V. King and O. F. Steinbach, *J. Am. Chem. Soc.*, **52**, 4779 (1930).
110. J. H. Baxendale, M. G. Evans, and J. K. Kilham, *Trans. Faraday Soc.*, **42**, 668 (1946).
111. I. M. Kolthoff and W. J. Dale, *J. Am. Chem. Soc.*, **69**, 441 (1947).
112. J. H. Baxendale, M. G. Evans, and J. K. Kilham, *J. Polymer Sci.*, **1**, 467 (1946).
113. H. Dostal, *Monatsh.*, **67**, 63 (1935).
114. H. Dostal, *Monatsh.*, **67**, 63–79 (1935).
115. H. Dostal, *Monatsh.*, **70**, 409 (1937).
116. G. Salomon, *Trans. Faraday Soc.*, **32**, 153 (1936).
117. G. V. Schulz and A. Dinglinger, *Z. physik. Chem.*, **B43**, 47 (1939).
118. H. Suess, H. Pilch, and H. Rudorfer, *Z. physik. Chem.*, **A179**, 361 (1937).
119. H. Suess and A. Springer, *Z. physik. Chem.*, **A181**, 81 (1937).
120. I. M. Kolthoff and F. A. Bovey, *J. Am. Chem. Soc.*, **70**, 792 (1948).
121. J. W. Breitenbach and L. Breitenbach, *Ber.*, **B75**, 505 (1942).
122. J. W. Breitenbach and A. J. Renner, *Can. J. Research*, **28**, 507 (1950).

123. H. Staudinger and G. V. Schulz, *Ber.*, **68**, 2320 (1935).
124. R. B. Carlin and N. E. Shakespeare, *J. Am. Chem. Soc.*, **68**, 876 (1946).
125. R. Spencer and L. R. Drake, *Physical Methods of Organic Chemistry*, edited by A. Weissberger, Vol. I, p. 146, Interscience Publishers, New York, 1945.
126. M. S. Kharasch, E. M. May, and F. R. Mayo, *J. Org. Chem.*, **3**, 175 (1938).
127. M. S. Kharasch, A. T. Read, and F. R. Mayo, *J. Soc. Chem. Ind.*, **57**, 752 (1938).
128. L. B. Morgan, *Trans. Faraday Soc.*, **42**, 169 (1946).
129. R. G. R. Bacon, *Trans. Faraday Soc.*, **42**, 140 (1946).
130. J. H. Baxendale, M. G. Evans, and G. S. Park, *Trans. Faraday Soc.*, **42**, 155 (1946).
131. F. Haber and J. Weiss, *Proc. Roy. Soc.* (London), **A147**, 332 (1934).
132. H. Wollthan and W. Becker, U. S. Patent 2,281,613.
133. K. Meisenburg *et al.*, U. S. Patent 2,321,693.
134. M. A. Youker, U. S. Patent 2,365,035.
135. P. J. Flory, *J. Am. Chem. Soc.*, **59**, 241 (1937).
136. H. W. Melville, *Trans. Faraday Soc.*, **32**, 258 (1936).
137. F. R. Mayo and C. Walling, *Chem. Revs.*, **27**, 351 (1940).
138. H. R. Snyder, J. M. Stewart, R. E. Allen, and R. J. Dearborn, *J. Am. Chem. Soc.*, **68**, 1422 (1946).
139. F. T. Wall, F. W. Banes, and G. D. Sands, *J. Am. Chem. Soc.*, **68**, 1429 (1946).
140. W. W. Hunter and R. V. Yohe, *J. Am. Chem. Soc.*, **55**, 1248 (1933).
141. R. A. Harman and H. Eyring, *J. Chem. Physics*, **10**, 557 (1942).
142. British Patent 401,297.
143. British Patent 432,196.
144. A. B. Hersberger, J. C. Reid, and R. G. Heiligman, *Ind. Eng. Chem.*, **37**, 1073 (1945).
145. F. C. Whitmore, *Ind. Eng. Chem.*, **26**, 94 (1934).
146. C. C. Price and M. Meister, *J. Am. Chem. Soc.*, **61**, 1595 (1939).
147. R. G. Beaman, *J. Am. Chem. Soc.*, **70**, 3115 (1948).
148. W. E. Hanford and R. M. Joyce, *J. Polymer Sci.*, **3**, 167 (1948).
149. P. Schlack, U. S. Patent 2,241,231 (May 6, 1941).
150. H. Leuchs, *Ber.*, **39**, 857 (1906).
151. W. Mund and W. Koch, *Bull. soc. chim. Belg.*, **34**, 119, 241 (1925).
152. S. C. Lind and D. C. Bardwell, *Science*, **62**, 422 (1925).
153. W. M. Garrison, *J. Chem. Physics*, **15**, 78 (1947).
154. P. Kusch, A. Hustrulid, and J. T. Tate, *Phys. Rev.*, **52** (2nd Ser.), 840 (1937).
155. F. C. Whitmore, *Chem. and Eng. News*, **26**, 668 (1948).

CHAPTER 9

Reaction Loci
in Polymerization Systems

Emulsion polymerizations are distinguished from mass or bead polymerizations by a number of outstanding characteristics. Two of the more important characteristics are:

1. Polymerizations in emulsions proceed at a faster rate than in homogeneous systems, and the molecular weights of the polymers are higher than in most other systems.
2. Many monomers which do not copolymerize in homogeneous systems copolymerize in emulsion systems.

The specific behavior of emulsion polymerization systems raises two important questions. First, what is the locus of the initiation of polymerization, and does it occur (1) in the dispersed or monomer phase, (2) in the dispersing or aqueous phase, or (3) at the interface of the two phases? Second, what is the manner of the propagation of the polymerization once initiation has taken place?

To help in understanding emulsion polymerizations, a number of other polymerizations will be considered first. These other systems, which are more simple than emulsion systems, can then be compared with emulsion systems, and the common features recognized.

MASS OR BULK POLYMERIZATIONS

Mass polymerizations represent the simplest polymerization system. All of them are characterized by an initial homogeneity and consist of monomer with or without added catalyst or other modifying agents. Once polymerization has been initiated, mass polymerizations may exhibit different modes of behavior; therefore, a number of modified systems are possible in mass polymerization. The variants of mass polymerization are considered in systems A and B.

System A. Polymer Is Soluble in Monomer

In a system in which the polymer is soluble in monomer at all stages of conversion, there is no question that initiation of polymerization occurs in the monomer or oil phase, since the system initially contains no other substances but monomer and catalyst, if the catalyst is used. Whenever catalysts are used, they are soluble in monomer. In a thermal polymerization, however, no added organic catalyst is present. As polymerization progresses, the viscosity noticeably increases, and the propagation occurs in a medium of associated polymers dissolved in, or swollen by, monomer until the monomer is consumed. Termination of polymer chains occurs by kinetic chain transfer or by collision and combination of two active growing chains. The energy of activation, as calculated from temperature dependence data, is usually 20,000 to 25,000 calories per mole, as, for example, 23,000 calories for styrene polymerization as calculated from the initial rates of polymerization.

System B. Polymer Is Insoluble in Monomer

In this system, initiation obviously occurs in the monomer or oil phase. Precipitation of polymer occurs without a noticeable increase in true solution viscosity. Vinylidene chloride and acrylonitrile are examples of such monomers which are not solvents for their corresponding polymers. Such systems have an activation energy corresponding to a mass polymerization, with initial rates proportional to the square root of the catalyst concentration. The molecular weight decreases with an increase in temperature or with an increase in catalyst concentration.

Furthermore, the molecular weight of the precipitated polymer far exceeds the solubility limit of the monomer for the polymer. For example, acrylonitrile monomer will not dissolve polyacrylonitrile of molecular weight of 10,000, yet molecular weights up to 1,000,000 may be obtained by the mass polymerization of acrylonitrile.[1] In view of these facts, it must be assumed that propagation of polymerization occurs in swollen precipitated polymer particles. Otherwise, if the molecular weight of the polymer obtained was determined by the maximum molecular weight of the polymer that was soluble in the monomer before the polymer was precipitated, then only the rate, but not the molecular weight, would be affected by an increase or decrease in catalyst concentration.

SOLUTION POLYMERIZATIONS

Solution polymerizations are substantially mass polymerizations in which the monomer is soluble to varying degrees in an added solvent. This added solvent may be a complete solvent, a partial solvent, or a non-solvent for the polymer. The various types of solution polymerizations are considered in systems C, D, and E, respectively.

System C. Monomer and Polymer Are Both Soluble in Solvent

Such a system may be represented by the polymerization of styrene in benzene, toluene, or ethylbenzene. Since all molecular species of monomer and polymer are soluble in the solvent, initiation and propagation occur in the organic or oil phase. In accordance with the mass action law, the rate of polymerization is lower than mass polymerizations, and the more dilute the solution, the lower the rate and the molecular weight of the polymer. The presence of non-polymerizable solvent means that kinetic chain transfer can occur more frequently as dilution is increased. If the solvent is active as a telomer or retarder, etc., it combines with growing chains. In this system, monomer- and solvent-soluble catalysts are used.

System D. Monomer Is Soluble in Solvent, but Polymer Is Only Partially Soluble, or Insoluble, in Solvent

Such a system may be represented by the polymerization of styrene in methanol. This system is substantially the same as system C in that initiation occurs in the oil phase. As polymerization progresses, there is some increase in viscosity with conversion, then precipitation occurs. The precipitated polymers are swollen by diffused and absorbed monomer, and further propagation and termination occur in these swollen particles or gels. As in system C, the presence of a non-polymerizable solvent increases the probability of kinetic chain transfer; and if the solvent is active as a telomer, it combines with the growing chain. In substance, this system corresponds to system B, in which the polymer is insoluble in monomer, but further complicated by the addition of solvent molecules.

The polymerization of vinyl chloride in benzene, or of acrylonitrile in chloroform or carbon tetrachloride, are further examples of such systems. In these systems the limit of solubility of the polymer in the diluent is very low; in fact, polyacrylonitrile of molecular weights of 5000 to 6000 is insoluble in chloroform. Yet when acrylonitrile is polymerized in a chloroform medium, polyacrylonitrile of a molecular weight in excess of 50,000, which contains attached (telomerized) chlorine atoms, is obtained.[1] These results can be explained only on the ground that both monomeric acrylonitrile and chloroform were either absorbed by or diffused into the low molecular weight swollen polymer chain during the growth reaction. Jenckel and Süss[2] polymerized styrene in benzene, in which polystyrene is soluble, and in ethyl alcohol, in which polystyrene is insoluble, and obtained the following average molecular weights:

Polymerization Temperature, °C	Polymerized in Benzene, Molecular Weight	Polymerized in Ethyl Alcohol, Molecular Weight
140	53,800	51,600
170	30,500	28,900
200	21,800	23,200

These results indicate that the molecular weight of the polymer is not lowered in a solution polymerization in which polymer precipitates, providing the diluent solvent does not possess high telomerizing activity.

System E. Monomer Is Partially Soluble in Solvent, and Polymer Is Insoluble in Solvent

Since most organic solvents are good solvents for monomers, the conditions of this system are best exemplified by the choice of water as the solvent. Some monomers, such as styrene, are only slightly soluble in water, whereas vinyl acetate and acrylonitrile are relatively soluble, that is, up to 5 to 7 per cent at room temperature. If an aqueous, saturated solution of acrylonitrile is polymerized in the presence of a water-soluble catalyst, the system behaves initially as a solution polymerization, that is, the molecular weight and the rate are lower than in a mass polymerization. The polymer will precipitate, since polyacrylonitrile, even of low molecular weight, is insoluble in water, monomeric acrylonitrile, or mixtures of the two. Yet, in the system described, molecular weights in excess of 50,000 are readily obtained.

As in system B, this may be considered as evidence that, though initiation occurred in the aqueous phase, that is, in solubilized monomer, propagation occurred in the polymer particle itself by diffusion of monomer, and termination occurred in the normal manner of collision of two chains, or by kinetic transfer, etc.

In contrast to acrylonitrile, styrene is practically insoluble in water, having a solubility of about 0.02 per cent at room temperature. If a saturated, aqueous solution of styrene is polymerized at room temperature, in the presence of a water-soluble catalyst, the rate and molecular weight correspond to a solution polymerization, and are lower than the values obtained in a mass polymerization. As polymerization progresses, the solution becomes opaque, even though the concentration of polymer is small. As in the case of the acrylonitrile polymerization, the initiation occurs in the aqueous phase, but propagation occurs in the polymer particles themselves.

In the five systems already considered, systems A to E, inclusive, the conditions of the systems were such that they were molecularly homogeneous at the beginning of the reaction. If excess acrylonitrile or styrene were present in system E, a heterogeneous system would have been present, consisting of an oil or organic phase, and a dissolved or aqueous phase, and an interface between the oil and water phase. These more complex systems will be considered under dispersion and emulsion polymerizations.

In Figure 1 the rates of polymerization of styrene as (1) a mass polymerization in which the polymer is soluble in its own monomer and

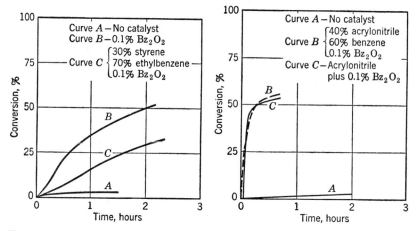

FIGURE 1. Polymerization of styrene at 100 C.

FIGURE 2. Polymerization of acrylonitrile.

(2) a solution polymerization in which both monomer and polymer are soluble in the solvent are compared to each other and contrasted to the rate of an uncatalyzed polymerization. The rates are in the expected order. The uncatalyzed reaction has the lowest rate, and the undiluted catalyzed reaction has the highest rate of polymerization, whereas the diluted catalyzed reaction has a rate that lies between these extremes.

Rate data are shown in Figure 2 for the polymerization of acrylonitrile. Curve A is for the uncatalyzed polymerization. Curves B and C are for polymerizations catalyzed by 0.1 per cent benzoyl peroxide.

Curve C represents the rate for the undiluted monomer in a system in which polymer precipitates from the monomer. Curve B represents the rate for the monomer diluted by benzene solvent, and in this sytem the polymer is insoluble in the diluent as well as the monomer. It should be noted that the conversion rates are almost identical in spite of the fact that on a concentration basis the rate for the undiluted monomer should be higher. This particular aspect will be considered later.

DISPERSED SYSTEMS

There are two types of dispersion polymerization systems, namely, suspension polymerizations and emulsion polymerizations.

System F. Suspension or Pearl Polymerizations

In a suspension polymerization, the monomer is mechanically dispersed in a liquid which is a non-solvent for the monomer or for all the polymer species derived from it. Styrene and its polymers are sufficiently insoluble in water to fulfill the requirements of a dispersion process. Where substantially no monomer exists in the aqueous phase, monomer-soluble catalysts would be expected to be more effective than water-soluble catalysts, and such has been found to be the case. For example, benzoyl peroxide was found to be five to nine times more effective in the initial rate of polymer formation than sodium persulfate or perborate, and about four times more effective than tertiary-butyl hydroperoxide, which is partly monomer soluble as well as water soluble.

The organic phase in a suspension polymerization exists in discrete macroscopic beads before, during, and after polymerization with a marked organic (oil) phase and interface. Although we may be led to believe that in such a system the initiation of polymerization might readily occur at the interface, the possibility remains of a certain amount of organic phase dissolving in the aqueous phase, initiating the polymerization in the aqueous phase, and then propagating the reaction in the organic phase. If the initiation occurs in the monomer or oil phase, and if the propagation is continued and terminated in the dispersed phase, no differences in rate should be expected between a "pearl" and a mass polymerization.

In fact, the pearl polymerization of styrene [3] appears to be essentially an effectively cooled mass polymerization which has been broken up into small globules by dispersion in water. Kinetic data have been published for styrene pearl polymerization [4] which shows that the initiation, propagation, and termination occur inside the pearl in the same way as in the mass polymerization.

As mentioned above, the ideal suspension polymerization utilizes monomers that are substantially insoluble in the dispersion medium, which usually is water. As is well known, no monomer is absolutely insoluble in water. For those monomers that are more water-soluble than styrene, the difference in initial rate of polymerization between the monomer-soluble catalyst and the water-soluble catalyst should not be as great as the difference in styrene. Conversely, if a monomer more insoluble than styrene is used, then a greater difference should be noted between the monomer-soluble and water-soluble catalysts in the initial rates of conversion. The data of Hohenstein and Mark,[4] summarized in Table 1, which gives monomers in order of increasing solubility in water, justify this conclusion.

TABLE 1

Monomer	Catalyst	% Catalyst Based on Monomer	Initial Rate of Polymer Formation	Ratio
Dichlorostyrene	Benzoyl peroxide	1	5.5	11:1
Dichlorostyrene	Potassium persulfate	1	0.5	
Styrene	Benzoyl peroxide	2	3.5	8.75:1
Styrene	Potassium persulfate	2	0.4	
Methyl methacrylate	Benzoyl peroxide	0.3	0.9	4.5:1
Methyl methacrylate	Sodium perborate	0.3	0.2	

The data in Table 1 show that as the monomer becomes more soluble in water, the ratio of the rates between monomer-soluble catalyst and water-soluble catalyst decreases. As solubility of the monomer in water increases, more polymerization occurs in the aqueous solution phase, a solution polymerization process becomes superimposed on the suspension process, and the amount of polymer formed in each phase depends on the solubility of the monomer in water, as well as on the type and distribution of the catalyst. Polymers prepared under such conditions sometimes have two distribution curve peaks, where the small peak corresponds to the lower molecular weight obtained by the portion that polymerizes in the aqueous solution.

No generalization can be made as to the behavior of a particular monomer dispersed in water with either a water-soluble or a monomer-soluble catalyst when the monomer shows considerable solubility in water and is in sufficient excess to form a separate oil phase. The polymerization of acrylonitrile in excess of its solubility in water represents such a system. Fryling and Harrington [5] polymerized acrylonitrile in a water system in the absence of an emulsifying agent and in the presence of potassium persulfate as a water-soluble catalyst. The results of their work indicate that polymerization may start in the aqueous phase. In fact, in an undispersed acrylonitrile-water-potassium persulfate layer system, they demonstrated visually that polymerization occurs exclusively in the aqueous phase. These investigators added purified acrylonitrile to a 6 per cent aqueous solution of potassium persulfate and allowed the mixture to stand unagitated at room temperature. The greater portion of the acrylonitrile separated as a well-defined upper layer, while a small portion of the monomer dissolved in the aqueous solution of catalyst. After the acrylonitrile stood undisturbed for a short time, the aqueous phase became cloudy and finally opaque, and polyacrylonitrile formed. No evidence of polymerization in the upper or monomer layer was detectable since it also remained clear. If polymerization occurred, the monomer phase should have become cloudy, since polyacrylonitrile is insoluble in acrylonitrile. Likewise, these results exclude the possible initiation of the polymerization at the interface of the two phases, since the water layer remained clear and transparent for about 5 millimeters below the interface, as though the acrylonitrile were diffusing into the aqueous phase to replenish the monomer removed by polymerization, and the monomer had insufficient time to undergo polymerization while diffusing through the 5-millimeter layer. It was also observed that if the partially polymerized system is partially stirred, the polyacrylonitrile is preferentially wetted by the acrylonitrile and passes immediately into the upper layer. Thus, if a system of monomer and water was submitted to continuous agitation while polymerization was occurring, the appearance of polymer in the dispersed monomer might lead erroneously to the conclusion that polymerization had occurred either in the acrylonitrile or at the interface of the phases.

In the presence of the oil phase, that is, excess monomer, the molecular weight of the polymer obtained is higher than in the corresponding solution polymerization, since in such a heterogeneous polymerization, the monomer, which diffuses from the oil phase into the aqueous phase, is also captured by the polymer molecules and propagation is continued. Similar results are obtained in the absence of a liquid interface when the acrylonitrile monomer in one flask is connected by a vapor tube to another flask containing water and a water-soluble catalyst, thereby indicating vapor diffusion of monomer from the oil phase to the aqueous phase. In contrast to these results, if in a layer polymerization, monomer-soluble (water-insoluble) catalyst is used, the main course of the polymer is that of a mass polymerization, and a minor portion is that of solution or "diffusion polymerization."

These conclusions may be verified by the following experiment, using layer polymerization. If a small amount of monomer-soluble (water-insoluble) inhibitor is added to the acrylonitrile, the course of polymerization is not changed if the catalyst is water-soluble, but is inhibited if the catalyst is monomer-soluble.

These considerations show that the complications of pearl or suspension polymerizations are minimized by the use of a medium in which the monomer is substantially insoluble, and by the use of a monomer-soluble catalyst. Obviously, additives in conjunction with water, such as acetone, ethyl alcohol, or the like, which solubilize monomers complicate the true mechanism of dispersion polymerization by the introduction of a simultaneous solution polymerization or other processes.

System G.   Emulsion Polymerizations

A simple emulsion system contains monomer, water, an emulsifying agent, and a catalyst.

Catalyzed emulsion polymerizations appear to have been disclosed first in the publications of Dinsmore [6] and Luther and Heuck.[7] Their patents disclose the simultaneous use of water- and monomer-soluble catalysts and soap or related substances, such as sodium or potassium oleate and sodium butylnaphthalene sulfonates.

A number of substances may be used as emulsifying agents, but since considerable data have been published on soap in emulsion polymerization systems, the terms *emulsifying agent* and *soap* are used interchangeably.

When a small amount of soap, RCOONa, is dissolved in water, dissolved soap, RCOONa, and ionized dissolved soap, $RCOO^-$ and Na^+, exist in the solution.

If the soap solution is not too dilute, a number of investigators [8-11] have assumed the existence of spherical micelles, and McBain [12] has proposed the existence of large lamellar micelles. Their existence was verified for concentrated soap solutions by X-ray measurements.[13-23]

In a number of papers, Harkins and his co-workers [24-27] offer evidence for single double layers of soap, which consist of 20 to 300 soap molecules, and these double layers of soap are referred to by Harkins and Debye [28] as *small micelles*.

The X-ray band for this single double layer of soap, called the d_2 band, can be measured even at soap concentrations of 2.5 per cent. When the soap concentration is increased, an X-ray band, d_1, becomes evident and measures the distances between micelles, each of which consists of single double layers of soap.

In dilute solution, Brownian movement keeps the micelles of single-double layers of soap in oscillation and rotation, thereby preventing them from lining up, and the d_1 band does not appear until the concentration of soap lies between 7 and 10 per cent, whereupon the lamellar micelles become evident, even though the d_2 line is evident at 2 per cent concentration of soap. When the concentration of soap lies between 7 and 10 per cent, the rotation of the single-double layers of soap is sufficiently restricted, so that the d_1 band is sufficiently intense to be measured.

When a laurate soap micelle (25 per cent soap in water) was saturated [29] with styrene, d_1 increased from 58.5 to 74.4 Å. When a single double layer is saturated with an oil, d_2 increases about 7 to 12 Å, depending on the solubility of the oil, as for example Δd_2 is 10 Å for heptane, and 12 to 13 Å for benzene. The original value of d_2 is essentially equal to double the length of the molecule of the particular soap, for example: 36.6 Å for potassium caprylate, 49.6 Å for potassium myristate.

The solubility of the oil (that is, styrene, benzene, etc.) in the soap solution, as measured by the addition of an oil to a soap solution, remains constant until the critical concentration is reached. This is indicated in Figure 3,[30] which correlates turbidity with the amount of

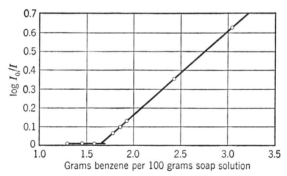

FIGURE 3. Solubility of an oil in a soap solution. (Reprinted by permission from the authors and the *Journal of the American Chemical Society*.)

benzene added to 100 grams of a 6.89 per cent potassium laurate solution. Harkins [29] showed that, according to Stearns, after the critical concentration is reached, the turbidity increases because of light scattering by droplets of benzene.

When a system of oil and aqueous soap solution is stirred or otherwise agitated, an oil-in-water emulsion is usually obtained, with oil droplets dispersed in the system. The droplets are not of uniform size but show a distribution curve as indicated in Figure 4 [30] for a benzene emulsion in 0.1 sodium oleate aqueous solutions.[31-32] It was shown that the position of the peak of this distribution is dependent on the concentration and nature of the soap, the concentration, the temperature and the viscosity of the oil, as well as on the type of agitation.

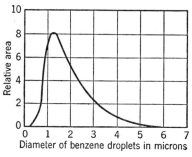

FIGURE 4.   Particle size distribution of a benzene emulsion. (Reprinted by permission from the authors and the *Journal of the American Chemical Society*.)

Since in an emulsion system there is insufficient soap to solubilize all the oil or monomer, each emulsion droplet is surrounded by a liquid, moderately packed monomolecular layer of soap molecules oriented with their hydrocarbon chains toward the monomeric oil and their ionic-polar groups toward the water, as in Figure 5.   The symbol, R——O, represents soap molecules wherein R is the hydrocarbon terminal, and the circle represents the water-soluble or heteropolar group of the soap.   The letter M or the letter S represents monomer.

In the absence of a catalyst, the material ingredients of a simple emulsion polymerization system consist of water, a monomer, and soap.

The soap therein is insufficient to solubilize all the oil, thereby resulting in a system which on agitation produces a dispersion system comprising essentially parts of the following:

1. *Monomer droplets surrounded by a monomolecular layer of soap.*   Most of the monomer exists in this form.[24, 33]

2. *Soap micelles swollen by monomer, considered to be micellar solubilized monomer.* A small portion of the monomer exists in this form.   Even though the

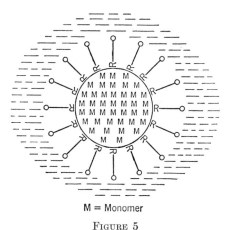

M = Monomer

FIGURE 5

exact shape and size of the soap micelles are at the present time not known, it is qualitatively irrelevant whether the micelles are spherical or lamellar or not too far from spherical, or whether the micelles consist of single or multiple double layers of soap.[24, 25, 33-35] The ionic polar groups present in the soap have a number of effects on the system. Because of the slight repulsion between these ionic-polar groups, the average area occupied per molecule of soap is greater than that of a liquid condensed film.[36] Furthermore, it has been shown [37] that the lowering, by electrolytes, of the critical concentration of the micellar formation of soaps is related only to the concentration of the ion of the added salt which bears a charge opposite to that of the colloidal aggregate. The nature of the other ion is without effect.

3. *Monomer dissolved in true solution in the water phase.* The amount of monomer dissolved by the water is dependent on the nature of the monomer itself.

Since such systems polymerize slowly, a catalyst and, often, other substances which modify the reaction are used. In such heterogeneous systems, it is obvious that initiation of the polymerization reaction could occur in the emulsion droplets, or in the micellar solubilized monomer, or in the dissolved monomer, or at the interface of the emulsion droplets. Once initiation has taken place, propagation can continue by a number of means.

A polymerization system in which sufficient soap is present to solubilize all the monomer cannot be considered either as a true emulsion polymerization system or as a true solution polymerization system. It may be considered a modified solution polymerization in which the insoluble monomer has been solubilized by means of an emulsifying agent, and therefore differs in character and quality from a true solution. More accurately, such a polymerization is a *micellar polymerization.* It must be stressed that even though reference is made to the oil in a micelle as solubilized oil, the oil still exists in the hydrocarbon portions of the micelles as an oil, and should be considered (Figure 22, p. 386) the micellar-oil phase to distinguish it both from the monomer-droplet-oil phase and the oil truly dissolved in the aqueous phase.

Before a possible mechanism is considered for emulsion polymerizations, a number of experimental data and historical facts are considered.

Staudinger believed that in emulsion polymerization many activated centers are formed on the surface of the dispersed monomer particles, and that these active centers are very reactive nuclei for promoting the reaction, and thereby accelerating the polymerization rate.[38] Fikentscher [39] concluded that the polymerization occurs in the aqueous phase. As Harkins [40] pointed out, the aqueous phase was not sufficiently identified to allow the mechanism to be defined specifically. Obviously, some type of reaction was occurring in the aqueous phase, as can be shown by the following experiment.[41]

Monomeric methyl methacrylate was poured over a layer of soap solution containing a catalyst, and the *layer system* allowed to stand at room temperature without agitation. In a short time the water became cloudy, owing to the formation of emulsified polymer, and simultaneously the upper layer of monomer decreased and finally vanished. No polymer formation occurred in the *oil layer* or oil phase. This experiment leaves unanswered the questions whether or not initiation takes place at the interface, and what is the mechanism of propagation. It may be considered that initiation could start in the dispersed phase, migrate to the interface, and propagate there, or that initiation may start at the interface and propagate in the dispersed phase. Gee and his co-workers answered this question [42] by eliminating the interface through the study of the polymerization of butadiene vapor above a solution of hydrogen peroxide in water containing no soap. The initial rate of conversion to polymer was found to be proportional to the concentration of peroxide and to the pressure of the monomer in the gas phase, that is, to the solubility of the monomer. If monomers which are more water-soluble than butadiene are used, the initial appearance of polymer occurs sooner and the rate of polymerization is increased, as shown by either a *layer polymerization* or a vapor diffusion polymerization with vinyl acetate or acrylonitrile as the monomer.

Furthermore, it can be shown that, in a layer polymerization, the presence of soap in the water phase accelerates the rate of polymerization in the aqueous phase.[43] Hohenstein and Mark [44] recently confirmed this in a similar layer system for styrene and found that the rate is roughly proportional to the solubility of monomer in water. If a small amount of inhibitor is added to the monomer, the course of polymerization in the aqueous phase is not altered; and if the same amount of inhibitor is added to the aqueous phase, the appearance of the polymer is retarded. Fryling and Harrington [43] further reported that emulsion copolymerizations of the type used in the preparation of synthetic rubbers (copolymers of butadiene and styrene, or of butadiene and acrylonitrile) will occur in the absence of a liquid interface, as when a mixture of monomers is separated by a vapor phase from the aqueous phase containing emulsifying agent. The monomers evaporate, pass into the aqueous phase, and copolymerize without any discernible evidence of a liquid monomer phase in contact with the solution phase.

Water-soluble catalysts such as potassium persulfate, hydrogen peroxide, and sodium perborate are especially effective initiators in emulsion polymerization. When monomer-soluble catalysts are used, the rate is greatly reduced.

The velocity observed in a number of soap solubilized polymerizations using styrene,[24, 43, 45-47] butadiene, and comonomers with butadiene showed that, at low concentration of soap, the velocity is almost linearly proportional to the concentration of the emulsifying agent. This behavior would indicate that initiation occurs in the aqueous phase. It has been observed that the more useful polymerization emulsifiers are found among those that exhibit considerable solubilization of the monomers.

In many experiments with emulsion polymerization systems, stable emulsification of the organic phase is not obtained until after polymerization has started.

An increase in the concentration of soap causes a decrease in the induction period. The induction period is a measure of the time required for reactive nuclei to react with and exhaust inhibiting substances in the system; the rate of inhibitor consumption is proportional to the reciprocal of the time of induction. By plotting the logarithm of the rate of inhibitor consumption, $1/t$, against the reciprocal of the absolute temperature, $1/T$, the activation energy can be calculated for a system of monomer and water, containing water-soluble inhibitor, and of monomer and water, containing both water-soluble inhibitor and soap. The data [48] of Hohenstein and Mark are summarized in Figure 6.

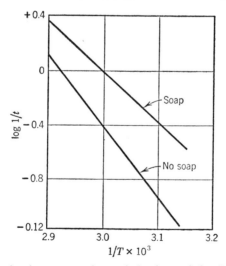

FIGURE 6. Effect of soap concentration on induction period. (From W. P. Hohenstein and H. Mark, "Polymerization of Olefins and Diolefins in Suspension and Emulsion II," *J. Polym. Sci.*, **1**, 552 [1946]. Interscience Publishers, Inc.)

The energy of activation for initiation for the system containing no soap was calculated to be about 25,000 calories per mole, which is of the same order of magnitude as found for the mass, solution, or suspension polymerization of styrene. In contrast, the energy of activation for the system containing soap is about 17,000 or approximately 8000 calories less. The effect of soap in the system is also illustrated by the collision constant, A, which for the soapless system is about 1.2×10^{16}, and for the emulsion system, is about 1.1×10^{11}. Values of similar magnitude have been reported previously by Vinograd and others.[49] Similarly, if

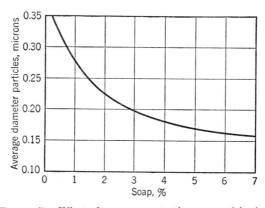

FIGURE 7. Effect of soap concentration on particle size.

the inhibitor is oil- or monomer-soluble, an increase in the soap concentration likewise decreases the period of inhibition. These observations indicate that solubilization increases the rate of nuclei formation and, therefore, the rate of polymerization, and that a system which increases the rate of nuclei formation will also shorten the induction period. Since soap also solubilizes monomer-soluble inhibitors, their rate of consumption is increased in the presence of soap.

As styrene is dispersed in soap solutions, the average diameter of the dispersed particle decreases as soap concentration increases [32] (Figure 7), and this average particle size is approximately the same whether a water-soluble or a monomer-soluble catalyst is present.[50] Turbidity and transmission measurements give the same results. The observations made when systems containing a progressively increasing amount of soap were subjected to both water-soluble catalysts and oil-soluble catalysts may be summarized as follows.

The rate of polymerization for both systems increased with an increasing amount of soap and the ratio of rate of polymerization with the water-soluble catalyst (cat_w) to the rate for the monomer-soluble catalyst (cat_m) also increased,[50] as in Figure 8. At zero concentration of soap, however, little or no polymerization occurred with the water-soluble catalyst, whereas the oil-soluble catalyst gave a rate of polymer formation corresponding to a mass or suspension polymerization. These results indicate that with an increase in the amount of soap, a suspension polymerization system containing monomer-soluble catalyst becomes progressively similar, in increments, to an emulsion polymerization system, but never completely so, even at 6 per cent soap, at which point it exhibits a fraction of the rate of a system using a water-soluble catalyst. With a water-soluble catalyst and a water-insoluble

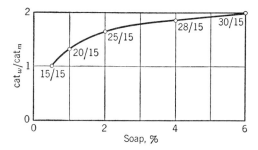

FIGURE 8.   Effect of soap on rate ratios.

monomer, no polymerization occurs unless at least part of the oil or the monomer is solubilized by the addition of soap. Since the rate increases with soap addition, there must be a maximum rate due to maximum solubilization, that is, a concentration of soap sufficient to locate all the monomer in single-double layer micelles or multilayer (lamellar) micelles. Thus Harkins and others [24, 25] have shown that when 0.75 gram of styrene was polymerized in 100 cubic centimeters of 6 per cent potassium laurate solution with aqueous catalyst, the polymerization was extremely rapid and the opacity of the solution did not increase as the polymerization progressed, the latter fact being explained by the small size of the polymer molecules formed. In such systems, the molecular weights are low, corresponding to the amount of the monomer contained within the micelle, and these polymerizations may be called *micellar polymerizations*.

An emulsion system, as previously defined, certainly does not conform to a micellar polymerization, but is obviously a system intermediate between a micellar polymerization and a suspension polymerization, that is, the soap must be insufficient to solubilize all the monomer but sufficient to solubilize part of the monomer and to disperse the remainder of the monomer. At a constant formulation of monomer, water, and soap, emulsion polymers are more readily prepared with water-soluble catalyst than with oil-soluble catalyst. At low concentration of soap, such as 1 or 2 per cent on the basis of the monomer, eight to ten times more beads or precipitate are formed with monomer-soluble catalyst than with water-soluble catalyst. As the soap is increased, not only does bead or precipitate formation decrease, but the ratio of the weight of solid polymer for the monomer-soluble catalyst (cat_m) to the weight of

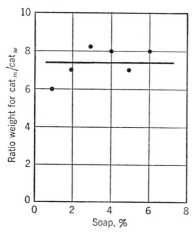

that for the water-soluble catalyst (cat_w) remains approximately constant,[50] as in Figure 9.

As the soap is increased, the deviation from the suspension polymerization system becomes greater, since particle size becomes smaller. It is possible, by suspension polymerization systems, to prepare beads having a diameter of 10 microns (0.01 millimeters). Mostly, however, the bead diameters range between 0.1 and 10 millimeters, whereas emulsified styrene particles have an average radius of 0.275 micron with 1 per cent of soap and 0.16 micron with 6 per cent of soap. The peak

FIGURE 9. Effect of soap on amount of precipitate.

of the diameters of polystyrene particles, polymerized in emulsion, was found at 1850 Å in a distribution ranging between 1000 and 4000 Å.

It becomes obvious that the particular system itself determines whether a suspension or the emulsion mechanism will dominate a process. If the same polymerization system can be made to function simultaneously, both as a bead- and as an emulsion-polymerization system, it must be concluded that the conditions for both systems are present. This may be readily verified by using a dual catalyst system, a water-soluble and a monomer-soluble catalyst, simultaneously with a monomer dispersed in a soap solution. Then both bead polymers and emulsion polymers are obtained by a dual-phase polymerization,[1] and the system is dominated by the faster reaction, namely, the reaction initiated in the aqueous phase. If, when the monomer-soluble catalyst is eliminated from such a system, bead polymers substantially disappear from the system, a mechanism must be derived, not only for the initiation reaction but also for a propagation reaction, which will explain the disappearance of dispersed monomer droplets that originally were responsible for bead polymer formation.

In all emulsion systems, it has been observed that as polymerization proceeds,[70] and as the yield of polymer increases, the diameter of the polymer particle also increases and the surface tension rises rapidly, as shown in Figure 11.

At the initiation of an emulsion polymerization, the formation of polymers is slow because of an induction period, followed by a period of increased rate of polymer formation. During the second period the

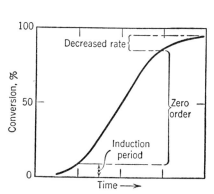

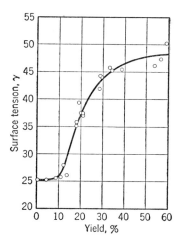

FIGURE 10. Emulsion polymerization time-conversion curve.

FIGURE 11. Variation of the surface tension with the yield (mutual formula at 50°) of isoprene-styrene copolymer in sodium oleate solutions. (Reprinted by permission from the authors and the *Journal of the American Chemical Society*.)

rate is virtually of zero order, and during it most of the polymerization occurs. Last, a decrease in the rate is observed as monomer concentration is decreased. The long-range zero order, as indicated in Figure 10, must be explained. It must also be observed that it is during the period of zero order that the greatest increase in surface tension occurs, as in Figure 11.[29]

THE MECHANISM OF EMULSION POLYMERIZATION

As a result of an excellent and rather extensive study with a number of co-workers, Harkins[29] published an article proposing a general theory on the mechanism of emulsion polymerization which appears to be in harmony with the experimental facts. It must be mentioned that in

1944 Trommsdorff [51] suggested a similar mechanism. It, however, was lacking in some of the details and refinements introduced by Harkins.

As indicated previously, Harkins and Debye consider a single double layer of soap a micelle that exists in dilute solutions of soap, in contrast to the lamellar micelles that exist in concentrated solutions. For purposes of clarity, reference will be made hereafter to the single double layers of soap as the Debye-Harkins micelles. The idealized picture of the Debye-Harkins micelle may be represented as in Figure 12. When

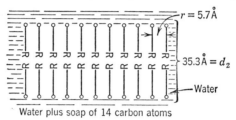

Water plus soap of 14 carbon atoms

FIGURE 12.   Single double layer micelle.

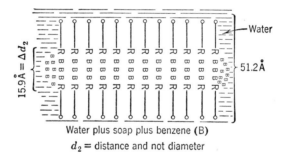

Water plus soap plus benzene (B)

d_2 = distance and not diameter

FIGURE 13.   Oil-swollen single double layer micelle.

saturated with styrene, it may be represented as a swollen micelle (see Figure 13).

In dilute solution these Debye-Harkins micelles are highly swollen, that is, are separated from each other by water, and therefore removed from neighbor micelles because of Brownian movement and rotation. In more concentrated solution, a group of two, three, or more Harkins micelles forms lamellar micelles considerably less swollen by water, which when saturated with styrene monomer may be represented as in Figure 14, based on data from Harkins. [30]

Before the introduction of the styrene, $d_1 = 58.5$ Å and $d_2 = 35.3$ Å with a value of Δd_1 of 15.9 and Δd_2 of 11.5 Å.

Since most emulsion polymerizations are performed in dilute solutions of soap or emulsifying agent—between 0.1 and 2.5 per cent—it is most probable that the polymerization involves the Debye-Harkins micelle rather than the lamellar micelle. In any case, the following polymerization mechanism is applicable to either micelle, provided not all the monomer is solubilized. The hydrocarbon layer between the single

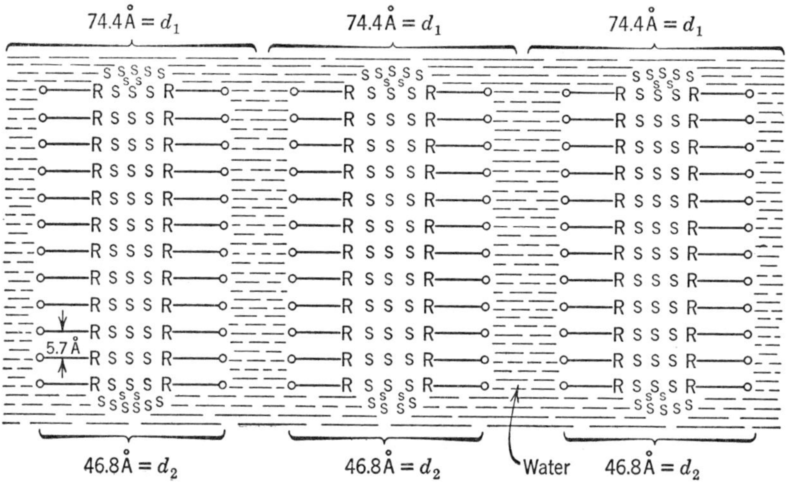

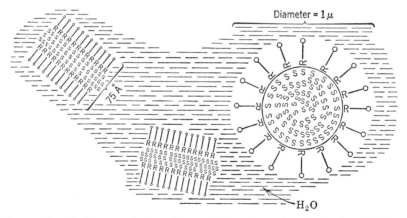

FIGURE 14. Oil- and water-swollen lamellar micelles.

layers of soap is known as solubilized oil, that is, the micellar oil phase, and according to Harkins will contain sufficient monomer to produce only low molecular weight polymers. Because of the high water-to-soap ratio, these micelles are highly swollen by water, and thereby permit the

FIGURE 15. Ideal representation of an emulsion system at start of polymerization.

free diffusion of water-soluble catalyst. In this manner, the formation of active nuclei takes place at the micelles.[45, 46] The system at this initial stage may be represented ideally as in Figure 15.

Initiation

The energy of activation of initiation of the emulsion polymerization of styrene was found [48] to be about 17,000 calories, or about 8000 calories lower than in mass or solution polymerization. It appears reasonable to assume that orientation and polarization of monomer molecules within soap micelles would cause changes in the value of the energy of activation and, therefore, in the rate of polymerization. This type of a change was noted [52] in the lowering of the energy of activation in the polymerization of an unsaturated fatty acid absorbed at an air-water interface as a monomolecular film. A large increase in the rate of reaction would be expected by a decrease of 8000 calories in the energy of activation if the collision factor (frequency of contact of monomers, catalysts, etc.) remained unchanged. Waring and others [53] have shown that the collision factor, A, is reduced in a water system that contains soap. Not only does this mean that in an emulsion system the accessibility of the catalyst to the monomer is reduced, but also that the accessibility of those particles responsible for chain termination is reduced, thereby allowing the molecular weight of the polymer to increase. However, the decrease in collision factor is amply compensated by the reduction of an energy barrier by 8000 calories. It was shown [54] that a reduction of 8000 calories would increase the rate of the reaction by a factor of 10^6 if the frequency factor remained unchanged, whereas the collision factor, A, was reduced by a factor of 6×10^4, when soap was removed from an emulsion system. This reduction of collision factor would also indicate a "fixing," that is, orientation or polarization of the monomer and polymer molecules by the soap, and even if every one of the reduced number of collisions was effective, an increase in rate would still be observed.

Thus it may be interpreted that the presence of an emulsion micelle allows the reaction to proceed faster by lowering the energy of activation by alignment or orientation of monomer molecules within the micelle. Furthermore, the fact that the energy of activation is lower locates the micelle as the principal locus of initiation. If the reaction is initiated by such water-soluble catalysts as hydrogen peroxide, the initiating radical, $HO\cdot$, will diffuse into the solubilized micellar oil to produce a polymer particle nucleus. A very small amount of monomer, beyond that solubilized in the micelle, is also dissolved in the "free" water. This water-dissolved monomer may react with catalyst radicals to be a minor locus of initiation. The initiating radical, after attachment to one monomer molecule, or to a very small number of monomer molecules, will diffuse into the micelle to form a polymer particle nucleus. The water-dissolved monomer is not the primary locus of initiation, as may be confirmed by the fact that, in the absence of micellar soap, as in a suspension polymerization system using a water-soluble catalyst, the energy of activation corresponds to the energy of activation of a mass polymerization. However, this locus is responsible for all particle nuclei in the complete absence of soap,[55] but becomes less important in the presence of soap, especially micellar soap, and becomes relatively unimportant as the amount of soap is increased.

With reference to the initiation reaction, therefore, the function of the soap (emulsifying agent) is to form micelles to orient and solubilize the monomer, thereby making the monomer more available to radicals originating in the water phase.

Propagation

Once the active loci have formed in the water-solubilized monomer micelles, the polymer can grow by the addition of the monomer molecules that exist in that specific micelle. It is obvious, however, that two systems are possible: one in which the soap is in excess, and another in which the monomer is in excess. Both systems will be considered. In these considerations we must bear in mind that a polymer chain, for example, polystyrene, is not fully extended in a water system. It is curled up into a closely packed random coil so that a polystyrene chain of about 250 D.P. in a fully extended state has a length of about 600 to 700 Å, while in a coiled state its length is about 50 Å and its diameter about 5 Å. We may visualize that a dispersed particle, having a radius of about 100 Å, can contain many coiled polymers of a relatively large degree of polymerization.

SYSTEM I. SOAP IN EXCESS—MICELLAR POLYMERIZATION

In a system that contains soap in excess, all the monomer is contained in micelles, and the active nuclei grow into polymers by exhaustion of monomer present in the micelles. If the assumption is made that such a micelle contains in the neighborhood of 200 to 1000 molecules of styrene, it would be expected that the D.P. of the polymer would be low, that the opacity of the solution would not increase as polymerization increases, and that the polymer would be solubilized in micelles or exist in very small dispersed particles in the aqueous phase by the adsorption of soap.

Harkins and others [24] have shown this to be true by polymerizing 0.75 gram of styrene in 100 cubic centimeters of 6 per cent potassium laurate solution. In contrast, it was shown that when styrene is polymerized in water without soap, an opaque solution is formed,[55] and the polymerization rate is 100 to 200 times slower than that of the soap emulsion experiment, and the molecular weights are low. Thus another function of the soap becomes evident, namely, to stabilize the polymer particles, thereby preventing coalescing and precipitation.

SYSTEM II.   MONOMER IN EXCESS—THE TRUE EMULSION SYSTEM

Obviously, if the growth of the polymer is to continue, monomer must be supplied to the active points of growth. This is accomplished by increasing the monomer-soap ratio. Eventually a restriction is reached on this increase in the rate of supply set by the amount of monomer that may be solubilized by the soap. Beyond this point, monomer droplets surrounded by a monolayer of soap are formed in the system. It must be stressed particularly that a monomer droplet has initially a volume of more than one thousand times, and very often more than a million times, that of the final polymer particle. During the polymerization the volume of the monomer droplet decreases by diffusion of monomer into the aqueous phase, whereby polymerization occurs outside the monomer droplet.[56] It can also be shown from thermodynamic considerations, as, for example, from the energy of activation and from other data,[56] that the monomer droplet likewise is not a primary locus of initiation in the presence of micellar soap. The monomer droplets, therefore, are reservoirs of monomer from which the growing particles in the micelle are fed. A mechanism of transport of monomer from the monomer droplet to the active micelle is required to explain the propagation reaction because the polymerization of the polymer particle nucleus can proceed only if the supply and absorption of monomer are sufficiently rapid to maintain the rate of monomer consumption. If the rate of supply were lower than that of monomer consumption, the molecular weight of the polymer as well as the rate of polymerization would be lowered. A monomer diffusion process from monomer droplet to the micelle is consistent with experimental facts. Debye in collaboration with Harkins has shown that the diffusion rate of monomers from monomer droplets surrounded by soap to growing polymer molecules is consistent with polymerization rates which have been observed, and that the diffusion of monomer from soap-surrounded monomer droplets is sufficiently rapid for the growing polymer chain.[24, 25] Thermodynamically, these conclusions are that the energy of activation of diffusion is lower than the energy of activation of propagation.

It has also been shown [47] (1) that the rate of diffusion of monomer from a dispersed monomer droplet increases with decreasing diameter of the droplet and (2) that, for identical droplet diameters, the diffusion rate increases with soap concentration as well as with temperature.

With respect to the propagation reaction, the soap serves as a means of producing the largest possible surface area in the form of stable monomer droplets, thereby insuring a high rate of diffusion of monomer into the aqueous phase. Experimentally, it has been shown [47] that diffusion is sufficient to maintain the rate of polymerization because long before the polymerization is complete, the monomer droplets, which act as reservoirs, disappear and diffuse into polymer particles. The propagation process may be visualized as a diffusion propagation whereby monomer from the monomer droplet diffuses into water and is captured by the micelle. The micelle, therefore, becomes not only the primary locus for the initiation but also the primary locus for the propagation by capturing monomer from the water phase which has diffused from the monomer droplet. That the micelle is the primary locus of growth was confirmed [30] by polymerization experiments carried out under X-rays, on which careful measurements were made, when it was found that at the end of the polymerization the micelles had returned to their original dimensions, namely, those of empty micelles.

The exhibit and the legend verifying the changes in X-ray spacings shown in Figure 16 are taken from the publication of Harkins [30] reporting measurements taken by Mattoon. Exposure C of Figure 16 is interpreted to mean that, as the polymer molecules grow larger than the micellar cores, the polymer particles begin an independent existence in the water with an absorbed layer of soap. This new phase—the polymer particle—reduces the amount of micellar soap by adsorbing a monolayer of soap for its own stabilizing. This polymer particle will also compete with micellar soap for monomer. Through this process, the soap in the micelle in which a free radical starts to grow becomes adsorbed soap associated with a new polymer molecule. Monomer is taken from monomer droplets and from other micelles until monomer equilibrium is established among the polymer particles, the monomer droplets, and the remaining micelles. Once polymerization has been initiated, the system represents one of changing equilibrium until all the micellar soap has been converted to adsorbed soap associated with a monomer-polymer particle. In this manner, all micellar soap disappears at a particular percentage conversion of monomer to polymer.

The process may be visualized as follows: (1) Monomer is solubilized in the hydrocarbon portion of a soap micelle and initiation of the polymerization occurs primarily in the micelle; (2) polymer growth starts in the micelle, utilizing monomers in the micelle; (3) diffusion of monomer from monomer droplets, or from other micelles, into the active micelle takes place and the micelle becomes polymer-swollen; (4) when the polymer particle becomes sufficiently large, the micellar soap becomes adsorbed soap, establishing new equilibrium conditions with old micelles and forming new empty micelles which can function again for the solubilization of fresh monomer; (5) polymer growth is continued in the polymer particle by the diffusion of monomer from monomer droplets and from other micelles under equilibrium conditions; (6) the old and new micelles formed under equilibrium conditions as polymeriza-

POLYMERIZATION REDUCES THE STYRENE LAYER IN THE
MICELLE

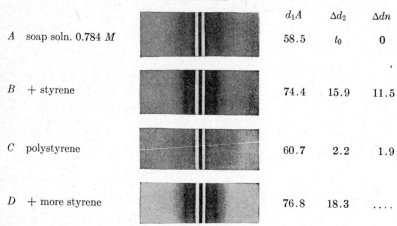

		$d_1 A$	Δd_2	Δdn
A soap soln. 0.784 M		58.5	t_0	0
B + styrene		74.4	15.9	11.5
C polystyrene		60.7	2.2	1.9
D + more styrene		76.8	18.3	....

Identical exposures throughout by R. W. Mattoon.

FIGURE 16. *A.* Exhibits two lines, one on each side of the center, which give the distance ($d_1 = 58.5$ Å) between the centers of micelles in a 0.784 M solution of potassium laurate and myristate (0.392 M for each soap). The background contains a band which gives the thickness of the micelle ($d_2 = 35.3$ Å). *B.* On saturation with styrene, d_1 increases by 15.9 to 74.4 Å and d_2 by 11.5 to 46.8 Å. *C.* On polymerization, with no free monomers present, the increase in thickness disappears, and the spacings become practically those found in the micelle without styrene. When the polymerization is produced by X-rays, the thickness of the monomer layer decreases with the time of exposure to the X-rays; the d_1 band remains as sharp as before, but merely shifts in position. The soap in the micelle in which a free radical starts to grow becomes adsorbed soap associated with the new molecule, and monomer is taken from other micelles until equilibrium with respect to monomer is established between the remaining micelles. *D.* On solubilizing styrene again, the value of d_1 rose to 76.8 Å, or essentially that found for micelles whose styrene had not been polymerized.

tion progresses repeat the solubilization and initiation processes, becoming adsorbed soap on a polymer particle until all micellar soap disappears.

As a result of this process, the soap micelles disappear and are converted into adsorbed soap at low polymer conversions. If the initial amount of soap is increased, the conversion of micellar soap into adsorbed soap occurs at higher polymer conversions. During the course of polymerization the system may be represented ideally as in Figure 17.

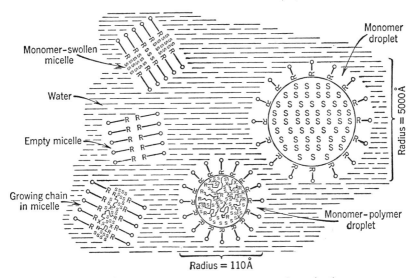

FIGURE 17. Ideal emulsion system during polymerization.

As already shown, the process of diffusion is not inconsistent with other systems where precipitation of polymer occurs, as in certain mass or solution systems. It was also shown that diffusion occurs in the absence of an interface to initiate and propagate the polymerization. The concept of diffusion is consistent with a system which orients or polarizes a monomer so that the collision factor is reduced, and the growing polymer cannot hunt for food (monomer). Therefore the monomer must come to it, thereby reducing terminations and increasing molecular weight. Montroll [57] pointed out that a zero-order reaction is to be expected if a constant number of active centers propagate at the expense of monomer supplied to them by a diffusion process, and the long-range order in Figure 10 is thereby explained. The data of Price and Adams [58] show that, after the induction period has passed, a zero-order reaction exists for conversions between 15 and 90 per cent.

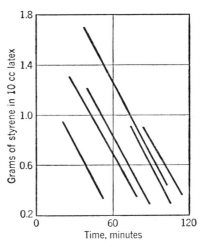

FIGURE 18. Residual styrene monomer as a function of conversion. (Reprinted by permission from the authors and the *Journal of the American Chemical Society*.)

Their data for an emulsion polymerization of styrene at 50 C, containing about 1×10^3 moles per liter of potassium persulfate, are shown in Figure 18.[58]

Since the polymer chain can be initiated in a micelle and can also start to grow in a micelle, and since the lower energy of activation indicates orientation, it would seem that the non-reactive part of the chain is immobilized and that only the reactive end is free to continue growth. This may be visualized in Figure 19.

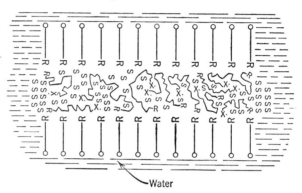

FIGURE 19.   Growing polymer chains in a micelle.

As polymerization continues by the diffusion of monomer, the micelles become polymer particles and then monomer-polymer droplets surrounded by an adsorbed layer of soap, as in Figure 20.

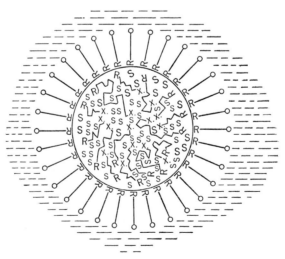

FIGURE 20.   Growing polymer chain in a monomer-polymer droplet.

Harkins has demonstrated the conversion of micellar soap into adsorbed soap by surface tension methods and by the dye method.[59] He has shown also that the micellar soap originally present in the emulsion is rapidly transformed into a monolayer of soap which surrounds the minute polymer-monomer latex particles formed by the polymerization. He shows,[60] as in Table 2, by using a 2.8 per cent solution of sodium

TABLE 2

Time in Hours	Conversion, %	Soap Left, Molar Concentration
0	0	0.91
3	8.1	
5	13.5	0.0049
6	21.1	0.0013
8	28.5	0.0008
10	32.8	0.0007
12	37.6	0.0005
14	46.8	0.0002

oleate $(0.091\ M)$ whose critical concentration lies between 7×10^{-4} and $1.2 \times 10^{-3}\ M$, that at about 14 per cent conversion all the free soap has disappeared.

These results also indicate that all the monomer had diffused into the polymer at relatively low conversions. Harkins [61] shows that with an initial soap concentration of about 0.1 M and with 180 grams of water and with 100 grams of monomer, diffusion had transported all the monomer into the polymer when a conversion of 60 per cent polymer had been reached. The ratio of monomer to polymer, M/P, is highest at low conversion and falls off as the yield increases. The ratio at any conversion is given by

$$\frac{M}{P} = \frac{[100 - (y + d + m)]}{y}$$

where y = the percentage conversion or yield,
d = percentage of initial monomer in the emulsion droplet,
m = percentage of initial monomer in the micelle and at above about 13 to 17 per cent yield, $m = 0$.

The yield of polymer at which all free monomer disappeared was determined in a number of cases by centrifugal technique to throw out emulsion droplets. In all cases, there was a yield of polymer above which no monomer could be centrifuged out even at 25,000 grams. In the standard synthetic rubber formulation using styrene and butadiene, this yield was found to be between 50 and 60 per cent, in which range d becomes zero.

A number of investigations by Fordyce and his co-workers [62-64] compare the copolymer compositions obtained in mass, solution, and emulsion copolymerizations, by using monomer-soluble and water-soluble catalysts in the emulsion systems and monomer-soluble catalyst in mass and solution polymerizations. The copolymer system,[62] styrene and acrylonitrile, was studied as (1) mass polymerization, using a monomer-soluble catalyst; (2) emulsion polymerization, using a monomer-soluble catalyst; and (3) emulsion polymerization, using a water-soluble catalyst.

Since the acrylonitrile is water-soluble and would exhibit a partition coefficient between the oil and water, it was expected that such a system would throw some light on the mechanism of emulsion polymerization. The polymerizations were allowed to proceed to low conversions, that is, 4 per cent or less, and the copolymer compositions determined when the molar concentrations in the initial monomer mixture were varied from high to low values. The proximity of the monomer-polymer composition curves for the mass polymerization and the emulsion polymerization was interpreted as giving support to an oil phase initiation for emulsion polymerization. These investigators, however, define the oil phase as the monomer droplet. Such an interpretation is not consistent with other data which their cumulative results show, that initiation occurs in the (micellar) water phase. It is logical to consider that the oil phase does exist while dispersed in the water phase, namely, the micellar solubilized oil. The solubilized monomer existing as "micellar oil" in a micelle in water solution is not identical with oil in true aqueous solution. In a study of retarders and inhibitors in the emulsion polymerization of styrene, Kolthoff and Bovey [65] also stress the difference between *true aqueous solution* and *solution* in a soap micelle. Fordyce [62] also points out that, "if polymerization occurs in the oil phase," less acrylonitrile should be found in the emulsion copolymer than in the corresponding mass polymerization. This was postulated on the basis that from solubility data we should expect the relative concentration of acrylonitrile to be lower in the oil droplet than that of acrylonitrile charged to the total reaction system. These authors add: ". . . it is virtually impossible that relative monomer concentration in the aqueous phase could be the same as the relative monomer concentrations added to the reactor for all the experiments reported. Unless aqueous phase concentrations equivalent to the charged monomers do exist, it is impossible to explain the proximity of the mass and emulsion curves on the basis of an aqueous phase mechanism of emulsion polymerization." Unfortunately, these statements ignore a number of pertinent facts in considering a mass and emulsion system. It does not necessarily follow that the copolymer composition curves must be different for a mass and emulsion polymerization, "if polymerization occurs in the oil phase" (droplet). The composition can be different because the distribution is disturbed by the presence of the water itself due to solubility effects, etc. The emulsion system must be compared to a mass polymerization containing similar quantities of water, such as an aqueous suspension polymerization. As has already been discussed under suspension polymerization processes, water-soluble monomers introduce complicating factors.

It has already been found [1] that the composition curve for styrene-acrylonitrile, prepared by an aqueous suspension process, which is a water-cooled mass polymerization, also differs from that prepared by an unmodified mass polymerization process. In a suspension process, the composition of monomer droplet also does not correspond to monomer composition charged to the system, but rather corresponds to a partition dependent on the ratios of styrene, acrylonitrile, and water in the system. If to such a suspension system an emulsifying agent is added in increasing quantities, sufficient to produce an emulsion but insufficient to convert all the monomer into micellar solubilized monomer, a dynamic system is obtained, containing the same monomer composition in the monomer droplet (true oil phase) and in the Debye-Harkins micelles. These micelles exist in the aqueous phase, with a monomer composition corresponding to that of the monomer droplets; and the solubilized monomer in the micelle exists as micellar-oil in the hydrocarbon portion of the micelle, that is, the monomer in the micelle exists as an oil phase in an aqueous phase. Because of the solubility of acrylonitrile in water, the composition of the oil phase, both in the droplet and in the micelle, cannot be equivalent to the ratio of monomers charged to the system.

The data of W. Smith on the partition of acrylonitrile between styrene and water confirm this.[66] If these data are used to calculate the acrylonitrile content of the oil phases present in the emulsion copolymerization, it is shown that the emulsion data are identical with bulk polymerization data in regard to the composition of polymer produced from a given oil phase.[66] The data of Fordyce and Smith can be considered convincing proof that the micellar-oil phase has the same composition as the droplet-oil phase, and that the initiation that occurs in the Fordyce oil phase is truly the micellar-solubilized oil phase.

If suitable corrections are made for the partition of the monomers among themselves and the water, the copolymer compositions as a function of comonomer composition should be identical because diffusion is sufficient to supply monomers from the comonomer droplet at a sufficient rate to conform with the coreactivity and selectivity constants of the monomers. Furthermore, the copolymer composition, as a function of monomer composition, should not change in an emulsion system with different soaps because as a system "in toto" diffusion will supply monomers to conform with the reactivity and specificity constants of the monomers.

The data obtained in the copolymerization of styrene and itaconic acid in solution and emulsion polymerization [63] were also interpreted in terms of oil phase (monomer droplet) mechanism for emulsion polymerization. It was proposed [62] that if this oil phase mechanism were generally valid, it was also predicted that a wide spread would be observed between the mass and the emulsion monomer-polymer composition curves for the case of a comonomer having a partition coefficient in favor of the water phase. For this study, itaconic acid was selected because it had a high solubility in water and a very low solubility in styrene. Because of the very low solubility of itaconic acid in styrene, it was necessary to carry out the copolymerization in dioxane, since copolymers could not be obtained by normal mass casting procedure. The comparison, therefore, was made for a solution and an emulsion system. The substitution of data from a solution polymerization for mass polymerization data was justified on results obtained for other copolymer systems wherein the mass monomer-polymer composition curves were shown to be coincidental with the dioxane solution curve.[64] These investigators show that a very wide divergence is obtained between the monomer-copolymer composition curves for the system, styrene-itaconic acid, determined in a solution of an organic solvent and in emulsion. These results are interpreted as indicating that in emulsion copolymerization, at least the initiation of polymerization proceeds within the oil droplet or at its interface. This interpretation may be questioned for a number of reasons. As stated above, styrene and itaconic acid cannot be copolymerized in a mass process because of the extreme insolubility of itaconic acid in styrene. There is no reason then to assume that itaconic acid will dissolve in styrene, either in the monomer droplet-oil phase or in the micellar-oil phase when solubility cannot be achieved in mass. Solubility can be expected even less in the presence of water, which acts as an extractant for any itaconic acid that might be dissolved in the styrene.

As in the acrylonitrile-styrene emulsion, the data from the styrene-itaconic acid emulsion system must be compared to those obtained in an aqueous suspension copolymerization of itaconic acid and styrene. In such a case,[1] because itaconic acid is not soluble in styrene, the composition corresponds to that of a mass casting,[63] and not to the composition of the charge; that is, the monomer droplet has a composition which corresponds to the partition of itaconic acid between styrene and water. In styrene and acrylonitrile copolymerization, there was some difference between the mass and suspension polymer, when uncorrected for partition, because there was a measurable partition of the acrylonitrile between styrene and water. Itaconic acid, on the other hand, has an extremely high partition in favor of water since it is practically insoluble in styrene.

It can be shown that in other similar systems, wherein one monomer is water-soluble and the other monomer is water-insoluble, and the monomers are insoluble in each other, similar results are obtained; for example, in a system consisting of styrene and fumaric acid.[1] In view of this, the validity may be questioned of extending the coincidence of the monomer-polymer composition for mass casting and solution polymerization from homogeneous to heterogeneous systems. The extension was based on data obtained [64] on monomer systems, such as styrene–vinyl chloride–methyl acrylate and styrene–vinyl chloride–acrylonitrile, wherein a homogeneous solution is obtained and the monomers are soluble in each other. Obviously, the addition of a solvent, such as dioxane, to such a system does not basically change the availability of one monomer to the other. Dilution may affect the rate of polymerization, and if the solvent is inert no chain transfer or telomerization will occur. On the other hand, the addition of a mutual solvent, such as dioxane, to a system in which the monomers are insoluble in each other, such as styrene and itaconic acid, does change the inherent character of the system. Styrene and itaconic acid thereby become available to each other for reaction, that is, the collision factor for reaction is greatly increased. Obviously, reaction cannot occur without collision, and, therefore, little or no copolymer can form readily with monomers that are completely or substantially insoluble in each other. It is likewise obvious that aqueous suspension or aqueous emulsion polymerization will not favor the mutual solubilization of styrene and itaconic acid.

These same investigators [64] likewise consider the data obtained on the styrene-vinyl chloride emulsion as indicating an oil phase (monomer droplet) mechanism. In view of related data, their results [64] appear to be best interpreted by postulating that the initiation does occur in the aqueous phase which contains an "oil phase" (micellar oil phase) in the Debye-Harkins micelle.

Termination

As has been previously shown, termination of the growing chain can occur by a number of means, due to the collision of the growing chain with another molecule which may also be another growing chain. Price and Adams [58] and Kolthoff and Dale [67] found that, in normal emulsion systems, after the inhibition period had passed, monomer consumption was proportional to the square root of the catalyst concentration, that the steady-state approximation was reasonably obeyed, and that termination in such a system occurs by the mutual collision of two active molecules. It appears, therefore, that the termination reaction in emulsion systems is substantially the same that occurs in mass and solution polymerization.

The molecular weights of emulsion polymers are much higher than those obtained in mass or solution systems, and obviously termination occurs between growing chains that have acquired a higher degree of polymerization than in other systems. A number of attempts have been made to explain the higher molecular weight. One explanation attributes it to the rapid destruction of inhibitor. It has been assumed that if the inhibitor is water-soluble it is destroyed more rapidly in an emulsion system than in a solution or mass system. Or if the inhibitor is monomer-soluble, it is destroyed rapidly by diffusion from dispersed droplets into micelles or dispersed polymer-monomer particles; and the greater the amount of soap, the greater the rate of diffusion of the inhibitor, and the shorter the inhibition period. This explanation is not very satisfactory because in a mass or solution polymerization the inhibitor is present in a homogeneous system containing active and growing molecules, and should be destroyed at the same or even lower degrees of conversion. Moreover, the experimental data of Norrish and Smith and other investigators [68–70] are interpreted [71] as indicating that the rate of monomer consumption and the polymerization degree of the resulting polymer are greater in a system in which there exists a polymer phase swollen by monomer than in a system in which the growth occurs in the monomer phase.

Another explanation for the higher molecular weight is based on the assumption that the increased viscosity of the medium in which polymerization occurs decreases the rate of termination noticeably without decreasing the rate of propagation. It must be noted, however, that, even in a mass polymerization in which the monomer and polymer are mutually soluble, a tremendous increase in viscosity occurs at low degrees of conversion, and it is still much simpler for a monomer to diffuse or "wander" to the growing end of a polymer chain than for the growing end of two macromolecules to find each other by collision and to terminate by reaction. Moreover, in those homogeneous mass polymer systems in which polymer precipitates from pure monomer, the system becomes essentially a process whereby (1) monomer must diffuse into polymer to effect growth, that is, the polymer cannot hunt for monomeric food, and (2) the polymer precipitates out in a partially or slightly swollen state considerably immobilized by the very high viscosity (a large amount of insoluble polymer containing some monomer), thereby reducing possible collision of growing chains. The same general condition applies to an emulsion system wherein a polymer is formed that is insoluble in the monomer from which it was derived. However, in an emulsion system in which the polymer and monomer are soluble in each other, such as polystyrene and styrene, the viscosity increase alone cannot account for the immobilization of the growing chains. As has already been shown,[27] substantial quantities of monomer have diffused into the polymer-monomer droplet at low conversion, for example, at 20 per cent conversion, the polymer-monomer droplet will contain 65 to 70 per cent monomer. In such a case, the viscosity of the polymer-monomer particle must lie between that obtained in (1) homogeneous mass polymerization in which polymer is soluble in monomer and (2) mass polymerization in which polymer is insoluble in monomer. The data of Harkins [55, 72, 73] indicate that the polymer must be a "coiled form in an emulsion droplet." This conclusion is based on his comments: "Consider that during the growth of the polymer-monomer particle, it gains a diameter of 300 Å at a certain yield. If the molecular weight were this high at this diameter, a straight chain molecule is sufficiently long to stretch across this diameter more than 100 times." One must also consider that another factor contributes to the immobilization of the polymer. Its initiation occurred in a micelle, and therefore it is subject to orientation or polarization at the interface. There is no reason to assume that as polymerization occurs, this interface disappears; otherwise stable polymeric emulsions would not be obtained in which polymer particles are surrounded by a monolayer of soap. It is irrelevant to a qualitative picture of the mechanism whether the active end or the inactive end of the growing macromolecule is attached to the organophilic residue of the soap. Under any condition, the system sets a restriction on the mobility of a growing chain with reference to another growing chain similarly restricted. In an emulsion system, therefore, we can visualize a growing molecule subjected to restrictions favoring growth and not termination:

(1) The polymer as formed is in a coiled state, or at least is not fully extended.

(2) It exists in a swollen state of high viscosity.

(3) Interfacial conditions are set by the existence of soap.

(4) Monomer supply is high, owing to the process of diffusion to the polymer.

If such a picture is qualitatively correct, it follows that agitation should exert great influence on the kinetics and on the molecular weight of the polymer obtained. Agitation would be expected to increase the rate of polymerization, since diffusion rates would be increased, as is evidenced by the rate difference between a layer polymerization and a system identical except for mild agitation. The difference in rate is indicated qualitatively in Figure 21. This difference in rate can be attributed to increased solubility, to increased fugacity as a function of particle size, to the reduction of the distance of diffusion between suspended monomer droplet and micelle, as well as to the increased number of droplets and to changes in interfacial surface. Graphically, the condition may be represented as in Figures 22 and 23.

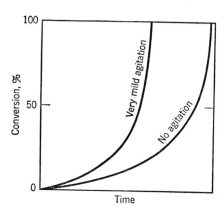

FIGURE 21.   Effect of mild agitation on polymerization rate.

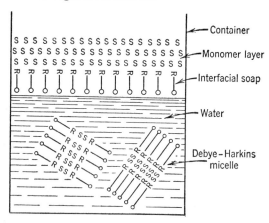

FIGURE 22.   Layer polymerization.

Trommsdorff [74] has shown that with gentle agitation polymerization is accelerated. As a consequence of agitation, the polymerization rate

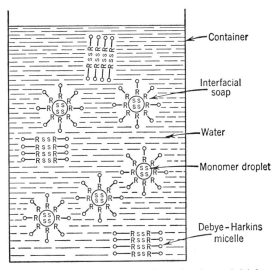

FIGURE 23.   Agitated emulsion polymerization at initial stage.

should increase with increased agitation to a certain point. As a corollary, the molecular weight should decrease owing to an increase in collisions, that is, the probability of collision between growing chains increases with agitation. Furthermore, the effect of stirring on the lowering of molecular weight should decrease with conversion because:

(1) At low degrees of conversion, the monomer droplets are quite fluid and in an agitated system correspond to a dynamic distribution as determined by amount of interfacial soap, etc. Stirring can produce mechanical motion within the drop.

(2) The polymer-monomer micelle or particle is highly swollen when the monomer-polymer ratio, M/P, is greater than one, and under these conditions stirring can produce motion within the particle.

(3) The monomer droplets disappear at low conversions (Harkins), after which the M/P ratio decreases, and with this decrease the viscosity and immobilization of the growing polymer chain increases, since stirring does not cause movement within the polymer-monomer particle.

In contrast to the increased polymerization rate resulting from mild agitation, violent agitation at zero or low conversions should produce the greatest retardation of polymerization as well as the greatest decrease in molecular weight, and the rate curve should appear to have an extended induction period. Trommsdorff carried out a number of experiments varying only in type of agitation, the results of which are summarized in Figures 24 and 25. According to these data (Figure 24) curve A represents a polymerization system which was agitated for one-half minute every 5 minutes, and this amount of agitation is considered mild. The polymer has a final $\eta_{\rm sp}/C$ of about 0.33 (curve A', Figure 25).

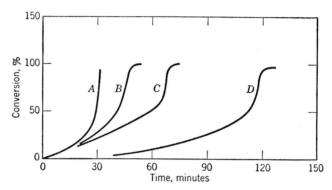

FIGURE 24. Effect of violent agitation on conversion rate.

Curve B represents the system agitated one-half minute for every 5 minutes until a conversion of about 35 per cent was obtained, followed by continuous vigorous agitation to a 100 per cent conversion. At 35 per cent conversion practically all the monomer droplets have diffused into the swollen polymer-monomer particles, and the viscosity of a 35 per cent polymer-monomer mixture is extremely high. In such a case agitation should not affect or seriously decrease the molecular weight. The final viscosity of polymer B was about 0.32 (curve B', Figure 25). Curve C represents agitation one-half minute every 5 minutes to about a 15 per cent conversion before continuous agitation was started and a drop in viscosity occurred (curve C', Figure 25). If continuous agitation is started at zero time, as in curve D, both the rate and viscosity are re-

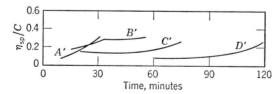

FIGURE 25. Effect of violent agitation on viscosity of polymer.

duced (curve D'). The rate curves were based on 0.4 gram of potassium per sulfate and 2 grams of emulsifier in 160 grams of methyl methacrylate, and there was no substantial difference in the velocity when an oxygen-free atmosphere was used. Similarly, the quantity of soap could be varied over a wide range without substantial difference in rates, provided catalyst concentration was not also varied widely.

The velocity curves of Figure 24 are quite similar to the velocity curve obtained as concentration of catalyst is decreased when agitation

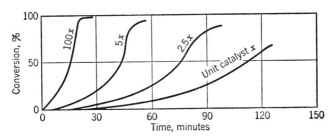

FIGURE 26.   Effect of catalyst on conversion rate.

is kept constant. These data are summarized in Figure 26, and the viscosity data of the corresponding polymers are shown in Figure 27. Fields [75] has also confirmed that the polymerization of liquid monomers, such as styrene and methyl methacrylate, is hindered and delayed by vigorous agitation.

A similar behavior is observed for monomer-soluble catalysts such as benzoyl peroxide or tertiary-butyl perbenzoate. In ordinary emulsion systems, water-insoluble catalysts are rather ineffective, indicating initiation as occurring in the aqueous phase. It may be observed that whereas a slow rate of polymerization, a consequence of low catalyst concentration, produces polymers of high molecular weight, a low rate of polymerization due to agitation also results in low molecular weight polymers.

As confirmatory evidence that initiation occurs in the solubilized monomer and that propagation is sustained in a polymer-monomer

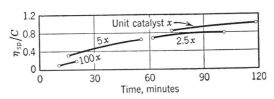

FIGURE 27.   Effect of catalyst concentration on viscosity of polymer.

particle, Trommsdorff polymerized styrene in the presence of sulfur in both a suspension system and an emulsion system. The bead polymerization was strongly inhibited by 0.20 per cent sulfur based on the weight of the monomer. Although in an emulsion polymerization the sulfur had no effect at low stages of conversion, at a conversion of about 35 per cent a marked retardation was noted. This value agrees qualitatively with Harkins' value at which free monomer droplets disappear and Trommsdorff's value below which violent agitation causes a reduction in the velocity of polymerization and in molecular weight.

These data are readily interpreted to mean that, at the early stages of conversion, initiation is occurring in water-swollen micelles in which sulfur is not soluble, but that, after monomer droplets have disappeared and the system consists of polymer particles containing monomer, retardation occurs, indicating propagation as continuing in an oil phase rather than a water phase. The data are given in Figure 28.

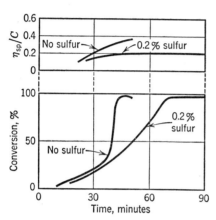

FIGURE 28. Effect of sulfur on conversion rate.

In a dual-phase catalyst system, using a water-soluble catalyst and a monomer-soluble catalyst simultaneously, little or no acceleration is observed at low conversions, whereas as the degree of conversion increases, that is, after the monomer droplets have disappeared, a definite acceleration is observed as compared to a system using a water-soluble catalyst alone.

Non-ideal Emulsion System

In the ideal emulsion system the polymerizable component, namely, the monomer or mixture of monomers, should be insoluble, or substantially so, in water in the absence of soap. As is well recognized, this is not so; in fact, many monomers have a relatively high solubility in water. As has already been shown for styrene, as a relatively water-insoluble monomer, and for vinyl acetate or acrylonitrile, as relatively water-soluble monomers, polymerization can be initiated and propagated in such solutions. In an emulsion polymerization, therefore, monomer dissolved in water containing catalyst may also be a minor locus of initiation and propagation which, however, becomes less important as the solubility of monomer in water decreases. This solubility factor becomes even more unimportant when some micellar soap is present and loses substantially all importance as the amount of micellar soap is increased.

A second minor locus of polymerization is the monomer droplet itself. In the consideration of suspension polymerization, it was noted that water-soluble catalyst caused some polymerization. In suspension polymerization, the size of the monomeric suspension is considerably larger than that of an emulsified monomer-droplet in an emulsion system. This means that in an emulsion system the ratio of soap to emulsified monomer-droplet is higher than the ratio of soap to a suspension monomer-droplet. Therefore the solubilizing effect, or the degree of contact of the monomer-droplet with the water-soluble catalyst, is higher in an emulsion than in a suspension system. Consequently, some polymerization can be expected in the monomer-droplet itself.

Diffusion of Regulators

A number of scientists have indicated that "regulators" or modifiers of polymerization follow a diffusion process in emulsion polymerizations. Smith [76-78] studied the effect of a number of mercaptans on the mass and emulsion polymerization of styrene and methyl methacrylate as well as on the copolymerization of these two monomers. He found that the relative rates at which the growing end of a polymer chain reacts with a monomer and a mercaptan are essentially the same for both the mass and the emulsion system if a short-chain mercaptan is used. As soon as a long-chain mercaptan is used, the relative rate of mercaptan addition in the mass and emulsion systems is no longer maintained; and in the emulsion system the rate of mercaptan addition is strictly dependent on diffusion.

Kolthoff and Harris [79-81] have also studied the promoter and modifier action of mercaptans in emulsion systems of styrene and butadiene, and have shown that the higher the molecular weight of the mercaptan, the lower the diffusion or consumption rate by the copolymer. In addition, the disappearance

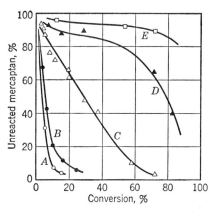

FIGURE 29. Effect of number of carbon atoms in primary mercaptans on their disappearance curves: A, octyl; B, decyl; C, dodecyl; D, tetradecyl; E, hexadecyl. (From I. M. Kolthoff and W. E. Harris, "Mercaptans as Promoters and Modifiers in Emulsion Copolymerization of Butadiene and Styrene Using Potassium Persulfate as Catalyst. II. Mercaptans as Modifiers," *J. Polym. Sci.*, **2**, 49–71 [1947]. Interscience Publishers, Inc.)

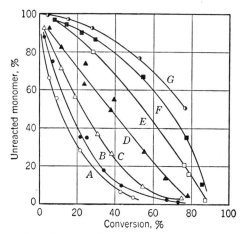

FIGURE 30.   Effect of number of carbon atoms in tertiary mercaptans on their disappearance curves: *A*, butyl (Phillips); *B*, octyl (Sharples); *C*, decyl (Sharples); *D*, dodecyl (W. C. MacTavish); *E*, tetradecyl (Sharples); *F*, pentadecyl (Sharples); *G*, hexadecyl (Sharples).   (From I. M. Kolthoff and W. E. Harris, "Mercaptans as Promoters and Modifiers in Emulsion Copolymerization of Butadiene and Styrene Using Potassium Persulfate as Catalyst. II.   Mercaptans as Modifiers," *J. Polym. Sci.*, **2**, 49–71 [1947].   Interscience Publishers, Inc.)

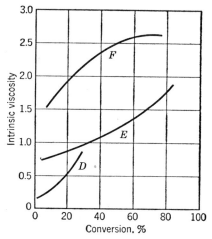

FIGURE 31.   Effect of mercaptan on polymer viscosity.   Disappearance and intrinsic viscosity curves with 0.5 per cent of various mercaptans: *D*, primary decyl; *E*, primary dodecyl; *F*, tertiary-hexadecyl.   (From I. M. Kolthoff and W. E. Harris, "Mercaptans as Promoters and Modifiers in Emulsion Copolymerization of Butadiene and Styrene Using Potassium Persulfate as Catalyst.   II.   Mercaptans as Modifiers," *J. Polym. Sci.*, **2**, 49–71 [1947].   Interscience Publishers, Inc.)

curves were found to be independent of concentration for tertiary-hexadecyl mercaptan, tertiary-dodecyl mercaptan, and primary tetra-decyl mercaptan. These data [80] are given in Figures 29 and 30. Accordingly then, those mercaptans with the highest diffusion rates should be more effective in reducing the molecular weight or viscosity of the polymer. The data shown in Figure 31 [80] verify this point also.

Energy of Activation for an Emulsion System

The total overall energy of activation, E_0, of a polymerization system is given as

$$E_0 = E_p + \tfrac{1}{2}(E_i - E_t)$$

where E_p = energy of activation of propagation,
E_i = energy of activation of initiation,
E_t = energy of activation of termination.

Cohen [82] recommends a value of 11,000 calories per mole for E_p and 4000 calories for E_t. With a value of 17,000 calories for E_i, the overall energy of activation, for an emulsion polymerization,

$$E_0 = 11,000 + \tfrac{1}{2}(17,000 - 4000) = 17,500$$

which is in good agreement with the value of 18,500 for E_0 derived by Price and Adams.[58] In contrast to this, the overall energy of activation for a mass polymerization is much higher, owing to the high energy of activation of initiation which is given as ranging between 26,000 and 33,000 [83-86] for polymerization in a number of solvents. Assuming the same energy of propagation and termination, the total overall energy of activation

$$E_0 = 11,000 + \tfrac{1}{2}(26,000 - 4000) = 22,000 \text{ calories}$$

$$E_0 = 11,000 + \tfrac{1}{2}(33,000 - 4000) = 25,500 \text{ calories}$$

lies between 22,000 and 26,000 calories, for a mass polymerization.

On the other hand, the redox system, as shall be shown later, has a lower total energy of activation than either a mass solution or normal emulsion polymerization.

The Concept of Diffusion-Propagation

In consideration of the increased rate of polymerization and of the increased molecular weight obtained in emulsion systems, the diffusion of monomer into a growing chain was established as a means of propagation. To explain high molecular weight, the concept of a polymer chain, immobilized primarily by coiling in a very viscous medium and secondarily by orientation was considered. In the consideration of mass polymerization systems, a similar mechanism was suggested for system B, in which a polymer is insoluble in its own monomer. Likewise, in solution polymerizations (systems D and E) consideration was given to systems in which the polymer is insoluble in solvent. In all such cases initiation of polymerization occurs when the monomer is in a soluble state in an organic solvent. In an emulsion system, the monomer is "solubilized" by residence in a micelle. In the solution polymerization, the polymer precipitates at some molecular weight, and therefore is not in a distended form but in a coiled or contracted form. The precipitated polymer can grow only by diffusion of the monomer to the polymer. In an emulsion system, the polymer chain in the emulsion droplet is also in a retracted and non-extended form and can grow only by diffusion of monomer. If in an emulsion system, the diffusion of monomer into an immobilized growing chain is responsible, at least in part, for the higher rate of monomer consumption and for increased molecular weights, then solution systems in which polymer precipitation occurs should produce polymers of higher molecular weight and at an increased rate than those systems in which no solvent is used but wherein the polymer is soluble in monomer, or in those systems containing solvent for both monomer and polymer.

The data of Norrish and Smith [68] substantiate this theory. Methyl methacrylate was polymerized at 40 C, using 0.0094 mole of benzoyl peroxide per liter of solution consisting of 40 per cent of monomer and 60 per cent of diluent. As diluents, these investigators used:

A. Butyl stearate, which is a precipitant for the polymer,
B. Cyclohexanol, which is also a precipitant for the polymer,
C. Amyl acetate, which is a poor solvent for the polymer,
D. Chloroform, which is a good solvent for the polymer,
E. Undiluted monomer.

The results are summarized in Figure 32. [68]

It may be observed that the rates of polymerization in the presence of precipitants are higher than those of the mass and solution polymerizations. According to the concentration law, the undiluted monomer should have the fastest rate, and the rates of curves A, B, C, and D should be identical. Undoubtedly, the deviations obtained are due to terminations or chain transfers, and the precipitated polymers are not subject to the same probability of collision terminations as polymers in solution. When pure monomer is polymerized, and the polymer is soluble in its own monomer, the molar concentration of monomer is higher than when a polymer solvent is used as a diluent; therefore the rate of

conversion should be higher. This is confirmed when curve E is contrasted with curves C and D.

Furthermore, when the pure monomer in the above system is polymerized, the viscosity is much higher at comparable conversions (as
50 per cent) than a similar system containing solvent. This factor
likewise contributes to a molecular weight increase by decreasing terminations. The shape of a polymer molecule in a solvent is determined

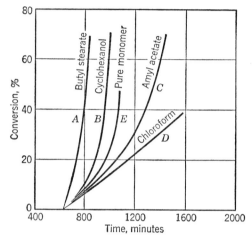

FIGURE 32. Effect of solvent on rate of conversion. (From R. G. W. Norrish and
R. R. Smith, "Catalyzed Polymerization of Methyl Methacrylate in Liquid Phase,"
Nature, **150**, 336 [1942].)

by the nature of the solvent, and a poor solvent should behave more
like a precipitant than a good solvent; that is, the polymer molecule
tends to coil more in a poor solvent than a good solvent, and chain
transfer should occur more frequently in a good solvent than a poor
solvent, reducing both rate and molecular weight. Good solvents,
therefore, will be more active telomerizing agents than poor solvents,
even when comparable chemical activity exists in both molecules. It
will be noted that the rate of polymerization for curve C is much higher
than for curve D, reflecting the collision factor due to the different
geometric structure of the polymers in solvents. The qualitative values
of the molecular weights of the polymers in these different systems are
also in accord with the postulated mechanism. The viscosity index of
the different polymers were:

Polymer A = 34   Polymer C = 25
Polymer B = 38   Polymer D = 12

In a solution polymerization in which polymer precipitation occurs, such as the butyl stearate solution of methyl methacrylate, the rate of polymerization is decreased with an increase in the concentration of solvent. At very low concentrations of monomer, the rate is very slow and the molecular weight is low. A comparable system is found in solution polymerization, in which the monomer is partially or slightly soluble in the solvent and the polymer is insoluble (system E). It explains the results obtained in the polymerization of styrene in water solution. The solubility of styrene in water is very low, and in such a system there is a deficiency of monomeric food to maintain propagation, thereby resulting in termination and low molecular weights.

It should be pointed out that those monomers, which in mass polymerization produce polymers insoluble in monomer, have rapid rates of polymerization and may be polymerized to very high molecular weights. The polymers of acrylonitrile, acrylic acid, vinyl chloride, and vinylidene chloride precipitate from their respective monomers; and under normal conditions the rates are rapid and their molecular weights are high. In contrast to acrylonitrile, methacrylonitrile produces polymers that are soluble in monomer, and the molecular weights of such polymers and polymerization rates are lower than those for acrylonitrile. The conversion curves for (1) a mass polymerization in which polymer is soluble in monomer (curve A'), (2) solution polymerization in which the polymer remains dissolved in the solvent (curve B'), (3) a solution polymerization in which polymer precipitation occurs (curve C'), (4) an emulsion polymerization (curve D'), and (5) a mass polymerization in which polymer precipitates from monomer (curve E') are generalized and summarized in Figure 33.

It may be observed that in those systems in which precipitation occurs, a comparatively long linear range is found after an inhibition period and the polymer formation within the linear range is zero order. This linear order is maintained until monomer is substantially consumed, thereafter resulting in a lowered rate of polymerization.

The similarity in the nature of curves C', D', and E' indicates a similar mechanism for these different polymerization processes. This mechanism may be called diffusion-propagation. The shape of these curves indicates that diffusion-propagation is identified with a zero-order polymer formation, and this means that the monomer supply must be sufficient to maintain propagation. Diffusion-propagation is responsible for increased rates and molecular weights in polymerization processes wherein polymers form in precipitated or coiled shape; as a consequence, the chains are immobilized, thereby reducing probability of termination, and propagation continues by diffusion of monomer into swollen polymer-monomer particles. The concept of propagation of polymerization as well as termination in a swollen polymer, even at high degrees of conversion, is consistent with other data. In the emulsion polymerization of styrene, the product obtained is a thermoplastic polymer derived from a monomer with a functionality 2. These polymers are responsive to thermal effects, and this is evident to a large extent in their molecular mobility, cold flow, viscosity, chemical reactivity, etc. In fact, the propagation of a polymerization will continue

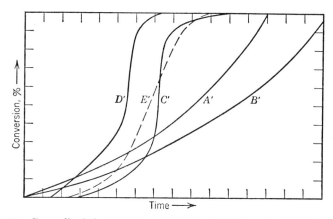

FIGURE 33. Generalized time-conversion curves for different systems: A' = methyl methacrylate. B' = methyl methacrylate + amyl acetate. C' = methyl methacrylate + butyl stearate. D' = methyl methacrylate in emulsion. E' = acrylonitrile.

even after crosslinking (gel point) has occurred in polymerization processes utilizing monomers or mixtures of monomers whose average functionality is greater than 2. Flory [87-90] applied statistical methods to the structural interpretation of three-dimensional polymers, exploring critical conditions for the occurrence of gelation both for condensation polymers and for addition polymerizations accompanied or followed by crosslinking. Walling [91] and particularly Stockmayer [92, 93] extended the size distribution relationship but were hesitant to extend the relationship beyond the gel point. More recently, Flory [94, 95] has shown that the derivation of the size distribution equations apply equally to the sol existing beyond the gel point, or to the polymer preceding gelation.

In the previous section dealing with functionality, the results of Walling [91] in his crosslinking studies of monovinyl compounds with divinyl compounds, and the discrepancies between the observed and theoretical values of gelation at high concentration of crosslinking agent, were qualitatively explained by an immobilization of the growing polymer chain. The conclusion was reached that a partially polymerized system of these two monomers consisted of swollen polymer molecules, and that these swollen molecules had a very slow rate of diffusion (polymer-immobilization) as compared to the rate of growth (that is, the rate of diffusion of monomer to the growing chain).

As a corollary, it may be stated that if those monomers which precipitate their own polymers are polymerized in the presence of a solvent that solubilizes the polymer, the rate and the molecular weight should be reduced. Acrylonitrile is an ideal monomer for such studies since not only is polyacrylonitrile of low molecular weight insoluble in acrylonitrile, but the polymer is also resistant to an extremely large number of chemical substances. A number of true solvents are now known; however, most of them telomerize the polymerization because they possess active hydrogens contained in such compounds as the nitrophenols, malonyl nitrile, dimethyl formamide, and the like. Dimethyl acetamide is more satisfactory for this study.[96] It was found that both rate and molecular weight of the polyacrylonitrile are reduced. A 1 per cent benzoyl peroxide catalyzed polymerization of a solution of 50 per cent acrylonitrile and 50 per cent dimethyl acetamide required 48 hours for a 50 per cent conversion whereas, in the absence of the amide, the same conversion was obtained in a matter of minutes. The molecular weight is reduced from about 120,000 to about 17,000 by the presence of the amide.

To explain why a 10 per cent solution of styrene in polystyrene polymerizes about ten times more rapidly than in other solvents, Walling et al.[97] treated the problem by the J. N. Brönsted rate equation[98] involving activity coefficients to determine the effect of changing medium upon reaction rates. These investigators concluded that the shape of the rate curve cannot be due to chain termination but to a diffusion controlled reaction.

It has been shown[99] in a study of the emulsion polymerization of methyl methacrylate, using a redox system of ferrous ions and hydrogen peroxide, that the rate of conversion is consistent with (1) initiation occurring in the aqueous phase and (2) propagation occurring in the suspended polymer-monomer particle.

These studies also show that a decrease in the value of k_t (termination constant) would account for an increase in molecular weight of the polymer and that the rate of termination is decreased as polymerization progresses because of the increasing viscosity of the monomer-polymer particles in which the active chains are embedded.

In light-scattering experiments of cellulose acetate,[100] the dissymmetry coefficients (q) were measured in acetone solution, and the distance between the ends of the polymer molecules was calculated from the q values. The length of the polymer was also calculated from molecular weight data and compared to the lengths calculated from q, assuming rigid rods and random coil forms for the polymer. These data are summarized in Table 3.[100]

TABLE 3

DIMENSIONS OF CELLULOSE ACETATE MOLECULES

| | | Distance between Ends in Å | | |
Molecular Weight	q	Assuming Rigid Rod	Assuming Random Coil	Calculated from Mol. Wt.
163,000	0.60	1900	1340	3100
135,000	0.60	1900	1340	2400
75,000	0.43	1550	1120	1440
65,000	0.43	1550	1120	1250
52,000	0.32	1380	960	1000

Reprinted by permission from the authors and the *Journal of the American Chemical Society*.

The data indicate that, below a molecular weight of 80,000, cellulose acetate molecules in dilute solution (1 per cent or less) are fairly well extended, but as the molecular weight increases, the molecules coil back on themselves very rapidly to a degree that increases with molecular weight.

Inoculation of an Emulsion System

It has been known for some time [29, 51, 102, 103] that the induction period found in an emulsion polymerization could be reduced by the inoculation or initial addition of another latex which previously had been partially polymerized. Trommsdorff showed that if a partially polymerized emulsion system is added to an unpolymerized emulsion of methyl methacrylate, not only is the rate of polymerization increased, but the resulting polymer is also of higher molecular weight. These data are summarized in Figure 34,

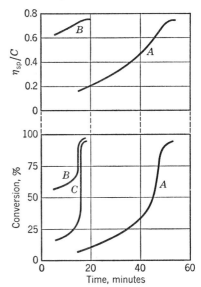

FIGURE 34.   Inoculation in an emulsion system.

where curve A represents the rate for the normal emulsion polymerization of methyl methacrylate and curve B when it is inoculated with an emulsion which has been polymerized to a 50 per cent conversion. Curve C represents the correction of curve B calculated on monomer only.

The increased rate and molecular weight are due to a diffusion-propagation into the swollen polymer-monomer particles added in the inoculation, whereas in curve A, a time interval is required to establish the dispersed polymer-monomer droplets. Expressed differently, the conditions for zero-order propagation had already been established in a system simply by the addition or inoculation of such particles. The difference in conversion rates as established in curve B for the total system and curve C for the total free monomer indicates that, simultaneously with the diffusion propagation into the added, dispersed, swollen polymer-monomer particles, part of the unpolymerized emulsion system is following its normal polymerization mechanism, but that the high rate is dominated by diffusion propagation.

In other studies, Trommsdorff points out [51] that heretofore it had been regarded as improbable that macromolecular substances added to or formed in the monomer could further influence the course of polymerization, since these polymers would lack the necessary reactive groups for such a change in reaction. Using 0.1 per cent benzoyl peroxide at 60 C in the mass polymerization of methyl methacrylate, he compared the polymerization rates of methyl methacrylate alone and with 10.4 per cent of prepolymerized methyl methacrylate. As shown in Figure 35, a noticeable increase in rate was observed. Curve A

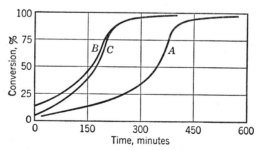

FIGURE 35. Inoculation in a mass casting.

represents the rate for the undiluted monomer, curve B represents the rate with the addition of polymer, and curve C represents the correction of curve B when calculated on the monomer present at the start of the reaction.

It may be suggested that the polymethyl methacrylate added to the monomer may not be "dead," that is, it still contains terminally reactive groups, and therefore acceleration should occur. The addition of some other high molecular weight substance dissolved in monomer would determine if such a mechanism is probable. Preferably, the polymer should consist of macromolecules that have not been prepared by a free radical addition polymerization. Cellulose propionate of low degree of polymerization is soluble in methyl methacrylate. Trommsdorff mass-polymerized methyl methacrylate at 50 C, using 1 per cent benzoyl peroxide as a catalyst, and compared its rate to comparable systems containing 20 and 30 per cent dissolved cellulose tripropionate, as in Figure 36. Curve A represents the rate of monomeric methacrylate; curves B and C represent the rates for solutions of methyl methacrylate containing 20 and 30 per cent, respectively, of cellulose tripropionate.

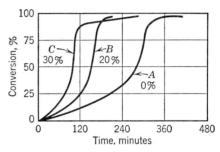

FIGURE 36.   Methyl methacrylate inoculated by a cellulose derivative.

These data indicate, at least to some extent, that the presence of polymeric substance is capable of increasing the rate of polymerization, even if the polymer added is foreign to the system. Conceivably, even in mass casting where polymer is soluble in monomer, immobilization of the growing chain can become a factor. It has already been demonstrated that if a polymerized acrylic ester is dissolved in a chlorostyrene monomer and this solution is polymerized,[104] a species of an acrylic polymer can be isolated which contains chlorine. This can readily be explained by the reaction of the acrylic polymer with a free radical R·, which thereby terminates the free radical, converting the dead acrylic polymer into a free radical chain which can grow then by the addition of monomer. The free radical initiating such a system may be derived from a catalyst or from a small growing chain, thus

$$\text{Catalyst} \rightarrow R_z\cdot$$

$$R_z\cdot + nM \rightarrow R_z(M)_n\cdot$$

wherein n is a small numerical value. If $R_z\cdot$ and $R_z(M)_n\cdot$ are generalized as $R'\cdot$, then $R'\cdot$ can react with a foreign polymer chain:

$$R'\cdot + R(CH_2CH)_nCH_2CHR \rightarrow RH + R(CH_2CH)_nCH_2\overset{\displaystyle R}{\underset{\displaystyle X}{\text{C}}}\cdot$$

and the resulting chain can add monomer, thus:

$$R(CH_2CH)_nCH_2\overset{\overset{\displaystyle R}{|}}{C}\cdot\ +\ nM\ \rightarrow\ R(CH_2CH)_nCH_2\overset{\overset{\displaystyle R}{|}}{C}\!\!-\!\!(M)_n\cdot$$
$$\underset{X}{|}\qquad\underset{X}{|}\qquad\qquad\qquad\underset{X}{|}\qquad\underset{X}{|}$$

If the polymer chains, $R(CH_2CH)_nCH_2\overset{\overset{\displaystyle R}{|}}{C}\cdot$ or $R(CH_2CH)_nCH_2\overset{\overset{\displaystyle R}{|}}{C}\!\!-\!\!(M)_n\cdot$,

are immobilized by reasons of a high viscosity medium or otherwise, propagation of the chain can occur only by diffusion, and provided sufficient monomer is present, the rate will be of zero order. There is no reason to doubt that cellulose propionate cannot be converted into a free radical, as indicated above, and that a copolymer of cellulose propionate and methyl methacrylate is obtained.

$$\text{Cellulose propionate (CP)}\ \xrightarrow{R'\cdot}\ R'H\ +\ CP\cdot$$

$$CP\cdot\ +\ nM\ \longrightarrow\ CP(M)_n\cdot$$

Similar reasoning can be applied to other polymers, and in favorable systems it should be possible to prepare a copolymer of vinyl monomers and condensation polymers as, for example, by polymerizing a solution of trimethylene glycol adipate in a soluble monomer in the presence of peroxide.[1] Such a conclusion is justified since thermoplastic condensation polymers of saturated dihydric alcohols and saturated dibasic acid can be crosslinked or vulcanized by benzoyl peroxide.[105] The free radicals generated by the benzoyl peroxide react with the polymers to produce polymer radicals. If more than one radical point is formed on a number of chains, crosslinking occurs by termination of the radical ends of one chain with another:

$$2[-OOC(CH_2)_nCOOCH_2CH_2CH_2OOC(CH_2)_nCOOCH_2CH_2CH_2-]$$

$$\Big\downarrow 4R'\cdot$$

$$2[-OOC(CH_2)_nCOOCH_2\!\!-\!\!\underset{\bullet}{C}H\!\!-\!\!CH_2OOC(CH_2)_nCOOCH_2\!\!-\!\!\underset{\bullet}{C}H\!\!-\!\!CH_2-]$$

$$\Big\downarrow$$

$$-OOC(CH_2)_nCOOCH_2\!\!-\!\!\overset{|}{C}H\!\!-\!\!CH_2OOC(CH_2)_nCOOCH_2\!\!-\!\!\overset{|}{C}H\!\!-\!\!CH_2-$$
$$-OOC(CH_2)_nCOOCH_2\!\!-\!\!\overset{|}{C}H\!\!-\!\!CH_2OOC(CH_2)_nCOOCH_2\!\!-\!\!\overset{|}{C}H\!\!-\!\!CH_2-$$

However, in the presence of monomer, the growth of the polymer radical would be represented as follows:

$$-OOCH(CH_2)_nCOOCH_2CH-CH_2OOCH(CH_2)_nCOOCH_2CH-CH_2-$$

$$
\begin{array}{cc}
(M)y & (M)n \\
M & M \\
M & M \\
M & M \\
M & M \\
\cdot & \cdot
\end{array}
$$

If such a radical were responsible for the termination of a growing "pure" polymer chain, $R(M)_n \cdot$, a molecular weight increase would be expected, thus:

$$-OOC(CH_2)_nCOOCH_2CH-CH_2OOC(CH_2)_nCOOCH_2CH-CH_2-$$

$$
\begin{array}{cc}
(M)y & (M)y \\
M & M \\
M & M \\
M & M \\
M & M \\
(M)n & (M)n \\
R & R
\end{array}
$$

Redox Emulsion Polymerization

Monomers have been shown to contribute to the rate of radical production in peroxide-catalyzed polymerizations. In such cases, monomer molecules react with the catalyst to initiate the reaction by the formation of a radical-producing complex.[106-108] The energy of activation for the formation of free radicals by the decomposition of organic acyl peroxides as, for example, benzoyl and acetyl peroxide in different solvents, was found to be between 26,000 and 33,000 calories per mole. In a normal emulsion polymerization, the energy of activation of initiation was indicated to be about 17,000 calories per mole. In an emulsion redox system, the value of the energy of activation of initiation is of the same order as that of a redox polymerization in aqueous solution, namely, about 10,100 calories, indicating that the redox system is a very efficient system for the production of radicals at low temperature, and that polymerization in emulsion is initiated in the aqueous (micelle-solubilized) phase. The data of Bacon [109] show in Figures 37 and 38 the similarity in the rate curves of the redox polymerization of acrylonitrile in an aqueous solution and of styrene in an emulsion. Bacon's data in Table 4 [109] show the difference in rates of a number of styrene

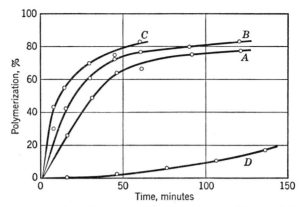

FIGURE 37.   Redox polymerization in aqueous solution.   (By permission from The
Faraday Society, London.)

        A.   Water   200 grams
             (NH₄)₂S₂O₈   0.3
             NaHSO₃   0.2
             Acrylonitrile   10.0
                under nitrogen at 30 C
        B.   Same as A, but at 40 C
        C.   Same as A, but at 50 C
        D.   Water   200 grams
             (NH₄)₂S₂O₈   0.3
             Acrylonitrile   10.0
                under nitrogen at 40 C

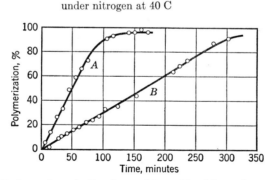

FIGURE 38.   Redox polymerization in emulsion.   Emulsion polymerization of styrene at 40 C, followed by change in specific gravity.   (By permission from The
Faraday Society, London.)

        A.   Water   400 grams
             (NH₄)₂S₂O₈   1.0
             Na₂SO₃   0.56
             Na oleic acid sulfonate   4.0
             Styrene   120
        B.   Same as A, except for the ab-
             sence of Na₂SO₃.

TABLE 4

AQUEOUS EMULSION POLYMERIZATION OF STYRENE AT 40 C AND pH 8; 30 GRAMS
STYRENE PER 100 MILLILITERS OF WATER CONTAINING 1 PER CENT SODIUM
SALT OF SULFONATED OLEIC ACID

Ammonium Persulfate, % on Water	Sodium Sulfite, % on Water	Polymerization Rate (grams polymer per liter per minutes)	η_r (0.1 gram polymer per 100 ml benzene sol. at 20 C)
0.5	.....	1.00	1.466
0.5	0.275	3.04	1.116
0.25	.....	0.97	1.768
0.25	0.14	2.91	1.305
0.1	0.055	1.88	1.567

Reprinted by permission from The Faraday Society, London.

emulsions prepared with various amounts of redox agents in contrast to
unactivated systems.

Since free radicals are readily generated in aqueous systems involving
ions, which can undergo oxidation-reduction, the reducing agent acts
as an electron donor to the peroxide, which is the oxidizing agent. Water
systems are most effective for redox systems.[110]   The peroxide in such
a system is considered the catalyst and the reducing agent the activator.   This effect is comparable to the increased rate of free radical
generation by benzoyl peroxide (the catalyst) by the monomer (the
activator).   That the non-ionic organic system is not as efficient as the
inorganic aqueous system is indicated by the fact that the addition of
organic reducing agents does not produce the same effect on the benzoyl
peroxide as an aqueous reducing agent does on an aqueous peroxide
solution.   If acrylonitrile in aqueous solution, or methyl methacrylate
in emulsion, is subjected to a redox polymerization, the rate of polymerization is directly proportional to catalyst concentration, that is

$$-\frac{dm}{dt} \propto c$$

where m and c represent the concentration of monomer and catalyst,
respectively.   In mass solution or normal emulsion polymerization, the
rate of monomer consumption is proportional to the square root of the
catalyst concentration.[111-113]   Josefowitz and Mark [70] attempted a redox
activation of vinyl acetate in a suspension polymerization using 20 grams
of monomer in 80 milliliters of water with benzoyl peroxide as the catalyst and 0.5 per cent of sodium bisulfite, calculated on the weight of the
monomer, as an activator.   In this system the monomer-soluble benzoyl

peroxide was the catalyst and the water-soluble bisulfite was the accelerator. The data of these experiments are shown in Table 5.[70]

TABLE 5

POLYMERIZATION OF VINYL ACETATE

Benzoyl Peroxide Concentration, C, %	$\sqrt{C}$, %	Polymerization Rate % per Hour Unactivated	% per Hour Activated
1.0	1	1.00	4.50
1.5	1.22	1.25	5.60
2.0	1.41	1.43	6.40
5.0	2.26	2.32	10.5

These data show that such a system is obeying the square-root law both for the unactivated and the activated system. Both rates are initial rates, and the initial rate in the presence of activator, which is about 4.5 times the unactivated rate, is due mainly to the removal of oxygen either initially present in the system or formed by side reactions of the peroxide catalyst decomposition. Morgan and others [114-116] have shown that in a redox system the reducing agent functions in two ways. First, it removes oxygen from the system and, second, it becomes an electron donor and facilitates the production of radicals by reaction with the peroxidic catalysts. For monomer phase polymerization as, for example, in mass suspension or solution polymerization, in which the catalyst exists in non-aqueous solution, a reducing agent is not indicated to be an activator. If activation is achieved by a substance which is not a reducing agent, the term *redox* (reduction activation) cannot be applied to such a system. A monomer phase activation will require the addition of a substance which will initiate free radicals by interaction with the peroxide catalyst with a lower energy of activation than 26,000 calories, this latter value being the energy of activation of initiation between the peroxide type catalyst (benzoyl peroxide) and the monomer:

E_i = 26,000 benzoyl peroxide + monomer → complex → free radical

E_i = <26,000 benzoyl peroxide + activator → complex → free radical

In aqueous solution two redox systems are possible by the interaction of the peroxide and the reducing agent.

In the first system, only one radical is formed, as in the reaction between hydrogen peroxide and a ferrous salt. The ferrous ion acts as electron donor:

$$H_2O_2 + Fe^{++} \rightarrow Fe^{+++} + HO^- + HO\cdot$$

The reactive hydroxyl radical can react with monomer, if present, as well as with all other components, thus:

$$HO\cdot + CH_2{=}CHX \rightarrow HOCH_2CHX\cdot \quad (k_i) \quad (2a)$$

$$HO\cdot + Fe^{++} \rightarrow HO^- + Fe^{+++} \quad (k_2) \quad (2b)$$

$$HO\cdot + H_2O_2 \rightarrow H_2O + HO_2\cdot$$

In the second system, two radicals are generated, one from the catalyst and the other from the activator. Such a system is represented by a persulfate catalyst and a thiosulfate activator:

$$S_2O_8^{=} + S_2O_3^{=} \rightarrow SO_4^{=} + SO_4^{-}\cdot + S_2O_3^{-}\cdot \quad (1)$$

In such a case the thiosulfate ion contributes an electron to the persulfate ion. In the presence of monomer these radicals undergo reaction:

$$SO_4^{-}\cdot + CH_2{=}CHX \rightarrow SO_4^{-}{-}CH_2CHX\cdot \quad (k_i)$$
$$S_2O_3^{-}\cdot + CH_2{=}CHX \rightarrow S_2O_3^{-}{-}CH_2CHX\cdot \quad (k_i) \tag{2}$$

and while in the absence of monomer the radicals will react among themselves, thus:

$$SO_4^{-}\cdot + S_2O_3^{-}\cdot + S_2O_3^{=} \rightarrow SO_4^{=} + S_4O_6^{=}\cdot \quad (3)$$

In both types of redox systems, the energy of activation of initiation, E_i, is about 10,000 calories. In equation 1 it appears that the rate of formation of the $SO_4^{-}\cdot$ and $S_2O_3^{-}\cdot$ radicals is proportional to the product of the catalyst (persulfate) concentration, c, and the activator (thiosulfate) concentration, a. In equation 3 the disappearance of these radicals is proportional to the thiosulfate concentration only, and the steady-state concentration of the radicals, R*, is given as

$$R^* = \frac{k_1ca}{k_2a} = \frac{k_1c}{k_2} \tag{4}$$

When such a radical reacts with a monomer the initiation occurs to give RM* (equation 2), and this step is given as

$$\frac{d(RM^*)}{dt} = k_iRM^* = \frac{k_ik_1cm}{k} \tag{5}$$

and the steady-state concentration of growing chains is given [112] in terms of rate constants of initiation, k_i, and of termination, k_t, as

$$RM^* = cm\sqrt{\frac{k_1k_i}{k_tk_2}} \tag{6}$$

The rate of monomer consumption, including the propagation-rate constant, is given [111] as

$$-\frac{dm}{dt} = k_p \sqrt{\frac{k_1 k_i}{k_2 k_t}} \, m^{3/2} c^{1/2} = k_p \sqrt{\frac{k_i}{k_t}} \, m^{3/2} c^{1/2} = k_{1.5} m^{3/2} c^{1/2} \qquad (7)$$

This equation indicates that the rate of monomer consumption is not dependent on activator concentration, since that term has disappeared. Morgan's data [114] is in agreement with this fact. Morgan further confirmed the dependence on the disappearance of monomer upon $m^{3/2}$ by following the aqueous redox polymerization of acrylonitrile over a wide conversion range; and, by correcting for the disappearance of catalyst with conversion, he was able to obtain a satisfactory agreement between the rate of monomer disappearance and the sesquimolecular order, $m^{3/2}$.[115] The overall energy of activation, E_0, of a redox system is lower than normal mass, solution, or emulsion polymers; it is about 10,000 to 12,000 calories. This compares with about 26,000 for mass and solution polymerization, and with about 17,500 calories for emulsion polymerizations.

The overall energy of activation, E_0, is represented by

$$E_0 = E_p + \tfrac{1}{2}(E_1 + E_i - E_2 - E_t) \qquad (8)$$

where E_i represents the energy of activation of the reaction of an $SO_4 \cdot^-$ or $S_2O_3^- \cdot$ radical with a monomer, E_2 represents the reaction of these same radicals with $S_2O_3^=$ ions, and E_1 and E_2 will have approximately the same values, so that the equation becomes

$$E_0 = E_p + \tfrac{1}{2}(E_1 - E_t) \qquad (9)$$

Using approximations of 10,000 calories for E_p, the energy of activation of propagation, 6000 calories for the energy of activation of termination, and about 10,000 calories for E_1 (the energy of activation for the persulfate and thiosulfate ion, the value for E_0 obtained is:

$$E_0 = 10,000 + \tfrac{1}{2}(10,000 - 6000) = 12,000 \qquad (10)$$

which is reasonably within the experimental order of magnitude.

Equation (7) indicated that the rate of monomer consumption was that of a square-root dependence on the catalyst concentration

$$-\frac{dm}{dt} \propto \sqrt{\text{cat}} \qquad (11)$$

However, the experimental data obtained [116] in a water-soluble redox system show a direct proportionality between the rate and the catalyst concentration,

$$- \frac{dm}{dt} \propto (\text{cat})$$

Hohenstein and Mark [117] indicate that a proportionality between the rate and the catalyst concentration can be obtained by assuming that the radicals generated by the reaction of the persulfate and thiosulfate can only form an unstable addition compound, u,[70, 108] with the monomer when collision occurs:

$$u = K \text{MR}^*$$

where K is the equilibrium constant, and if this complex is converted to an active center by collision with a catalyst molecule,

$$\frac{d(\text{MR}^*)}{dt} = \frac{k_1 k_i K}{k_2} m c^2 \tag{12}$$

and the overall rate is given as

$$\frac{-dm}{dt} = k_p \sqrt{\frac{k_1 k_i K}{k_2 k_t}} \, m^{3/2} c \tag{13}$$

This formal method of treatment shows that the dependence of the rate on $m^{3/2}$ has not changed, whereas it is now proportional not to the square root of the catalyst concentration but to its first power. As has been pointed out, there has been no experimental evidence published for the existence of an addition compound.[108]

OXYGEN EFFECT IN REDOX SYSTEMS

As indicated previously, a large number of investigators [118-120] have shown that oxygen influences the course of a polymerization. Kolthoff and his co-workers [121, 122] have shown that the induction period caused by oxygen in an emulsion polymerization of styrene was approximately inversely proportional to the amount of persulfate used as a catalyst.

By isolating polystyrene peroxide these investigators showed that oxygen could be considered a comer with styrene and that the initial rate of polymerization was reduced. Bacon [123] also showed that oxygen had a marked retarding effect on the aqueous polymerization of acrylonitrile even in the presence of a powerful redox system. Retardation was noticed by the presence of an induction period whose length depended on the amount of oxygen present in the system.

The experimental data of Baxendale [124] indicate that oxygen has the same effect in a redox emulsion system using methyl acrylate as the monomer. For example, when the concentration of the ferrous ion and hydrogen peroxide were $10^{-4}\,M$, no polymerization occurred in the presence of air. When the solutions were thoroughly deaerated, however, extensive polymerization occurred, the results were reproducible, and the induction period disappeared.

REFERENCES

1. G. F. D'Alelio, Unpublished results.
2. E. Jenckel and S. Süss, *Naturwissenschaften*, **29**, 339 (1931).
3. G. F. D'Alelio, *Experimental Plastics and Synthetic Resins*, p. 72, John Wiley and Sons, New York, 1946.
4. W. P. Hohenstein and H. Mark, *J. Polymer Sci.*, **I**, 127 (1946).
5. C. F. Fryling and E. W. Harrington, *Ind. Eng. Chem.*, **36**, 114–117 (1944).
6. R. P. Dinsmore, U. S. Patent 1,732,795 (October 22, 1929).
7. M. Luther and M. Heuck, U. S. Patent 1,864,078 (June 21, 1932); German Patent 558,890 (January 9, 1927).
8. A. Reychler, *Kolloid-Z.*, **12**, 277 (1913).
9. J. W. McBain and T. R. Bolam, *J. Chem. Soc.* (London), **113**, 825 (1918).
10. J. W. McBain, *Trans. Faraday Soc.*, **9**, 99 (1913).
11. G. S. Hartley, *Aqueous Solutions of Paraffin Chain Salts*, p. 41, Hermann & Cie, Paris, 1936.
12. J. W. McBain, *Advances in Colloid Science*, Vol. I, p. 124, edited by E. O. Kraemer, New York, Interscience Publishers, Vol. I, 1942.
13. K. Hess and J. Gundermann, *Ber.*, **70**, 1800 (1937).
14. W. Philippoff and K. Hess, *Ber.*, **70**, 1808 (1937).
15. K. Hess, H. Kiessig, and W. Philippoff, *Naturwissenschaften*, **26**, 184 (1938).
16. K. Hess, W. Philippoff, and H. Kiessig, *Kolloid-Z.*, **88**, 40 (1939).
17. J. Stauff, *Kolloid-Z.*, **89**, 224 (1939).
18. J. Stauff, *Naturwissenschaften*, **27**, 213 (1939).
19. H. Kiessig and W. Philippoff, *Naturwissenschaften*, **27**, 593 (1939).
20. H. Kiessig, *Kolloid-Z.*, **96**, 252 (1941).
21. W. Philippoff, *Kolloid-Z.*, **96**, 255 (1941).
22. H. Kiessig, *Kolloid-Z.*, **98**, 213 (1942).
23. K. Hess, *Fette u. Seifen*, **49**, 81 (1942).
24. W. D. Harkins, R. W. Mattoon, and M. L. Corrin, *J. Am. Chem. Soc.*, **68**, 220 (1946).
25. W. D. Harkins, R. W. Mattoon, and M. L. Corrin, *J. Colloid Sci.*, **1**, 105 (1946).
26. R. W. Mattoon, R. S. Stearns, and W. D. Harkins, *J. Chem. Physics*, **15**, 209 (1947).
27. W. D. Harkins, *J. Am. Chem. Soc.*, **69**, 1432 (1947).
28. W. D. Harkins, *J. Am. Chem. Soc.*, **69**, 1433 (1947).
29. W. D. Harkins, *J. Am. Chem. Soc.*, **69**, 1428–1444 (1947).
30. W. D. Harkins, *J. Am. Chem. Soc.*, **69**, 1436 (1947).
31. W. D. Harkins and N. Beeman, *J. Am. Chem. Soc.*, **51**, 1674 (1929).
32. E. K. Fischer and W. D. Harkins, *J. Phys. Chem.*, **36**, 98 (1932).
33. W. D. Harkins, F. E. Brown, and E. C. H. Davies, *J. Am. Chem. Soc.*, **39**, 354 (1917).
34. W. D. Harkins, E. C. H. Davies, and G. L. Clark, *J. Am. Chem. Soc.*, **39**, 541 (1917).

35. Irving Langmuir, *J. Am. Chem. Soc.*, **39**, 1848 (1917).
36. G. C. Nutting and W. D. Harkins, *J. Am. Chem. Soc.*, **61**, 1181 (1939).
37. M. L. Corrin and W. D. Harkins, *J. Am. Chem. Soc.*, **69**, 683 (1947).
38. A. Koch, *Ind. Eng. Chem.*, **32**, 464 (1940).
39. H. Fikentscher, *Angew. Chem.*, **51**, 433 (1938).
40. W. D. Harkins, *J. Am. Chem. Soc.*, **69**, 1429 (1947).
41. H. Fikentscher, *Kunststoffe*, **28**, 179 (1938).
42. G. Gee, C. B. Davies, and W. H. Melville, *Trans. Faraday Soc.*, **35**, 1298 (1939).
43. C. F. Fryling and E. W. Harrington, *Ind. Eng. Chem.*, **36**, 114 (1944).
44. W. P. Hohenstein and H. Mark, *J. Polymer Sci.*, **I**, 551 (1946).
45. W. D. Harkins, *J. Chem. Phys.*, **13**, 381 (1945).
46. W. D. Harkins, *J. Chem. Phys.*, **14**, 47 (1946).
47. R. S. Stearns and W. D. Harkins, *J. Chem. Phys.*, **14**, 214 (1946).
48. W. P. Hohenstein and H. Mark, *J. Polymer Sci.*, **I**, 552 (1946).
49. R. J. Vinograd, L. L. Fong, and W. M. Sawyer, *Abstracts* of the 108th Meeting of the American Chemical Society, Division of Colloid Chemistry, p3E, New York, September 13, 1944.
50. E. A. Hauser and D. S. Le Beau, *J. Phys. Col. Chem.*, **52**, 27 (1948).
51. E. Trommsdorff, Paper read at High Polymer Colloquium at Freiburg, July 14, 1944.
52. G. Gee, *Trans. Faraday Soc.*, **32**, 187 (1936).
53. C. D. Waring and P. Becker, *Abstracts* of American Chemical Society Meeting, Division of Physical and Inorganic Chemistry, p. 4, Memphis, April 10, 1942.
54. W. P. Hohenstein and H. Mark, *J. Polymer Sci.*, **I**, 556 (1946).
55. W. D. Harkins, *J. Am. Chem. Soc.*, **69**, 1439 (1947).
56. W. D. Harkins, *J. Am. Chem. Soc.*, **69**, 1441 (1947).
57. E. W. Montroll, *J. Chem. Phys.*, **13**, 337 (1945).
58. C. C. Price and C. E. Adams, *J. Am. Chem. Soc.*, **67**, 1674 (1945).
59. M. L. Corrin and W. D. Harkins, *J. Am. Chem. Soc.*, **69**, 679 (1947).
60. W. D. Harkins, *J. Am. Chem. Soc.*, **69**, 1438 (1947).
61. W. D. Harkins, *J. Am. Chem. Soc.*, **69**, 1430 (1947).
62. R. G. Fordyce and E. C. Chapin, *J. Am. Chem. Soc.*, **69**, 581 (1947).
63. R. G. Fordyce and G. E. Ham, *J. Am. Chem. Soc.*, **69**, 695 (1947).
64. E. C. Chapin, G. E. Ham, and R. G. Fordyce, *J. Am. Chem. Soc.*, **70**, 538 (1948).
65. I. M. Kolthoff and F. A. Bovey, *J. Am. Chem. Soc.*, **70**, 797 (1948).
66. W. V. Smith, *J. Am. Chem. Soc.*, **70**, 2177–2179 (1948).
67. I. M. Kolthoff and W. J. Dale, *J. Am. Chem. Soc.*, **67**, 1672 (1945).
68. R. G. W. Norrish and R. R. Smith, *Nature*, **150**, 336 (1942).
69. J. Abere, G. Goldfinger, H. Naidus, and H. Mark, *Ann. N. Y. Acad. Sci.*, **44**, 267 (1943).
70. D. Josefowitz and H. Mark, *Polymer Bull.*, **I**, 140 (1945).
71. W. P. Hohenstein and H. Mark, *J. Polymer Sci.*, **I**, 559 (1946).
72. W. D. Harkins, *J. Am. Chem. Soc.*, **69**, 1437 (1947).
73. W. D. Harkins, *J. Am. Chem. Soc.*, **69**, 1443 (1947).
74. E. Trommsdorff, British Intelligence Objectives Sub-Committee, pp. 34, 35, 38–40, Item 22, *Final Report* 363, London, H.M. Stationery Office.
75. C. M. Fields, U. S. Patent 2,289,765 (July 14, 1942).
76. W. V. Smith, *J. Am. Chem. Soc.*, **68**, 2059 (1946).
77. W. V. Smith, *J. Am. Chem. Soc.*, **68**, 2064 (1946).
78. W. V. Smith, *J. Am. Chem. Soc.*, **68**, 2069 (1946).

79. I. M. Kolthoff and W. E. Harris, *J. Polymer Sci.*, **2**, 41–48 (1947).
80. I. M. Kolthoff and W. E. Harris, *J. Polymer Sci.*, **2**, 49–71 (1947).
81. I. M. Kolthoff and W. E. Harris, *J. Polymer Sci.*, **2**, 72–81 (1947).
82. S. G. Cohen, *J. Am. Chem. Soc.*, **67**, 17 (1945).
83. K. Nozaki and P. D. Bartlett, *J. Am. Chem. Soc.*, **68**, 1686 (1946).
84. P. D. Bartlett and R. Altschul, *J. Am. Chem. Soc.*, **67**, 812, 816 (1945).
85. C. E. Barnes, *J. Am. Chem. Soc.*, **67**, 217 (1945).
86. S. G. Foord, *J. Chem. Soc.* (London), **1940**, p. 48.
87. P. J. Flory, *J. Am. Chem. Soc.*, **63**, 3083 (1941).
88. P. J. Flory, *J. Am. Chem. Soc.*, **63**, 3091 (1941).
89. P. J. Flory, *J. Am. Chem. Soc.*, **63**, 3096 (1941).
90. P. J. Flory, *J. Phys. Chem.*, **46**, 132 (1942).
91. C. Walling, *J. Am. Chem. Soc.*, **67**, 441 (1945).
92. W. H. Stockmayer, *J. Chem. Phys.*, **12**, 125 (1944).
93. W. H. Stockmayer, *J. Chem. Phys.*, **11**, 45 (1943).
94. P. J. Flory, *Chem. Revs.*, **39**, 137 (1946).
95. P. J. Flory, *J. Am. Chem. Soc.*, **69**, 30 (1947).
96. G. F. D'Alelio, U.S. Patent 2,531,406.
97. Cheves Walling, Emorene R. Briggs, and Frank R. Mayo, *J. Am. Chem. Soc.*, **68**, 1145–1149 (1946).
98. J. N. Brönsted, *Z. physik. Chem.*, **100**, 139 (1922).
99. J. H. Baxendale, M. G. Evans, and J. K. Kilham, *J. Polymer Sci.*, **1**, 466–474 (1946).
100. R. S. Stein and Paul Doty, *J. Am. Chem. Soc.*, **68**, 159–167 (1946).
101. J. W. Zemba and G. H. Coleman, U. S. Patent 2,311,615 (Feb. 16, 1943).
102. E. C. Britton and G. H. Coleman, U. S. Patent 2,331,263 (Oct. 5, 1943).
103. V. H. Turkington and L. R. Whiting, U. S. Patent 2,367,810 (Jan. 23, 1945).
104. R. B. Carlin and N. E. Shakespeare, *J. Am. Chem. Soc.*, **68**, 876 (1946).
105. B. S. Biggs and C. S. Fuller, *Chem. Eng. News*, **21**, 962 (1943).
106. S. Kamenskaya and S. Medvedev, *Acta Physicochim.* (U.R.S.S.), **13**, 565 (1940).
107. G. V. Schulz and F. Blaschke, *Z. physik. Chem.*, **B51**, 75 (1942).
108. M. S. Matheson, *J. Chem. Phys.*, **13**, 584 (1945).
109. R. G. R. Bacon, *Trans. Faraday Soc.*, **42**, 140–155 (1946).
110. J. H. Baxendale, M. G. Evans, and G. S. Park, *Trans. Faraday Soc.*, **42**, 167 (1946).
111. L. B. Morgan, *Trans. Faraday Soc.*, **42**, 169 (1946).
112. J. H. Baxendale, M. G. Evans, and G. S. Park, *Trans. Faraday Soc.*, **42**, 155 (1946).
113. C. C. Price, *Ann. N. Y. Acad. Sci.*, **44**, 351 (1943).
114. L. B. Morgan, *Trans. Faraday Soc.*, **42**, 174 (1946).
115. L. B. Morgan, *Trans. Faraday Soc.*, **42**, 175 (1946).
116. L. B. Morgan, *Trans. Faraday Soc.*, **42**, 171–176 (1946).
117. W. P. Hohenstein and H. Mark, *J. Polymer Sci.*, **I**, 574 (1946).
118. H. Staudinger and A. Schwalbach, *Ann.*, **488**, 8 (1931).
119. H. S. Taylor and A. A. Vernon, *J. Am. Chem. Soc.*, **53**, 2527 (1931).
120. H. Staudinger and H. W. Kohlschutter, *Ber.*, **64**, 2091 (1931).
121. I. M. Kolthoff and W. J. Dale, *J. Am. Chem. Soc.*, **69**, 441 (1947).
122. F. A. Bovey and I. M. Kolthoff, *J. Am. Chem. Soc.*, **69**, 2143 (1947).
123. R. G. R. Bacon, *Trans. Faraday Soc.*, **42**, 144 (1946).
124. J. H. Baxendale, M. G. Evans, and G. S. Park, *Trans. Faraday Soc.*, **42**, 163 (1946).

CHAPTER 10

Copolymer Compositions
and Stability of Polymers

POLYMER VERSUS MONOMER COMPOSITION

In the preparation of a homopolymer, such as polystyrene from monomeric styrene, all the polymer chains formed will be identical in their composition, that is, they are composed only of styrene segmers, but the polymer chains will not be homogeneous because of molecular weight distributions. In vinyl copolymerization processes, the polymers formed differ not only in the length of the individual polymer chains but also in the composition of the different polymer chains.

Figure 1 shows the composition of a styrene-acrylonitrile copolymer [1] as a function of the concentration of acrylonitrile in the monomer composition. Curve A represents the theoretical amount of acrylonitrile that would be expected in the copolymer; curve B represents the actual amount found in the composition at low conversions.

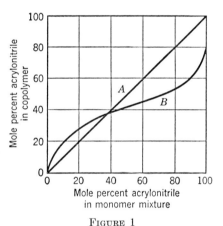

FIGURE 1

(Reprinted by permission from the authors and the *Journal of the American Chemical Society*.)

Wall [2] considered the structure of copolymers theoretically and deduced that copolymers consisted of a mixture of polymers whose copolymer composition was subject to a composition distribution function. Thus in a system consisting of two monomers, M_1 and M_2, the following relations are obtained:

$$\frac{d[M_1]}{dt} = K_1[M_1] \tag{1}$$

413

and

$$\frac{d[M_2]}{dt} = K_2[M_2] \qquad (2)$$

and

$$\frac{d[M_1]}{d[M_2]} = \frac{K_1}{K_2} \times \frac{[M_1]}{[M_2]} = \alpha\frac{[M_1]}{[M_2]} \qquad (3)$$

If M_1^* is defined as the mole fraction of M_1 segmer in the polymer at any particular instant, the relation becomes:

$$M_1^* = \frac{\alpha[M_1]}{\alpha[M_1] + [M_2]} \qquad (4)$$

If α is greater than one, the first polymer formed will be richer in M_1 than the concentration of M_1 in the original monomer mixture. As polymerization proceeds, M_1 will be depleted, and the last polymer to form will contain only M_2. When α is less than one, the polymer will originally be richer in M_2 than the concentration of M_2 in the original monomer mixture, and eventually the last polymer to form will contain only M_1 monomer. Only when α is one will the composition of the resulting copolymer, at least within statistical limits, correspond to the concentration of the monomers.

It has been shown that copolymers of vinyl chloride and vinyl acetate [3] could be separated by solvents to yield fractions of different chlorine contents.

In dehalogenation experiments which were concerned with the constitution of vinyl chloride–vinyl acetate copolymers, Marvel [4] correlated the composition of the polymer with the composition of the monomer mixture. It was found that the polymer molecules produced in a given case differed widely in composition and that the first polymer chains were richer in vinyl chloride than the monomer mixture. It was found that α, for vinyl chloride, had a value of 1.5. Further studies were carried out [5] by interrupting the copolymerization of p-chlorostyrene and methyl methacrylate. The α for p-chlorostyrene in this copolymerization was 1.46 and remained constant when the temperature, solvents, and relative concentrations of the monomers were varied.

Wall's original equation was shown to apply to the ideal case where a polymer chain radical ending in M_1 or M_2 had the same relative preference for reacting with M_1 or M_2 monomer and α varied with the original proportions of the reactants. As a result, the equation

$$\frac{d[M_1]}{d[M_2]} = \frac{[M_1]}{[M_2]} \times \frac{r_1[M_1] + [M_2]}{r_2[M_2] + [M_1]} \qquad (5)$$

was suggested,[6-8] where r_1 and r_2 are two ratios of reaction rate constants, and copolymerization is thus expressed in terms of *relative reactivity constants and selectivities.*

Monomer Reactivites and the Copolymer Equation

This new relation coordinates the selectivity of the monomers with their reactivities. The selectivity of monomers had been noticed in copolymers containing maleic anhydride.[9-12] Mayo and Lewis have indicated that many other monomers show this phenomenon to a large degree.[7] They state that no copolymer will form if each radical prefers to react with the monomer from which it was derived and that this selectivity may be based on complex formation between monomers [7] or to steric or dipole effects.[13]

The original Wall [2] equation,

$$\frac{d[M_1]}{d[M_2]} = \alpha \frac{[M_1]}{[M_2]} \tag{3}$$

may be considered as describing an ideal copolymerization system. It is possible to describe the system,[14] assuming the free radical growth mechanism for a copolymer system as containing four different growth reactions. If M_1 and M_2 are the monomers and $M_1 \cdot$ and $M_2 \cdot$ their respective radicals, the four steps may be represented as

$$M_1 \cdot + M_1 \xrightarrow{K_{11}} M_1 \cdot \tag{6}$$

$$M_2 \cdot + M_1 \xrightarrow{K_{21}} M_1 \cdot \tag{7}$$

$$M_1 \cdot + M_2 \xrightarrow{K_{12}} M_2 \cdot \tag{8}$$

$$M_2 \cdot + M_2 \xrightarrow{K_{22}} M_2 \cdot \tag{9}$$

The disappearance of monomers and their interrelationship may be expressed as follows:

$$\frac{-d[M_1]}{dt} = K_{11}[M_1][M_1 \cdot] + K_{21}[M_1][M_2 \cdot] \tag{10}$$

$$\frac{-d[M_2]}{dt} = K_{12}[M_2][M_1 \cdot] + K_{22}[M_2][M_2 \cdot] \tag{11}$$

and

$$\frac{d[M_1]}{d[M_2]} = \frac{K_{11}[M_1][M_1 \cdot] + K_{21}[M_1][M_2 \cdot]}{K_{12}[M_2][M_1 \cdot] + K_{22}[M_2][M_2 \cdot]} \tag{12}$$

If the assumption is made that a steady state is reached and maintained at the rate where $M_1\cdot$ radicals are being converted to $M_2\cdot$ radicals at the same rate that $M_2\cdot$ radicals are converted to $M_1\cdot$ radicals,

$$K_{12}[M_2][M_1\cdot] = K_{21}[M_1][M_2\cdot] \tag{13}$$

and

$$[M_1\cdot] = \frac{K_{21}[M_1][M_2\cdot]}{K_{12}[M_2]} \tag{14}$$

Substituting the value of $M_1\cdot$ in equation 12 gives

$$\frac{d[M_1]}{d[M_2]} = \frac{[M_1]}{[M_2]} \times \frac{(K_{11}/K_{12})[M_1] + [M_2]}{[M_1] + (K_{22}/K_{21})[M_2]} \tag{15}$$

and, defining K_{11}/K_{12} as r_1, and K_{22}/K_{21} as r_2, we have

$$\frac{d[M_1]}{d[M_2]} = \frac{[M_1]}{[M_2]} \times \frac{r_1[M_1] + [M_2]}{r_2[M_2] + [M_1]} \tag{16}$$

The differential equation (equation 16) may be used directly in experiments where the relative concentrations of the unreacted monomers remain essentially constant. Unless the conversions are low, the integrated equation is required.

Mayo and Lewis integrated equation 16 to the form given in equation 17.

$$\ln \frac{[M_2]}{[M_2{}^0]} = \frac{r_2}{1 - r_2} \ln \frac{[M_2{}^0][M_1]}{[M_1{}^0][M_2]}$$

$$- \frac{1 - r_2 r_1}{(1 - r_2)(1 - r_1)} \ln \frac{(r_1 - 1)([M_1]/[M_2]) - r_2 + 1}{(r_1 - 1)([M_1{}^0]/[M_2{}^0]) - r_2 + 1} \tag{17}$$

and, by definition,

$$\frac{1 - r_1}{1 - r_2} = P \tag{17a}$$

Then,

$$r_2 = \frac{\ln \dfrac{[M_2{}^0]}{[M_2]} - \dfrac{1}{P} \ln \dfrac{(1 - P)([M_1]/[M_2])}{(1 - P)([M_1{}^0]/[M_2{}^0])}}{\ln \dfrac{[M_1{}^0]}{[M_1]} + \ln \dfrac{(1 - P)([M_1]/[M_2])}{(1 - P)([M_1{}^0]/[M_2{}^0])}} \tag{18}$$

where M_1^0 and M_2^0 are the concentrations of styrene and methyl methacrylate, respectively, at the start of the polymerization, and M_1 and M_2 are the concentrations at the point where polymerization is stopped.

Equation 18 was evaluated [7,13] in the copolymerization of styrene and methyl methacrylate by varying the ratio of these two monomers and by interrupting the polymerization to varying yields between 7.57 and 13.23 per cent conversion. The values of r_1 (for styrene) and r_2 (for the methacrylate) averaged about 0.5. These values were determined as follows.

An experimental determination gives a set of values for M_1^0, M_1, M_2^0, and M_2. Arbitrary values of P are chosen and the corresponding value of r_2 is computed, using equation 18. The value for r_1 is then obtained by substituting this value of r_2 in equation 17a. A plot of r_1 against r_2 gives a straight line (Figure 2).[7] A second experiment is run

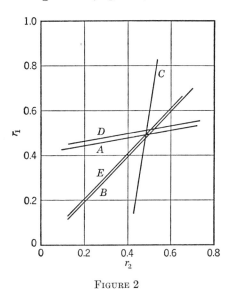

FIGURE 2

(From F. R. Mayo, "Copolymerization. I. A basis for Comparing the Behavior of Monomers in Copolymerization; the Copolymerization of Styrene and Methyl Methacrylate," *J.A.C.S.*, **66**, 1594 [1944].)

and a second r_1,r_2 line is obtained. The intersection of two such lines gives the unique values for r_1 and r_2. In practice usually three or more experiments are performed, resulting in three or more lines. Usually, the intersection of three lines forms a triangle, the area of which is a measure of the experimental errors. Mayo and Lewis [7] calculated the best values of r_1 and r_2 from the following data:

Experiment	M_1^0	M_2^0	M_1	M_2
A	0.7980	0.2020	0.7435	0.1813
B	0.5010	0.4990	0.4571	0.4556
C	0.2021	0.7979	0.1828	0.7468
D	0.8064	0.1996	0.7450	0.1796
E	0.5020	0.4980	0.4552	0.4520

In the copolymerization system of styrene and methacrylate, the value of r_1 was determined to be 0.5. Since r_1 is the ratio, K_{11}/K_{12}, of two reaction constants, the value of 0.5 means that the styrene radical has only one-half the preference for reaction with a styrene monomer that it has for reaction with a methacrylate monomer. Similarly, the 0.5 value of r_2, K_{22}/K_{21}, means that the methacrylate radical has only one-half the preference for a methacrylate monomer that it has for a styrene monomer. Expressed inversely, the styrene radical has twice the preference for a methacrylate monomer than for a styrene monomer, and the methacrylate radical has twice the preference for a styrene monomer than for a methacrylate monomer.

Wall [8] considered mathematically some other systems where r_1 and r_2 have values other than those found in the styrene-methacrylate system of Mayo and Lewis, where $r_1 = r_2 = 0.5$. He also pointed out that numerous examples are available for systems where r_1 or r_2 equals zero. The work of Wagner-Jauregg [9] shows that the maleic anhydride does not polymerize with itself but readily coreacts with substances like styrene to form a 1:1 polymer. Similarly, other systems, such as the maleic imide copolymers,[15] may be explained by setting r_1 or r_2 nearly equal or actually equal to zero.

The monomer reactivity ratios for several monomer pairs using styrene, methyl methacrylate, acrylonitrile, and vinylidene chloride were determined.[13] The experimental results are shown in Table 1.

TABLE 1

	r_1		r_2
Styrene	0.50 ± 0.02	Methyl methacrylate	0.50 ± 0.02
Styrene	0.41 ± 0.08	Acrylonitrile	0.04 ± 0.04
Styrene	2.00 ± 0.1	Vinylidene chloride	0.14 ± 0.05
Methyl methacrylate	1.20 ± 0.14	Acrylonitrile	0.15 ± 0.07
Methyl methacrylate	2.53 ± 0.1	Vinylidene chloride	0.24 ± 0.03
Acrylonitrile	0.91 ± 0.1	Vinylidene chloride	0.37 ± 0.1

Quantitatively, the data in Table 1 have the following meaning. The r_1 and r_2 values for the reactions of the styrene radical with styrene and methacrylate monomers and of the methacrylate radical with the methacrylate and styrene monomers have already been considered. In the copolymerization of styrene and acrylonitrile, the acrylonitrile molecule adds to the styrene radical two and one-half times as fast as the styrene molecule, whereas the styrene monomer adds to the acrylonitrile radical twenty-five times as fast as the acrylonitrile monomer. Furthermore, styrene monomer adds twice as fast to the styrene radical as the vinylidene chloride monomer, but the vinylidene chloride monomer adds to the vinylidene chloride radical only approximately one-seventh as fast as the vinylidene chloride monomer.

With the rate constant used for the reaction of the styrene-type radical with styrene as unity, the *relative* values of the rate constants for the reaction of four *monomers* with the styrene-type radical are given in Table 2.[13]

TABLE 2

Monomer Relative Reactivity with Four Radicals

		Radicals		
Monomer	Styrene	Methyl Metha-crylate	Acrylo-nitrile	Vinyli-dene Chloride
(a) Styrene	1	2.0	25	7
(b) Methyl methacrylate	2	1.00	7	4.1
(c) Acrylonitrile	2.5	0.83	1.00	2.7
(d) Vinylidene chloride	0.5	0.4	1.1	1.00

Reprinted by permission from the authors and the *Journal of the American Chemical Society.*

In line *a* of Table 2, the relative reactivity of styrene, methyl methacrylate, acrylonitrile, and vinylidene chloride radicals are compared respectively with styrene monomer. The relative reactivities of these same four radicals were also calculated with the methyl methacrylate monomer in line *b* of Table 2 with acrylonitrile in line *c*, and with the vinylidene chloride in line *d*. It must be noted that a different rate constant is taken in each column; hence the absolute values in one column have no relation to the absolute values in another column.

These authors [13] also summarize rates of polymerization and copolymerization of these monomers at 60 C in the presence of 0.1 per cent of Bz_2O_2. In the copolymers the rates refer to equal molar mixtures, they are initial rates, and they are expressed in weight percentage per hour. Their data are summarized in Table 3.[13]

TABLE 3

RATES OF POLYMERIZATION AND COPOLYMERIZATION OF FOUR MONOMERS

Polymerization of				
Acrylo-nitrile	Methyl Metha-crylate	Vinyli-dene chloride	Styrene	with
91	...	...	...	Acrylonitrile
4.7	7.8	...	...	Methyl methacrylate
4.9	3.9	3.3	...	Vinylidene chloride
4.5	1.7	1.14	1.6	Styrene

Reprinted by permission from the authors and the *Journal of the American Chemical Society*.

It may be seen that though styrene polymerizes alone more slowly (1.6, Table 3) than any other monomer, it enters relatively faster in copolymers with acrylonitrile (25, Table 2) and vinylidene chloride (7, Table 2). Similarly, methyl methacrylate enters the copolymer faster than acrylonitrile (7, Table 2), in spite of the fact that acrylonitrile polymerizes faster than methacrylate (91 to 7, Table 3). In contrast, styrene-vinylidene chloride copolymerizes at a rate of 1.14 (Table 3), which is slower than the value for either styrene (1.6, Table 3) or vinylidene chloride (3.3, Table 3). However, most combinations polymerize at a rate intermediate between the rates of the monomers alone.

By defining M_1/M_2 as G, equation 16 can be converted to the forms

$$\frac{d[M_1]}{d[M_2]} = G\frac{(r_1G + 1)}{(G + r_2)} \tag{16a}$$

or

$$\frac{d[M_1]}{d[M_1] + d[M_2]} = \left[1 + \frac{1}{G}\frac{(G + r_1)}{(r_2G + 1)}\right]^{-1} \tag{16b}$$

where $d[M_1]/(d[M_1] + d[M_2])$ is the mole fraction of monomer M_1 units in the polymer.

The instantaneous composition of a copolymer formed from a mixture of monomers, M_1 and M_2, depends on the values of r_1 and r_2 for these monomers. A plot of the mole fraction of monomer, M_1, that is $M_1/(M_1 + M_2)$, in the monomer mixture against the mole fraction of the same monomer in the copolymer produces a straight line only if both r_1 and r_2 equal one. By the use of equation 17, it is possible to obtain a number of plots for various values of r_1 and r_2 parameters such as are shown [16] in Figures 3, 4, and 5. In these three figures, the straight line corresponds to a polymer composition that is identical to the monomer composition and r_1 and r_2 are both equal to one. In Figures 4

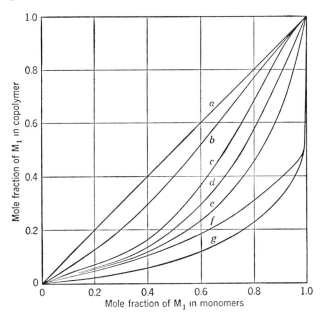

FIGURE 3.   Plot of instantaneous mole fraction of monomer, M_1, in a copoylmer as a function of the mole fraction of M_1 in a monomer mixture. (From R. Simha, "Copolymerization," *J. Research*, **41**, 521 [1948].)

(a) $r_1 = 1, r_2 = 1$ (d) $r_1 = 5, r_2 = \frac{1}{2}$
(b) $r_1 = 2, r_2 = 1$ (e) $r_1 = 5, r_2 = \frac{1}{5}$
(c) $r_1 = 5, r_2 = 1$ (f) $r_1 = 5, r_2 = 0$
               (g) $r_1 = 10, r_2 = 0$

and 5, the curves intersect the diagonal at some point, and it is at this point only that the polymer composition is identical to the monomer composition.

The limiting trend of the curves is readily visualized. In Figure 3 large values of r_1 and small values of r_2 produce copolymers with M_2-M_2 and M_1-M_2 repeating segmers, having a deficiency of M_1 monomers even when a large concentration of M_1 is used in the monomer mixture. This is especially true in curves f and g in Figure 3. If both r_1 and r_2 are very small, the copolymer will be of the alternating type, and the mole fraction of M_1 in the polymer will be about 0.5 as in curve l of Figure 4.

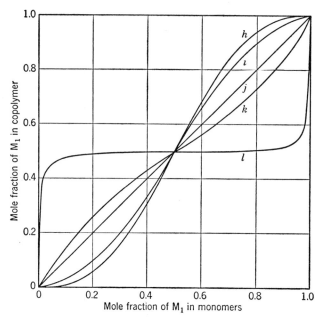

FIGURE 4.   Plot of instantaneous mole fraction of monomer, M_1, in a copolymer as a function of the mole fraction of M_1 in a monomer mixture. (From R. Simha, "Copolymerization," *J. Research*, **41**, 521 [1948].)

(h) $r_1 = r_2 = 100$ $\qquad\qquad$ (j) $r_1 = r_2 = 1$
(i) $r_1 = r_2 = 5$ $\qquad\qquad$ (k) $r_1 = r_2 = 0.5$
(l) $r_1 = r_2 = 0.01$

If r_1 and r_2 are both very large, no copolymer will be formed except in a very narrow range close to a mole fraction of 0.5, in which range there occurs a transition from pure polymer of M_2 to pure polymer of M_1. Curve h in Figure 4 approaches such a copolymer system.

Composition curves of the type shown in Figures 1, 3, 4, and 5 are useful in determining the values of the constants, r_1 and r_2. To do this a number of experiments must be performed and the monomer-polymer compositions determined and plotted. The values of r_1 and r_2 can be determined if the limiting slopes, when M_1 and M_2, respectively, approach zero, are known, since

$$\frac{d\left[\dfrac{M_1}{M_1 + M_2}\right]_{\text{polymer}}}{d\left[\dfrac{M_1}{M_1 + M_2}\right]_{\text{monomer}}} = \frac{1}{r_1} ; \quad \text{when} \quad \frac{M_1}{M_1 + M_2} \to 0$$

and

$$\frac{d\left[\dfrac{M_1}{M_1 + M_2}\right]_{\text{polymer}}}{d\left[\dfrac{M_1}{M_1 + M_2}\right]_{\text{monomer}}} = \frac{1}{r_2} \; ; \quad \text{when} \quad \frac{M_1}{M_1 + M_2} \rightarrow 1$$

At the present state, there is no correlation between the rates of polymerization of two monomers by themselves and their relative tendencies to react with free radicals and form a copolymer.

Marvel and others [4] showed that even when an excess of diethyl maleate was polymerized with styrene, the styrene segmers combined in the copolymer were greater than a 1:1 ratio to the maleate. This in itself would not indicate that r_2 for the maleate is low. Even if r_2 is zero in this case, it does not mean that it will be zero in all systems as it appears to be for maleic anhydride. It is conceivable that the maleate in certain systems could copolymerize alone or that, at least, oligomers

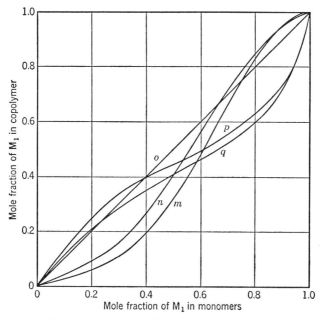

FIGURE 5.   Plot of instantaneous mole fraction of monomer, M_1, in a copolymer as a function of the mole fraction of M_1 in a monomer mixture.   (From R. Simha, "Copolymerization," *J. Research*, **41**, 521 [1948].)

$(m)\ r_1 = 10,\ r_2 = 4$ $(o)\ r_1 = 1,\ r_2 = 1$
$(n)\ r_1 = 5,\ r_2 = 3$ $(p)\ r_1 = 0.5,\ r_2 = 0.2$
$(q)\ r_1 = 0.8,\ r_2 = 0.2$

would be obtained. The maleic and fumaric esters have been polymerized by means of heat and light and such catalysts as benzoyl peroxide and triethyl lead acetate. More recently, Marvel and his co-workers [17] have shown that when dimethyl maleate (two moles) is treated with large quantities of benzoyl peroxide (one mole) a number of distillable reaction products are obtained in conjunction with 30 to 40 per cent of non-volatile material containing more than two maleic ester segmers.

Alfrey [18] studied the copolymerization of styrene with diethyl maleate, and with diethyl chloromaleate, respectively, and found an r_2 value of zero for both the diethyl maleate and the diethyl chloromaleate. The relative rates of copolymerization of styrene with these two monomers were found to be:

	r_1 K_{11}/K_{12}	r_2 K_{22}/K_{21}
Styrene and diethyl maleate	5	0
Styrene and diethyl chloromaleate	2.5	0

In this case, the rate constant K_{22} is zero, within experimental error, but the rate constants K_{11}, K_{12}, and K_{21} have finite values.

Lewis and his co-workers [19] reported a value of 6.52 ± 0.50 for the r_1 for styrene with a value of 0.005 ± 0.01 for r_2 for diethyl maleate. The reactivity of the styrene radical to these two maleate esters was in contrast to maleic anhydride and to diethyl fumarate, as in Table 4.

TABLE 4

Styrene Radical with	K_{12}
Maleic anhydride	24
Diethyl fumarate	2.5
Diethyl chloromaleate	0.4
Diethyl maleate	0.2

These data mean that, even though the copolymerization of the diethyl maleate proceeds faster than the copolymerization with the diethyl chloromaleate, the chloromaleate ties in twice as fast as the maleate, and maleic anhydride ties in 120 times faster and diethyl fumarate twelve times faster than the diethyl maleate.

Dipole and Steric Effects in Copolymerization

Price attempted to explain these differences in the maleate and chloromaleate and in a number of other cases by considering generally the factors that effect polymerization. First, he considered the effect of substitution on the double bond, and the nature of the substituent which changes the polarity of the monomer. It was observed that those pairs of monomers copolymerize easily wherein one monomer contains electron-releasing substitution (a substituent promoting aromatic substitution) and the other electron-attracting substitution (a substituent retarding aromatic substitution).

Any substituent attached to the double bond will polarize the labile π electrons and denote or withdraw electrons. Alkyl groups and halogen atoms will polarize the π electrons towards the β carbon atoms. The alkyl groups will increase the overall electron density at the double bond (Type A), while the halogen will decrease the density (Type B), a condition indicated as follows:

$$
\begin{array}{cc}
\text{R} & \text{Cl} \\
\searrow \overset{\oplus}{\text{CH}}=\overset{\ominus}{\text{CH}_2} & \nwarrow \overset{\oplus}{\text{CH}}=\overset{\ominus}{\text{CH}_2} \\
\underbrace{\quad\quad}_{\ominus} & \underbrace{\quad\quad}_{\oplus} \\
\text{Type A} & \text{Type B}
\end{array}
$$

If the substituent is the type that normally directs meta in the benzene ring, such as COOH, COOR, CONR$_2$, CN, NO$_2$, it withdraws electrons from the double bond but polarizes the π electrons in the opposite direction (Type C):

$$
\begin{array}{c}
\text{ROOC} \\
\nwarrow \overset{\ominus}{\text{CH}}=\overset{\oplus}{\text{CH}_2} \\
\underbrace{\quad\quad}_{\oplus} \\
\text{Type C}
\end{array}
$$

Experimental data tend to show that ready copolymerization occurs in those pairs of monomers where one monomer is represented by an electron-rich double bond (Type A) and an electron-poor double bond (Type B or C). The assumption is made that substituents, which influence the polarity of the double bond in one monomer, can similarly influence the polarity of an adjacent free radical, and the attraction of the negative radical for the positive double bond might be an important factor in facilitating polymerization.

Another influencing factor in polymerization or copolymerization is the steric factor. This steric and polarity effect is demonstrated in the relations between maleic anhydride, diethyl maleate, diethyl fumarate, and diethyl chloromaleate. Experimental results indicate that only in those monomers containing a double bond with a substituent on each carbon atom which undergo free radical polymerization are the two substituents members of a five-membered ring. Thus maleic anhydride copolymerizes readily, but when the ring is opened as in maleic acid or maleic esters there is a great reduction in the tendency to copolymerize. Indene and coumarone also polymerize well in contrast to the maleic esters. The increased tendency of the chloromaleate over the maleate to copolymerize can be attributed to the electrical effect of the chlorine atom. The difference in the maleate and fumarate is explained by the fact that all the atoms with the exception of the ethyl groups in the fumarate can be coplanar, whereas in the maleate not more than one carboxyl group at a time can be coplanar with the double bond.

Alfrey and Harrison [20] studied copolymerization of styrene and allyl chloride. Their results show that allyl chloride is less reactive than styrene as far as addition to either type of free radical chain is concerned. The rate of polymerization and the polymerization degree of the co-polymer decrease with increasing concentration of allyl chloride. Allyl chloride does polymerize alone to low molecular weight polymers.

Nozaki [21] re-examined Wall's original equation,

$$\frac{d[M_1]}{d[M_2]} = \alpha \frac{[M_1]}{[M_2]} \tag{3}$$

in the copolymerization of acrylonitrile, methacrylonitrile, methyl α-chloroacrylate, vinylidene chloride, and vinyl acetate with equimolar quantities of other monomers in the presence of benzoyl peroxide. The derived value of α for these copolymers and their analysis indicated a relative sequence of monomer activity with radicals, listed in Table 5.[21]

TABLE 5

RELATIVE RATES OF MONOMER REACTION WITH RADICALS

Monomer	Relative Value of k	Monomer	Relative Value of k
Methyl-α-chloroacrylate	60	2-Chloroprene	5.4
Styrene	54	Vinyl chloride	4.6
Methyl methacrylate	48	Allyl chloride	2.0
Methacrylonitrile	40	Vinyl acetate	1.5
Acrylonitrile	20	Ethylene (estimated)	1.0
Indene	16	Crotyl acetate	0.6
Vinylidene chloride	14	1-Chloropropene	0.28

From K. Nozaki, "Reactivity of Monomers in Copolymerization," *J. Polym. Sci.*, **1**, 455 (1946).

Limiting factors were considered in arranging this table. The value of α is rather sensitive to errors in the analysis of the copolymers, especially when α is very small or very large; and α is determined most accurately when it lies between 0.7 and 1.5. In this range, an agreement to ± 0.20 was found for a number of samples.[4]

From this table Nozaki makes certain generalizations about the effect of structure on the reactivity of ethylene derivatives with radicals.

Apparently conjugation aids the rate since all the monomers above vinylidene chloride have conjugated structures. With particular reference to ethylene substitution, the order in which the substituents on ethylene aid reactivity may be given as

$$-CH{=}CH_2 > -C_6H_5 > -CN > -COOCH_3 > -Cl > -OCCH_3$$

It appears that a second substituent on the same carbon atom is as effective as the first and that the same relative order of increase is observed. It is apparent that the replacement of a non-terminal hydrogen by a methyl group, as may be noted in the comparison of acrylonitrile with methacrylonitrile, and of methyl acrylate with methyl methacrylate, increases the rate of reaction of the monomer with radical. In contrast, a second substitution at the other end of the ethylene molecules to produce a symmetrically substituted ethylene decreases the rate of the reaction, probably because of steric hindrance.

Deviations from the predicted sequence of monomer reactivities are known, and the author derives two copolymerization equations, one in which the assumption is made that the selectivity is due to dipole, steric, or other factors independent of concentration, and the other in which the assumption is made that the selectivity is due to complex formation between monomers. The copolymerization of styrene and methyl methacrylate was studied in diluted and undiluted systems, and the results obtained by Nozaki indicated that selectivity due to factors independent of concentration, for example, steric or dipole factors, is more important than selectivity due to complex formation. Such a concept seems reasonable in explaining to some degree, at least, why such monomers as α-chlorostyrene, $CH_2{=}C{-}C_6H_5$, 2-chloropropene-1,

$$\overset{|}{Cl}$$

$CH_2{=}C{-}CH_3$, α-chloroacrylonitrile, $CH_2{=}C{-}CN$, and symmetrical

$\overset{|}{Cl}$ $\qquad\qquad\qquad$ $\overset{|}{Cl}$

diphenylethylene, $\langle\;\rangle CH{=}CH\langle\;\rangle$, do not polymerize well. Price [22] has already suggested that the polarity of the double bonds and the steric nature of the monomer are important governing factors in copolymerization.

Nozaki [21] compared the experimental data of Mayo and Lewis [7] dealing with copolymerization of styrene and methyl methacrylate with data obtained for the same copolymers in diluted systems (benzene and ethyl acetate). The check obtained offers strong support that copolymerization can be expressed in terms of a relative reactivity constant and selectivity constant. He points out that if selectivity is due to complex formation, that is, the complex between a monomer and a radical, the disappearance of the monomers is given by

$$\frac{-d[M_1]}{dt} = k_{m_1}[M_1][R\cdot]k_s{}^1[M_1M_2][R\cdot] \tag{19}$$

$$\frac{-d[M_2]}{dt} = k_{m_2}[M_2][R\cdot]k_s{}^1[M_1M_2][R\cdot] \tag{20}$$

where $[M_1M_2]$ = concentration of reactive complex and $[R\cdot]$ = total radical concentration.

By letting

$$K_c = \frac{[M_1M_2]}{[M_1][M_2]} \tag{21}$$

and

$$k_s = k_s{}^1 K_c \tag{22}$$

and dividing equation 19 by equation 20, we obtain

$$\frac{d[M_1]}{d[M_2]} = \frac{[M_1]}{[M_2]} \times \frac{k_{m_1} + k_s[M_2]}{k_{m_2} + k_s[M_1]} \tag{23}$$

Equation 23 may be integrated, and if $\alpha = k_{m_1}/k_{m_2}$ and $\beta = k_s/k_{m_2}$, the integrated equation becomes

$$\alpha' = \beta \frac{[M_1] - [M_1{}^0] - [M_2] + [M_2{}^0]}{\ln([M_2]/[M_2{}^0])} + \frac{\ln([M_1]/[M_1{}^0])}{\ln([M_2]/[M_2{}^0])} \tag{24}$$

To obtain the solution for α and β it is necessary to conduct the copolymerizations at two different concentrations and to determine the intersection of the two lines obtained by substituting the results in equation 24.

However, the method of Mayo and Lewis,[7] which involves three experiments and the area of the triangle included by the three lines, is more reliable.

If the selectivity is due to dipole interactions or to steric effects, the disappearance of monomers is expressed as

$$-\frac{d[M_1]}{dt} = k_1[M_1][M_1\cdot] + k_4[M_1][M_2\cdot] + k_{sa}[M_1][M_2\cdot] \tag{25}$$

$$-\frac{d[M_2]}{dt} = k_2[M_2][M_1\cdot] + k_3[M_2][M_2\cdot] + k_{sb}[M_2][M_1\cdot] \tag{26}$$

and, assuming selectivity is symmetrical, we have

$$k_{sa}[M_1][M_2\cdot] = k_{sb}[M_2][M_1\cdot] \tag{27}$$

Dividing equation 25 by equation 26, we obtain

$$\frac{d[M_1]}{d[M_2]} = \frac{k_1[M_1][M_1\cdot] + k_4[M_1][M_2\cdot] + k_{sb}[M_2][M_1\cdot]}{k_2[M_2][M_1\cdot] + k_3[M_2][M_2\cdot] + k_{sb}[M_2][M_1\cdot]} \tag{28}$$

and, if the steady state is assumed to be reached rapidly, so that

$$k_4[M_1][M_2\cdot] = k_2[M_2][M_1\cdot] \tag{29}$$

then, by letting $k_1/k_2 = k_4/k_3 = \alpha$, we obtain

$$\frac{dM_1}{dM_2} = \frac{M_1}{M_2} \times \frac{\dfrac{[M_1]}{\dfrac{1}{\alpha} + \dfrac{k_{sb}}{k_1}} + [M_2]}{\dfrac{[M_2]}{\alpha^2\left(\dfrac{1}{\alpha} + \dfrac{k_{sb}}{k_1}\right)} + [M_1]} \tag{30}$$

and, by letting $k_{sb}/k_1 = r$,

$$\frac{dM_1}{dM_2} = \frac{M_1}{M_2} \times \frac{\dfrac{[M_1]}{\dfrac{1}{\alpha} + r} + [M_2]}{\dfrac{[M_2]}{\alpha^2\left(\dfrac{1}{\alpha} + r\right)} + [M_1]} \tag{31}$$

According to the Lewis and Mayo derivation,

$$r_1 = \frac{1}{\dfrac{1}{\alpha} + r} \tag{32}$$

and

$$r_2 = \frac{1}{\alpha^2\left(\dfrac{1}{\alpha} + r\right)} \tag{33}$$

and, since α^2 equals r_1/r_2, the values of α and r may be calculated if r_1 and r_2 are known.

It may be seen that if the selectivity is due to complex formation, the concentration of the complex and, therefore, the selectivity contribution to copolymerization should drop off with dilution. Conversely, a selectivity contribution due to dipole or steric effects should not be changed by dilution, and the calculated values of α and β or r should be more constant in the correct case. A test of these equations was applied to the styrene–methyl methacrylate system studied by Mayo and Lewis [7] and the values of α, β, and r compared with data obtained in diluted systems, as summarized in Table 6.[21]

TABLE 6

STYRENE–METHYL METHACRYLATE COPOLYMERIZATION AT 60 C

Experiment	r_1	r_2	Results Using Equation 24		Results Using Equation 31	
			α	β	α	r
Run 4 *	0.54 ± 0.01	0.50 ± 0.01	1.05	0.118	1.039	0.886
Run 5,*						
undiluted	0.55 ± 0.01	0.47 ± 0.01	1.08	0.125	1.082	0.895
Benzene dilution	0.68 ± 0.05	0.46 ± 0.05	1.21	1.3	1.212	0.655
Ethyl acetate						
dilution	0.63 ± 0.05	0.57 ± 0.05	1.03	1.05	1.052	0.640

* Data from Mayo and Lewis, *J. Am. Chem. Soc.*, **66**, 1594 (1944).
From K. Nozaki, "Reactivity of Monomers in Copolymerization," *J. Polym. Sci.*, **1**, 455 (1946).

A comparison of the α values by both methods shows approximately the same values for diluted and undiluted experiments, but it may be observed that r is relatively constant, whereas the value of β varies tenfold on dilution. This indicates that factors such as dipole and steric effects as well as other factors independent of concentration are more important in copolymerization than complex formation between monomers.

Steric effects may be produced by excessive substitution on the

basic $CH_2=CH_2$ group, such as $CH_2=C$, and symmetrical

substitution is bad, for example, CH=CH .

Effect of substitution at the non-terminal positions on the reactivity of ethylene derivatives with radicals may be interpreted in terms of the stability of the new radicals formed.[22]

If the product is stabilized by resonance, reaction occurs more readily. Thus resonance forms in conjugated systems, in which the odd electrons enter the substituent, make important contributions.[23] Similarly, halogen substitution results in resonance forms of the type, $RC\overset{H}{\underset{H}{-}}C::\overset{..}{X}\cdot$, and methyl group substitution produces possible hyperconjugation forms.

The monomer reactivity ratios in a copolymerization system appear to be independent of the presence of solvents or of other non-polymerizable components in the system. The non-polymerizable component may be a solvent such as benzene, toluene, or xylene, as in the solution polymerization of styrene, or it may be a modifying agent such as an inhibitor or a retarder (see Chapter 8). In both instances such substances act as modifiers by telomerizing the polymerization. We should not expect that the presence of telomerizing bodies would affect the monomer reactivity ratios, since the telomer will influence only the molecular weight of the copolymer by chain termination or chain transfer. It has been shown [24] that monomer-polymer compositions are identical for the acrylonitrile–vinylidene chloride system performed as a mass casting in the presence or absence of carbon tetrachloride. As expected, however, the molecular weight of the copolymer prepared in the presence of carbon tetrachloride was lower than that of the unmodified system, and it was found to contain attached chlorine atoms.

Data have been presented [19] which show that such solvents as benzene, acetonitrile, and methanol are also without effect on the monomer reactivity ratios of the system, styrene–methyl methacrylate.

The Tripolymer Equation

Walling and Briggs,[25] Alfrey and Goldfinger,[26] and Skeist[27] have extended the copolymerization equation to those systems that contain more than two monomers.

The equation for predicting the initial copolymer composition from a monomeric mixture containing three components is given as:

$$\frac{d[M_1]}{d[M_2]} = \frac{\dfrac{[M_1][M_2]}{r_{21}r_{32}} + \dfrac{[M_1]}{r_{31}}\left(\dfrac{[M_1]}{r_{21}} + \dfrac{[M_3]}{r_{23}}\right)}{\dfrac{[M_1][M_2]}{r_{12}r_{31}} + \dfrac{[M_2]}{r_{32}}\left(\dfrac{[M_3]}{r_{12}} + \dfrac{[M_3]}{r_{13}}\right)} \cdot \frac{[M_1] + \dfrac{[M_2]}{r_{12}} + \dfrac{[M_3]}{r_{13}}}{[M_2] + \dfrac{[M_1]}{r_{21}} + \dfrac{[M_3]}{r_{23}}} \tag{34}$$

$$\frac{d[M_1]}{d[M_3]} = \frac{\dfrac{[M_1][M_2]}{r_{21}r_{32}} + \dfrac{[M_1]}{r_{31}}\left(\dfrac{[M_1]}{r_{21}} + \dfrac{[M_3]}{r_{23}}\right)}{\dfrac{[M_1][M_3]}{r_{13}r_{21}} + \dfrac{[M_3]}{r_{23}}\left(\dfrac{[M_2]}{r_{12}} + \dfrac{[M_3]}{r_{13}}\right)} \cdot \frac{[M_1] + \dfrac{[M_2]}{r_{12}} + \dfrac{[M_3]}{r_{13}}}{[M_3] + \dfrac{[M_1]}{r_{31}} + \dfrac{[M_2]}{r_{32}}} \tag{35}$$

where $[M_1]$, $[M_2]$, and $[M_3]$ represent monomer concentrations of the three components; $d[M_1]$, $d[M_2]$, and $d[M_3]$ represent the amounts of combined comonomers in the polymer molecules first formed; and r_{12}, r_{21}, r_{13}, r_{31}, r_{23}, and r_{32} are the monomer reactivity ratio parameters for the three 2-component systems involved.

Chapin, Ham, and Fordyce [28] examined the validity of the tripolymer equation for the systems styrene–vinyl chloride–methyl acrylate and styrene–vinyl chloride–acrylonitrile, and the agreement between the predicted and actual copolymer compositions was within the limit of experimental error.

The Characterization of Individual Monomers

Alfrey and Price [29] proposed a method that would characterize an individual monomer by relating the two copolymerization ratios r_1 and r_2 to a definite set of constants Q and e. The constant Q is related to the reactivity of the radical adduct formed from a given monomer as primarily influenced by the possibilities of resonance stabilization. Thus styrene exhibits a marked tendency to add to any given free radical because the resulting adduct free radical is stabilized by resonance. Vinyl acetate, as distinct from styrene, shows a weak tendency to add to any given free radical because the resulting radical adduct is not stabilized by resonance. The constant e is related to the polar effects of the substituent groups in the monomer.

The substituent group may be one that withdraws electrons from the polarizable double bond, and such a group will give the double bond a positive character; consequently, the free radical will have a positive character. Such a substituent is the nitrile group, which in aromatic compounds directs further substitution to a meta position. The opposite type of substituent is electron donating and contributes a negative polarity to the double bond of the monomer and to the corresponding free radical. A free radical with a positive polarity reacts preferentially with a monomer with a highly negative double bond, and a free radical with a negative polarity reacts with a monomer with a positive double bond. These authors [29] analyzed the data of Mayo, Lewis, and Hulse [13] and derived an approximate relation for the addition of a monomer of type two, M_2, to the radical of type one, $M_1 \cdot$, as

$$K_{12} = A_{12} e^{-(p_1 + q_2 + e_1 e_2)} \qquad (36)$$

where A_{12} represents the probability factor,

  p_1 is an activation factor related to the general reactivity of the polymer end group,

  q_2 is an activation factor related to general monomer reactivity,

e_1 and e_2 are two electrical factors.

On the general consideration that all vinyl monomers have one free methylene end, the assumption is made that the factor A will be constant, and the equation can be modified to

$$K_{12} = P_1 Q_2^{-e_1 e_2} \tag{37}$$

where P_1 is characteristic of the radical, $M_1 \cdot$,

Q_2 is the mean reactivity of monomer, M_2,

e_1 is proportional to the charge on the end of the radical, $M_1 \cdot$,.

e_2 is proportional to the charge on the double bond of monomer, M_2.

The expression for the rate at which the monomer, M_1, competes for its own radical, $M_1 \cdot$, is given by

$$K_{11} = P_1 Q_1^{-e_1} \tag{38}$$

and the relative rate is

$$r_1 = \frac{K_{11}}{K_{12}} = \frac{P_1 Q_1^{-e_1}}{P_1 Q_2^{-e_1 e_2}} = \left(\frac{Q_1}{Q_2}\right) e^{-e_1(e_1 - e_2)} \tag{39}$$

Similarly,

$$r_2 = \frac{K_{21}}{K_{22}} = \left(\frac{Q_1}{Q_2}\right) e^{-e_2(e_1 - e_2)} \tag{40}$$

Alfrey and Price calculated the Q and e values from published data [13] (see Table 2) on copolymers of styrene, methyl methacrylate, acrylonitrile, and vinylidene chloride. They were determined to be:

Monomer	Q	e
Styrene	1.00	−1
Methyl methacrylate	0.64	0
Acrylonitrile	0.34	+1
Vinylidene chloride	0.16	0

The decreasing values of Q seem to agree well with the theoretical expressions based on resonance stabilization. Styrene exhibits the greatest number of resonance structures for the radical formed by the addition to its chain and, therefore, appears as the most reactive of these four monomers. Methyl methacrylate is second, acrylonitrile is third, and vinylidene chloride, which has no true conjugation, is last. The values of e are also consistent with the hypothesis that the double bond in styrene is electron-rich and, therefore, negative; the double bond in acrylonitrile is electron-poor and, therefore, positive; and the double bonds in methyl methacrylate and vinylidene chloride are approximately neutral. It may be concluded, therefore, that the rela-

TABLE 7

MONOMER REACTIVITY FACTORS

Monomer₁	e	Q	Monomer₂	References
(1) α-Methylstyrene	−1.2	0.70	Methyl methacrylate	8
	−1.1	0.55	Acrylonitrile	10
	−0.8	0.50	Methacrylonitrile	10
(2) p-Dimethylamino-styrene	−1.2	1.35	Styrene	7
	−1.55	1.66	Methyl methacrylate	7
(3) Isobutylene	−1.1	0.2	Vinyl chloride	6
(4) p-Methoxystyrene	−1.0	1.0	Styrene	7
	−1.1	1.22	Methyl methacrylate	7
	−1.1	1.23	p-Chlorostyrene (A)	7
(5) p-Methylstyrene	−0.9	1.05	Methyl methacrylate	7
	−0.9	0.92	p-Chlorostyrene (A)	7
(6) m-Methylstyrene	−0.8	0.95	Methyl methacrylate	7
(7) α-Vinylthiophene	−0.8	3.0	Styrene	8
(8) Styrene	(−0.8)	(1.0)	. . . . .	
(9) Butadiene	−0.8	1.33	Styrene	6
(10) p-Chlorostyrene (A)	−0.8	0.88	Styrene	7
p-Chlorostyrene (B)	−0.6	1.20	Methyl methacrylate	7
(11) p-Iodostyrene	−0.3	1.08	Styrene	7
	−0.6	1.28	Methyl methacrylate	7
(12) m-Chlorostyrene	−0.2	0.96	Styrene	7
	−0.5	1.05	Methyl methacrylate	7
(13) o-Chlorostyrene	−0.5	1.41	Styrene	8
	−0.2	1.15	Methyl methacrylate	8
(14) p-Bromostyrene	−0.2	0.88	Styrene	7
	−0.5	1.27	Methyl methacrylate	7
(15) m-Bromostyrene	−0.1	0.98	Styrene	7
	−0.4	1.20	Methyl methacrylate	7
(16) α-Vinylpyridine	−0.1	1.07	Styrene	8
	−0.6	1.09	Methyl methacrylate	8
(17) Vinyl acetate (A)	−0.1	0.022	Vinylidene chloride	1
Vinyl acetate (B)	−0.3	0.028	Methyl acrylate [a]	4
	−0.4	0.026	Methyl methacrylate [b]	4
	−0.3	0.047	Allyl chloride	1
	−0.5	0.010	Vinyl chloride (A)	1
	−0.8	0.015	Vinyl chloride	4
	−0.9	0.022	Vinylidene chloride	5
(18) Vinyl bromide	0.1	0.1	Vinyl acetate (B)	4
(19) Vinyl chloride (A)	0.2	0.024	Styrene	5
	0.0	0.035	Methyl acrylate	2
	0.4	0.074	Methyl methacrylate	1
(20) p-Cyanostyrene	0.3	1.61	Styrene	7
	(−0.7?)	(2.26?)	Methyl methacrylate	7
(21) p-Nitrostyrene	0.4	1.86	Styrene	7
	0.4	1.06	p-Chlorostyrene (A)	7
(22) 2,5-Dichlorostyrene	0.4	1.67	Methyl methacrylate	1
(23) Methyl methacrylate	0.4	0.74	Styrene	3
(24) Vinylidene chloride	0.6	0.2	Styrene	5
(25) Allyl chloride	0.6	0.052	Vinylidene chloride	1
(26) Methyl acrylate	0.6	0.42	Styrene	3
(27) Methyl vinyl ketone	0.7	1.0	Styrene	6
(28) β-Chloroethyl acrylate	0.9	0.46	Styrene	6

TABLE **7** (*Continued*)

MONOMER REACTIVITY FACTORS

Monomer₁	e	Q	Monomer₂	References
(29) Methacrylonitrile (A)	1.0	1.0	Styrene	6
	0.9	1.15	Styrene	10
	0.9	1.06	Vinyl acetate [c]	10
	1.3	1.5	Methyl methacrylate	6
(30) Acrylonitrile (A)	0.9	0.68	Methyl vinyl ketone [d]	6
Acrylonitrile (B)	0.9	0.37	Vinyl acetate (B)	4
Acrylonitrile (C)	1.0	0.67	Vinyl acetate (B) [e]	10
	1.2	0.44	Styrene	9
	1.3	0.37	Vinyl chloride	2
	1.6	0.9	Vinylidene chloride	5
	1.6	0.75	Vinyl chloride [f]	5
(31) Diethyl fumarate	1.2	0.77	Styrene	3
	1.4	0.028	Vinylidene chloride	5
	1.9	0.28	Vinyl chloride	5

References. The values of Q and e were calculated from the data given in the following references:

1. P. Agron, T. Alfrey, J. Bohrer, H. Haas, and H. Wicksler, *J. Polymer Sci.*, **3**, 157 (1948).
2. E. C. Chapin, G. E. Ham, and R. G. Fordyce, *J. Am. Chem. Soc.*, **70**, 538 (1948).
3. F. M. Lewis, C. Walling, W. Cummings, E. R. Briggs, and F. R. Mayo, *J. Am. Chem. Soc.*, **70**, 1519 (1948).
4. F. R. Mayo, C. Walling, F. M. Lewis, and W. F. Hulse, *J. Am. Chem. Soc.*, **70**, 1523 (1948).
5. K. W. Doak, *J. Am. Chem. Soc.*, **70**, 1525 (1948).
6. F. M. Lewis, C. Walling, W. Cummings, E. R. Briggs, and W. J. Wenisch, *J. Am. Chem. Soc.*, **70**, 1527 (1948).
7. C. Walling, E. R. Briggs, K. B. Wolfstirn, and F. R. Mayo, *J. Am. Chem. Soc.*, **70**, 1537 (1948).
8. C. Walling, E. R. Briggs, and K. B. Wolfstirn, *J. Am. Chem. Soc.*, **70**, 1543 (1948).
9. F. R. Mayo, F. M. Lewis, and W. F. Hulse, *J. Am. Chem. Soc.*, **67**, 1701 (1945).
10. R. G. Fordyce, E. C. Chapin, and G. E. Ham, *J. Am. Chem. Soc.*, **70**, 2489 (1948).

[a] The value for r_2 is given as 0.1 ± 0.1; the value used for the calculations was chosen as 0.05.

[b] The value for r_2 is given as 0.015 ± 0.015; the value used for the calculations of Q and e in the table was 0.025. Using $r_2 = 0.015$. $e = -0.7$, and $Q = 0.022$.

[c] Using $r_1 = 12.0$ and $r_2 = 0.02$.

[d] The values for r_1 and r_2, 1.78 ± 0.22 and 0.61 ± 0.04, respectively, give a product greater than the theoretical maximum of unity. The lower limits in each case were therefore used in the calculation of Q and e.

[e] Using $r_1 = 6.0$ and $r_2 = 0.03$.

[f] The value for r_1 is given as 0.02 ± 0.02; the value used for the calculations was chosen as 0.04.

From C. C. Price, "Some Relative Monomer Reactivity Factors," *J. Polym. Sci.*, **3**, 772 (1948). Interscience Publishers, Inc.

tive rate of addition of a neutral monomer to any radical, or a neutral radical to any monomer, will be determined by the overall reactivity, Q, of the monomers. Likewise, it would be expected that the rate of addition of styrene to styrene radical, and of addition of acrylonitrile to acrylonitrile radicals, should be lower than the value expected on the basis of their mean reactivities because of electrostatic repulsion. On the other hand, the rate of addition of styrene monomer to acrylonitrile radicals, or of acrylonitrile monomer to styrene radicals, should be increased by electrostatic attraction.

Price has recently published [30] the list of Q and e values for thirty-one monomers. These values, summarized in Table 7,[30] show that the calculated values agree quite satisfactorily with the expected values, and that the constants calculated from independent data are largely within the expected limit of experimental error. It is evident that the most notable deviations occur where a steric hindrance could be a complicating factor, such as the case in which one or both of the monomers possess two bulky substituent groups, as, for example, in the copolymerization of diethyl fumarate with vinylidene chloride.

Walling and his co-workers [31] have shown that there was a satisfactory agreement between the copolymerization ratio and Hammett's σ (sigma) constant [32] for the copolymerization of substituted styrenes with styrene, but not for the substituted styrene with methyl methacrylate. This apparent inconsistency was interpreted in terms of resonance stabilization of a one-electron transfer complex as a contributing structure to the transition state. Price [30] points out that, since Hammett's σ constant is derived from the influence of substituent groups

TABLE 8

Substituent	Δe	σ
p-Dimethylamino	−0.6	−0.44
p-Methoxy	−0.3	−0.27
p-Methyl	−0.1	−0.17
m-Methyl	0	−0.07
Hydrogen	(0)	(0)
p-Chloro	0.35	0.23
p-Iodo	0.35	0.28
p-Bromo	0.15	0.23
m-Chloro	0.45	0.37
m-Bromo	0.55	0.38
p-Cyano	1.1	1.0
p-Nitro	1.2	1.27

From C. C. Price, "Some Relative Monomer Reactivity Factors," *J. Polym. Sci.*, **3**, 772 (1948). Interscience Publishers, Inc.

in benzene derivatives on polar reactions and is, therefore, a polar factor, it is more reasonable to expect the correlation of Hammett's constant with the only polar factor in copolymerization, the e constant. The excellent correlation is shown in Table 8.[30]

Thus, in copolymerization the Q and e treatment appears to be in accord both with the theoretical considerations and with the experimental data.

SUMMARY OF CONDITIONS AFFECTING POLYMERIZATION

Copolymerization processes may be summarized as being very complicated systems in which the rates of copolymerization, as well as the composition of the copolymer as functions of the monomers, depend on many factors. Probably the first factor is the initiation of the reaction which may vary with the nature of the monomer and free radical type or source of generation. This rate and the tendency of a monomer to add to a radical are deciding factors. Some of the general factors affecting copolymerization as well as polymerization are conjugation in the monomer, the polarity of the double bond, the effect of substitution on this polarity, the extent and type of substitution and the resulting steric disturbance, the coplanar characteristics of the disubstituted monomers, the presence of another monomer and the derived monomer radical, the preference of one monomer to add to another radical in preference to a radical derived from its own species, or the change in the rate of addition of a monomer to add to its own monomer radical in the presence of another different monomer or radical, and the possible formation of radical monomer complexes. The complicated nature of copolymerization is evident in systems of monomer pairs such as styrene and vinyl acetate which individually polymerize very well, but copolymerize poorly. A similar situation is known for the monomer pair of vinyl chloride and dichlorostyrene, which as yet have not been reported to have been copolymerized.[33] Conversely, there are monomer pairs which individually do not polymerize, such as stilbene and maleic anhydride, but do copolymerize.

It is evident from the preceding discussion that many factors influence the polymerization of ethylenic compounds. The first and most important is the monomer itself, and includes the nature, type, and

extent of substitution in the basic ethylene group, $\begin{matrix} R_I & R_{III} \\ | & | \\ C{=}C \\ | & | \\ R_{II} & R_{IV} \end{matrix}$. The electronegative substitution and steric facts appear to be the dominating factors. The next important factor is the method of initiation, as to whether it is accomplished by thermal, photochemical, catalytic, or ionic radiation methods. The catalytic methods are most common, and many monomers which are not initiated by the R· type of radical are readily polymerized by an ionic mechanism. The normal radical type may be subjected to reduction activation and the inhibition period reduced.

The conditions under which the polymerizations are performed is next in importance. The final properties of the polymer depend on the amount of catalyst used. High concentrations of catalyst increase the rate of polymerization but decrease the molecular weight. An increase in temperature has the same effect. When the polymerization is performed in solution, the molecular weight is lowered; and the lower the concentration of the monomer, the lower the molecular weight. Pearl polymerization is substantially a mass polymerization system, but owing to the dispersion process thermal control is more effective. On the other hand, emulsion systems are complicated when contrasted with mass and solution polymerization, and the molecular weights are higher than those obtained by solution or mass polymerization methods. Furthermore, reduction activation is readily applied to emulsion systems.

The presence of modifiers of any type complicates any polymerization system, regardless of whether they are called inhibitors, retarders, regulators, activators, or telomers. Fragments of carbon tetrachloride were shown to be combined in the polymer molecule. Dodecyl mercaptan, which may be used to prevent branching and crosslinking in diene polymers, was also shown to be combined in the polymer molecule.

Copolymerization systems are especially complicated. Comonomers, which do not form copolymers in mass or solution, sometimes form copolymers in emulsion, and, conversely, if copolymers form in an emulsion system they may or may not form in mass or solution. Similarly, a molecule which does not polymerize alone may copolymerize with another monomer which does polymerize alone. More interesting than this is the fact that two molecules, neither of which polymerizes alone, will coreact to give a copolymer.

The reactivity and specificity of the comonomers and comers used for the preparation of copolymers are a most important variable. The composition of the copolymer was shown to depend not only on these factors but also on steric and electrical factors, and in a copolymer derived from two molecules, four rate steps occur in the initiation. It was also shown that the rate of copolymerization of a specific monomer, M_1, with two different monomers, M_2 and M_3, respectively, may be faster with M_2 than with M_3, although the ratio of M_1 to M_3 monomers in the polymer is higher than M_1 to M_2. As will be shown later in this chapter, the arrangement of the copolymer units may take different orders and the polymer may be head to tail,

$$—CH_2—CH—CH_2—CH—, \text{ or tail to tail, } —CH_2—CH—CH—CH_2—$$
$$\qquad\ \ |\qquad\quad |\qquad\qquad\qquad\qquad\qquad\quad |\quad\ |$$
$$\qquad\ \ X\qquad\quad X\qquad\qquad\qquad\qquad\qquad\ X\quad X$$

and the stability, both thermal and photochemical, depends on the ratio of the components of the copolymer and on its arrangement.

RATE CONSTANTS OF POLYMERIZATION STEPS

A number of investigators have attempted to determine the absolute rate constants for the elementary steps of initiation, propagation, and termination. Melville [34] determined the mean lifetime of the free radicals in a methyl methacrylate polymerization induced by hydrogen atoms photochemically produced. This study was accomplished by the rotating-sector method. The exciting light is interrupted by means of a slotted disk rotating at controlled speeds and yielding equal periods of darkness and of light. The dependence of the overall rate of polymerization on the sector speed yielded [35] the determination of the average life of the free radicals. Bartlett and Swain [36, 37] applied the rotating-sector method to the determination of the rate constants in the polymerization of liquid vinyl acetate. Melville and Burnett [38] have also studied and derived the rate constant values for vinyl acetate polymerization.

Bartlett and his co-workers [21, 37] determined the value of the decomposition of benzoyl peroxide in ethyl acetate, k_1, to be 3.9×10^{-8} mole per liter per second, and the energy of activation of the decomposition to be 28.3 calories. This k_1 value was derived from a ratio of the measured rates of polymerization (8.4×10^{-5} mole per liter per second) and the determination of the rate constants of the spontaneous (k_1) and the radical induced peroxide polymerization (k_i). In this case,

$$k_1 = \text{rate constant for initiation} = 0.02k_i$$

$$= 3.9 \times 10^{-8} \text{ mole per liter per second}$$

$$k_2 = \text{the rate constant for propagation value}$$

$$= 1.1 \times 10^3 \text{ mole per liter per second}$$

$$k_3 = \text{the termination} = 8 \times 10^7 \text{ moles per liter per second}$$

Dewar and Bamford [39, 40] have determined the rate constants in the irradiation polymerization of methyl methacrylate and reported the following values:

$$k_p = 150 \text{ moles per liter per second}$$

$$k_t = 1.3 \times 10^7 \text{ moles per liter per second}$$

DEGRADATION OF POLYMERS

All polymers, whether they are prepared by an addition or condensation reaction, can be degraded. The degradation can be produced by chemical or physical methods or by a combination of both. Physical means, such as the milling of a polymer, are equivalent to a thermal treatment since mechanical energy is converted to thermal energy in such a process. The degradation of a polymer does not necessarily regenerate the materials from which the polymer was prepared.

Condensation Polymers

CHEMICAL DEGRADATION

The simplest chemical degradation that could be studied involves the reversal of the condensation reaction, that is, since the polymer was built up by the elimination of a simple molecule the addition of a simple molecule to the polymer should cause degradation. The hydrolysis of a polyester with water to produce the original hydroxy acids is a typical example. The hydrolysis in strong acids by splitting of the β-glucoside linkages between the structural units of the cellulose chain was studied by Kuhn [41, 42] and Freudenberg and his co-workers.[43, 44] These investigators found a continuous increase in the first-order velocity constant of the linkages over the range of hydrolysis from 10 to 100 per cent, corresponding to a $\overline{DP}_n$ change from 10 to 1. This change showed that the linkages initially present split with greater difficulty than the linkages remaining near the completion of the degradation. These investigators examined the hydrolysis in 51 per cent sulfuric acid at 18 C of several lower polysaccharides, where n in the following formula equals 2, 3, and 4, respectively:

$$HO(C_6H_{10}O_4)-[O(C_6H_{10}O_4)]_{n-2}-O(C_6H_{10}O_4)OH$$
a   [c   ]   b

and determined the initial rate constants expressed as the fraction of linkages disappearing per minute, as summarized in Table 9.[42]

TABLE 9

Value of n	Polysaccharide	Initial Rate Constant	Schematic Structure
2	Cellobiose	1.07×10^{-4}	$a \mid b$
3	Cellotriose	0.65×10^{-4}	$a \mid c \mid b$
4	Cellotetrose	0.51×10^{-4}	$a \mid c \mid c \mid b$
Up to 10	Cellulose, low mol. wt.	0.305×10^{-4}	$a \mid [c]_{n-2} \mid b$

These investigators showed that cellobiose bonds were hydrolyzed according to a first-order expression, whereas when n became greater than 2, as in the triose, tetrose, and cellulose, the first-order rate constants increased as the reaction progressed. The course of hydrolysis is in good agreement with Kuhn's calculations of consecutive reactions [42] that one or both of the terminal linkages, a and b, in these polymers hydrolyze more readily than the c or internal linkages. It is assumed that in a polymer of n greater than 2, the a and b linkages hydrolyze at a rate equal to the cellobiose linkages, that is, at 1.07×10^{-4} per minute, and the rest of the link at a rate of 0.305×10^{-4} per minute. The degradation of cellulose with $\overline{DP}$ values 130 to 1500 by phosphoric acid was studied by Schulz and Lohmann.[45] They found that at regular intervals of $\overline{DP}$ of 500, linkages occur which are hydrolyzed more readily than β-glucoside linkages. From a degree of polymerization of 500 or more, the hydrolysis of linkages in the cellulose chain is of the first order. In general, however, the results indicated that the internal linkages are equivalent in their reactivity toward hydrolysis regardless of the location in the chain and regardless of the length of the chain.

The studies of the hydrolytic degradation of gelatin by a number of investigators, Scatchard and his co-workers,[46] Montroll and Simha,[47] and Sakurada and Okamura,[48] appear to show that all the linkages in the gelatin molecules are equally susceptible to hydrolysis and that their rates are independent of molecular weight.

The hydrolyses of polyamides of aminocaproic acid by 40 per cent sulfuric acid at 50 C were investigated by Matthes [49] and were found to be in strict accordance with a first-order splitting of the amide linkage over the $\overline{DP}$ range of 220 to 6. Flory [50] studied the degradation of polyesters by alcoholysis rather than by hydrolysis, according to the equation

$$-[OC(CR_2)_x COO(CR_2^1)_y O]_n - \xrightarrow{R''OH}$$

$$-[OC(CR_2)_x COO(CR_2^1)_y O]_{\overline{n-1}} - OC(CR_2)_x COOR'' + HO(CR_2^1)_y O-$$

This reaction was investigated by means of the relation between molecular weight and melt viscosity.[51] If all the ester groups were equally reactive, the alcoholysis degradation reaction should be first order with respect to the alcohol. Decamethylene adipate polyesters of $\overline{DP}$, 35 to 40, were degraded by small amounts of lauryl alcohol or decamethylene glycol at 109 C with 0.1 equivalent per cent of p-toluenesulfonic acid. The $\overline{DP}$ values of the degraded polymers ranged between 15 and 20, and the reaction was of the first order. In polyesterification degradation, such as in hydrolysis and alcoholysis, it may be concluded that the mechanism of the polyester degradation follows the reverse course of the polymerization reaction. In an analogous manner to the alcoholysis reaction, amide interchange appears to be responsible for the growth of a number of polyamides. As an example may be mentioned the polymerization of the cyclic lactams, specifically caprolactam. Once polymerization is initiated,[52-54]

$$NH(CH_2)_5 CO + H_2O \rightarrow HOOC(CH_2)_5 NH_2$$

growth of the polymer chain occurs by amide exchange on either the carboxyl or the amino group, or both of the amino acids, thus:

$$HOOC(CH_2)_5 NH_2$$

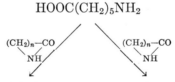

$$HOOC(CH_2)_n NHOC(CH_2)_5 NH_2 \qquad HOOC(CH_2)_5 NHOC(CH_2)_n NH_2$$

and the continued amide exchange along the chain results in a polymer. If the polymerization is initiated by relatively few amino (or carboxyl) groups, equivalent in this case to the molar quantity of water, the final molecular weight will be sharp.[55] If the reaction conditions are such that interchange reactions can also occur, that is, that all the reactants are in the form of amino acids, $NH_2(CH_2)_5 COOH$, which corresponds to the limiting case of one mole of water per mole of amino acid, a wider distribution curve will be obtained.

The mechanism of ring opening for the initiation reaction and the amide exchange reaction for the propagation, as indicated above, is equivalent to the carbonium ion mechanism indicated in a previous chapter. With water as the initiating substance, the carbonium ion reaction for caprolactam polymers may be indicated as follows:

$$HOH \rightarrow H^+ + {}^-OH$$

$$H^+ + (CH_2)_5 \overset{NH}{\underset{CO}{\diagup\big|\diagdown}} \rightarrow NH_2(CH_2)_5CO^+ \xrightarrow{\quad n(CH_2)_5 \overset{NH}{\underset{CO}{\diagup\big|\diagdown}} \quad}$$

$$H[NH(CH_2)_5CO]_n NHCH_2CO^+$$

or

$$H_2O + (CH_2)_5 \overset{NH}{\underset{CO}{\diagup\big|\diagdown}} \rightarrow NH_2(CH_2)_5COOH \rightarrow NH_2(CH_2)_5CO^+ + {}^-OH$$

$$NH_2(CH_2)_5CO^+ \xrightarrow{\quad n(CH_2)_5 \overset{NH}{\underset{CO}{\diagup\big|\diagdown}} \quad} H[NH(CH_2)_5CO]_n NHCH_2CO^+$$

and the termination reaction becomes

$$H[NH(CH_2)_5CO]_n NH(CH_2)_5CO^+ + {}^-OH \rightarrow$$
$$H[NH(CH_2)_5CO]_n NH(CH_2)_5COOH$$

THERMAL DEGRADATION

Formation of rings. Most condensation polymers undergo pyrolytic decomposition when heated sufficiently high, and this is particularly true if the polymer is crosslinked, as in the phenol-formaldehyde, melamine-formaldehyde polymers, etc. A number of linear condensation polymers can be converted to compounds which represent the segmer of the polymer or a multiple of the segmer. Usually these products of thermal degradation are cyclic monomeric or dimeric compounds. Generally, it may be stated that those linear condensation polymers which can undergo exchange reaction to form five- or six-membered rings may be thermally degraded to cyclic compounds. The reversibility of these polymers has already been considered in a previous chapter, where reference was made, among others, to (1) the six- and seven-membered rings obtained through the reversibility of the polyesters of ω-hydroxy acids, (2) the dimers from polyesters of α-hydroxy acids, and (3) the seven-membered rings of the polyalkylene formals.

Interchange reactions. Flory has studied [56, 57] the degradation of condensation polymers that occur during interchange reactions between polymers themselves. With polyesters used as examples, the interchange may occur between:

1. The terminal hydroxyl of one polymer chain and the ester group in another polymer chain.
2. The terminal carboxyl group of one polymer chain and the ester group in another polymer chain.
3. Polyester chains of two identical polymer molecules of different $\overline{DP}$ values, that is, one of low molecular weight and the other of high molecular weight; for example, two polyethylene succinates, one of low and the other of high molecular weight.
4. Polyester chains of two different polymer molecules, of either the same or different $\overline{DP}$ values; for example, a low or high molecular weight polyethylene succinate and a low or high molecular weight polytrimethylene adipate.

The occurrence of interchange reactions between a low average molecular weight and a high average molecular weight polydecamethylene adipate was studied [56] in the presence of p-toluene sulfonic acid. Flory studied this reaction by means of melt viscosity and weight average molecular weights, $\overline{M}_w$. The $\overline{M}_w$ value is shifted as molecular weight distribution is altered at constant $\overline{M}_n$. These data are shown in Figure 6.

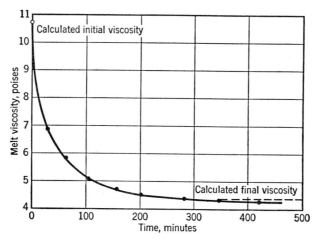

FIGURE 6. Interchange reaction between two polydecamethylene adipate polymers at 109 C catalyzed by p-toluenesulfonic acid. Melt viscosity vs. time of reaction. Initial mixture: 42.4 per cent of polymer for which $\overline{M}_n = 6200$, and 57.6 per cent of polymer having $\overline{M}_n = 1860$. The horizontal broken line indicates the viscosity calculated for the theoretical equilibrium molecular-weight distribution. (From P. Flory, "Principles of Condensation Polymerization," *Chemical Reviews*, **39**, 168 [1946]. The Williams and Wilkins Company, Baltimore, publishers.)

The distribution is identical with that obtained directly from the random intermolecular condensation, and the final viscosity of the interchange reaction is reasonably close to the calculated equilibrium distribution having the number-average molecular weight dictated by the proportions and molecular weight of the original reactants. Brubaker and his co-workers [58] have shown that exchange reactions occur in polyamides. They studied the exchange between two different polyamides from two different sets of comers. One polymer was formed from trimethylenediamine and adipic acid, and the other from hexamethylenediamine and adipic acid. When these two polymers were reacted at 285 C for about 30 minutes, a polymer mass differing from both initial polymers is obtained.

Many polymers may be prepared by either an addition or a condensation reaction. As an example, the polyamide of ϵ-aminocaproic acid may be prepared by condensation of the aminocaproic acid itself (equation a) or by the self-addition of caprolactam under catalytic influence (equations b or c).

(a) $(n + 1)NH_2(CH_2)_5COOH \rightarrow H[NH(CH_2)_5CO]_nNH(CH_2)_5COOH$

(b) $(CH_2)_5 \begin{smallmatrix} NH \\ | \\ CO \end{smallmatrix} + H^+ \rightarrow NH_2(CH_2)_5CO^+ \quad n(CH_2)_5 \begin{smallmatrix} CO \\ | \\ NH \end{smallmatrix} \longrightarrow$

$$H[NH(CH_2)_5CO]_nNH(CH_2)_5CO^+$$

(c) $(CH_2)_5 \begin{smallmatrix} NH \\ | \\ CO \end{smallmatrix} + H_2O \rightarrow NH_2(CH_2)_5COOH \quad n(CH_2)_5 \begin{smallmatrix} CO \\ | \\ NH \end{smallmatrix} \longrightarrow$

$$H[NH(CH_2)_5CO]_nNH(CH_2)_5COOH$$

The mechanism of the addition polymerization of ring compounds, for example, ethylene oxide, ethylene imine, caprolactam, is not similar to the addition polymerization of the vinyl or $CH_2{=}C\diagdown^{\diagup}$ compounds. The overall polymerization of ring compounds does not represent a kinetic chain reaction. The specific rate of the ring opening step is comparable to the specific rate of each succeeding monomer addition.

Usually they proceed by interchange reactions under the influence of catalysts or end-producing groups.[56] All the polymers in a ring-chain polymerization undergo practically simultaneous growth throughout the polymerization, and as the polymerization is continued, not only is the amount of polymer increased but also the average molecular weight is increased. Expressing it differently, the molecular weight of the ring addition polymerizations may be controlled by discontinuing the reaction at any stage, and isolating monomer and polymer, whereas in the vinyl-type addition polymerization, interruption of polymerization results only in a lower conversion of monomer to polymer. However, continuing the polymerization does not increase the molecular weight of the polymers already formed. Polymers prepared from ring addition compounds follow the kinetics of condensation polymers and resemble vinyl addition polymers *only* in that they add monomer to polymer.

Addition Polymers

CHEMICAL DEGRADATION

In addition polymers, except for those polymers that are susceptible to simple degradation reactions, such as hydrolysis, catalytic degradations are usually too drastic to be of technical value. Fundamental information, however, can be readily obtained by studying the reactions or degradations that can be carried out on the substituents or side chains attached to the polymer.

Side chain reactions and proof of structure. Ostromislensky [59] was among the first to attempt the proof of the structure of polyvinyl halides by treating the polymers with zinc and obtaining a rubberlike product. He believed that the dehalogenated polyvinyl bromide was related to butadiene, and on making certain comparisons to polybutadiene bromide concluded that these polymers were identical, thus:

$$n\text{CH}_2\text{=}\text{CHBr} \rightarrow (\text{—CH}_2\text{CH—})_n$$
$$\underset{\text{Vinyl bromide}}{} \qquad \underset{\substack{| \\ \text{Br} \\ \text{Polymer}}}{}$$

$$(\text{—CH}_2\text{—CH=CH—CH}_2\text{—})_n \xrightarrow{\text{Br}_2} (\text{—CH}_2\text{—CH—CH—CH}_2\text{—})_n$$
$$\underset{\text{Polybutadiene}}{} \qquad \qquad \underset{\substack{| \quad | \\ \text{Br} \quad \text{Br} \\ \text{Polybutadiene dibromide}}}{}$$

Harries [60] objected to this conclusion, and no further evidence was offered until Staudinger [61] reinvestigated the reaction of zinc on polyvinyl bromide. The evidence establishing the relation of halogen atoms along the chain, however, was not conclusive. Marvel et al.[62]

found that when a dilute solution of polyvinyl chloride in dioxane is heated with zinc, steady removal of the chlorine occurs, and the polymer remains soluble. After 84 to 86 per cent of the chlorine is removed, no further removal of the chlorine occurs, even when the heating is continued for several hundred hours. From a study of these data, the question arises as to the relation of the chlorine atoms to each other along the chain. When a substituted vinyl monomer polymerizes, it may take two regular arrangements:

Head-to-Tail Arrangement:

$$n\text{CH}_2\text{=CH} \rightarrow \text{—CH}_2\text{CH—CH}_2\text{CH—CH}_2\text{CH—CH}_2\text{CH—}$$
$$\quad\;\; | \qquad\qquad | \qquad | \qquad | \qquad |$$
$$\quad\;\; \text{X} \qquad\qquad \text{X} \quad\;\; \text{X} \quad\;\; \text{X} \quad\;\; \text{X}$$

and the halogens are substituted 1,3.

Head-to-Head or Tail-to-Tail Arrangement:

$$n\text{CH}_2\text{=CH} \rightarrow \text{—CHCH}_2\text{—CH}_2\text{CH—CHCH}_2\text{—CH}_2\text{CH—}$$
$$\quad\;\; | \qquad\qquad | \qquad | \qquad | \quad\; | \qquad |$$
$$\quad\;\; \text{X} \qquad\qquad \text{X} \quad\;\; \text{X} \quad\;\; \text{X} \quad\; \text{X}$$

and the halogens are paired 1,2.

Flory,[63] Wall,[64, 65] and Simha [66] treated the removal of substituents mathematically, and statistically derived probabilities for pairs of groups in a chain which might react with each other to form ring closures, etc. There was the chance as well that occasional groups would become isolated, thus:

$$\text{—CH}_2\text{CH—CH}_2\text{CH—CH}_2\text{CH—CH}_2\text{CH—CH}_2\text{CH—CH}_2\text{CH—CH}_2\text{CH—}$$

Their calculations show that 86.47 per cent of the groups will react in pairs and that 13.53 per cent will be isolated. It is obvious that all the halogen would be removed from the 1,2 substitution. Marvel's value of 84 to 86 per cent agrees remarkably well with the statistically calculated data for a 1,3 substitution.

Since the dehalogenated polymer was soluble, and since it contained no unsaturation, cyclopropane units were apparently formed along the chain,

$$\text{—CH}_2\text{—CH——CH—CH}_2\text{—CH—CH}_2\text{—CH——CH—CH}_2\text{—}$$
$$\qquad\quad \backslash\;/ \qquad\qquad | \qquad\qquad \backslash\;/$$
$$\qquad\quad \text{CH}_2 \qquad\qquad \text{Cl} \qquad\qquad \text{CH}_2$$

In contrast to this, polyvinyl bromide reacts with zinc to give complete removal of bromine.[67] The fact that neither the bromide nor the chloride liberates iodine from KI would indicate that neither is a 1,2 arrangement. Marvel explained these contradictory facts by determining the stability of the bromide in the absence of zinc. It was found that when polyvinyl bromide is refluxed alone in dioxane most of the bromine was liberated as hydrogen bromide.

Marvel and his co-workers [4] extended their studies of dehalogenation to the vinyl chloride–vinyl acetate copolymer series. Wall [64, 65] calculated statistically how much chlorine would be removed by zinc from such copolymers, assuming that the orientation of each monomer was "head-to-tail" and that the vinyl chloride and vinyl acetate were distributed in the chain according to chance. He also calculated the amount of chlorine that would be removed if the orientation of the monomers were entirely at random.

For the 1,3 orientation he derives the formula

$$f = e^{-2x}$$

and for the random distribution, the equation

$$f = e^{-x(1-x/2)}$$

where f is the fraction of chlorine left in the polymer and x is the mole fraction of the vinyl chloride in the polymer. In a series of copolymers having a high chlorine content, Marvel obtained the data summarized in Table 10.

TABLE 10

DEHALOGENATION OF VINYL CHLORIDE COPOLYMERS OF HIGH CHLORINE CONTENT

% Vinyl Chloride in Polymer	Value of x, Wall's Formula	Value of f Found	Value of f Calculated as 1,3	Value of f Calculated as Random
60	0.674	0.278	0.260	0.338
65	0.720	0.242	0.237	0.311
77	0.822	0.193	0.194	0.260
87	0.902	0.198	0.162	0.221

From C. S. Marvel, "Organic Chemistry of Vinyl Polymers," Chapter VII in *The Chemistry of Large Molecules* (*Frontiers in Chemistry*, Vol. I). Interscience Publishers, Inc., New York, 1943.

These results indicated in general that a 1,3 orientation existed in the polymer and that vinyl chloride and vinyl acetate had copolymerized in a random arrangement. The discrepancies, however, led these investigators to examine copolymers of lower chlorine content. The results of these later experiments are tabulated in Table 11.

TABLE 11

Dehalogenation of Vinyl Chloride Copolymers of Low Chlorine Content

% Vinyl Chloride in Polymer	Value of x, Wall's Formula	Value of f Found	Value of f Calculated as 1,3	Value of f Calculated as Random
20.65	0.264	0.320	0.780	0.830
23.25	0.350	0.409	0.546	0.638
36.9	0.446	0.290	0.410	0.497

From C. S. Marvel, "Organic Chemistry of Vinyl Polymers," Chapter VII in *The Chemistry of Large Molecules* (*Frontiers in Chemistry*, Vol. I). Interscience Publishers, Inc., New York, 1943.

The discrepancies between calculated and found values were large. In an attempt to explain these results, these investigators carried out a series of interrupted polymerizations, analyzing the polymer and determining the molecular weight. Some of their experiments are listed in Table 12, to which references have been made in an earlier part of this chapter.

TABLE 12

Interrupted Polymerizations

Experiment Number	% Chlorine in Monomer Mixture	% Yield of Polymer	% Chlorine in Polymer
1a		45	17.65
1b	12.48	65	15.08
1c		78	13.9
1d		95	12.48
2a		3.4	37.4
2b	30.2	26	37.3
2c		16	35.3
2d		80	30.2

From C. S. Marvel, "Organic Chemistry of Vinyl Polymers," Chapter VII in *The Chemistry of Large Molecules* (*Frontiers in Chemistry*, Vol. I). Interscience Publishers, Inc., New York, 1943.

These results show clearly that the composition of the polymer changes as the monomer composition changes, because of different rates of entry into the polymer chain. It is also obvious that, although an analysis of a copolymer at 100 per cent yield will agree with the chlorine content of the monomer concentration, such a polymer is not homogeneous but is a mixture in which almost every polymer chain is different from every other one. In view of the fact that vinyl chloride and vinyl acetate do not copolymerize at random, but according to relative reactivity constants and specificities, it is not surprising that there are large discrepancies between the found and calculated values on the studies of the vinyl chloride–vinyl acetate copolymers.

Marvel and Levesque [68] determined the structures of methyl vinyl ketone polymers by studying them pyrolytically. If methyl vinyl ketone polymerizes head to tail, a 1,5 diketone should be obtained:

$$-CH_2CH^2-CH_2{}^3CH^4-$$

$$
\begin{array}{cc}
CO^1 & CO^5 \\
| & | \\
CH_3 & CH_3
\end{array}
$$

whereas in a head-to-head, tail-to-tail polymerization, a 1,4 diketone should be obtained:

$$-CH_2CH^2-CH^3CH_2-$$

$$
\begin{array}{cc}
CO^1 & CO^4 \\
| & | \\
CH_3 & CH_3
\end{array}
$$

On heating, both types of ketones lose water. The 1,4 diketone will give a furane derivative, and the 1,5 diketone will give a cyclohexanone derivative.

1,4 diketone → Furane derivative

1,5 diketone → Cyclohexanone derivative

It may be seen that the 1,4 diketone will lose half its water to form the furane, and then no further condensation will occur till cracking occurs. The 1,5 diketone will lose half its water in forming the cyclohexanone derivative, but the condensation could continue between methyl groups and ketone groups until most of the oxygen has been eliminated. Flory [69] and Wall [70] have calculated statistically that, if the polymer is a diketone structure, 81.6 per cent of the oxygen will be removed and 18.4 per cent will remain in the polymer. If the polymer is a random mixture of 1,4 and 1,5 ketones, Wall calculated that only 68.8 per cent of the oxygen will be lost. Marvel heated the polymer and obtained a loss of oxygen of 79 to 85 per cent, indicating a 1,5 ketone, and therefore a head-to-tail structure. Further evidence of a head-to-tail structure was obtained by cracking the polymer and isolating 3-methyl-2-cyclohexenone-1.

$$
\begin{array}{c}
CH_2 \\
\diagup \quad \diagdown \\
CH_2 \qquad CH_2 \\
\mid \qquad \mid \\
CH_3-C \qquad CO \\
\diagdown \quad \diagup \\
CH
\end{array}
$$

No furane derivatives were obtained. The polyketone was converted to an oxime derivative by means of hydroxylamine hydrochloride. Dehydration of a 1,5 dioxime should result in a pyridine derivative:

$$-[CH_2-CH]_{2n}- + nNH_2OH \rightarrow$$

$$
-\left[\begin{array}{c}
-CH_2-CH \text{————} CH_2-CH- \\
\mid \qquad\qquad\qquad \mid \\
C=NOH \;\; HON=C \\
\mid \qquad\qquad\qquad \mid \\
CH_3 \qquad\qquad\qquad CH_3
\end{array} \right]_n
$$

$$
\left[\begin{array}{c}
CH \\
\diagup\diagup \quad \diagdown \\
-CH_2-C \qquad C\text{————} \\
\mid \qquad\qquad \parallel \\
CH_3-C \qquad C-CH_3 \\
\diagdown \quad \diagup \\
N
\end{array} \right]_n
$$

Experimentally, the reaction proceeded to about 85 per cent, which is in excellent agreement with the statistically calculated value of 86.47 per cent previously mentioned for the interaction of two functional groups in a chain.

In a related manner the structure of polyvinyl alcohol was determined [71] by oxidation with chromic acid to produce a 1,3 polyketone, which on hydrolysis yields acetic acid and acetone.

$$
\begin{array}{c|c|c|c}
-CH_2CO & CH_2CO & CH_2COCH_2 & CO- \\
HO & H \quad HO & H \qquad\quad H & OH
\end{array}
$$

Most of the polymers of the vinyl addition type have been found to be of the head-to-tail arrangement. The α-haloacrylic esters appear to be of the head-to-head, tail-to-tail type:

$$\begin{array}{ccc} & Cl & Cl \\ & | & | \\ -CH_2-C & - & C-CH_2- \\ & | & | \\ & COOR & COOR \end{array}$$

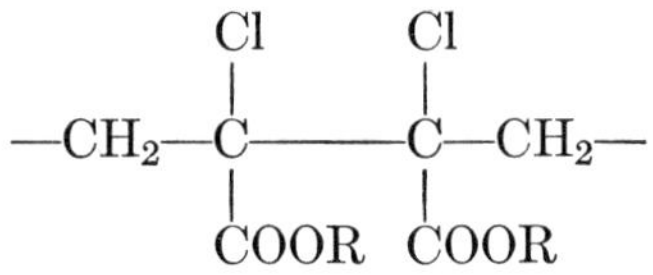

Studies on polymers of this type [72] show that they liberate iodine from KI and that zinc completely removes the halogens. These investigators studied the liberation of iodine from KI by esters of related structure which would correspond to a head-to-tail, and a head-to-head, tail-to-tail configuration. The α-haloacrylic ester polymers were compared with the α-halosuccinic and α-haloglutaric esters of the following structures:

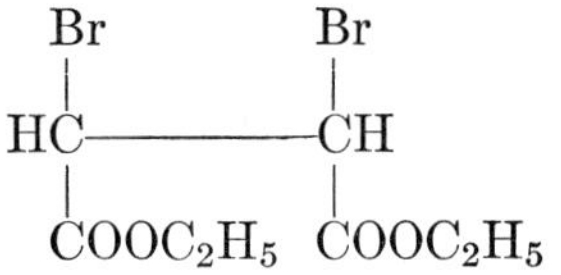

$$\begin{array}{ccc} Br & Br \\ | & | \\ HC & \underline{\hspace{1cm}} & CH \\ | & | \\ COOC_2H_5 & COOC_2H_5 \end{array} \qquad \begin{array}{ccc} Br & Br \\ | & | \\ HC\underline{\hspace{0.5cm}}CH_2\underline{\hspace{0.2cm}}CH \\ | & | \\ COOC_2H_5 & COOC_2H_5 \end{array}$$

Head-to-head, tail-to-tail type. Ethyl α,α'-dibromosuccinate

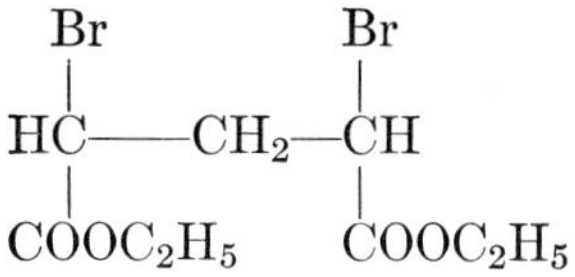

Head-to-tail type. Ethyl α,α'-dibromo-glutarate

$$\begin{array}{ccc} Br & Br \\ | & | \\ H_5C_2C\underline{\hspace{1cm}}CH_2\underline{\hspace{0.2cm}}C-C_2H_5 \\ | & | \\ COOC_2H_5 & COOC_2H_5 \end{array}$$

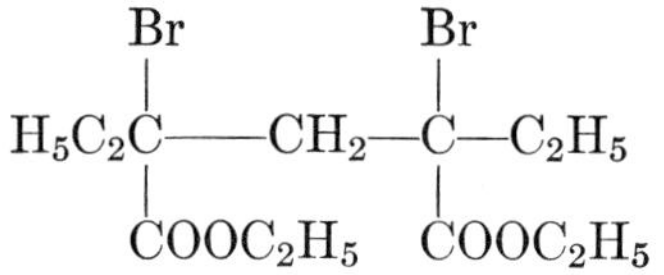

Head-to-tail type. Ethyl α,α'-dibromo-α,α'-diethyl glutarate

The results are given in Table 13.[72]

TABLE 13

LIBERATION OF IODINE BY BROMOESTERS

	% Iodine Liberated			
	Acetone, 24 hr, 25 C	Acetone Reflux, 24 hr	Dioxane, 24 hr, 25 C	Dioxane Reflux, 72 hr
Polymethyl α-bromoacrylate	30	49	24	92
Ethyl α,α'-dibromosuccinate	33	53	26	96
Ethyl α,α'-dibromoglutarate	4	6	4	21
Ethyl α,α'-dibromo-α,α'-diethyl glutarate	2	5	..	..

This evidence is offered to show that at least a substantial part of the polymer chain exists in a head-to-head, tail-to-tail configuration. Other evidence would indicate that head-to-tail configurations also exist in the polymers. The α-bromoacrylate polymers are unstable and discolor under heat and light. Discoloration in polymers is attributed to conjugated unsaturation of the polyene type $(-CH=CH-)_n$.[72] Conjugated unsaturation could only be obtained from a head-to-tail configuration of the α-chloroacrylate polymer.

THERMAL DEPOLYMERIZATION OF ADDITION POLYMERS

Depolymerization-equilibrium. Depolymerization is considered the reverse of polymerization; monomers and polymers may be considered to be in equilibrium, as, for example, in styrene:

$$nCH_2=CHC_6H_5 \rightleftharpoons -(CH_2-CHC_6H_5)_n-$$

The energy of activation for the polymerization of styrene is about 26,000 to 28,000 calories; the value of the depolymerization lies between 21,900 and 23,000 calories.[73] Equilibrium reactions that differ by activation energies of 7000 to 8000 calories are considered reversible. This reversibility or degradation may be brought about by energy in the form of mechanical treatment, light, chemical substances, heat, etc. At room temperature, the degradation is usually very small or very slow and usually increases with an increase in temperature. As already shown, polymerization involves the addition of monomer to the end of a growing chain, and in a true depolymerization, the degradation should be the removal of monomers, one at a time, from the polymer chain. Tuckett,[74] using statistical thermodynamics, has derived expressions for size distributions in degraded polymers, assuming (1) random degradation, and (2) non-random degradation with preferential splitting at the ends of the chains. Kuhn,[41] Montroll,[47] Simha,[75] and Schulz,[76] in a kinetic treatment of this problem as based on statistical analyses, assumed that all bonds connecting monomeric units have the same probability of being broken at a high degree of degradation. Simha and Mark [77] also considered polymer systems statistically with a low degree of degradation, wherein one link was broken and the adjacent one not broken, and derived the probability relationships. The relationships of these investigators are generally true only in a few specific instances, for while polymethacrylate and polyoxymethylene may be depolymerized smoothly to rather high yields, by-products are obtained from a large number of polymers subjected to degradation.

As mentioned in other chapters, polyethylene glycol produces acetaldehyde, divinyl ether, dioxane, and a number of other products, indicating that rupture takes place between carbon and oxygen as well as between carbon and carbon. Polyacrylonitrile does not degrade to monomer but to basic substances and a carbon residue; polyvinyl chloride liberates hydrogen chloride with charring, as does vinylidene chloride. It is obvious that secondary reactions predominate in the thermal degradation of a number of linear addition polymers, and that the nature of the polymers themselves determines whether monomers or secondary products are obtained. Some of the factors are given in the numbered paragraphs below.

1. The nature of the substitution on the linear carbon chain, and the bonding forces of the substituent group. Thus HCl and HCN may form more readily than the breaking of a carbon-to-carbon bond, as in the degradation of polyvinyl chloride, polyvinylidene chloride, and polyacrylonitrile. If side chain decomposition occurs, the polymer chain may become crosslinked or otherwise stabilized.

2. The influence that the substituent group, if it is stable, will have on the location of the rupture of the carbon-carbon bond. Thus in a head-to-tail polymer, the bond may be influenced to rupture as in scheme A or in B.

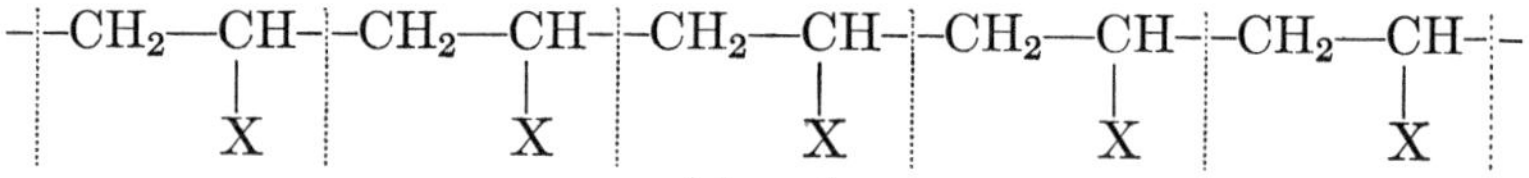

$$-\!-CH_2-CH-\!-CH_2-CH-\!-CH_2-CH-\!-CH_2-CH-\!-CH_2-CH-\!-$$
$$XXXXX$$

Scheme A

$$-\!-CH_2-CH-CH_2-\!-CH-CH_2-CH-\!-CH_2-CH-CH_2-CH-\!-$$
$$XXXXX$$

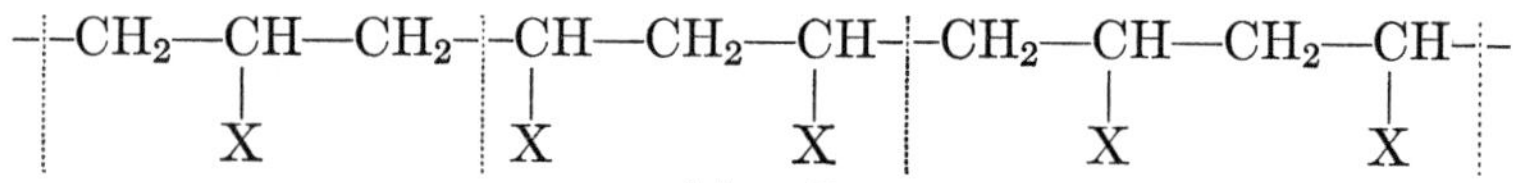

Scheme B

In a tail-to-tail structure, the bond break may occur as in scheme C or scheme D.

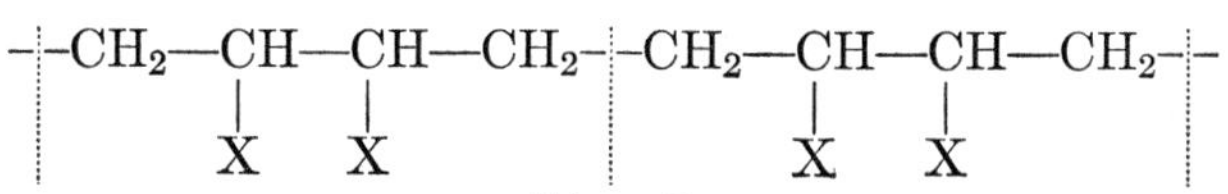

$$-\!-CH_2-CH-CH-CH_2-\!-CH_2-CH-CH-CH_2-\!-$$
$$XXXX$$

Scheme C

$$-\!-CH-CH_2-CH_2-CH-\!-CH-CH_2-CH_2-CH-\!-$$
$$XXXX$$

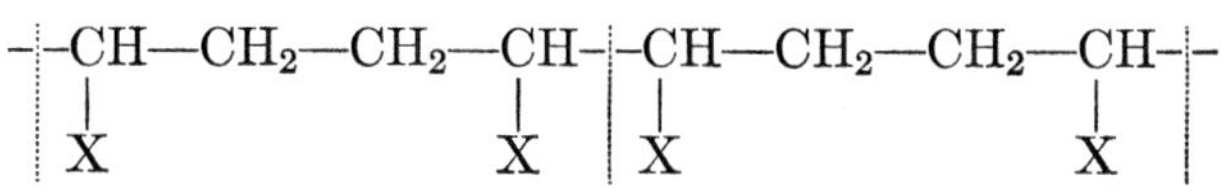

Scheme D

3. The disorder of the chain due to substituent groups may influence the degradation. Thus polymers of methyl methacrylate are degraded to higher yields of monomer than those of methyl acrylate, and the same holds true for methacrylonitrile, whereas acrylonitrile polymers

yield no monomer. On the other hand the yield of monomer from polystyrene is about four times greater than the monomer yield from polymers of α-methyl styrene.

4. The type of heteroatom in a chain is important. As discussed in another chapter, polyoxymethylene may be considered a linear poly-acetal rather than an ether and forms formaldehyde by an exchange reaction, whereas polyethylene glycols are true ethers and do not readily undergo exchange. Carothers' work on the depolymerization of linear esters showed that, if cyclic compounds could form by ester exchange, they were produced by an ester exchange reaction.

5. Crosslinkages seriously affect degradation reactions. Little or no divinylbenzene is obtained by depolymerizing polydivinylbenzene. The yield of monomeric styrene obtained from a copolymer of styrene and divinylbenzene, on the basis of the styrene content, is reduced disproportionately as the divinylbenzene content is increased.[24]

6. Monomer recovery from copolymers is poor because of the disturbing factors summarized in items 1 to 5.

7. Molecular weight of the polymer may influence the degradation. This was indicated by Bachman and Hellman [78] whose data are given in Table 14.

TABLE 14

MONOMER YIELD AS FUNCTION OF MOLECULAR WEIGHT OF POLYSTYRENE

Molecular Weight of Sample	Temperature of Polymerization	Telomer	% Monomer Yield
3,680	60	CCl$_4$	52
4,670	60	CCl$_4$	48
5,700	60	CCl$_4$	49
7,000	85	CCl$_4$	31
37,000	..	.....	62
60,000	80	None	55
74,000	..	.....	62
169,000	60	None	62
190,000	60	None	63
>190,000	25	None	67

The molecular weight of these polymers was calculated from the viscosity of the polymers according to Staudinger's equations. No correlation of molecular weight to any branching in these polymers was made, nor were telomerizing effects of carbon tetrachloride considered. However, these results do indicate that high polymers of molecular weights greater than 20,000 give better yields of monomer than those of lower molecular weights.

These same authors correlate the yield of monomer to the chemical structure of the polymer; their data are given with other data in Table 15. In the styrene copolymers the yields were calculated on the amount of styrene combined in the copolymer.

TABLE 15

Polymer	% Monomer Yield
Methyl methacrylate	90–95
Styrene	60–65
α-Methyl styrene	18–19
Dichlorostyrene	60–70
Styrene-maleic anhydride	11–12
Styrene-methyl methacrylate	66
Acrylonitrile [24]	0
Methacrylonitrile [24]	70–75
Dimethyl methylene malonate [24]	10–15

The methods of thermal depolymerization. Rapid heating at high temperatures usually produces better yields of monomer than slow heating at low temperatures. At low temperatures, cracking usually produces stable complex structures which are isolated with the monomer. On the other hand, high temperatures cause cracking along bonds other than those that will produce monomers. In a previous chapter, reference was made to the depolymerization of polystyrene by Staudinger and others,[79] showing a number of simple stable products like benzene and toluene which were isolated from the cracking products of polystyrene. As a rule, polymers vary considerably in the temperatures at which they depolymerize and also in the temperatures at which the best yield of monomer is obtained. These conditions are best determined experimentally.

When heat is applied to a polymer to produce monomer, most polymers first soften and viscous melts are produced, resulting in caking and poor heat-transfer conditions. The addition of inert materials, such as sand, molten metal, and fused salts, is claimed to improve heat transfer and to eliminate caking. Superheated steam is also claimed to be beneficial.[80, 81] The monomer is liberated as soon as cracking temperatures are reached. Since at these high temperatures polymerization may reoccur and air has a deleterious effect, it is advisable to carry out the degradation in the presence of an inhibitor and in the absence of air, preferably under reduced pressures.

DEPOLYMERIZATION BY FREE RADICALS

Substances which generate free radicals and thereby act as catalysts for polymerization may likewise act as catalysts for depolymerization.

Under thermal influences such effects are quite marked, and become readily noticeable at temperatures corresponding to the free-radical generating temperature of the particular catalyst under the specific conditions of the experiment. Depolymerization by free radical can be considered a process involving both a chemical and thermal process. That degradation is not primarily due to thermal influences on the polymer is readily demonstrable. For example, if a high molecular weight polyisobutylene, polyethylene, or polystyrene is processed on a rubber mill as in standard commercial practice, breakdown of the polymer occurs relatively slowly, the extent and rate of depolymerization being dependent on the usual factors of time, temperature, oxidizing atmosphere, etc. However, if the treatment is repeated under otherwise identical conditions, but with the addition of small amounts of benzoyl peroxide, the degradation is more rapid, the molecular weight is considerably lower, and the distribution curve markedly different from that obtained in the absence of the peroxide.[24]

Solution methods are especially adapted to the study of these polymerization-depolymerization systems. Mesrobian and his co-workers [82-84] have shown that, in toluene solutions, both the polymerization of styrene and the depolymerization of polystyrene occur simultaneously under similar conditions of temperature, concentration, and catalyst. Usually the steady states or equilibrium states for the polymerization and depolymerization are obtained at different rates under identical catalyst concentration with the rate of depolymerization being the slower of the two rates. The rate of approach to the steady state in depolymerization experiments of polystyrene in toluene at reflux temperatures can be increased by the addition of large amounts of benzoyl peroxide.

The technique of using very large amounts of peroxide catalyst for a more rapid approach to the steady state was the subject of a recent investigation.[84] In the polymerization experiments of Mesrobian, monomeric styrene in a concentration of 16 per cent in toluene was polymerized at reflux, using initially 0.001 per cent of benzoyl peroxide, as based on the weight of the styrene, as the catalyst. Thereafter, a similar amount of benzoyl peroxide, namely, 0.001 per cent, was added at regular intervals until a total of 1.0 per cent catalyst had been added. In the degradation experiment, polystyrene in a 16 per cent concentration in toluene was refluxed with 1.0 per cent benzoyl peroxide, followed by the addition of a similar amount at regular intervals. At definite intervals, aliquot samples were removed, the amount of precipitable polymer determined, and the molecular weight of the polymer measured. The results of these experiments [84] are summarized in Figure 7 and Table 16.

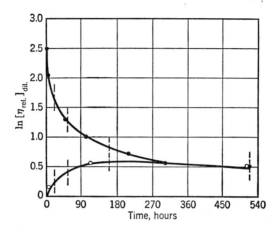

FIGURE 7. Polymerization degree vs. time; concentration of styrene, 16 g/100 cc toluene; 111 C; (●) polymer solution, 0.5 g benzoyl peroxide added every 8 hours; (○) monomer solution, 0.005 g benzoyl peroxide added every 8 hours. (From H. W. Spodheim, W. J. Badgley, and R. B. Mesrobian, "Polymerization-Degradation of Styrene in Solution," *J. Polym. Sci.*, **3**, 410 [1948]. Interscience Publishers, Inc.)

TABLE 16

POLYMER RECOVERABLE AND CATALYST ADDED FOR STYRENE SOLUTIONS UNDER-GOING DEGRADATION AND POLYMERIZATION

Degraded Polymer Solution

Time, Hours	Recovery of Polymer, %	Total Catalyst Added,* %
0	94	. . . .
21	92.2	4.24
54	83.6	8.20
158	85.9	25.21
518	81.1	95.6

Polymerized Monomer Solution

21	25.2	0.03
54	62.3	0.07
158	67.8	0.25
518	77.8	0.92

* Based on weight of styrene.

From H. W. Spodheim, W. J. Badgley, and R. B. Mesrobian, "Polymerization-Degradation of Styrene in Solution," *J. Polym. Sci.*, **3**, 410 (1948). Interscience Publishers, Inc.

The data of Table 16 show that only 1 per cent of benzoyl peroxide total was used in the polymerization experiment. In the degradation experiment, approximately 95 per cent benzoyl peroxide had been added in 518 hours, although degradation was substantially completed in 10 hours. However, under different conditions of addition of peroxide and on a different time scale, it has been shown that almost complete degradation to the steady state can be accomplished with as little as 1.0 per cent total peroxide addition.[82]

The experimental evidence to date is still insufficient to specify the exact role of the catalyst in effecting the degradation of the polymer or of determining the relation of the number of catalyst radicals to the number of cleavages. It may be reasonable to assume that in the depolymerization experiments the solvent telomerized the degraded polymer, since this is known for the polymerization of styrene in the presence of toluene (see Chapter 3). Otherwise, the molecular weight average for both systems, as in Figure 3, would possess the same steady-state viscosity average only by chance.

Discoloration in Polymers as a Result of Degradation

Marvel, Sample, and Roy [62] assumed that discoloration arising in polyvinyl halides is due to the polyene structure, $(-CH=CH-)_n$, produced by the dehydrohalogenation of the polymer:

$$-CH_2CH-\left(\begin{matrix}CH_2-CH\\ | \\ Cl\end{matrix}\right)_n-CH_2CH- \rightarrow$$
$$\begin{matrix}| \\ Cl\end{matrix}\begin{matrix}| \\ Cl\end{matrix}$$

$$n\text{HCl} + -CH_2CH-(CH=CH)_n-CH_2CH-$$
$$\begin{matrix}| \\ Cl\end{matrix}\begin{matrix}| \\ Cl\end{matrix}$$

It was as a result of this and other investigations [63-67] that the head-to-tail structures of polyvinyl chloride and of vinyl chloride–vinyl acetate copolymers were established.

Boyer [85] carried out statistical calculations for the expected distribution of n values, both for random and non-random loss of hydrogen chloride from polyvinylidene chloride. He calculated the expected color or light transmission curve of a degraded polymer, using the known light-absorption characteristics of polyene compounds. The comparison of his calculated values with experimental data on the degradation of vinylidene chloride indicated fair agreement. He pictures polyvinylidene chloride as having the structure

assigned by Reinhardt.[86]   In this structure hydrogen chloride will tend to be lost from a segmer in the same monomer radical rather than from adjacent segmer units.   Only one molecule of HCl is lost per segmer unit, since the remaining chlorine atom is stabilized by the presence of the double bond, and the degraded polymer will have the structure

after it has been exposed to light, heat, or chemical reagents, and if one molecule of HCl has been lost from each segmer.   If, however, less than one molecule of HCl is lost, the loss will be random.   Along the chain there will be structures of the type, $(-CH=CCl-)_n$, adjacent to the original, $-CH_2CCl_2-$ segmer and n will be an integer.   The value of n will depend on probability laws and the extent of the dehydrohalogenation.   Boyer expresses this mathematically:

$$P_n(p) = (1 - p^2)p^n \tag{41}$$

where P_n is the probability of an unsaturated system of value n, and p is extent of degradation.   Thus at a low degree of degradation, the value of n is one; at high percentages of degradation the percentage of $n = 1$ decreases and the percentages of $n > 1$ increases.   Thus at 20 per cent degradation there will be about

$$65\% \text{ of } (-CH=CCl-)_{n=1}$$
$$27\% \text{ of } (-CH=CCl-)_{n=2}$$
$$5\% \text{ of } (-CH=CCl-)_{n=3}$$
$$3\% \text{ of } (-CH=CCl-)_{n=4}$$

whereas at 40 per cent degradation there will be about

$$37\% \ (-CH{=}CCl-)_{n=1}$$
$$29\% \ (-CH{=}CCl-)_{n=2}$$
$$17\% \ (-CH{=}CCl-)_{n=3}$$
$$11\% \ (-CH{=}CCl-)_{n=4}$$
$$6\% \ (-CH{=}CCl-)_{n=5}$$

It may be observed that as degradation increases the conjugation of double bond increases in frequency. Brode[87] and Lewis and Calvin[88]

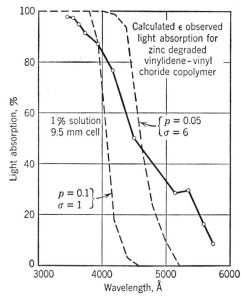

FIGURE 8. The curve marked $p = 0.1$ was calculated for a 10 per cent random loss of hydrogen chloride; the curve marked $p = 0.05$ assumes a 5 per cent non-random loss of hydrogen chloride. σ greater than unity implies a preferential building up of long conjugated systems. (From R. F. Boyer, "A Statistical Theory of Discoloration for Halogen-Containing Polymers and Copolymers," *J. Phys. and Colloid Chem.*, **51**, 80 [1947]. The Williams and Wilkins Company, Baltimore, publishers.)

have summarized the relation of structure to constitution in organic compounds, and the authors point out the work of Hausser, Kuhn, and Smakula[89] on the diphenylpolyenes of the structure R—(—C=C—)$_n$R′, where n reaches a value of 7. The intensity of absorption and the square of the wavelength of the first absorption maximum were found to be functions of n.

β-carotene, which has eleven double bonds in conjugation, has an intense yellow color. The polymers of phenylacetylene[90] and of phenoxyacetylene [91] are known to be a reddish color. Boyer refluxed a dioxane solution of vinylidene chloride–vinyl chloride copolymer (82 to 18 per cent) in the presence of excess purified zinc. In 8 hours, HCl had been removed from 10 per cent of the segmer units. The polymer was isolated and dried. The light absorption of the polymer was measured and contrasted to calculated absorption values, as in Figure 8.[85] The relation can be considered as fairly well established, particularly when chain ruptures, crosslinking, oxidation, etc., have not been taken into account. The degradation is not random, since once a double bond forms, an allyl chloride type structure may result:

$$—CH_2[—CCl_2—CH_2—CCl_2—]_nCH_2CCl_2— \rightarrow$$

$$HCl + —CH_2[—CCl_2CH{=}CCl—]_nCH_2CCl_2—$$
Allyl structure

and since the chlorine atom of the allyl type is quite labile, an adjacent double bond would form more readily than an isolated one.

Boyer considered the presence of the vinyl chloride in this copolymer and concluded that, since pairs of vinyl chloride segmers along the chains would be infrequent, we should not expect a serious discrepancy. At this point, it is well to point out that in the reaction of zinc and polyvinyl chloride, the chlorine atom is removed in pairs along the same chain, cyclopropane rings are formed,[62] and no color develops in the presence of zinc.[67] These data agree with the X-ray structure assigned [92] to polyvinyl chloride:

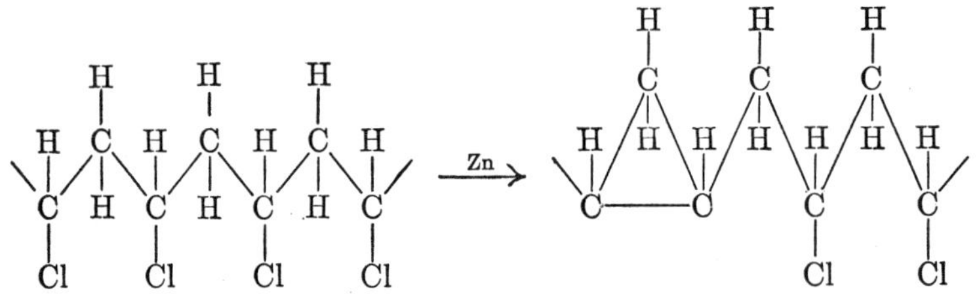

The discoloration of a polyvinyl chloride or polyvinylidene chloride polymer may be retarded or prevented by destroying the double bond conjugation. Boyer suggests that esters of maleic and aconitic acid stabilize vinylidene chloride polymers by undergoing a Diels-Alder reaction with the conjugated double bonds formed in the degraded polymer. This type of stabilizer, tributyl aconitate, has been disclosed by Hanson and Goggin [93] for polyvinylidene chloride and by D'Alelio [94, 95] for polyvinyl chloride polymers using itaconic esters. If the Diels-Alder reaction is effective in the prevention of color formation, it probably acts by preventing the formation of long conjugated systems:

$$
\begin{array}{c}
\text{Cl} \qquad\qquad\qquad\qquad\qquad\qquad\qquad\qquad\qquad \text{Cl} \\
| \qquad\qquad\qquad\qquad\qquad\qquad\qquad\qquad\qquad\qquad | \\
-\text{CH}_2-\text{C}-\text{CH}=\text{CCl}-\text{CH}=\text{CCl}-\text{CH}=\text{CCl}-\text{CH}_2-\text{C}- \\
| \qquad\qquad\qquad\qquad\qquad\qquad\qquad\qquad\qquad\qquad | \\
\text{Cl} \qquad\qquad\qquad\qquad\qquad\qquad\qquad\qquad\qquad \text{Cl}
\end{array}
$$

$$
\begin{array}{c}
+\ \text{CH}-\text{COOR} \\
\parallel \\
\text{CH}-\text{COOR}
\end{array}
$$

$$\downarrow$$

$$
\begin{array}{c}
\text{Cl} \qquad\qquad\qquad\qquad\qquad\qquad\qquad\qquad\qquad \text{Cl} \\
| \qquad\qquad\qquad\qquad\qquad\qquad\qquad\qquad\qquad\qquad | \\
-\text{CH}_2-\text{C}-\text{CH}-\text{CCl}=\text{CH}-\text{CCl}-\text{CH}=\text{CCl}-\text{CH}_2-\text{C}- \\
| \quad | \qquad\qquad\qquad\qquad\qquad\qquad\qquad\qquad | \\
\text{Cl} \ \ \text{CH}\text{------}\text{CH} \qquad\qquad\qquad \text{Cl} \\
\qquad | \qquad\qquad\ \ | \\
\qquad \text{COOR} \qquad \text{COOR}
\end{array}
$$

This system is equivalent then to a copolymer system of vinylidene chloride and a comonomer which cannot split out HCl. In fact, it goes further and implies that the comonomer should not degrade to produce unsaturation. Such unsaturation can be produced by the loss of H_2O, HCN, HCOOH, CH_3COOH, from segmers in a polymer.

Ideal comonomers are styrene, acrylic esters, methacrylic esters, ethylene, isobutylene, itaconic esters, etc. For a given loss of HCl, copolymers of these monomers with vinyl chloride or vinylidene chloride should not develop as deep a red color as the corresponding homopolymer. Boyer's investigation of copolymers of vinylidene chloride and ethyl acrylate, and the stabilization that resulted, are shown in Figure 9,[85] in the transmission values he obtained as the percentage of acrylate is increased.

Simha [85,96] derived a statistical theory which is in qualitative accord with the results of Figure 5. Similarly, the copolymers of vinyl chloride and the itaconic esters are more stable than polyvinyl chloride.[97] As examples of the types of polymers which become conjugatedly unsaturated, thereby acquiring color, the following may be mentioned.

1. Land and West [98] found that on dehydrating oriented polyvinyl alcohol, a slight darkening occurred and a strong positive dichroism, or the ability to polarize light, was produced. They attribute the existence of polyene groups, $(-\text{CH}=\text{CH}-)_n$, in an oriented polymer as the cause of selective light absorption.

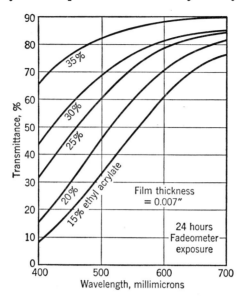

FIGURE 9. Beneficial effect of increasing amounts of neutral comonomer (ethyl acrylate) on the light stability of vinylidene chloride-ethyl acrylate copolymers. These films did not contain a light stabilizer. (From R. F. Boyer, "A Statistical Theory of Discoloration for Halogen-Containing Polymers and Copolymers," *J. Phys. and Colloid Chem.*, **51**, 80 [1947]. The Williams and Wilkins Company, Baltimore, publishers.)

2. Polyvinyl acetate will lose acetic acid when heated, becoming yellow before darkening:

$$(-CH_2CH-)_n \rightarrow nCH_3COOH + (-CH=CH-)_n$$
$$\underset{OCOCH_3}{|}$$

3. Polyacrylonitrile prepared at lower temperatures is colorless but loses HCN when heated and acquires a yellow cast. A nitrogen analysis of polyacrylonitrile accounts for only 96 to 97 per cent of the nitrile nitrogen. The odor of HCN is always present in solvent, mass, or emulsion polymerization of acrylonitrile. When treated with concentrated aqueous NaOH solutions, polyacrylonitrile turns a deep red before completely hydrolyzing the —CN groups to —COONa groups. The color formation is attributed to loss of HCN under alkaline catalytic influences.[24]

4. Polyacrylonitrile is less stable to thermal discoloration than its copolymers with ethyl acrylate,[99] itaconic esters,[100] fumaric esters,[24] styrene,[24] monochlorostyrene,[24] dichlorostyrene,[24] but it is not stabilized

by vinyl chloride,[24] vinylidene chloride,[24] methacrylonitrile,[24] fumaryl nitrile,[24] methyl-β-cyanoacrylate,[24] β-cyanoacrylic amide,[24] etc.

5. The tendency toward discoloration of the copolymers of styrene, methyl acrylate, methyl methacrylate, dimethyl itaconate, respectively, with fumaryl nitrile is increased as the ratio of the fumaryl nitrile in the copolymer is increased.[24]

REFERENCES

1. R. G. Fordyce and E. C. Chapin, *J. Am. Chem. Soc.*, **69**, 581 (1947).
2. F. T. Wall, *J. Am. Chem. Soc.*, **63**, 1862 (1941).
3. H. Staudinger and J. Schneiders, *Ann.*, **541**, 151 (1939).
4. C. S. Marvel, G. D. Jones, T. W. Mastin, and G. L. Schertz, *J. Am. Chem. Soc.*, **64**, 2356 (1942).
5. C. S. Marvel and G. L. Schertz, *J. Am. Chem. Soc.*, **65**, 2054 (1943).
6. T. Alfrey, Jr., and G. Goldfinger, *J. Chem. Phys.*, **12**, 205 (1944).
7. F. R. Mayo and F. M. Lewis, *J. Am. Chem. Soc.*, **66**, 1594 (1944).
8. F. T. Wall, *J. Am. Chem. Soc.*, **66**, 2054 (1944).
9. T. Wagner-Jauregg, *Ber.*, **63**, 3213 (1930).
10. A. Voss and E. Dickhäuser, German Patent 540,101.
11. T. Alfrey, Jr., and E. Lavin, *J. Am. Chem. Soc.*, **67**, 2044 (1945).
12. P. D. Bartlett and K. Nozaki, *J. Am. Chem. Soc.*, **68**, 1495 (1946).
13. F. M. Lewis, F. R. Mayo, and W. F. Hulse, *J. Am. Chem. Soc.*, **67**, 1701 (1945).
14. R. G. W. Norrish and E. F. Brookman, *Proc. Roy. Soc.* (London), **A171**, 147 (1939).
15. H. W. Arnold, M. M. Brubaker, and G. L. Dorough, U. S. Patent 2,301,356.
16. R. Simha, *J. Research*, **41**, 521 (1948).
17. C. S. Marvel, E. J. Prill, and D. F. DeTar, *J. Am. Chem. Soc.*, **69**, 52 (1947).
18. T. Alfrey, Jr., E. Merz, and H. Mark, *J. Polymer Research*, **1**, 37 (1946).
19. F. M. Lewis, C. Walling, W. Cummings, E. R. Briggs, and F. R. Mayo, *J. Am. Chem. Soc.*, **70**, 1519 (1948).
20. T. Alfrey, Jr., and J. G. Harrison, *J. Am. Chem. Soc.*, **68**, 299 (1946).
21. K. Nozaki, *J. Polymer Sci.*, **1**, 521 (1946).
22. C. C. Price, *J. Polymer Sci.*, **1**, 83 (1946).
23. C. F. Koelsch and V. Boekelheide, *J. Am. Chem. Soc.*, **66**, 412 (1944).
24. G. F. D'Alelio, Unpublished results.
25. C. Walling and E. R. Briggs, *J. Am. Chem. Soc.*, **67**, 1774 (1945).
26. T. Alfrey, Jr., and G. Goldfinger, *J. Chem. Phys.*, **12**, 322 (1944).
27. Irving Skeist, *J. Am. Chem. Soc.*, **68**, 1781–1784 (1946).
28. E. C. Chapin, G. E. Ham, and R. G. Fordyce, *J. Am. Chem. Soc.*, **70**, 538 (1948).
29. T. Alfrey, Jr., and C. C. Price, *J. Polymer Sci.*, **2**, 101–106 (1947).
30. C. C. Price, *J. Polymer Sci.*, **3**, 772–775 (1948).
31. C. Walling, E. R. Briggs, K. B. Wolfstirn, and F. R. Mayo, *J. Am. Chem. Soc.*, **70**, 1537 (1948).
32. L. P. Hammett, *Physical Organic Chemistry*, p. 188, McGraw-Hill Book Co., New York, 1940.
33. J. C. Michalek and C. C. Clark, *Chem. and Eng. News*, **22**, 1559 (1944).
34. H. W. Melville, *Proc. Roy. Soc.* (London), **A163**, 511 (1937).
35. F. Briers, D. L. Chapman, and E. Walters, *J. Chem. Soc.* (London), **129**, 562 (1926).

36. C. G. Swain and P. D. Bartlett, *J. Am. Chem. Soc.*, **68**, 2381 (1946).

37. P. D. Bartlett and C. G. Swain, *J. Am. Chem. Soc.*, **67**, 2273 (1945).

38. G. M. Burnett and H. W. Melville, *Nature*, **156**, 661 (1945).

39. M. J. S. Dewar and C. H. Bamford, *Nature*, **158**, 380–381 (1946).

40. C. H. Bamford and M. J. S. Dewar, *Nature*, **157**, 845 (1946).

41. W. Kuhn, *Ber.*, **63**, 1503 (1930).

42. W. Kuhn, *Z. physik. Chem.*, **A159**, 368 (1932).

43. K. Freudenberg and C. Blomquist, *Ber.*, **68**, 2070 (1935).

44. K. Freudenberg, W. Kuhn, W. Dürr, F. Bolz, and G. Steinbrunn, *Ber.*, **63**, 1510 (1930).

45. G. V. Schulz and H. J. Lohmann, *J. prakt. Chem.*, **157**, 238 (1941).

46. G. Scatchard, J. L. Oncley, J. W. Williams, and A. Brown, *J. Am. Chem. Soc.*, **66**, 1980 (1944).

47. E. W. Montroll and R. Simha, *J. Chem. Phys.*, **8**, 721 (1940).

48. I. Sakurada and S. Okamura, *Z. physik. Chem.*, **A187**, 289 (1940).

49. A. Matthes, *J. prakt. Chem.*, **162**, 245 (1943).

50. P. J. Flory, *J. Am. Chem. Soc.*, **62**, 2255 (1940).

51. P. J. Flory, *J. Am. Chem. Soc.*, **62**, 1057 (1940).

52. P. Schlack, U. S. Patent 2,241,321.

53. W. E. Hanford, U. S. Patent 2,241,322.

54. R. M. Joyce and D. M. Ritter, U. S. Patent 2,251,519.

55. P. J. Flory, *J. Am. Chem. Soc.*, **62**, 1561 (1940).

56. P. J. Flory, *J. Am. Chem. Soc.*, **64**, 2205 (1942).

57. P. J. Flory, *J. Chem. Phys.*, **12**, 425 (1944).

58. M. M. Brubaker, D. D. Coffman, and F. G. McGrew, U. S. Patent 2,339,237.

59. I. Ostromislensky, *J. Russ. Phys.-Chem. Soc.*, **44**, 240 (1912).

60. C. Harries, *Ann.*, **395**, 216 (1913).

61. H. Staudinger, M. Brunner, and W. Feist, *Helv. Chim. Acta*, **13**, 805 (1930).

62. C. S. Marvel, J. H. Sample, and M. F. Roy, *J. Am. Chem. Soc.*, **61**, 3241 (1939).

63. P. J. Flory, *J. Am. Chem. Soc.*, **61**, 1518 (1939).

64. F. T. Wall, *J. Am. Chem. Soc.*, **62**, 803 (1940).

65. F. T. Wall, *J. Am. Chem. Soc.*, **63**, 821 (1941).

66. R. Simha, *J. Am. Chem. Soc.*, **63**, 1479 (1941).

67. C. S. Marvel and E. H. Riddle, *J. Am. Chem. Soc.*, **62**, 2666 (1940).

68. C. S. Marvel and C. L. Levesque, *J. Am. Chem. Soc.*, **60**, 280 (1938).

69. P. J. Flory, *J. Am. Chem. Soc.*, **64**, 177 (1942).

70. F. T. Wall, *J. Am. Chem. Soc.*, **64**, 269 (1942).

71. C. S. Marvel and C. E. DeNoon, Jr., *J. Am. Chem. Soc.*, **60**, 1045 (1938).

72. C. S. Marvel and J. C. Cowan, *J. Am. Chem. Soc.*, **61**, 3156 (1939).

73. A. Votinov, P. Kobeko, and F. Marei, *J. Phys. Chem.* (USSR), **16**, 106 (1942).

74. R. F. Tuckett, *Trans. Faraday Soc.*, **41**, 351 (1945).

75. R. Simha, *J. Applied Phys.*, **12**, 569 (1941).

76. G. V. Schulz, *Z. physik. Chem.*, **51**, 127 (1942).

77. H. Mark and R. Simha, *Trans. Faraday Soc.*, **36**, 611 (1940).

78. G. B. Bachman and H. Hellman, *J. Org. Chem.*, **12**, 111, 115 (1947).

79. H. Staudinger and A. Steinhofer, *Ann.*, **517**, 35 (1935).

80. U. S. Patent 2,248,512.

81. U. S. Patent 2,359,212.

82. R. B. Mesrobian and A. V. Tobolsky, *J. Am. Chem. Soc.*, **67**, 785 (1945).

83. R. B. Mesrobian and A. V. Tobolsky, *J. Poly. Sci.*, **2**, 463 (1947).

84. H. W. Spodheim, W. J. Badgley, and R. B. Mesrobian, *J. Poly. Sci.*, **3**, 410 (1948).
85. R. F. Boyer, *J. Phys. and Colloid Chem.*, **51**, 80 (1947).
86. R. C. Reinhardt, *Ind. Eng. Chem.*, **35**, 422 (1943).
87. W. R. Brode, *Chemical Spectroscopy*, Chapter VII, John Wiley and Sons, New York, 1939.
88. G. N. Lewis and M. Calvin, *Chem. Revs.*, **25**, 273 (1939).
89. K. W. Hausser, R. Kuhn, and A. Smakula, *Z. physik. Chem.*, **B29**, 384 (1935).
90. J. Stitcher and J. D. Piper, *Ind. Eng. Chem.*, **33**, 1567 (1941).
91. W. P. Tuttle, Jr., and T. L. Jacobs, *Abstracts of the Buffalo Meeting of ACS*, September 7–11, 1942.
92. C. S. Fuller, *Chem. Revs.*, **26**, 161 (1940).
93. A. W. Hanson and W. C. Goggin, U. S. Patent 2,273,262.
94. G. F. D'Alelio, U. S. Patent 2,297,290.
95. G. F. D'Alelio, U. S. Patent 2,340,108.
96. R. Simha, *J. Research*, **41**, 541 (1948).
97. G. F. D'Alelio, U. S. Patent 2,299,740.
98. E. H. Land and C. D. West, *Linear Dichroism Dichroic Polarizers and Applications*, Vol. VI, p. 160, *Colloid Chemistry*, Jerome Alexander (Editor), Reinhold Publishing Corp., New York, 1946.
99. G. F. D'Alelio, U. S. Patent 2,412,034.
100. G. F. D'Alelio, U. S. Patent 2,366,495.

Author Index

Adams, C. E., *see* Price, C. C., 377, 384, 393
Adams, R., *see* Lycan, W. H., 274
Agron, P., Alfrey, T., Jr., Bohrer, J., Haas, H., and Wicksler, H., 435
Aleksandrov, A. P., and Lazurkin, Ya S., 147
Alfrey, T., Jr., 424
——, *see* Agron, P., 435
——, Bartovics, A., and Mark, H., 238
—— and Goldfinger, G., 431
——, Goldfinger, G., and Mark, H., 132
—— and Harrison, J. G., 426
—— and Price, C. C., 432, 433
Alyea, H. N., *see* Jeu, Kia-Khwe, 289
Avogadro, A., 80, 257, 258, 260, 297

Bachman, G. B., and Hellman, H., 455
Bacon, R. G. R., 314, 316, 325, 403, 409
Badgley, W. J., *see* Spodheim, H. W., 458
Baekeland, L. P., 26
Baeyer, A., 171
—— and Villiger, V., 172
Baker, W. O., 122
—— and Fuller, C. S., 108
——, Fuller, C. S., and Heiss, J. H., Jr., 225
Bamford, C. H., *see* Dewar, M. J. S., 440
Bardwell, D. C., *see* Lind, S. C., 346
Bartlett, P. D., 439
—— and Cohen, S. G., 276
—— and Swain, C. G., 439
Bartovics, A., *see* Alfrey, T., Jr., 238
Baxendale, J. H., 334, 336, 409
——, Evans, M. G., and Park, G. S., 333
Beckmann, E., 254
Beer, A., 286
Bekkedahl, N., 128
Berg, R. M., *see* Clash, R. F., Jr., 152
Berkeley, Earl of, and Hartley, E. G. J., 222
Berzelius, J., 6, 7
Bingham, E. C., 240
Bohrer, J., *see* Agron, P., 435
Boissonnas, C. B., *see* Meyer, K. H., 221
Bolland, J. L., *see* Melville, H. W., 314
Bourdillon, J., 221

Bovey, F. A., and Kolthoff, I. M., 316, 317, 318
——, *see* Kolthoff, I. M., 323, 380
Boyer, R. F., 459, 460, 461, 462, 463, 464
—— and Heidenreich, R. D., 256
—— and Spencer, R. S., 124, 128, 129, 130, 131, 132, 144, 145, 146, 147, 148, 149, 151, 152, 153
——, *see* Spencer, R. S., 134
Brauker, E., *see* Jenckel, E., 130
Breitenbach, J. W., 97, 191, 303, 324, 325
—— and Raff, R., 285
—— and Renner, A. J., 325
Breusch, F., *see* Staudinger, H., 182
Bridgman, W. B., 66
Briggs, E. R., *see* Lewis, F. M., 435
——, *see* Walling, C., 431, 435
Brockman, E. F., 305
——, *see* Norrish, R. G. W., 304
Broda, E., *see* Obogi, R., 222
Brode, W. R., 461
Brönsted, J. N., 398
Brubaker, M. M., 445
Bunn, C. W., 104, 116, 117
Busse, W. F., *see* Davies, J. M., 147

Calvin, M., *see* Lewis, G. N., 461
Carlin, R. B., and Shakespeare, N. E., 331
Carothers, W. H., 15, 30, 62, 63, 84, 86, 172, 175, 178, 179, 275, 314, 455
—— and Dorough, G. L., 273
——, *see* Hill, J. W., 171, 186
——, *see* Spanagel, E. W., 173
—— and Van Natta, F. J., 230, 273
Caspari, W. A., 219
Chapin, E. C., *see* Fordyce, R. G., 435
——, Ham, G. E., and Fordyce, R. G., 432, 435
Clapeyron, B. P. E., *see* Clausius, R. J., 251
Clash, R. F., Jr., and Berg, R. M., 152
—— and Rynkiewicz, L. M., 152
Clausius, R. J., and Clapeyron, B. P. E., 251
Cohen, S. G., 393
——, *see* Bartlett, P. D., 276

469

Subject Index

Esterification, of methyl alcohol with fatty acids, 290
rate constants, 290
reactivity constants, 290
Esters, cyclic, from β-hydroxyisobutyric acids, 177
synthesis of, 172
Esters, cyclic, dimeric, from β-hydroxy-isobutyric acids, 177
Ethyl acrylate, acrylonitrile copolymers, stability of, 464
suspension polymerization of, 210
vinylidene chloride polymers, light stability of, 464
Ethyl alcohol, functionality of, 16
Ethyl methacrylate, Raman spectra of, 287
Ethylbenzene, 135
plasticizer for polystyrene, 143, 144
Ethylcellulose, 64, 135
molecular weight determination, in ultracentrifuge, 250
structure of and repeating unit in, 9
Ethylcyclohexane, by hydrogenation of styrene, 63
from styrene, 63
Ethyl-α,α'-dibromo-α,α'-diethyl glutarate, reaction with potassium iodide, 452
structure of, 452
Ethyl-α,α'-dibromoglutarate, reaction with potassium iodide, 452
structure of, 452
Ethyl-α,α'-dibromosuccinate, reaction with potassium iodide, 452
structure of, 452
Ethylene, 32
benzene from, 181
butadiene from, 181
cyclic compounds from, 181
cyclohexene from, 181
dispersion polymerization of, 190
polyethylene from, 190
polymerization, 190
gaseous, of, 190
stages in, 190
solution polymerization of, 190
structure of, 139
substituted, polymerization tendency of, 184
Ethylene imine, addition polymerization of, 445
Ethylene diacetate, end groups in, 62
Ethylene glycol, molecular weights, comparison by different methods, 271

Ethylene glycol, and succinic acid, condensation polymerization of, 31
polyesterification of, 214
Ethylene imine, 36, 37
effect of telomers in polymerization of, 47
structure of, 37
Ethylene maleate, 57
Ethylene oxide, 7, 36, 37
addition polymerization of, 445
dimerization of, 12, 185
dioxane from, 185
effect of telomers in polymerization of, 47
functionality of, 56
intermolecular reactions of, 185
intramolecular reactions of, 185
polymerization of, 12, 31, 62, 185, 272
by dimethylamine, 275
by methylamine, 275
polymers, end groups in, 62
structure of, 37
Ethylene succinates, molecular weights, from cryoscopic determination, 273
from end group analysis, 273
from melting point depression, 273
Eucolloids, description of, 19
molecular weight of, 20
Eupolymer, description of, 19
Exchange resins, cation, 213
Expansion curves, polystyrene, 133, 134

Ferrous ions, reaction with hydrogen peroxide, 333
Fiber state, 5
Fibers, physical properties of, 27
as polymers, 5
volume used, 28
Fibrin, 23
Fibrinogen, 22
First-order reaction, equation for, 294
Fit value, of chloroprene, 120
deviations, 118, 119
effect on, by substitution in polyethylene chain, 140
of polybutadiene, 120
of polyethylene, 115
of polyisobutylene, 118, 119
of polymers, 115
of polyvinyl acetate, 119
of polyvinyl alcohol, 116
of polyvinyl chloride, 115, 119
of polyvinylidene chloride, 116, 119
Flax, 24
Fluidity, definition of, 224

Succino-nitrile, polymerization catalysts, 340

Sulfates, insoluble, in suspension polymerization, 211

Sulfinic acid salts, as emulsifying agents, 202

Sulfites, as reduction activation agents, in emulsion polymerization, 203

Sulfonated styrene-divinylbenzene copolymers, 213

Sulfonic acid salts, as emulsifying agents, 202

Sulfoxylates, as reduction activation agents, in emulsion polymerization, 203

Sulfur, effect on polymerization rate of styrene, 390

  inhibitor, in emulsion polymerization of styrene, 389

    in suspension polymerization of styrene, 389

Sulfur dioxide in polymerizations, with olefins, 46

Sulfuric acid catalyst, 14

Sulfurous acid, as reduction activation agent in emulsion polymerization, 203

Surface active agents, alcohol phosplates, 209

  alcohol sulfates, 209

  alcohol thiosulfates, 209

  anionic, 209

    alcohol sulfonates, 209

    examples of, 209

    fatty acid soaps, 209

  cationic, 209

  deflocculation by, 211

  foaming, 210

  non-ionic, 209, 210

  soaps, 209

  sodium alkyl sulfonates, 209

  solubilizers, 210

  washing, 210

  wetting, 210

Surface tension, effect of electrolytes on, 209

Surface tension change, in emulsion polymers, 369

Suspension agents (anionic organic), 211

  carboxymethylcellulose, 211

  polysodium acrylate, 211

  sodium alginate, 211

Suspension agents (cationic organic), 211

  chitin, 211

Suspension agents (non-ionic organic), 211

Suspension agents (non-ionic organic), hydroxyethylcellulose, 211

  methylcellulose, 211

  polyvinyl alcohol, 211

Suspension agents (polymeric organic), nature of, 211

Suspension copolymerization of acrylonitrile and ethyl acrylate, 213

Suspension polymerization, of acrylonitrile, 207

  advantages of, 213

  agglomeration in, 207

  agitation, continuous, in, 208

  aluminum salts, insoluble, in, 211

  barium salts, insoluble, in, 211

  calcium salts, insoluble, in, 211

  carbonates, insoluble, in, 211

  catalysts in, 206

    monomer-soluble, 206

    water-soluble, 206

  conditions of, 357

  dispersion medium in, 206

  effect of catalyst solubility in, 358

  effect of monomer solubility in, 358

  of ethyl acrylate, 210

  factors affecting, 212

    catalyst type, 213

    dispersion agent type, 213

    monomer amount, 213

    monomer reactivity, 213

    polymerization temperature, 213

    stirring rate, 213

  initiation in, 357

  kinetics of a, 206

  magnesium carbonate in, 211

  magnesium salts, insoluble, in, 211

  as a mass polymerization, 357

  of methyl methacrylate, 211

  monomer influence on, 212

  particle size in, 205

  phosphates, insoluble, in, 211

  polymerization rates in, 358

  propagation in, 357

  silicates, insoluble, in, 211

  solution additives, 360

  stabilizers, 207

  of styrene, 213

    in presence of sulfur, 389

  sulfates, insoluble, in, 211

  termination in, 357

  of vinyl chloride, 207

  of vinylidene chloride, 207

  viscous stage in, 207

  water, use of, 206

Suspension stabilizers, as protective colloids, 212